Foreword

ORVILLE L. FREEMAN, *Secretary of Agriculture*

WE CANNOT MEASURE in tons or dollars or even in terms of stomachs filled and bodies clothed the accomplishments of these hundred years in agriculture, for the achievement is not alone in numbers or amounts but in challenges met and responsibilities laid upon us.

We can say that American farmers produce many times more than American farmers did a hundred years ago. We can say also that the number of our people who are ill fed and ill clothed has been reduced to a small fraction. Or that the technological revolution we are now in is far beyond the Industrial Revolution in scope and possibilities. Or that we have enough food in storage to see us through any emergency. All that is true, and we are grateful. But this is not the time for boasting; accomplishment makes vainglory unworthy of us.

Rather, as the Department of Agriculture enters its second century, our productive genius, the elements of men and machines and resources that underlie our progress, and the abundance they have given us impose on us new opportunities and responsibilities. The goals are finite, not synthetic. They arise from our attainment of a point where it is possible to produce enough so that nobody in the world need lack food and clothing; from an ability to produce that has outstripped the social and economic adjustments necessary for the full use of our productive capacity; and from forces that have made the world smaller and the family of man larger. We cannot stop at that point. We must march confidently beyond it if we are to survive and the free world is to survive.

Our first responsibility is to American farmers, who have not received a fair return for the abundance they have given us and equal to the labor, capital, risk, and managerial competence they have put into it. We need a continuing, well-defined, well-understood program that will guarantee adequate incomes for farmers without penalizing consumers of farm products. Such a policy has to be more than a year-by-year expedient. It must embrace not only an assurance of fair income, but an expansion of the sources of strength that have made our agriculture great: Serious support of the owner-operated family farm; the retraining of farmers displaced or made underemployed by technological developments; diversified vocational opportunities in rural areas; help to young men who wish to enter farming; recognition of the place and needs of those we too easily call "small" or "marginal" farmers; an assurance of continuity in a business that, unlike industry, cannot control its returns and some of its operations; and a willingness to act on the conviction that farming is a way of life that influences the lives of all of us.

Another goal is to provide for basic human needs. That goal is nearly within our grasp for ourselves. Nearly all of us are well fed and well clothed—but every one of us has to be nourished and clothed adequately. We have food, fibers, and some of the devices of distribution for that, but we do not have the full conviction that it is necessary or possible. We need adjustments in marketing, economics, social agencies, attitudes, and, in places, laws. We need, as well, to use our abundance to help the hungry and naked in the universal family of which we are a part. Our humanity, our position in a free world dictate this obligation to promote peace and security. This we can do by sharing our plenty and our experience in ownership and operation of land and our scientific skills. This is more than simple charity; it is an investment in the economic growth and national maturity of countries whose development began later than ours.

We have a responsibility to the future. In growing, we exploited our resources. The period of misuse and overuse is largely past, but a new obligation arises in the need of our growing population for space, the movement of people to cities and suburbs, the use of land for highways and airports and cities, the expanding requirements of water and timber. If we are not foresighted, Americans will not have a proper place to live. We need an expanded program of care and use that will insure the best utilization of land, water, and forests to meet future needs; protect and expand our parks, seashores, wild areas, places of natural beauty, and other places for recreation of all citizens; keep and develop the beauties of the countryside, now endangered by urban and industrial developments. Planning is needed, and a determination to do this task properly.

We have a duty to the American community—not to farmers as a group or to city people as a group, but to all Americans. The realization that farm policy is no longer made only by farmers or only for farmers and that many of the results of agricultural research benefit nonfarmers more than farmers will lead to a better understanding of farm problems and their relationship to the whole economy. Mechanization on the farm affects city people, just as automation in the factory affects farmers; the dislocations or personal hardships or the abundance they bring about affect the whole

87TH CONGRESS, 2D SESSION
HOUSE DOCUMENT NO. 279

The Yearbook

of Agriculture

1962

Arthur A. Martin

AFTER A

THE UNITED STATES GOVERNMENT PRINTING OFFICE

HUNDRED YEARS

YEARS

The Yearbook of Agriculture 1962

THE UNITED STATES DEPARTMENT OF AGRICULTURE • Washington, D.C.

Growth Through Agricultural Progress

economic and social structure we all belong to. This duty to the American community embraces education, public discussion, and reaching decisions on policy on the basis of participation by farmers and the nonfarm public. Out of them will develop social, political, and economic growth that will insure steady, even, universal progress. As Thomas Jefferson said, "Laws and institutions must go hand in hand with the progress of the human mind; as that becomes more developed, more enlightened, as new discoveries are made, new truths discovered and manners and opinions change, with the change of circumstances, institutions must advance also to keep pace with the times."

These goals are attainable. These responsibilities can be met. Not by farmers alone. Not by the Department of Agriculture—or, indeed, by the Government—alone. Not by one or a few of us. All of us. The time is not some time in the next hundred years. The time is now.

VIII

Preface

ALFRED STEFFERUD, *Editor of the Yearbook*

THIS YEARBOOK OF AGRICULTURE, one of a series that began before the Department of Agriculture was even thought of, is a sampler of progress in the hundred years since the Department was established. Just that; no more. It is not intended to be a history, although there is much of history in it. It is not a treatise of technology, although we consider many scientific developments. It is not a boastful report, although we who work in agriculture have much to boast of. It is not a complete survey of all that has happened in farming; for that, the reader is referred to the previous Yearbooks of Agriculture and the thousands of other publications about agriculture, some of which we list in a later section, and to *Century of Service: The First 100 Years of the United States Department of Agriculture,* the Centennial history of the Department's organizational development and response to changing conditions.

This sampler gives a few samples of the accomplishments on American farms and in laboratories in a century; a few indications of the problems so as to point up the extent of the achievements; a few of the ways that have helped our farmers produce so abundantly; a few of the tasks performed by the Department and its related institutions for the well-being of all Americans; a few of the reasons why agriculture is so important to everybody and why a healthy agriculture is important to a healthy general economy.

Most farmers know all that. This book, therefore, unlike previous Yearbooks, is addressed more to nonfarmers than to farmers. Our thinking is along these lines: We know that progress in agriculture in this century has meant as much to consumers as to farmers, that whatever differences there once were between rural and city people have nearly vanished, that policies and programs for farmers actually are farmer-consumer programs. We believe that city people should become better acquainted with farmers or, because many city people came from the land, reacquainted with the farmers of 1962 and reacquainted with the America that exists beyond the city limits and is changing rapidly. We have tried to make this a happy, pleasant, informative book, because our story, for the most part, is a happy one, and our country, for the most part, is a pleasant one. Our purpose is allied with this thought: The greatness of achievement demands greatness of response.

The book is organized simply. It begins with several introductory chapters, which tell something about the history of agriculture and the Department, the scope and methods of research, the land-grant institutions, and a survey of American farming in terms of representative farmers. We chose to tell about milestones in the development of agriculture in terms of persons, none of whom is now living, who had major influence in shaping the work and directions of the Department and of farming. The body of the book is devoted to the fields of work—plant science, forests, soils and conservation, animal industry, insects, machines and equipment, processing and utilizing farm products, marketing, economics, the dissemination of information, and homes.

Throughout, for clarity and brevity, wherever we could we let one example—a disease, a State college, a State fair, and so on—tell a story of much larger dimensions, but when we chose these examples we thought of them primarily as devices of writing; we did not pass judgment on other factors. For each of them we could have chosen others by a flip of a coin. We have emphasized photographs because they can tell better than words many details that we wanted to stress and because most of the previous Yearbooks, for various reasons, have had few illustrations.

Acknowledgment of the help of contributors, photographers, and others is made at the end of the volume. Here, though, it is fitting to express special gratitude to the many persons of the United States Government Printing Office whose skills, experience, and craftsmanship have manufactured this and preceding Yearbooks of Agriculture, particularly Frank H. Mortimer, Assistant Planning-Production Manager for Typography and Design, and Clifford W. Shankland and Muriel Chamberlain of his staff.

Members of the 1962 Yearbook Committee, which planned the scope of the book, are: R. Lyle Webster, Office of Information, Chairman; Martin A. Abrahamsen, Farmer Cooperative Service; Robert T. Beall, Rural Electrification Administration; Philip S. Brown, Farmers Home Administration; Albert B. Foster, Soil Conservation Service; Arthur W. Greeley, Forest Service; H. L. Haller, Agricultural Research Service; Gerald H. Huffman, Federal Extension Service; George S. James, Forest Service; Joseph G. Knapp, Farmer Cooperative Service; Nathan M. Koffsky, Economic Research Service; W. A. Minor, Foreign Agricultural Service; H. A. Rodenhiser, Agricultural Research Service; Kennard O. Stephens, Agricultural Stabilization and Conservation Service; Murray Thompson, Agricultural Stabilization and Conservation Service; Darnell M. Whitt, Soil Conservation Service.

Contents

ANIMALS

INSECTS

TECHNOLOGIES

THE SUN IS ON HIS BROW, *and iron in his hand. Humanity is in his heart, and wisdom in his head. In his eye, the far horizon; however he sits, wherever he walks, his feet are on the ground. To him, the American farmer, to him, in friendship and admiration, we dedicate this book.*

After a Hundred Years

Backgrounds

1862

THE YEAR the Department of Agriculture was born, 1862, was a year of test and trial. Nine months had gone since President Lincoln declared the existence of an insurrection and called for 75 thousand volunteers to put it down. Now people in the North were singing and whistling "John Brown's Body" and learning "Battle Hymn of the Republic." Boys and men fought and killed each other at places nobody had heard of: Mill Springs, Pea Ridge, White Oak Swamp, Chickasaw Bayou, Prairie Grove. New words and names entered the weft of the young Nation's history: Copperhead, Gatling, Monitor, Confederacy, Conscription Act, abolition.

Thus the country faced its Armageddon. The sun rose and set, though; harvest followed seedtime. People ate, slept, worked, loved, dreamed, hoped, as people do, in fear and faith. There were fewer than 32 million Americans then, one-sixth of the population a century later. About 7 million farmworkers produced the food for themselves and the others, a ratio roughly of 1 to 5; a century later it was about 1 to 26.

On farms, food was mostly grown and preserved at home. Much of the clothing was homespun. Homemade candles and the flicker of the fireplace provided light. Animals and men were the power that tilled the soil. Buildings were erected from home-sawn trees or from the sod of the prairie. Fuel came from the woodlot or was the cow chips that littered the range.

The Homestead Act in 1862 opened half a continent to the plow. Machines were being made to help the farmer, but not yet could the agricultural revolution be foreseen. The sticky, root-matted soil of the prairie demanded the steel plow. The mechanical reaper, the drill, the cornplanter, and the threshing machine were the wonders of the farm. The 30 thousand miles of railroad started to grow into a giant that carried farm goods to consumers in every section.

Isaac Newton, the new Commissioner of Agriculture, took pen in hand to write an introduction to his first annual report to the President. His rounded periods about the satisfactions of farming may have had a strange sound to those who read them in those days of war, money problems, expansion, uncertainty. Maybe they gave comfort and good advice to people then, as similar words may give comfort, advice, and a hopeful glimpse in this day of test and

Central Pacific Railroad, Utah, 1869.

trial—or to any society that believes man cannot live by bread
alone.

Thus wrote Isaac Newton: ". . . Having reached this agricultural
vantage ground by honest toil, guided by the lights of experience
and science, it is an interesting question, to every American, What
are the conditions of a still grander progress and prosperity?

"The essential conditions, it seems to me, are—peace; a continued
and increasing demand for agricultural products, both at home and
abroad; an increased respect for labor; a more thorough knowledge
and practice of agriculture as an art and science; and, finally, a
more thorough education of our farmers in the physical sciences,
in political economy, in taste, and general reading. . . .

"The farmer should breathe that general atmosphere of thought,
which, coming to us from distant ages and across the sea, is
fanned by pulpit, press, and printed book. Our fathers endured
many hardships and privations; but the young farmer of to-day

3

Ranch in Custer County, Nebraska (date unknown).

Great Bend, Kansas (date unknown).

City Point, Virginia (1864).

possesses a wealth of advantages for general culture enjoyed by no other people. In some portions of our country these advantages are being improved, and the yield of cultivated mind, like that of the earth, is, indeed, wonderful; but as there is no royal road to agriculture, neither is there to knowledge. The latter must be acquired by long mental husbandry, but, like that of the soil, it yields many solid pleasures. . . .

"I hardly deem it necessary to attempt to convince our intelligent countrymen of the vast importance of such a department, inasmuch as whatever improves the condition and the character of the farmer feeds the lifesprings of national character, wealth, and power. What agricultural societies and publications have done for single counties and States, this department should do for the whole country, but with a liberality, wisdom, and catholicity commensurate with the resources of the nation, the importance of agriculture, and the co-operation of individuals both at home and abroad.

"It is hard to realize, and yet as true as Holy Writ, that some who shall read, to-day, these lines, will live to see one hundred millions of freemen dwelling in this dear land of ours. With peace and union restored, based on equity and freedom; with all the conditions of agricultural and mental progress fulfilled; with iron bands stretching from the pines of Maine to the Golden Gate; with the hum of factories on ten thousand streams, and swift-winged commerce flying to distant lands, what pen can sketch the possibility of this young giant of the west?

"Old Rome, with all her elements of decay constantly at work, lasted nearly one thousand years, and carried her culture, civilization, and arms to a wondrous pitch of glory. May we not hope and devoutly pray that, taking warning from history and the signs of the times, our republic may so learn lessons of wisdom, that, eradicating all destructive tendencies, she will fortify herself against decay, and become, what Rome was not—eternal?" *(A.S.)*

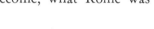

Alabama (date unknown).   *Custer County, Nebraska (1887).*

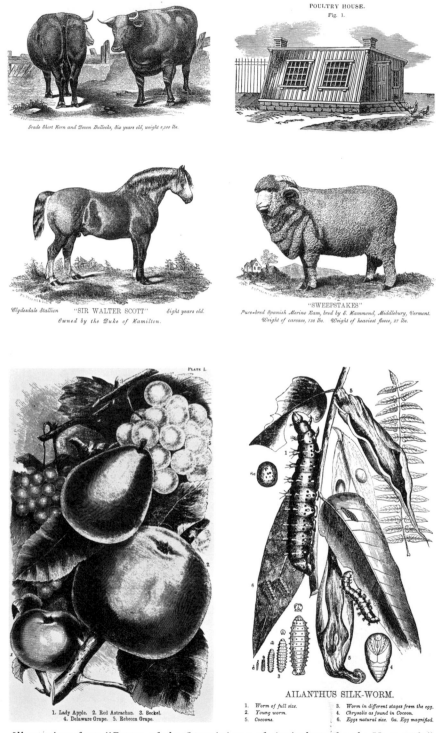

Grade Short Horn and Devon Bullocks, six years old, weight 2,100 lbs.

POULTRY HOUSE.
Fig. 1.

Clydesdale Stallion "SIR WALTER SCOTT" Eight years old.
Owned by the Duke of Hamilton.

"SWEEPSTAKES"
Pure-bred Spanish Merino Ram, bred by E. Hammond, Middlebury, Vermont.
Weight of carcass, 138 lbs. Weight of heaviest fleece, 27 lbs.

PLATE 1.

1. Lady Apple. 2. Red Astrachan. 3. Seckel.
4. Delaware Grape. 5. Rebecca Grape.

AILANTHUS SILK-WORM.

1. Worm of full size.
2. Young worm.
5. Cocoons.
3. Worm in different stages from the egg.
4. Chrysalis as found in Cocoon.
6. Eggs natural size. 6a. Egg magnified.

Illustrations from "Report of the Commissioner of Agriculture for the Year 1862".

The Department Is Built

PRESIDENT ABRAHAM LINCOLN on May 15, 1862, signed a bill that established the Department of Agriculture. The bill was one of three designed to serve the interests of the family farmer. The other two were the Homestead Act, May 20, and the Land-Grant College Act, July 2. Isaac Newton took the oath of office as first Commissioner of Agriculture on July 1. He inherited the staff of nine employees and facilities of the Agricultural Division of the Patent Office. The new Department a year later had a horticulturist, a chemist, an entomologist, a statistician, an editor, and 24 others.

The Department occupied six rooms in the basement of the Patent Office Building, now known as the Civil Service Commission Building. Its experimental work was done in a propagating garden between present-day Madison and Adams Drives and Fourth and Sixth Streets, Northwest. A larger area, between Independence and Constitution Avenues and Twelfth and Fourteenth Streets, was transferred to the Department for an experimental farm when the Union Army no longer needed it as a cattle yard. The Congress appropriated 80 thousand dollars for the Department's expenses the first year.

Commissioner Newton began in 1863 to try to get an appropriation for an office building. The Congress appropriated 100 thousand dollars for the purpose in 1867. The building was ready the following year. It was near the site of the present Administration Building. It served as headquarters for the Department until 1930.

Even before the Department was established, its advocates urged that it be made an Executive Department, headed by a Secretary who would be a member of the Cabinet. Agriculture, the single most important economic activity in the Nation, they said, should be represented in the innermost councils of Government. Finally, in 1889, the Congress elevated the Department to Cabinet status. The Department then had 488 employees and an annual appropriation of 1.1 million dollars. The number of employees jumped to 1,577 in 1891, when the weather service of the Army Signal Corps was transferred to the Department and the Weather Bureau was established.

The appointment of James Wilson of Iowa as Secretary of Agriculture in 1897 began a new era in the Department's history. He

7

The Department of Agriculture (in the foreground) in 1908.

The old Administration Building.

served 16 years and set guidelines that made it an outstanding research organization.

Personnel and appropriations reflected the physical growth: The Department had 2,444 employees in 1897 and 13,858 in 1912. The Congress appropriated 2.5 million dollars for the 1897 fiscal year and 20.4 million in 1912. Secretary Wilson had asked for 2.5 million dollars for a new administration building to be flanked by laboratory wings. He got 1.5 million dollars. He directed that the wings be constructed and that the central part be left to a future time. The wings were completed in 1907.

The Department had a few employees working outside Washington almost from its beginning. Some carried out research projects. Others, including employees of the Bureau of Animal Industry, were working on disease eradication and similar programs. The Department established experimental farms and laboratories in various parts of the country to work on specific problems. There was, for example, an experimental tea farm at Summerville, S.C., from 1880 to 1887. Most experimental work, however, was carried out in State agricultural experiment stations, established on a nationwide basis with the passage of the Hatch Act in 1887.

The Arlington Farm, a tract of about 400 acres on the Virginia side of the Potomac River opposite Washington, was acquired in 1900. The Bureau of Plant Industry used the land until 1941, when it was transferred to the War Department as a site for the Pentagon. The experimental work was transferred to Beltsville, Md., 15 miles from Washington, where a farm of 475 acres had been acquired in 1910 for the investigations of the Bureau of Animal Industry in animal husbandry and dairying. Before long, the greatly enlarged Beltsville farm had become the Agricultural Research Center. To get information about scientific developments to farmers in a usable form, the Department began issuing farmers' bulletins in 1889 and in 1894 started to publish as the Yearbook of Agriculture the books that since 1849 had been known as *Part II: Agriculture* of the annual reports of the Commissioner of Patents and *Agricultural Report*.

It also was necessary to adapt results of research to local conditions. So, in 1906, the first county agent was appointed to do something about boll weevils, which were destroying cotton in Texas. Other agents were appointed in the South and elsewhere. The Congress extended the system throughout the United States in 1914, with the passage of the Smith-Lever Act, which provided for the cooperative financing of the county agent system, operated in each State under the direction of the land-grant college.

The First World War meant increased emphasis on production—and therefore on methods and equipment—to meet military and civilian needs. The number of employees rose sharply during the

The lake on the grounds of the Department (about 1895).

The west wing.

The Administration Building and part of the east wing.

The Department of Agriculture buildings (1961).

11

war and, after a postwar drop, increased slowly beginning in 1922. The Department by 1926 had 20,742 employees, of whom 4,707 were stationed in Washington. Little had been done since 1907 to provide space, and many employees worked in rented buildings all over the District of Columbia.

Construction of the main Administration Building, connecting the laboratory wings that had been completed in 1907, was authorized by the Congress in 1926. Construction began in 1928 and was completed in 1930. One construction engineer called it "the most beautiful edifice of any kind in the world." Authority also was given to build the Cotton Annex, which was finished in 1937, and an "expansible" building—the South Building.

The South Building was much larger than the Administration Building and Cotton Annex together. Construction began on June 1, 1930, on two wings. Now there are seven. The entire project, including the James Wilson and Seaman A. Knapp Memorial Arches, which connect the Administration and South Buildings, was completed in 1937. It cost 10 million dollars. The South Building has 4,292 rooms and a floor space of 1,335,522 square feet.

Outside Washington, additional installations at Beltsville, the new Forest Products Laboratory in Madison, Wis., and four regional laboratories dedicated to developing industrial uses for farm products were particularly important during the 1930's.

The Congress passed the Agricultural Adjustment Act in 1933. The act and later legislation assigned the Department responsibility for assisting in the stabilization of farm prices, with a goal of securing for farmers parity of income with other parts of the economy. The Department later was assigned responsibility for new farm credit programs, soil and forest conservation, rural electrification, and research in many branches of economics and science.

The new functions, basic departures from the earlier duties of research and regulation, required a larger staff. The Department had 26,544 employees in 1933. The high point in Department employment was in 1937, when there were 106,217 employees, of whom 12,420 worked in the District of Columbia and 93,797 were stationed elsewhere.

On June 30, 1961, the Department had 87,262 employees, of whom 11,686 worked in the District of Columbia and 75,576 were stationed elsewhere. These employees worked in nearly 10 thousand offices located in every State and Territory of the Union and in about 55 cities abroad. They were responsible for handling 7.3 billion dollars, appropriated for the conservation of agricultural and forest resources, foreign assistance, investment in repayable resource and farm loans, and the protection of the farm part of our economy and the Nation's food supply. *(Wayne D. Rasmussen* and *Gladys L. Baker)*

People's Colleges

THE PEOPLE who surged westward a century ago dreamed of a new kind of education. They wanted colleges that would meet the practical needs of all citizens more directly than did the institutions that stressed classical studies and training for a few learned professions. They wanted "people's colleges" that their sons and daughters could attend at minimum cost and that would put emphasis on research and instruction that might increase agricultural production, improve the conditions of rural life, and support the young Nation's growing industry.

A Vermont man, the son and grandson of blacksmiths, got national action for this idea. Senator Justin Smith Morrill's first bill was vetoed by President James Buchanan in 1859. He introduced it again in 1862. It proposed that portions of federally owned land be sold and the proceeds used for the "perpetual endowment" in each State of at least one college whose main aim would be "without excluding other scientific and classical studies, and including military tactics, to teach such branches of learning as are related to agriculture and the mechanic arts, in such manner as the legislatures of the States may respectively prescribe, in order to promote the liberal and practical education of the industrial classes in the several pursuits and professions in life." Senator Morrill's bill, as enacted by the Congress and signed by President Lincoln, became the foundation of our land-grant college system, whose 68 members have set a pattern in democratic education.

As interested as any in the legislation and the opportunities it offered were Iowans, who were establishing a new State in the fertile prairie. No sooner had they begun to till their land than their thoughts and efforts turned toward a school of agriculture. In the new capital of Des Moines, three young legislators presented a draft of a bill for an agricultural college to the General Assembly in 1858. The bill was passed quickly and signed into law by the Governor. When Senator Morrill's bill became a Federal law in 1862, the General Assembly was in special session to consider concerns of the Civil War. The Assembly promptly took advantage of the proffered aid, and thus Iowa became the first State to accept the provisions and responsibilities of the Land-Grant College Act. Iowa State University is an example of the land-grant institutions, each adapted to the special needs of its State.

The campus of Iowa State University in the 1890's.

The Memorial Union.

The agronomy building.

The administration building at Iowa State University.

When the first students arrived at the new college in Ames, they came as boys and girls together—a departure from the accepted pattern of the day, when coeducation on the college level was practically nonexistent. Ever since, Iowa State's only requirements for admission have pertained to scholarship. No one has been turned away because of sex, race, creed, lack of wealth, or inability to play football. The new education was popular from the beginning. The first freshman class numbered 173. There were 800 students in 1900 and 10 thousand in 1961.

Iowa State has changed, expanded, and broadened to meet changed needs. At first only a "course in agriculture" and a "course of mechanics" were offered. Today students are enrolled in 80 undergraduate and graduate disciplines and subdisciplines in five major areas: Agriculture, engineering, home economics, science and humanities, and veterinary medicine. To carry knowledge to all the people, Iowa State has developed extension services that have made the campus as broad as the State.

From the beginning, the United States Department of Agriculture and Iowa State have been working partners. Many names, among them those of James Wilson ("Tama Jim") and Seaman Asahel Knapp, are writ large in the histories of both.

Iowa State established an experimental creamery in 1879. It began a course in dairying in 1880 and in 1897 inaugurated the first college curriculum for a degree of bachelor in science in dairy industry. It offered a course in forestry in 1874 and in 1904 began the professional training of foresters. Instruction began in 1905 in agricultural journalism—another pioneering effort. Iowa State first offered a course in farm mechanics in 1902 and graduated its first full-fledged agricultural engineer in 1910 to keep up with the growing mechanization of farming.

The young college and the Iowa General Assembly already were laying foundations for an experiment station when Federal aid was granted through the Hatch Act. The Iowa Agricultural Experiment Station was established on March 2, 1888. Research since has been carried on at a quickened pace and in close partnership with the Department of Agriculture and other State experiment stations.

The early experiments were important, but they cannot begin to match the tremendous advances since 1940. Many of the first studies were in the art of agriculture rather than in the science of agriculture. They concerned themselves with the rate of seeding, the manner of pruning, the types of feeding. Then came the introduction of more knowledge from the advancing sciences of mathematics, physics, chemistry, botany, zoology, bacteriology, genetics, and nucleonics and the wider application of the principles of engineering. Today the emphasis is not on how to grow corn but on how corn grows.

Men at Iowa State in the 1930's began work on inbred lines of corn that have been used almost exclusively in Iowa hybrids. One new variety of oats after another was developed to keep ahead of new threats of disease and to produce stiffer straw. The State and the Midwest received a new crop in the form of soybeans, and Iowa farmers began to plant varieties developed and proved at Iowa State. Yields were increased further by the application of fertilizers and better methods of tillage. The results of research helped send livestock to market earlier and more economically.

Iowa State still works with Iowa farmers for increased productivity, but the emphasis has shifted to broader areas. It has encompassed farm management and how to get the greatest return from labor and capital. It has entered the realm of consumer preference. It has stressed quality, better processing, and better handling of food. It has sought new, larger, and more profitable markets for farm products. It has shown increased interest in economics and sociology as means of insuring stable and attractive living conditions for rural and urban families.

Iowa State University in a typical year has enrolled more undergraduates in agriculture (about 1,800) than any other institution. The largest single group of graduates from the College of Agriculture goes into business and industry associated with agriculture. Another large group enters agricultural education. Agricultural service claims a third group; research, another; and agricultural communications, still another. A growing area is conservation and outdoor recreation activities. About one-fifth of the graduates become farmers. More than 500 occupations in eight major fields of endeavor are open to graduates in agriculture.

College instruction in agriculture has come to be centered on three principal needs: For farming, for specialized work in agricultural businesses and industries, and for public service in agriculture. Like many other institutions, Iowa State has been developing an advanced curriculum for the gifted student, who takes additional work in mathematics, statistics, physics, biology, and the social sciences.

An outstanding accomplishment of the land-grant colleges is the development of ways to carry the new knowledge in agriculture to the people who can use it best. The colleges long ago invited farmers to the campuses to see good farming practices and to hear what the professors had to say. Iowa State was one of the first to go to the farmers. Shortly after the institution was established, the idea of sending some of the faculty to conduct institutes away from Ames was put forth. At the first, in 1870, President A. S. Welch conducted a 5-day course for farmers.

Iowa farmers and educators undertook pioneer work that led to the Cooperative Extension Service in Agriculture and Home Eco-

Tests during freshman days.

A class in summer.

Familiar in Iowa towns 50 years ago were trains of agricultural exhibits.

Iowans at an extension demonstration.

Measuring wind and moisture in an Iowa cornfield.

Irradiation equipment used in studying biological materials.

Theory and practice in the laboratory.

nomics as an integral part of the land-grant institutions. In 1903, near Terrell, Tex., Seaman Knapp supervised an early farmer-conducted farm demonstration that opened the idea to the South. He was the man who had helped establish some of the agricultural research and teaching at Iowa State, where he had served as a professor of agriculture and as president and where in 1882 he drafted an early bill for Federal support of agricultural research.

P. G. Holden, a professor of agronomy, was speaking in 1903 to the annual meeting of the Sioux County Farmer's Institute. The farmers wanted a county demonstration farm, and Holden said he would ask Iowa State to furnish the educational and technical help. The county supervisors agreed to meet the cost of labor and other local expenses. Thus was born a cooperative movement based on the initiative of farmers, supported by county appropriations on land furnished by the county, and conducted in cooperation with the college and the Department of Agriculture.

The Iowa General Assembly established an agricultural extension service in 1906. The movement continued to grow as fast as funds would permit. The Cooperative Extension Act, known as the Smith-Lever Act, was passed by the Congress in 1914. All counties were brought into county extension work by 1918, and at least one agent was employed in each county.

Extension work in Iowa, as in other States, has changed greatly as the concerns and interests of people have broadened. Modern programs embrace the major areas of efficiency in agricultural production; marketing, distribution, and utilization of farm products; conservation and development of natural resources; management; family living; leadership; community improvement and resource development; and public affairs. The Extension staff in Iowa totals more than 400 persons, two-thirds of whom are employed in county extension offices. The total budget in 1962 was about 4 million dollars, which Federal, State, and county governments shared.

Mrs. Mary B. Welch, the wife of President Welch, taught "domestic economy," which was primarily cookery. From this foundation developed the new science of home economics. Other household arts, such as sewing and laundering, were added. A course in home management was offered as early as 1885. The idea from the start was that this program would apply to the entire family. Some graduates in home economics work in industry and education, but nearly all of them sooner or later become homemakers. Courses in home economics therefore retain a primary interest in the family and are broad enough to include a background for civic responsibilities.

The college introduced a 4-year course in veterinary medicine in 1903. Now the College of Veterinary Medicine has a diagnostic laboratory, a research institute, and a veterinary medical program.

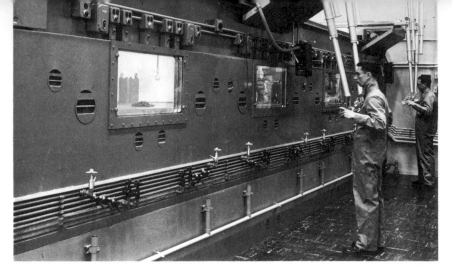

The Institute of Atomic Research at Iowa State University.

The modern land-grant institution has a flexibility that enables it to meet new demands. Iowa State's official name illustrates the point. Founded as Iowa Agricultural College and Model Farm, it was known later as Iowa State College of Agriculture and Mechanic Arts. The Iowa General Assembly in 1958 changed the name to Iowa State University of Science and Technology. The change recognized the fact that the institution is in fact a university, whose interests embrace the agricultural sciences, the basic sciences, all technology, the humanities, and the social sciences.

This is no backwoods institution, no "cow college," as some used to call these colleges. A research laboratory of the United States Atomic Energy Commission is operated as part of the university's Institute for Atomic Research. There are departments of aerospace engineering and nuclear engineering. A statistical center equipped with digital computers aids scientific research of many kinds. Two radio stations and a television station operated by the university take the campus to the people of Iowa. The National Animal Disease Laboratory, operated by the Department of Agriculture, employs hundreds of scientists and assistants near the campus.

Land-grant institutions enrolled one-fifth of the total college population in 1962. They granted 40 percent of the doctoral degrees in all subjects. These doctorates included about half of the Nation's total in the science, engineering, and health professions; all of those in agriculture; and approximately one-fourth of the total in the arts and languages, business and commerce, and education. But the purpose of land-grant institutions is the same as it was 100 years ago: To provide educational opportunities for all, to conduct research for the betterment of man, and to disseminate knowledge and information to all people. *(C. R. Elder)*

Men and Milestones

MANY MEN long ago planted the seeds that produced modern agriculture and the Department of Agriculture. The discoverers, explorers, colonists, and pioneers; yes. After them the farmers, inventors, scientists, administrators. The seeds they sowed were great, but we need not use that label for them, because to Nature one seed is not greater than another. What counts, in total, is a symbiosis, in which different organisms live, work, and progress in an association that is of advantage to all. The seedbed was well prepared before 1862. An inventive generation produced a cast-iron plow, a plow with interchangeable parts, mowing machines, barbed wire, a steel plow, a refrigerator, and other machines that moved agriculture to the threshold of the machine age. One of the inventors was Cyrus Hall McCormick (1809–1884), who carried forward the project his father had worked on for 20 years. One day in July of 1831 young McCormick tried out on the family farm in Rockbridge County, Virginia, the crude machine that he called a reaper. It worked. It cut 6 acres of oats. He advertised that he would sell the machine for 50 dollars, but he had no sale until 1840. Two years later he sold seven at 100 dollars each. He moved his factory to Chicago in 1847. Farmers of the Middle West welcomed the machine: It helped them settle and work new land; with it they could cut their grain with less work when it was ready. McCormick's use of modern business methods enabled him to eclipse some of his competitors, who also had invented practical reapers.

Of a different type was the contribution of Henry Leavitt Ellsworth (1791–1858), who has been called the founder of the Department of Agriculture. Ellsworth was a lawyer, farmer, leader of an agricultural society, and head of an insurance company in Hartford, Conn., before he became head of the newly established Patent Office in 1836. He received from naval and consular officers overseas certain seeds and plants, which he distributed to farmers, without Government authority or aid. He pleaded forcefully and constantly for Government aid to agriculture, and in 1839 he got an appropriation of a thousand dollars to collect and distribute new and valuable seeds and plants, carry on agricultural investigations, and collect agricultural statistics. He foresaw the importance of crop improvement through selection of outstanding varieties: "If the application of the sciences be yet further made to husbandry, what

21

vast improvements may be anticipated! Mowing and reaping will, it is believed, soon be chiefly performed on smooth land by horse power. Some have regretted that modern improvements make so important changes of employment—but the march of the arts and sciences is onward, and the greatest happiness of the greatest number is the motto of the patriot."

Daniel Lee, M.D., a former editor of the Genesee Farmer and professor of agriculture, was hired in 1849 as a "practical and scientific agriculturist" to supervise agricultural matters in the Patent Office and to prepare separate annual reports on agriculture. The first, dated 1849, was the seed of the Yearbooks of Agriculture. Lee decried the "universal impoverishment" of the soil: "Neither the earnest recommendation of the illustrious farmer of Mount Vernon, nor the prayers of two generations of agriculturists, nor the painful fact that nearly all tilled lands were becoming less and less productive, could induce any Legislature to foster the study of agriculture as a science." He estimated that a farmer lost 175 dollars' worth of soil constituents every time he raised and sold 1 thousand dollars' worth of produce. His reports covered a wide range—tillage, runoff, drainage, insects, fertilizers, the improvement of farm animals, rural science, statistics of weather. Few now are aware of his name, but the principles he stood for—the spirit of scientific inquiry, practical wisdom, intellectual honesty, and forthright advocacy of what he considered necessary for agricultural progress—have been guiding principles of the Department of Agriculture.

The work of the Division of Agriculture of the Patent Office expanded. A chemist, a botanist, and an entomologist joined the staff. Townend Glover (1813-1888), a British entomologist, who was 23 years old when he came to the United States, was hired to collect statistics and other information on seeds, fruit, and insects in the United States. He made a thorough study of insects of the Southern States and gathered an extensive collection of insects, birds, models of fruit, and herbarium plants. In 1865, he represented the Department of Agriculture at an exposition in Paris of insects useful or injurious to crops. In his report he warned: "As European insects are liable at any time to be introduced into this country in roots, bark, wood, grasses, and seeds, their nature and habits cannot be too well studied or understood here. It is well known that several of the insects most destructive to our crops are of European origin, and I would suggest that all foreign seeds and plants imported by this department be subjected to a careful investigation."

Isaac Newton (1800-1867) grew up in Pennsylvania, where he managed a model dairy farm. He carried on a butter trade with special customers, including the White House in Washington. After the formation of the United States Agricultural Society, he was delegate to many of its meetings, at which he repeatedly introduced

Cyrus Hall McCormick.   *Henry Leavitt Ellsworth.*

Left to right: Major H. A. Meyers, Superintendent of Seed Unit; William Saunders, Superintendent of Gardens; Colonel E. M. Whitaker, Chief of Correspondence; Major G. B. Newton, Chief Clerk of Department; Isaac Newton, Commissioner of Agriculture; W. E. Gardiner, Private Secretary; J. R. Dodge, Statistician; Thomas Antisell, M.D., Chemist; Isaac Newton, Jr., Superintendent of Experimental Farm; Townend Glover, Entomologist. Photograph was made about 1867.

23

Marion Dorset.

Oliver Hudson Kelley.

Harvey Washington Wiley.

resolutions calling on Congress to establish a Department of Agriculture. In 1861 he was appointed Superintendent of the Agricultural Division of the Patent Office. When the Department of Agriculture was organized the next year, President Lincoln, whose friend he had become, made him the first Commissioner of Agriculture. Newton established an agricultural library and a museum. He selected the present grounds of the Department of Agriculture, a 40-acre tract some distance from his office in the old Patent Office Building. One July afternoon in 1866, as a storm was approaching, he remembered that some wheat samples on the experimental tract had been cut but had not been taken in. He rushed over to attend to them. He bustled about in his high silk hat and frock coat until he suffered a sunstroke. He never fully recovered and died the following summer. Lincoln in his Message to Congress in 1864 said: "The Agricultural Department, under the supervision of its present energetic and faithful head, is rapidly commending itself to the great and vital interest it was created to advance. It is peculiarly the people's Department, in which they feel more directly concerned than in any other."

One of Newton's appointments was William Saunders (1822–1900), scion of a family of noted gardeners in Scotland, who was called to Washington in 1862 for consultation about laying out the Department grounds and planning its horticultural work. As botanist and superintendent of the propagating garden, he filled an important place in the Department for 38 years. He laid out many of the parks in Washington. He was instrumental in introducing a number of useful plants from abroad, among them the navel orange. His interest in rural social conditions led him to join with Oliver Hudson Kelley (1826–1913) in organizing the Patrons of Husbandry.

Kelley, a New Englander, had settled on a farm near Itasca, Minn. He went to Washington as a clerk in the Department of Agriculture and was sent through the Southern States to survey agricultural conditions. He was struck by what he called a lack of progressive spirit among the agricultural classes. On the trip he got the idea of organizing the farmers into a fraternal association. In 1867, with six other men, he organized the Patrons of Husbandry, later known as the National Grange. Kelley was elected secretary. A few months later he started for the West, dispensing charters for local granges to pay his expenses. He continued the organization work and emphasized the social, intellectual, and fraternal benefits of the order; others saw in it a way to attack the monopolies that were thought to be oppressing the farmers. The organization flourished and grew, a landmark in cooperative effort and an example of the power of united endeavors.

Agriculture (but not only agriculture) at times has encountered roadblocks to further progress in one or another of its overlapping segments. The actions to remove the hindrances—pests, diseases, economic maladjustments, inadequate experimentation and sharing of knowledge, or whatever—are the milestones of farm progress, especially since the 1880's, when agriculture was becoming more extensive and intensive and problems therefore were building up. Each is worth a book, but there is space here only for brief mention of a few. One example is the work of F. L. Kilborne, Cooper Curtice, Theobald Smith, and Dr. D. E. Salmon, a distinguished veterinarian who headed the new Bureau of Animal Industry, in solving the puzzle of the spread of cattle-tick fever. Another example was the work of Dr. Harvey Washington Wiley (1844–1930), who came to the Department of Agriculture in 1883 as Chief of the Bureau of Chemistry. He often said that he developed the Bureau from a room in a basement, where four scientists and one dishwasher led an isolated life, into 16 practical laboratory divisions. His first work with the Department included chemical studies of sugar and sugar-producing crops, but even more noteworthy was his campaign against misbranded and adulterated food, which led to the passage of the first Food and Drug Act in 1906. Another was Marion Dorset (1872–1935), who entered the Department in 1894 as a biochemist and later became Chief of the Biochemic Division of the Bureau of Animal Industry. His scientific contributions had many applications in the livestock, meat, and dairy industries and in public health. He was known especially for his discovery of the anti-hog-cholera serum. He was one of the first scientists to make chemical analyses of the tubercle bacillus. He organized the system of Federal inspection in establishments licensed by the Government to manufacture serums, viruses, toxins, and related veterinary biological products. He formulated also the laboratory procedures in the administration of the Federal Meat Inspection Act.

The first State agricultural experiment station in the United States was organized largely through the efforts of Wilbur Olin Atwater (1844–1907) in Connecticut in 1875. He was its director for 14 years. The Hatch Act in 1887 provided for the establishment of similar stations in all States and Territories in the Union. The Office of Experiment Stations was formed in the Department of Agriculture as a central agency for the stations. Dr. Atwater was its first director. In his first annual report he wrote: "In studying the food of animals we have no right to neglect the food of man. The principles involved are essentially the same. The majority of our people and practically all wage-workers spend and must spend at least half the money they earn for food. . . . The need and the wisdom of such studies require no urging." When the Congress appropriated funds for investigations of human nutrition, Dr. Atwater returned to the Connecticut station to become chief of the

26

Wilbur Olin Atwater.

Seaman Asahel Knapp.

Henry Wallace (father of Henry C. and grandfather of Henry A.) and James Wilson.

investigations. He prepared our first extensive table of food values, a pioneering and revolutionary work.

Alongside his achievements are those of Seaman Asahel Knapp (1833–1911), a farmer, teacher, and publisher, who urged farmers to produce more stock and abandon the one-crop system. Knapp in 1886 began growing rice in Louisiana and later in other States for a corporation engaged in agricultural development. Secretary of Agriculture James Wilson sent him overseas to seek new varieties of rice. The result was the introduction of Japanese rice and improvements in growing the crop. During his work in the South, he recognized the importance of crop diversification. He began to set up demonstration farms to show what could be done in growing crops other than cotton. When the cotton boll weevil became widespread in 1903, Dr. Knapp and Secretary Wilson visited the infested region. Dr. Knapp was put in charge of bringing to the farmer on his own farm information that would enable him to grow cotton despite the weevil. In 1906, the first county agent was appointed. Within a few years, Knapp's Farmers Cooperative Demonstration Work had been expanded to include boys' and girls' club work and home demonstration work.

James Wilson (1836–1920) served as Secretary for 16 dynamic years, under Presidents McKinley, Theodore Roosevelt, and Taft. Wilson was born in Scotland and came to this country in 1851. He settled first in Connecticut and then in Tama County, Iowa. He was elected to the House of Representatives, where he became a member of the Committee on Agriculture and began to be called "Tama Jim" to differentiate him from Senator James Falconer Wilson, also of Iowa. As Secretary of Agriculture, Wilson advanced the Department's status as a scientific institution, increased the number of its professional employees, persuaded Congress to appropriate money for new buildings, encouraged farm demonstration and cooperative extension work, started investigations in agricultural economics and farm credit, and, when the National Forests were placed in the Department's custody, put reforestation and conservation in positions of importance. He transformed his burgeoning agency into an outstanding research, regulatory, educational, and custodial institution, all of whose parts and functions he knew so well that he could answer the questions of congressional committees without first consulting a battery of experts.

Gifford Pinchot (1865–1946), the first professional forester in the United States and the first Chief of the Forest Service, began crusading for forestry the very day he was graduated from Yale. He began the first systematic forestry work in the United States when he became forest manager of the George W. Vanderbilt estate in North Carolina. When he became head of the Division of Forestry in 1898, lumber interests were slashing their way through the Nation's forests with little thought of what might be left. He introduced better forestry methods into the operations of owners of timberland by helping them make working plans and by demonstrating good practices on the ground. When the Forest Service was created in 1905 and the National Forests were placed in the custody of the Department, Pinchot developed effective protection and administration for them. He made the conservation of natural resources a national issue. During a controversy between Pinchot and Richard A. Ballinger, then Secretary of the Interior, over the leasing of public coal lands and other issues, President Taft dismissed Pinchot, who later became Governor of Pennsylvania and then professor of forestry at Yale. A year before he died he said, "I am a forester all the time—have been, and shall be, to my dying day." He was. At the time of his death, when he was 81 years old, he was working on a new forest management plan for his estate at Milford, Pa., and crusading for conservation.

Two other men are outstanding for their work in conservation— Hugh Hammond Bennett (1881–1960) and Curtis Fletcher Marbut (1863–1935). Dr. Marbut, a soil scientist who revolutionized the American conception of soil development and influenced world thought in this field, was for many years Chief of the Soil Survey Division. He has been called the father of the modern soil survey as we know it today. During his career, he traveled in practically every county of the United States and many countries to study soils. His great contribution to soil science was the development and application of a consistent, comparable system of soil classification, based entirely on soil characteristics. The citation accompanying an honorary doctor's degree from the University of Missouri in 1916 read: "The one who knows more about the soils of the United States than any other man has ever known."

Hugh Bennett received recognition as the "father of soil conservation." His crusade against soil erosion lasted for more than half a century. The publication of his bulletin, "Soil Erosion, A National Menace," in 1928 was a milestone in his fight to secure recognition of soil erosion as a national problem. The Congress appropriated funds in 1929 for research on the cause and control of soil erosion, and Dr. Bennett was given responsibility for directing the soil erosion investigations, which were carried on as a cooperative project with State agricultural experiment stations. In 1933 he organized and administered the Soil Erosion Service, which was established as an emergency agency of the Department of Interior, and carried on a nationwide program to provide technical assistance for farmers and ranchers in erosion-control projects. Legislation passed in 1935 declared it to be the policy of Congress "to provide permanently for the control and prevention of soil erosion" and established the Soil Conservation Service in the Department of Agriculture to replace the Soil Erosion Service. Dr. Bennett became its first Chief, a position he held until October 1951. His program provided for an integrated attack against erosion. His slogan was "to use each parcel of land according to its capability and treat it according to its needs." Beginning in 1937, the Soil Conservation Service began shifting its emphasis from demonstration projects to providing technical assistance for organized groups of farmers. Twenty-two States passed enabling legislation for the establishment of soil conservation districts in 1937. Other States followed. He retired from active service in 1952, but he continued to work for soil conservation. He advised other countries on land use problems and continued to speak and write. At the time of his death, the Milwaukee Journal editorialized, "Great men usually are memorialized in stone or metal but the earth itself is being carved into a memorial to Hugh Bennett."

The National Farmers Union was born during Tama Jim's tenure. In its history, the name of Charles S. Barrett (1866-1935) is prominent. He was its leader from 1906 to 1928. He was a farmer and teacher in his native Georgia, a leader in progressive movements, and one of the first to join the Farmers Union in Upson County. When the Georgia State Union was organized in 1905, he became president of it. As national president, he was in close touch with representatives of the Government. He was a member of important commissions. He represented farmers at the Paris Peace Conference in 1919. When cotton brought 8 cents a pound in 1908, he started a "plow-up" campaign. During the money crisis of 1907-1908, he attacked the commodity exchanges. A man of conviction, he made his organization one also of conviction.

Edward Asbury O'Neal (1875-1958) was born on a farm in Alabama, and he returned to it when he finished college. He believed always that agriculture was best served when it was in the hands of farmers operating their own farms, working for and managing for themselves. He served in turn as president of his county Farm Bureau and vice president and president of the Alabama Farm Bureau Federation and the American Farm Bureau Federation. Hard work, mental alertness, a friendly interest in people, a genius for cooperation and organization, and an abiding faith in the ability of united farmers to help themselves made him a leader in American agriculture: "Farmers in every part of the country must think and act together through their own organization under leaders of their own choosing. There must be a sound national program for all agriculture." He fought for equality for agriculture as a major aim of the Farm Bureau. He and other farm leaders had a role in securing the enactment of the original Agricultural Adjustment Act and other legislation to secure parity for agriculture.

Louise Stanley (1883-1954) was head of the Home Economics

30

Gifford Pinchot.   *Curtis Fletcher Marbut.*

Department of the University of Missouri when she and other home economists were called to Washington by Secretary Henry C. Wallace in 1923 to discuss the organization of a Bureau of Home Economics in the Department of Agriculture, and she became Chief of the new Bureau. She directed the first national survey of farm housing; more than 600 thousand families supplied facts on the physical conditions of farmhouses, and from it came nationwide

Hugh Hammond Bennett.   *Charles S. Barrett.*

Louise Stanley.

Edward Asbury O'Neal.

programs for improving rural conditions. She stressed the application of science to the solution of day-to-day problems of families. She served as chairman of the committee on education for home and family life of the White House Conference on Child Health and Protection in 1930. She was a member of the Food and Nutrition Board, National Research Council, for several years. She was official representative of the Department of Agriculture to the

John Hollis Bankhead.

Howard Ross Tolley.

American Standards Association—the first woman to hold such an appointment. During the war she helped our country and others on matters of research, nutrition, and dietary deficiencies of diverse groups of people. To her work she brought the ability and wisdom of a practical homemaker, scientist, and administrator and the thoughtfulness of a kind woman.

Howard Ross Tolley (1889–1958) was a leader in developing agricultural economics as a field of research and in shaping agricultural policy during a period of change. As Chief of the Program Planning Division of the Agricultural Adjustment Administration, he helped develop a long-range, conservation-oriented approach to farm problems that became the basis of the Soil Conservation and Domestic Allotment Act of 1936. Dr. Tolley was given responsibility for translating his ideas into action with his appointment as Administrator of the Agricultural Adjustment Administration in 1936. He became Chief of the Bureau of Agricultural Economics in 1938 and had the task of shifting the emphasis in the Bureau from straight research to long-range policy planning for the Secretary and the Department as a whole. He took on another pioneering job in 1946 as chief economist for the newly established Food and Agriculture Organization of the United Nations. That position as well as a later one, vice president of the Ford Foundation, gave him opportunity to utilize his experience and his creative mind in helping to solve world problems as well as American farm problems. The Washington Post commented editorially at the time of his death in 1958: "Tolley helped to plant and nurture the seeds of agricultural policy that during the last 25 years have grown into programs which are now as familiar a part of the American farm scene as a silo."

John Hollis Bankhead (1872–1946), of Alabama, served in the Senate from 1930 until his death. As a Senate leader for the administration in handling important farm legislation, he had a big role in the fight for farm parity. He sponsored the Bankhead Cotton Control Act of 1934, which established marketing quotas for cotton with a penalty tax on cotton ginned in excess of individual quotas. Later legislation provided for the use of marketing quotas to control the supplies of other major crops marketed. He was instrumental in securing the enactment of legislation providing price-supporting loans for cotton and other crops. The Bankhead-Jones Farm Tenant Act of 1937 provided loans to enable farm laborers, sharecroppers, and tenants to become farmowners, and authorized a continuation of the rehabilitation loan program, which had been carried on for the relief of destitute and low-income farmers. The act directed the Secretary of Agriculture to develop a program of land conservation and utilization, including the retirement of submarginal land. Senator Bankhead also sponsored legislation to increase Federal support for State agricultural experiment stations and extension services. Senator Lister Hill said at the time of Bankhead's death: "He labored long and tirelessly for American agriculture and was recognized throughout the Nation as the valiant champion of the American farmer and agriculture's foremost leader in Congress."

George William Norris (1861–1944), a Nebraskan, served in Congress from 1903 through 1943 and in the early twenties became the symbol and leader of progressive legislation. He was an outspoken advocate of the necessity of relief for agriculture. He worked for conservation of the Nation's natural resources and public ownership of the generation, transmission, and distribution of hydroelectric power. He sponsored the Tennessee Valley Authority Act of 1933, which brought to a successful conclusion his prolonged fight to save valuable Government properties at Muscle Shoals, Ala., from private exploitation. The first large dam built in Tennessee by TVA was named for him.

Charles Linza McNary (1874–1944), the son of a pioneer family of Oregon, grew up on a farm near Salem and later owned and managed a fruit farm. His 27-year career in the Congress was one of prestige and influence. His interests and visions were broad, but his chief concerns were the welfare of agriculture, the advancement of reforestation, irrigation, reclamation, and development of water power. He introduced the McNary-Haugen bill in the Senate in 1924. Its objective was to secure economic equality for agriculture. It passed twice and was vetoed. He sponsored the Clarke-McNary Act, which broadened Federal participation in the better management of forest lands and increased fire protection. The act made possible the purchase of lands on the watershed of navigable streams for timber production. Most of the National Forests east of the Mississippi River have been formed under this act and the Weeks Law. The McSweeney-McNary Law in 1928 set up a 10-year program that included a system of forest and range experiment stations, expanded research in forest products, and a nationwide survey of forest resources and requirements.

George Washington Carver (1864–1943) was a pioneer of agricultural research and chemurgy. He was born of slave parents on a farm in Missouri. After receiving a master's degree in agriculture from Iowa State College, he was placed in charge of the greenhouse. Booker T. Washington invited him to join the faculty at Tuskegee Institute as director of agriculture in 1896. Later Dr. Carver became the director of the Tuskegee Agricultural Research and Experiment Station. By creative research, he developed pigments for paints, wood stains, wallpapers, and ceramic products from the clays of Alabama. He developed more than 118 products from the sweetpotato. He made more than 300 products from peanuts. He produced

Charles Linza McNary.   *George William Norris.*

paving blocks, cordage, paper, fiber for rope, and many other products from cotton. From the soybean he made several types of flour and many other products. His contribution to the field of agricultural chemistry greatly expanded the agricultural economy of the South.

Liberty Hyde Bailey (1858–1954) grew up on a fruit farm in Michigan. After serving as professor of horticulture and landscape gardening at Michigan Agricultural College, he became director of the College of Agriculture of Cornell University in 1888. Theodore Roosevelt made him chairman of his Commission on Country Life in 1908, and he made the most of that opportunity and responsibility to work for the improvement of rural life. He was the editor and author of many volumes on agricultural subjects. He edited three Cyclopedias of Horticulture and Agriculture.

David Fairchild (1869–1954) joined the staff of the Section of Plant Pathology in 1889, when he was 19 years old. He resigned after 4 years to become the first occupant of the Smithsonian Table of Research at Naples Zoological Station. He returned to Washington in 1897 and organized a section of foreign seed and plant introduction. He made many trips as a special agent for the Department of Agriculture. He introduced dates from Egypt and the Persian Gulf; nectarines from Afghanistan; paprika from Spain; rhodesgrass from South Africa; sweet peppers, broccoli, and a seedless raisin grape from Italy; a hardy variety of avocado from Chile; grain sorghums; cotton from Egypt; flowering cherry trees from Japan; tung trees, the beginning of a profitable business; and other plants.

Morris Llewellyn Cooke (1872–1960), a mechanical engineer, embarked upon a career of public service in 1911, when he became

Director of Public Works in Philadelphia. His hatred of waste in any form was to form the basis for much of his most outstanding work in later years. When Gifford Pinchot was Governor of Pennsylvania, he made Dr. Cooke director of the Giant Power Survey Board to recommend a policy that would secure for industries, railroads, farms, and homes of the State an abundant and cheap supply of electrical current. He worked with utilities people and farmers to make workable plans for getting electricity to isolated farms. In a report on the Mississippi Valley, made to President Roosevelt, Dr. Cooke recommended a 20-year anti-erosion program; plans for flood control, basin by basin; power installations; independent, self-liquidating projects for rural electrification; and plans for the Forest Service to acquire and protect the forest cover. President Roosevelt issued an Executive Order creating a Rural Electrification Administration in 1935 and appointed Mr. Cooke its administrator.

William A. Jump (1891–1949) served under 11 Secretaries of Agriculture from his appointment in 1907 as a messenger at a salary of 360 dollars a year. His first major staff appointment was as personal secretary to Secretary Henry C. Wallace in 1921. The next year he became budget officer of the Department, a post he held 26 years. To him a budget was a plan of work; the problems of his onerous work he met with tact, honesty, and ability. His ideal was the advancement of public administration. On his retirement, President Truman wrote: "Your example of selfless effort to improve public administration has blazed a wide and clear trail which is already being followed by many of your associates and will be followed by many others for a long time." *(A. S.)*

George Washington Carver.

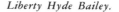

Liberty Hyde Bailey.

David Fairchild and Henry A. Wallace.

Morris Llewellyn Cooke.   *William A. Jump.*

37

Beltsville

IF YOU WANT to know what revolution is, said Victor Hugo, call it progress; if you want to understand what progress is, call it tomorrow. We can say, if you want to know progress in agriculture, visit the Agricultural Research Center near the town of Beltsville in Maryland, 15 miles northeast of the Nation's Capital, on U. S. Route 1. The Center has been the core of revolution and progress in agriculture since it began in 1910, when the Department of Agriculture bought 475 acres for an experimental farm. The land had been owned by the Snowden family, once known as the iron kings of America. One of the Snowden houses still stands; the rolling, partly wooded land thus has a link with Revolutionary times.

Beltsville, as we know it, is the focus of a research system that reaches into all the States and Territories. It is the home office of 4,800 scientists, who carry on a research program that cost 120 million dollars in 1962 and comprised 3 thousand projects. About one-fourth of the scientists are at Beltsville. They work primarily on broad, national research problems. The others work at 315 field stations, among which are facilities used cooperatively by the Department and land-grant colleges and universities. The Center is truly a center. It cooperates in agricultural research in the Federal field stations and with the State agricultural experiment stations, which generally deal with State and local farm problems.

The Center is unique in its concentration and diversity of skills. Specialists in the life sciences, physical sciences, and social sciences work at Beltsville. An agronomist who studies weeds in field crops need take only a short walk to get the views of chemists, botanists, hydrologists, and soil scientists that bear on his problems. An investigation of anaplasmosis, an insect-transmitted disease of cattle, brings together physiologists, pathologists, entomologists, and chemists, all of whom are easily accessible.

Beltsville is unique also as a center for basic research, which seeks new knowledge to advance science rather than the solution of a specific problem. Basic—or fundamental—research always has been a vital part of all research in the Department, but it attained new stature in 1957 with the establishment of pioneering laboratories, in which small groups of outstanding scientists probe beyond the borders of knowledge into the unknowns of how and why. They look deep into life processes—the changes in living cells, the physi-

The Plant Industry Station at Beltsville.

The Beltsville Research Center.

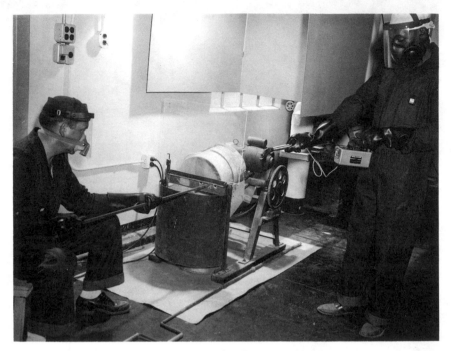

Mixing radioactive phosphorus with fertilizer.

An infected insect may disclose how a virus is reproduced in a plant.

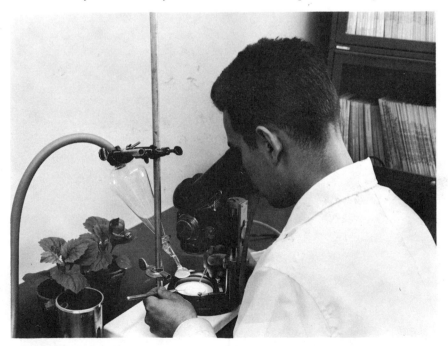

ology and nutrition of plants, the physiology of insects, virology, light and growth. They need not limit their investigations to specific crops or animals. They have no routine administrative duties. They are free to think, observe, experiment, and analyze. They are not called on each year to justify the "practicality" of their studies; we have come to appreciate that science needs the broadest possible base in order to develop fully. Seven of the 16 pioneering laboratories are at Beltsville. The work of one is done at Beltsville and Purdue University in Indiana. The others are in Washington, Peoria, New Orleans, Albany and Berkeley, Calif., and Wyndmoor, Pa., near Philadelphia.

Agricultural research reflects needs of the times. Radioactive fallout has become a worrisome fact. Engineers at Beltsville began investigations of ways to remove radioactive fallout from soils, and scientists in the Department, the Atomic Energy Commission, and the Department of Health, Education, and Welfare undertook cooperative work to develop an economical process for taking strontium 90 out of milk should it reach dangerous levels.

The Center has a laboratory that makes radioactive fertilizers for use in research. It is the only plant in the United States that supplies these tracer fertilizers to the agricultural experiment stations for experimental work with soils and crops. Many other tools of modern research are at Beltsville. Spectrophotometers make it possible to identify chemical substances instantaneously. Electron microscopes permit study of organisms too small to describe with older instruments. Oscilloscopes are electronic instruments for recording high-speed electric phenomena. Gas and paper chromatography offers a sensitive technique for separating and identifying chemical compounds.

Beltsville is big. Its farm now has 10,500 acres of experimental pastures, fields, gardens, orchards, and woods. Its 1,160 buildings provide office and laboratory space, housing for livestock and poultry, shops for making farm equipment, heating plants, a library, and auditoriums. The 35 greenhouses place 5 acres under glass. The spacious grounds look like a college campus. The buildings are grouped according to the kind of work done in them: At the Plant Industry Station the work on field crops, ornamentals, soil and water conservation, entomology, and weed control is brought together. Other groupings are animal husbandry, engineering, poultry, home economics, and research on parasites. The Center houses two notable collections. One has 60 thousand lots of parasites that affect man and animals. The National Fungus Collection contains more than 665 thousand specimens of fungi and plant disease organisms. Scientists the world over refer to them to identify and classify specimens.

Nearly 3 thousand head of cattle, swine, sheep, and goats and 10 thousand chickens and turkeys are kept for research in management,

41

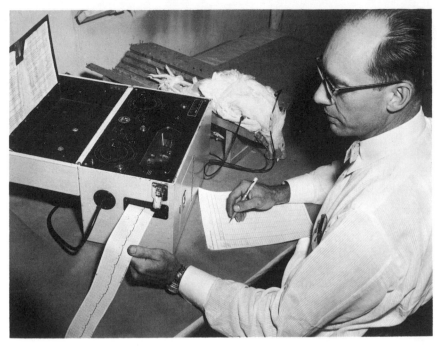

An electrocardiograph indicates the effect of stress on a hen.

Testing a device for spraying chemicals on plants.

Measuring how much of a cow's diet goes into milk production.

Women from overseas inspect a laborsaving kitchen.

feeding, breeding, and production. The Center has 3,300 small experimental animals, like rabbits and guinea pigs, for special studies. Research in infectious diseases of domestic livestock was moved from Beltsville in 1961 to the new National Animal Disease Laboratory at Ames, Iowa.

Thousands of scientists, students, farmers, housewives, gardeners, seedsmen, and others visit the Center. More than 3 thousand visitors from more than 90 countries came in 1962 to look over the shoulders of the scientists or to stay a while to do work in their own specialties. The visitors see many results of research: Chrysanthemums that bloom on a prescribed schedule, a meat-type hog, a record-setting Holstein herd, the Beltsville turkey, plants treated with chemicals to make them giants or dwarfs, a kitchen that is a housewife's dream, and models of machines to harvest cherries or pick cotton—and much more.

What they do not see is the work, the inspiration, and the dedication that precede the discoveries. An example is the relationship between plants and light. The first step was in 1918, when scientists learned about photoperiodism, the principle that the relative length of day and night controls the flowering and development of plants. The finding led to the discovery and isolation in 1959 of phytochrome, the light-absorbing pigment within the plant that triggers the mechanism for its development. To study photoperiodism more fully, scientists built plant growth chambers, in which light could be clocked to go on and off at desired intervals. They built a device for breaking light into its different color bands to study their effects on plants. They worked with incandescent and fluorescent lights and with red and blue filters. They applied light from various parts of the spectrum to the whole plant, to seeds, and to a single leaf. They used artificial light to add seconds, minutes, and hours to the normal daylength. They worked with the normal daylength and then added light periods at various intervals during normal darkness. They recorded every detail of response and timing as carefully as if their lives depended on it. The discovery of phytochrome came four decades after the discovery of photoperiodism. Scientists at Beltsville continue the research, convinced that still greater findings lie ahead.

The knowledge that is built up in one line of research opens new avenues in another, and gradually all of man's knowledge is pushed forward another step. In much of their work at Beltsville, scientists look into the mysteries of life itself. Will they be able some day to modify existing organisms? Can they learn to use light or chemicals or something else to alter genetic traits and characteristics of organisms, plants, insects, and animals? They cannot alter the past, but science can help shape the future. *(Marguarette M. Hedge)*

Old Products; New Uses

SCIENTISTS of the Department of Agriculture apply chemistry, engineering, microbiology, physics, mathematics—the sciences that have produced thousands of new goods and services, largely from nonagricultural resources—to develop new uses for agricultural products. It is a broad field. The research, which we call utilization research, often discovers ways to preserve and protect the native good qualities of farm commodities and to make modified and new products. It explores all outlets for processed products—for foods, feeds, clothing, shelter, industrial chemicals, equipment, the whole, vast range of man's needs. In its studies of the composition of farm crops, it develops new knowledge that can be used in developmental research.

Utilization research has been a major effort in the Department since 1938, when an act of the Congress created four regional utilization laboratories. Long before that, people knew the need for it, and some research on utilization had been conducted in the Department and State agricultural experiment stations. Four Utilization Research and Development Divisions of the Agricultural Research Service now are engaged in it.

Each is assigned the major crops of its region. To the Eastern Division, in Wyndmoor, Pa., near Philadelphia, are assigned animal products, such as dairy, meat, fats, and leather; plant products, such as eastern fruits and vegetables; tobacco; honey; maple; new crops; and studies of allergens. To the Northern Division, in Peoria, Ill., are assigned cereal grains, such as corn, wheat, barley, grain sorghum, and oats; oilseeds, such as soybean, flaxseed, safflower, and those that contain erucic acid; and new crops. To the Southern Division, in New Orleans, are assigned cotton and cottonseed; tung fruit; pine gum; southern fruits and vegetables, including citrus, sweetpotatoes, cucumbers, and sugarcane; rice; peanuts; and new crops. Crops assigned to the Western Division, in Albany, Calif., near San Francisco and Berkeley, are western fruits, nuts, vegetables, rice, poultry products, forage crops, wheat, barley, wool, mohair, sugarbeets, dry beans and peas, castor seed, and new crops.

We visit the laboratory at Albany to get an idea of the work of all four. We begin with the offices of administration—the part of the three-story building that joins two long wings. There research is planned, coordinated, directed, managed, and reported. Some is done under contract by groups elsewhere, including foreign coun-

The Western Regional Research Laboratory at Albany, Calif.

The food processing laboratory at Albany.

tries. Various producing and processing groups advise the Department, and their advice is assimilated, discussed, and put to use here. The wings house the scientific workshops. The numerous laboratories have complex apparatus, other paraphernalia of research, and large spaces for the engineers' processing equipment, an essential part of the total research organization. The staff of the Western Division numbers about 360, of whom about 200 are professional people. Twenty work in the Division's station in Pasadena, Calif. Five work in two stations in Washington, at Prosser and Puyallup.

We learn that thousands of chemical analyses and thousands of physical tests and taste-panel tests are required. One project has measured the effects of various temperatures and time periods on the rates of losses of color, flavor, texture, and vitamin content of frozen foods. These qualities are farm values, and they must be protected by appropriate industrial handling. For the project, more than 100 thousand sample packages of the foods were obtained under deep refrigeration from various producing regions. Then followed long hours of work to plan the experiments, collect data on the changes disclosed by the tests, analyze the data for soundness and significance, and finally make the findings known. Products of new processes—new juice powders, dehydrofrozen or dehydrocanned fruit and vegetables, dehydrated mashed potato—all require this detailed study of retention of quality. The removal of the natural moisture, partially in dehydrofrozen and dehydrocanned products and almost wholly in powders and granules, is the basis of much of the processing research on foods. The object is to reduce weight to make possible marketing at greater distances at lower cost.

Scientific methods advance continuously and extend the horizons of utilization research. Many used now were unavailable when the utilization laboratories started operations. For example, research on foods at the Western Laboratory depends heavily on a technique pioneered there. It is called gas-liquid-partition chromatography, and it makes possible quantitative analysis of flavor and aroma components so subtle that the human nose cannot detect them. Such investigations, along with organoleptic studies—sensory evaluations by panels of trained judges—are producing information on flavor preferences and flavor changes during processing. This knowledge provides guidelines for producing foods that please people of various races and cultures.

Electron microscopy is used to follow changes in the surfaces of wool fibers when resins are applied to provide resistance to mussing and shrinkage. Ultraviolet irradiation is used in studies of the effect of light on wool. A nuclear magnetic resonance spectrometer analyzes compounds in terms of the environments of their hydrogen atoms. Other instruments used in studies of the structure and chemical composition of raw molecules include the electron spin reso-

The "meat" component of this dish is restructured from wheat protein.

nance spectrometer, the X-ray diffractometer, infrared spectrophotometers, amino acid analyzer, ultracentrifuge, particle size counter,
and several countercurrent distribution devices. Laboratory findings
are translated into a semicommercial scale in the pilot plant area,
which is as big as some factories. Here are dehydrators, conveyors,
kettles, and equipment for various unit operations. Procedures and
equipment items developed here have gone on to take an important
place in American industry.

The food processing laboratory, a large, two-story room, is a feature of the Western Laboratory. It has equipment for the study of
variables in canning, freezing, and dehydrating foods. A wide range
of conditions of temperature, vacuum, airflow, steam treatment, atmospheric humidity, and so on can be applied throughout all stages
of processing. More specialized processing installations, designed to
study particular commodity problems, have been built with the advice, assistance, and in some instances financial support of industry.

A pharmacology laboratory at Albany serves the Department's
entire utilization research program. A broad program of research is
underway on the safety of new compounds in foods and feeds, on
toxic and allergenic substances occasionally present in farm crops,
and on growth-promoting and growth-inhibiting substances that indicate or contraindicate use of certain crops for feeding livestock
and poultry. Also at Albany is one of the Department's pioneering
research laboratories. Its special province is enzymes, the substances
formed in living cells that speed up chemical reactions but do not
change during the process. Its reason for being is that the development of technology and of new industrial uses for farm crops depends largely on fundamental knowledge of the properties of the
constituents of the crops. Basic research therefore is part of every
program. *(C. H. Harry Neufeld* and *Russell T. Prescott)*

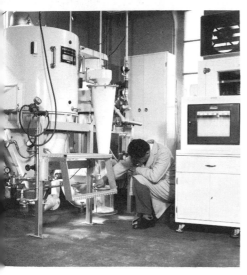

A spray drier is used in tests to develop new or improved egg products.

Nuclear magnetic resonance is used to identify flavor components of fruit and vegetables, determine radiation damage, and characterize complex molecules.

Trained judges evaluate the taste of foods.

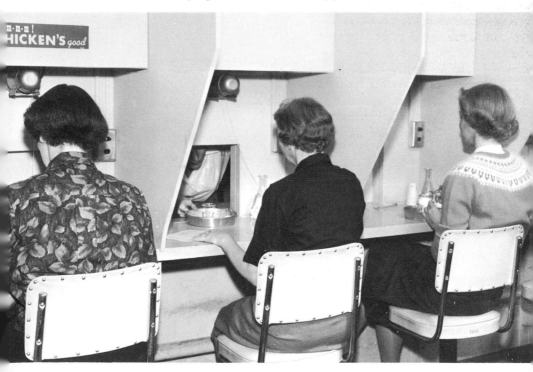

State Experiment Station

CITIZENS of Bertie County in North Carolina had wanted for years to expand opportunities for work in the county. To improve efficiency on farms was fine, but fewer farmers then could produce the peanuts, soybeans, and corn. If only we had some industry, they said, preferably industry that uses farm products. They began to organize to reach their goal. While they were organizing, scientists at the North Carolina Agricultural Experiment Station were working. Dr. Daniel T. Pope and Dr. L. N. Nielsen developed a sweet-potato that was better for processing. Then Dr. Maurice Hoover took the sweetpotato and perfected a new product—flaked sweet-potatoes. This was what Bertie citizens were looking for.

So an industry rose from the flat and fertile fields of Bertie and gave farmers a new market, new jobs for more people, and a new type of food for consumers. For the people of Bertie, the State experiment station has opened a multitude of new doors, just as it has been doing for all North Carolinians for generations and just as experiment stations are doing in all the States. When it was established in 1877, primarily to test commercial fertilizers, the North Carolina station was the second such institution in the Nation. (Connecticut was first.) It consisted of a one-man workbench in the basement of Smith Hall at the University of North Carolina, but it was a place where farmers could direct their questions and receive answers based on the latest achievements of science.

Today every phase of North Carolina's billion-dollar agricultural economy is undergirded with research findings from the station. Instead of one chemist, the station has 400 scientists, most of whom also teach in the college classrooms. Instead of a basement workbench, the station has laboratories, greenhouses, and farms scattered across North Carolina. Instead of testing fertilizers only, the station is an integral part of the teaching, research, and extension responsibilities of the School of Agriculture of North Carolina State College in Raleigh.

The scientists' research projects are as varied as the State's agricultural needs from which they spring. An economist, for example, may work on a cheaper method of loading broilers. An entomologist develops a new program to control cotton insects. An agricultural engineer works on machines for growers of tobacco. An agronomist studies the needs of apple trees for boron. A poultry

A hay drier developed at the North Carolina Agricutural Experiment Station.

The Mountain Research Station at Waynesville, N.C.

Farmers inspect a new wheat at the Piedmont Research Station, Salisbury, N.C.

Plots of tobacco at the Central Crops Research Station, Clayton, N.C.

nutritionist charts the relationship between vitamins and fowl typhoid. Plant breeders release a continuous stream of new and better
varieties of crops. Geneticists, bacteriologists, and biochemists delve
into the secrets of life. Rural sociologists and home economists study
the needs of farm families. Far from his laboratories at State College, a plant breeder searches the Andes for wild and cultivated
peanut plants. A station geneticist scours islands of the Caribbean
for wild cottons. Back home, a plant pathologist screens a collection of wild tobaccos from all over the world in the hope of finding a trait that can be used in a program to breed better tobacco.
Whatever the specialty, the goal is always the same: To push back
the horizons of agriculture.

Much of the work is done at branch stations. Anyone who travels
south along U.S. Route 117 realizes he is in a distinct farming area
as he nears Wilmington, N.C. Light, sandy soil gives way to
darker earth. Fields of corn and tobacco give way to fields of lettuce, beans, strawberries, gladiolus, and iris. Near the center of this
rich vegetable- and flower-growing area are greenhouses and hundreds of plant-filled research plots of the Horticultural Crops Research Station. Fifty miles to the west is another distinct agricultural
area, the Border Tobacco Belt. Here also is a branch station. There
are 14 others; they test in the field under rigorous farmlike conditions the ideas that are born in State college laboratories and are
nurtured in college greenhouses. In a State of many different agricultural and geographic conditions, the branch stations are important. Growing conditions at Waynesville, for example, may be more
like growing conditions in Maine than those in the North Carolina
Sandhills, only 200 miles to the east. Furthermore, branch stations
are the windows of the scientists' laboratories, through which a tobacco grower can see a promising new variety, or a swine producer
can look at a new kind of farrowing house. After all, the scientists'
work is not done until their knowledge is given to people who
can use it.

Cooperation is the keystone of the entire research effort. Farmers
cooperate by volunteering to test new techniques in their fields on
a scale that is bigger and more practical than is possible in a laboratory but is just as precise and carefully planned. The North
Carolina Department of Agriculture cooperates by providing staff
workers and some facilities. Station scientists provide technical information for the department's regulatory officials. The officials, in
return, advise the scientists on research needs uncovered in the field.
Station and department workers cooperate closely in the State Soil
Testing Laboratory and in the State's animal disease diagnostic laboratories. The United States Department of Agriculture cooperates
by supporting projects that could have value beyond the borders of
North Carolina.

53

Peanuts, corn, and soybeans in a study of rotations at Lewiston, N.C.

Tobacco is North Carolina's major crop.

A test of egg quality.

Measuring the progress of nutrition trials.

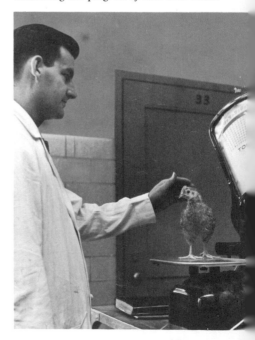

Tagging a chick, the first step in charting her lifetime performance.

Two years after the station was established, Albert R. Ledoux, the first director, wrote: "Thus we were able to offer to the farmers of the State complete and free protection against frauds in commercial fertilizers. . . ." Dr. R. L. Lovvorn, the present director, can write today with equal confidence: "Thus we were able to offer to farmers of the State a tobacco crop"—a crop worth 500 million dollars to them annually. On two occasions, station scientists have developed resistant varieties in time for Tar Heel farmers to roll back fatal diseases that threatened their tobacco. Such accomplishments still occur, but usually it is the multitude of diverse, and often seemingly small, research findings that raise continuously the efficiency of agriculture in North Carolina.

For the first 60 years, work of the experiment station was supported by the United States Department of Agriculture with some allocations from the North Carolina Department of Agriculture. Since 1937, however, the North Carolina General Assembly has been making larger and larger direct appropriations. The State now provides nearly half of the station's budget of 4.2 million dollars. National foundations provide 900 thousand dollars more. Farmers make a contribution by assessing themselves 5 cents on each ton of feed and fertilizer they buy. They call it their "Nickels-for-Know-How" program. Scientists at the North Carolina Agricultural Experiment Station call it a continuing testament to the faith that farmers have placed in their research. *(Tom Byrd)*

Profile of Farming

YOU CAN USE adjectives like diverse, big, and changing to describe American agriculture, but they are too general to give a good description. For that, you need information about farms and farmers, because each is different; about temperature, rainfall, length of growing season, and other details of the many climates in this big country; about traditions and backgrounds; and about economic conditions. There are, for instance, more than 70 thousand kinds of soil in the United States; you could almost say that on that basis alone there are 70 thousand kinds of farms in the United States, because a high correlation exists between soils and types of farming. Each of the kinds would have differences due to climate and topography—rainfall varies from an inch or two in the southwestern deserts to more than 60 inches a year in southern coastal and lowland places. Pests and animal and plant diseases also have a bearing on how and where a farmer farms. So do prices, distance to market, costs of production, credit, and the ease or difficulty of adopting one or another technological development. Men have tried, not too successfully, to classify types of farms. One classification lists 9 major agricultural regions, 61 subregions, and 165 generalized type-of-farming areas.

One is the Corn Belt, a midwestern region of feed grains and livestock, where the land is generally level, with deep, warm, fertile soils that are well adapted to the production of corn. Enough rainfall, well distributed through the growing season, hot days, and warm nights favor corn. Corn Belt farmers generally have cropping systems that may include corn, oats, wheat, soybeans, and hay and pasture crops. Corn is used chiefly for feeding hogs, beef cattle, and sheep. What we call the Cotton Belt, the largest cotton-producing region in the world, embraces all or large parts of nine Southern States and smaller parts of four more, but cotton also is grown in irrigated areas in California, Arizona, and New Mexico.

Dairy farming is concentrated in the Northeast, in the Lake States, along the North Pacific coast, and in smaller areas adjoining large cities. Generally speaking, soils and topography there are not favorable for cereal crops in competition with the Corn Belt and other grain-producing regions. The broken terrain limits the use of large tillage machines. The cool climate and ample rainfall favor hay and pasture. Wheat has a wide climatic range and is grown

56

commercially in most of the United States, except in sections with less than 12 to 15 inches of rainfall and parts of the Deep South where rainfall is excessive.

Rangeland in the Western States covers more than 700 million acres. From the Dakotas and the sandhills of Nebraska, it extends westward and south over much of southwestern Texas, New Mexico, and Arizona, the Mountain and Intermountain States, and the Pacific Coast States. Soils, elevation, topography, and climate make the production of range livestock more profitable than crops. Rainfall usually is scant and uncertain. Fruit and truck-crop farming is widely dispersed. The principal specialized deciduous fruit areas are in intermountain valleys and on protected slopes. In such areas, late spring and early fall frosts are not likely to occur, slopes provide air drainage, bodies of water moderate temperature changes, and soils are well drained. The citrus fruit and truck-crop areas are on the central California coast, in southern California and southwestern Arizona, the lower Rio Grande Valley, and central Florida. Climate is a chief factor. The largest group of contiguous general farming areas is in the section between the Corn Belt and dairy regions in the North and the Cotton Belt in the South. The tobacco and general farming region comprises four subregions, which are in the east-central part of the United States. Production of tobacco requires much labor per acre, much of it hand labor. Family-operated tobacco farms therefore are small in terms of acres. The so-called special crops, including potatoes, sugarbeets, dry beans, peanuts, rice, and sugarcane, are grown as a main enterprise or as supplementary cash crops in a general system of farming.

Other facts help particularize the broad picture. More persons worked on farms in 1961 than in the public utilities, communications, steel, automobile, and transportation industries combined. The investment in agriculture in 1961 was nearly 200 billion dollars. About two-thirds of the 2 billion acres in the land area of the United States was in farms. The average size of American farms in 1959 was 302 acres; most had 100 to 259 acres, but some had fewer than 10 acres and some had more than 10 thousand acres. More than two-thirds of all farms did not provide the major source of income for the farm family. About a third are part-time farms. Many farms had yearly gross incomes of more than 25 thousand dollars in 1961, but net income varied considerably. Almost three-fourths of all farms were operated by their owners or part owners; the rest by tenants. The average age of farmers—51 years in 1959—has been rising. About 17 percent of farm operators were 65 or older. The pages that follow give a closer look at some farms and farmers—each of them an individual but all of them alike in several ways—their ability to adapt to change, their love of farming, and the unity of their family life.

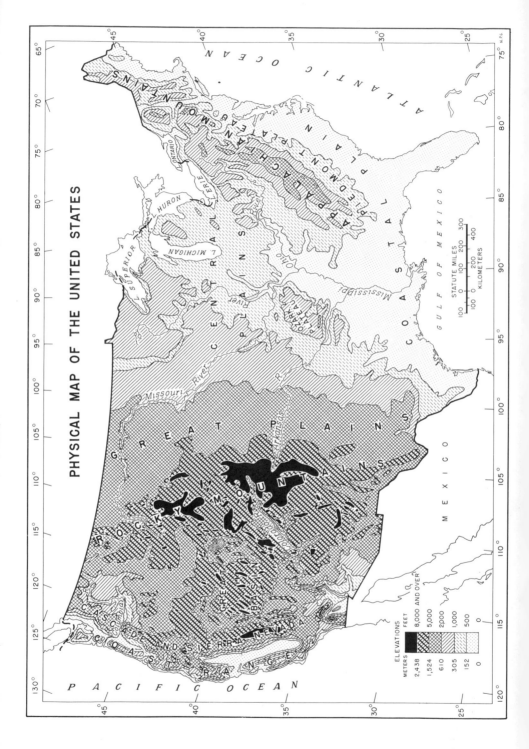

PHYSICAL MAP OF THE UNITED STATES

ELEVATIONS

FEET	METERS
8,000 AND OVER	2,438
5,000	1,524
2000	610
1,000	305
500	152
0	0

STATUTE MILES
100   200   300   400

KILOMETERS
100   200   300   400

PACIFIC OCEAN

ATLANTIC OCEAN

GULF OF MEXICO

MEXICO

CASCADE AND SIERRA NEVADA

COAST RANGE

GREAT BASIN

ROCKY MOUNTAINS

GREAT PLAINS

CENTRAL PLAINS

APPALACHIAN MOUNTAINS

PIEDMONT PLATEAU

COASTAL PLAIN

NORTHERN MOUNTAINS

L. SUPERIOR

L. MICHIGAN

HURON

L. ERIE

L. ONTARIO

Mississippi River

Missouri River

Arkansas R.

Ohio

OZARK PLATEAU

58

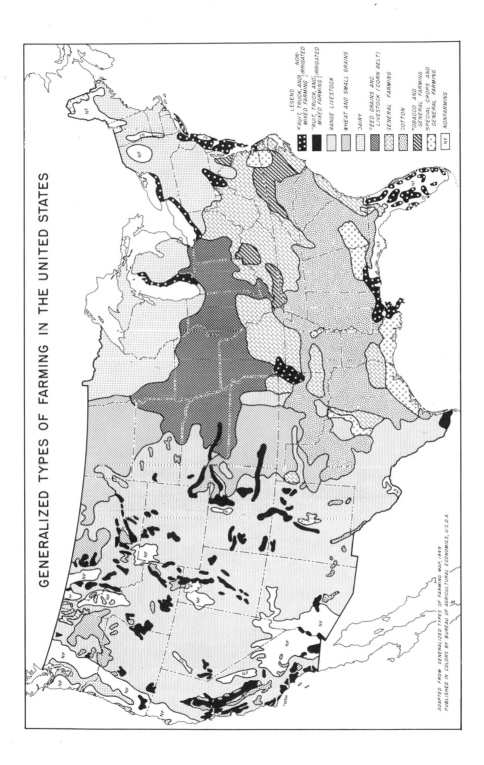

GENERALIZED TYPES OF FARMING IN THE UNITED STATES

LEGEND

FRUIT, TRUCK, AND NON-
MIXED FARMING IRRIGATED

FRUIT, TRUCK, AND IRRIGATED
MIXED FARMING

RANGE LIVESTOCK

WHEAT AND SMALL GRAINS

DAIRY

FEED GRAINS AND
LIVESTOCK (CORN BELT)

GENERAL FARMING

COTTON

TOBACCO AND
GENERAL FARMING

SPECIAL CROPS AND
GENERAL FARMING

NF NONFARMING

ADAPTED FROM GENERALIZED TYPES OF FARMING MAP, 1949
PUBLISHED IN COLORS BY BUREAU OF AGRICULTURAL ECONOMICS, U.S.D.A.

59

Ralph Gadbury went to Fairbanks, Alaska, from Kansas in 1951, when he was 35 years old. He worked in the heating plant at Fort Wainwright, the army post outside Fairbanks, and started homesteading. He quit his job in 1959 and began to concentrate on dairy farming. He, his wife, Jean, and their two sons, Ray and Dick, were well on their way in 1962 in what is considered by some to be the toughest farming country in the world. They had completed a new granary and a heating plant for the farmstead, farmhouse, and milkhouse and had 38 Brown Swiss, which had a herd average of better than 10 thousand pounds. They work hard, but they have time for fishing and hunting moose, bear, ducks, and geese. They farm about 180 acres, some of it rented land. They go in heavily for silage because of the difficult weather conditions for curing hay. In 1961 they raised 75 acres of oat-pea silage, 70 acres of barley for grain, 50 acres of bromegrass for hay and silage, and 10 acres of oats for grain. Mr. Gadbury is a member of the local soil conservation subdistrict and the local Farmers Home Administration committee. He is vice president of the Tanana Valley Dairy Association. He is a community leader and adviser to other homesteaders in his neighborhood.

Ralph Gadbury, of Alaska.

Mrs. Lillian E. Riggs, of Arizona.

Mrs. Lillian E. Riggs operates a ranch of 7 thousand acres in the "Geronimo Country" of southeastern Arizona, 21 miles southeast of the post office at Dos Cabezas. Her parents were born in Sweden and came to America in their late teens. She was born at Fort Bowie, Arizona Territory, and was brought as a baby to the homestead in Bonita Canyon at the foot of the Chiricahuas, which has been her home ever since. As a young girl she was sent to school in Illinois and later to Knox College. She taught school for 10 years at Bowie, Ariz., and returned to the ranch at the time of the First World War. Lillian and her sister, who later moved to California, enlarged the holding and did all the ranch work, including riding at the roundups and assisting at the brandings. Three years later Lillian married the oldest son of the oldest son of a neighboring family, Edward Murray Riggs. Mrs. Rigg's hearing began failing at an early date, and 20 years ago she lost her eyesight completely after she fell from a bucking horse. Mr. Riggs died in 1950, and Lillian Erickson Riggs has since operated the ranch. At least once a week she rides the range with one of her staff. A short rope tied to her companion's saddle helps her to direct her horse. Her mental image of that mountainous terrain is so clear that almost always she is aware of what part of the range she is riding and what landmarks are close by. She has a mental record of her cattle and stresses the value of knowing each as an individual. At shipping time, old cows are run into the chute, and she goes over them with her hands and "tooths" them to learn about their condition and make the decision as to whether they are to be sold. In 1961, when nearly all the ranchers in southern Arizona had to resort to supplemental feeding because of the worst drought since 1896, Mrs. Riggs kept her stock fat and happy and had a fine calf crop without extra feeding by watching closely her herd and the condition of the grass. She employs a foreman and housekeeper.

Farming on the Navajo Reservation near Window Rock in Arizona.

Harvey A. McDougal, president of McDougal Livestock Company, Birds Landing, Calif., has been in the cattle business all his life. He was born on a farm near Lewiston, Minn., and majored in animal husbandry at the University of Minnesota. He was a cattle buyer for Swift & Co. for 16 years and has operated a feedlot since 1940. His ranch consists of 3,300 acres, 260 of which are used in the feedlot operation. The rest is pasture. The company feeds about 37 thousand head a year. One-half of the cattle the company owns; the rest are commercially fed, mainly for range producers who raise feeders. Mr. McDougal's son and son-in-law are active in the business. Cattle feeding has been profitable, and Mr. McDougal is not interested in enlarging the operations. The ranch is almost completely mechanized. There is a ready market for all cattle produced, because the company feeds only to the quality and weight desired in the area. Mr. McDougal has been an officer of a number of cattlemen's organizations.

Harvey A. McDougal, of California.

James Svedman was born and reared on a farm and is a third-generation member of a pioneer Colorado family. He has a bachelor's degree in animal husbandry from Colorado State University, where he did a year of graduate work in business law and economics. His city-reared wife, Shirley, has a degree in dietetics and nutrition from the University. They have three daughters. The Svedmans assumed management in 1952 of 1,480 acres near Fort Collins, some rented from Jim's father and the rest leased from three other landowners. It was not a very good time for a young man to begin farming. The cost-price squeeze was particularly tight then. The severe effects of a drought were beginning to be felt. Jim's father had been farming only the dryland part of the family farm, renting out the irrigated land to other operators. Putting units of the farm back together, combining them with rented land, getting equipment to handle a sizable operation, and developing a management program to make it pay was a formidable task. The Svedmans tackled the job on a businesslike basis, without benefit of inheritances or gifts. Jim's father cosigned his notes at the bank the first few years.

Jim Svedman was born at Windsor, Colo., in 1926 and grew up on the homestead established by his grandfather in 1885. He started raising cattle in 4-H Club work in 1939. Income from his 4-H cattle project and a merit scholarship financed his 5 years of college work. Of the 1,480 acres he operates, 550 acres are irrigated and 930 are dryland. Cropland accounts for 1,250 acres; 230 acres are in pasture. He grows corn, alfalfa, barley, and sugarbeets on irrigated land. The dryland is devoted to barley, winter wheat, and summer fallow. Wheat and sugarbeets are the cash crops. The rest of the crops are marketed through cattle, which he feeds in partnership with his father—about a thousand head a year. The farm, which is in sight of the Rocky Mountains, produces most of the feed. He has a registered Angus herd of about 100 animals and a commercial herd of Angus.

He pays close attention to fertilizing, rotating crops, strip-cropping, contour farming, stubble mulching, controlled irrigation, and land leveling. His careful management of cattle has brought substantial reductions in death losses and improvements in the fattening ration and the feeding system. He has added equipment—whether tractors, hay harvesting equipment, or automatic feeding systems—only when he was convinced it would pay off in savings of crops and reductions in production costs. He designed and built his automatic cattle feeding system himself, utilizing an old railroad boxcar and buying the augers and motors. He employs two or three men the year around. During rush seasons he brings in temporary help.

The Svedmans are active in a number of civic, church, community, and cattlemen's organizations. Jim is a member of the Survival Club (a somewhat informal group of farmers who are determined that they can "survive" as farmers) and the Farm Bureau. He has received technical assistance from such agencies as the Extension Service, the Soil Conservation Service, and the Agricultural Stabilization and Conservation Committee. Mrs. Svedman helps her husband with the detailed records that are essential to modern farming operations. One reason she has the time to do this and to assist in the overall management program is that the house has time- and labor-saving appliances. One useful device is a two-way radio. From his pickup truck, in which is installed a citizens-band radio, he can get in touch with Mrs. Svedman from any place on the farm. She in turn can telephone for such things as repair parts and the veterinarian when the need arises. The telephone at farm headquarters is under the Fort Collins exchange. The telephone at "the other place," where the livestock feeding operation is carried out, goes through the Windsor exchange. Telephone communication between the two places—if neither of the party lines happens to be busy—must therefore be long distance. The two-way radio eliminates long-distance calls and waits to "get the line."

But it's not all work with the Svedmans. They try to take regular vacations at times when the pressures of work are at a minimum. They like to play bridge and enjoy both ballroom and square dancing. In winter they and the children often go sledding on the hills on the farm. The major problem—to make the farm pay—is not unique. Like all farmers, they have the pressures of costs and prices. Shortly after Jim began to farm for himself, his total liabilities came uncomfortably close to equaling total assets. His liabilities have increased to a little more than two and one-half times what they were initially, but his assets have risen to four and one-half times what they were worth at the start.

James Svedman, of Colorado.   *Mrs. Svedman.*

Harold B. Short, of Delaware.

Harold B. Short, of Georgetown, Del., began his modern market egg production business in 1951, when he was 22 years old. He counts on this experience and the modest capital he has accumulated to expand gradually his flock of 6 thousand hens to 15 thousand. The key factor in the expansion, he believes, is labor efficiency and production of homegrown feeds. Automation offers him a great opportunity. An egg grader was his first major piece of automatic equipment. In 1961 he installed an automatic feeder, which grinds, mixes, and transports feed to the hens. The next step is equipment for picking, shelling, drying, and storing corn, his major feed ingredient, because "I never could see the point in growing corn, sending it away, then buying it back." Mr. Short owns 150 tillable acres, and he rents 100 acres more. He grows 150 acres of corn and feeds all of it to his hens. He is gradually increasing his acreage in soybeans, with the plan in mind to swap beans for soybean oilmeal and thereby further reduce his off-farm costs for feed. In the 10 years he has cut down his labor requirements from six men to two, including himself, and still increased production.

Born on a farm near Georgetown, Mr. Short moved into the village as a youth, but kept up his interest in agriculture by keeping a backyard flock of hens and peddling the eggs after school on his bicycle. He began full-time farming immediately after he and his wife, Virginia, were married in 1951. They have two daughters, Nancy Lee and Patti, and two sons, Benjamin and David. They have a comfortable, modern home, which Mrs. Short, who was graduated from the University of Delaware School of Home Economics in 1951, manages efficiently. Mr. Short finds time for community activities. He is an elder of his church and the superintendent of the Sunday school.

John L. Simpson, Alachua, Fla., and his son, John S. Simpson, produce certified meat-type hogs on an 80-acre farm. Corn, the main crop, yields more than 65 bushels an acre. Corn is stored in metal bins for use throughout the year. The hogs graze crops of wheat in winter and millet in summer. For breeding stock, the Simpsons buy only certified meat-type hogs that have passed back-fat tests and are known to be prolific breeders.

Howard Hartle joined his father in the management of citrus groves near Clermont, Fla., soon after he was graduated from Ohio State University in 1940. Their holdings in central Florida total 85 acres.

C. A. Vinson, 61, of Fort Valley, Ga., has a diversified operation on the 684-acre farm where he was born and reared. He also farms 110 acres that once belonged to his wife's family. The original farm was a land grant to the Vinson family and has remained in the family since. Mr. Vinson has been on the farm since he finished Fort Valley High School. He has about 50 acres of pecans. By good management he has raised production and in 1961 got 140 pounds a tree in a large grove of Schleys. A few years ago the average production in the State was about 17 pounds a tree; an Extension program to improve this valuable crop raised the average to almost 35 pounds in 1961. A crop of 38 million pounds of pecans, worth some 12 million dollars, was grown in Georgia in 1960; the 1961 crop was expected to total 60 million pounds. The increase is due largely to improved fertilization and better control of diseases and insects. Pecans, a native nut, are produced commercially in only a few States in the South. Pecans are only one of Mr. Vinson's crops. He averaged about two bales to the acre on 60 acres of cotton in 1961. He has some 7 thousand peach trees, but he is reducing the number to make for a better balance of enterprises. "We're building for cotton, pecans, cattle, small grain, and pines," he explains. He averaged 50 bushels to the acre on 50 acres of wheat and 95 bushels on 6 acres of barley in 1960. He feeds more than 100 cows and is building his herd up to 200 cows.

C. A. Vinson, of Georgia.

For the papaya grower of the Puna district of Hawaii, a threat he cannot control or combat is a volcanic eruption, an event not to be taken lightly on an island still being built by active volcanoes. Twice in recent years vents opened along the rift zone cutting across the district, spewing molten lava, which devastated the land as the lava flowed to the sea. An eruption occurred near the town of Pahoa in 1955, when lava destroyed about 109 acres, more than 50 percent of the papaya orchards, and sulfur dioxide fumes damaged other crops in Puna and the neighboring Hilo district. An eruption occurred along the same rift zone, near Kapoho town, in 1960. An estimated 106 acres of papaya orchards were destroyed by lava, and large areas of other orchards were damaged by volcanic ash and fumes. Nevertheless, Puna has grown to be the major papaya-producing area in Hawaii, and the acreage has expanded from less than 200 in 1954 to more than 500 in 1961. The growth of the papaya industry in Puna is due in large part to natural conditions favoring the crop. The coastal area of the district, where papaya is grown, is located far enough east from the mountain masses of Mauna Loa and Mauna Kea, which are more than 13 thousand feet high, so that it is not affected by the inland cloud banks formed as the mountains disrupt the prevailing trade winds. The climate in this coastal area is ideal for the production of tropical fruit, particularly a crop such as the papaya *(Carica papaya)*, a melonlike fruit that requires a warm, sunny climate and ample water for optimum growth. Winds are generally mild, an important condition for papaya orchards, which can suffer great damage under heavy winds. Average annual rainfall exceeds 100 inches and is distributed evenly through much of the year.

The greatest contributions to the total State production of papaya are being made by a number of large growers in Puna, some of whom process and distribute the fruit they grow. The future growth of the industry, however, may depend on the small or part-time farmers, many of whom see a bright future for papaya production on the island of Hawaii. Kiyoshi Inada is among these small farmers who are working toward expansion of their own enterprise and of the industry as a whole. A part-time farmer, he works for the County of Hawaii, and operates an 18-acre papaya orchard in Kapoho. He started growing papaya in 1959 on about a dozen acres of land in Kapoho, where he was born and reared on a farm. Some 8 months later, when 7 acres were near maturity, a volcanic eruption in land adjoining his field wiped out his orchard. Immediately, he acquired a lease on land southeast of a prehistoric cinder cone near his first farm and began planting papaya once more. Part of his orchard was in production in 1962. The fruit is harvested by two or three hired workers, who pick the fruit by hand and crate them for shipment to a local distributor. With his partner, Claus

Kiyoshi Inada, of Puna District, Hawaii.

Hayselton, Mr. Inada is planning to farm more land, the most recently acquired being some 6 acres covered by cinders of the 1955 eruption—land which is being cleared under the 1961 Hawaii Agricultural Conservation Program for farmers willing to take part in a land reclamation program. There Mr. Inada is planting poha *(Physalis peruviana)*, a small, cherrylike, tropical fruit, which makes excellent preserves.

As a farmer, Mr. Inada's greatest preoccupation is not the natural elements, which he submits to when he must and fights when he can, but the economics of papaya production and marketing. The greatest potential of papaya is as an export crop. Shipments of fresh and processed fruit to the mainland United States have been increasing, so that about 20 percent of Hawaii's estimated 14.4-million-pound production is exported. In order to keep increasing exports of papaya, however, farmers, processors, and distributors must find ways to expand the market for the product, to improve and maintain the quality of the fresh fruit as it is transported, to increase the shelf life of the fresh fruit, and to develop more processed products. Also, regular transportation facilities from Hawaii to Honolulu and from Honolulu to the West Coast must be assured. Mr. Inada is a member of an association of Puna papaya growers that he hopes can solve the complex marketing problems. Then, he says, he will be able to devote full time to his first love, farming, specifically production of papaya, saving his spare time for his favorite pastime, fishing. Mr. Inada lives in Hilo with his wife, Lily Masue, and their son, Carlton.

Third in dollar value among agricultural commodities produced in Hawaii, coffee rates first in the agriculture of Kona, a district along the sloping, western coast of the "Big Island." Here, on a strip 25 miles long, 2 miles wide, and 800 to 2,200 feet above sea level, are a thousand coffee farms. Its soils are shallow, rocky, and fertile. The climate varies greatly, according to elevation, but conditions in the coffee belt favor the crop. An average of 2,690 pounds of parchment coffee per acre is harvested annually. The first commercial coffee farms were started in Kona around 1850. The Kona coffee industry is firmly established in Hawaii. Its relative stability despite growing competition on the world market is due to the hardy, independent farmers who operate the small farms, which average 6 acres. To the individualistic Kona coffee growers, farming is a way of life not to be given up easily. Mechanization has not overtaken coffee farms because the land is steep and unsuited to tractors, and no mechanical means has been found to facilitate the most time-consuming job of the grower, harvesting the ripe cherries. Almost all the farms are family operated—harvesttime comes in October, and all able members of the family work in the orchards, picking the coffee cherries by hand.

Coffee growers are coming to believe that the best insurance against the bad years when world coffee prices drop is to grow an additional crop—a tree crop, such as macadamia, avocado, banana, or citrus, all of which grow well in Kona. Kiyoshi Nishimoto is a typical coffee grower in Kona. He became a coffee farmer in 1933, when he was 28. With his wife, Sakae, he operates a 6-acre farm, which he purchased in 1947, when land prices in Kona were low. He paid off the mortgage within 5 years. He runs his farm in the time-honored way, as a family operation. He employs no hired hands even during the harvest season. One year, when the ripening season was short, he and Mrs. Nishimoto harvested the entire crop themselves. The orchard consists of Hawaiian and Guatemalan varieties of coffee, probably first planted 50 or 60 years ago. He has

Kiyoshi Nishimoto, of Kainaliu, Kona, Hawaii.

Kenneth Westfall, of Idaho.   Joe Marshall, of Idaho.

planted macadamia nut trees as an intercrop in a small corner of his orchard.

Except for 3 years at McKinley High School in Honolulu, Oahu, Mr. Nishimoto has spent his entire life in Kona. He was born in Kainaliu. His hobby is bonsai—the art of cultivating miniature trees—which helps to fill out the time when he is not working on his farm or enjoying community social events with his neighbor-farmers. Mr. Nishimoto says that bonsai often requires a greener thumb than is needed for coffee culture; it demands loving care of the dwarfed trees and a knowledge of the esthetics of the bonsai as it has developed in Japan.

Kenneth Westfall, of Aberdeen, Idaho, grows about 100 acres of Russet Burbank potatoes each year on his 600-acre farm. He began farming in 1946, when he was 24. While he was attending the University of Idaho he was called into the Army. On his return, he began farming in partnership with his father, Frank Westfall, who has retired, leaving responsibility for the farm to him. He raises sheep, cattle, sugarbeets, grain, hay, and potatoes. His feeding and farming operations are highly mechanized.

Joe Marshall of Twin Falls, Idaho, during his 80-plus years probably has grown more potatoes than any other living man. People in Idaho call him the potato king of America. He and members of his family have several acreages on which yields and quality are consistently high. Throughout his long farming career, which dates from the time when nearly all potatoes were picked by hand, he has been noted for two things besides potatoes. He always has a beard and never a necktie.

72

Lee Roy Copple has been farming 200 acres near Trivoli, Ill., in partnership with Mrs. C. L. Wilkins, since 1949. Once it was called "Cocklebur Farm," but no more. Mr. Copple tackled the burrs first with a hoe and later with sprays. More than 100 acres are contoured; 40 acres each year get green-manure crops. He applies fertilizer as determined by regular soil tests. He began with 11 purebred Guernseys, all offspring of 4-H project animals. Now his herd consists of 40 to 50 head of Holsteins. He has numerous awards from the Peoria County Health Association for outstanding production of Grade-A milk. Hogs also are an important phase of his farming enterprise.

Mr. Copple received the Outstanding Young Farmer Award of Peoria County. He was active in 4-H Club work. He and his wife, Marjorie, and their two sons, David and Donald, often are hosts to 4-H and FFA boys and girls and livestock-judging groups. Schoolchildren, bankers, and college students tour the farm each year. The Copples like to show them around and answer their questions. Mrs. Copple helps her husband with many of the dairy chores, takes care of their large yard and garden, and cans and freezes about 270 quarts of vegetables and fruit every year. She sews most of her own clothes and some of the boys'. She helps with the farm bookkeeping and records of livestock and crops.

Lee Roy Copple and family, of Illinois.

Ron, Erland, and William Rothenberger, of Indiana.

The Rothenberger farm, 3 miles northwest of Frankfort, typifies Indiana agriculture in two ways. Hogs are its largest source of income, as they are in Indiana. The changes that are taking place in the operation of the farm also are typical—continuous corn and cattle feeding, for example. William and Erland Rothenberger and their families have been running the 425-acre farm on a partnership basis since 1939. Until 1960 they had the counsel and help of their father, George, who during his lifetime taught his sons the importance of character, hard work, and saving in good farming. His mother and father homesteaded the original 200 acres in 1829.

The brothers share the work. William works more with the hogs, because the buildings and grounds for hogs are closer to his home. Erland works more with the cattle, because they are closer to his house. Both do whatever needs to be done, though. They have held their labor supply constant by substituting capital, which has mostly gone into equipment. The farm is an example of intensive management without too much land per man. By putting technology to work at saving labor, the brothers have developed a highly efficient farm. Changes in cropping practices illustrate the transition. The first rotation was corn-oats-meadow. They cut the corn and shocked it for roughage and made hay with a loader. Then they went to silage, with no hay or pasture, and can put up 225 tons a day. About 95 percent of the tillable land is in continuous corn, which averages 105 bushels an acre. Once they put the ear corn in a crib. Then they converted their horse barn to a corn-crib, and finally they lined the crib for dry shelled corn. They feed

William and Erland Rothenberger, of Indiana.

all of their 360 acres of continuous corn to their animals, using heavy amounts of fertilizer and seeding for 21 thousand plants to the acre. Not many years ago this was a good general farm, with dairy cattle, horses for power, and hogs. Now only the hogs remain as a mainstay of the business. Where once they had a two-litter hog system, with individual farrowing houses, pasture, alfalfa, and shade problems, they now raise 1,500 pigs a year on a four-litter system. They keep the hogs on concrete, with nursing barns for the sows, a central farrowing building with floor heat, and two finishing units that will hold about 300 pigs each. They added their cattle feeding program in 1959. They can feed 250 head in 30 seconds, and their feedlots are equipped with silos for the roughage, automatic unload feeding tube, and concrete floors. They figure about two hours of labor per steer from shipping in to shipping out.

Both the Rothenbergers are graduates of Purdue University in agriculture and engineering. Each family has a son and a daughter.

"A farmer is pretty well situated if he really wants to farm," the men say. "Borrowing and paying—that's the way it is in the farm business. And as long as you can do both, you have a pretty good time." They intend to stay in the hog and cattle business because they like both. They intend to continue working as a partner-team because it gives each man a chance to relax occasionally and enjoy a trip with his family or a little extra time around his handsome farm home.

Farmer Manley (second from right), of Kentucky.

Mr. and Mrs. Farmer Manley live southwest of Lexington, Ky., on their 330-acre farm. Of their four sons, one is in partnership with his father; all have been active in 4-H work. The Manleys raise tobacco, corn, alfalfa, soybeans, and millet. The tobacco base is 11.87 acres. About 55 acres are in cultivation; the rest is in pasture and forage crops. Seven hundred loads of barnyard manure a year help to keep the corn and tobacco land in a high state of productivity. The Manleys own and operate another farm, some 7 miles distant, of 251 acres. It has a tobacco base of 7 acres. They milk 110 of their 230-head herd of Holsteins. They sold 108 thousand pounds of milk in August of 1961. The son has half interest in the herd and takes primary responsibility for it. They employ six men regularly. During the growing season they hire some part-time workers.

Mr. Manley began farming during the depression of the thirties as a tenant farmer on a 50-acre tract. His first dairy herd consisted of 10 cows, which he and Mrs. Manley milked. Later Mr. Manley added to the herd by buying aged cows at local stock sales and reselling them after they had produced calves. Before going into farming, Mr. Manley worked as a janitor at the University of Kentucky. He was born in Kentucky. He had to quit school after completing the eighth grade to help his father, who was in debt and in poor health. He has served on the board of directors of the Fayette County Farm Bureau and a Lexington cooperative. He is a deacon in his church.

Harold J. Patten and his son, Richard, grow carnations in extensive greenhouses near Tewksbury, Mass. The business was established in 1870 by their father and grandfather and is part of the third-ranking agricultural industry in Massachusetts. Floriculture follows poultry and dairying in the State; nearly 600 growers, with nearly 9 million square feet of greenhouse area, sell about 20 million dollars' worth of flowers each year. The total production includes about 40 million blooms of carnations. Since 1910 carnations have been the Pattens' only crop. Mr. Harold J. Patten took over the business on the death in 1921 of his father, who had encouraged him to hybridize carnations. He produced two famous varieties, Mikado and Princess Dagmar. Rooted cuttings of them and many others have been shipped to Europe and throughout the Western Hemisphere. This success encouraged many others to take up hybridizing; one result was that 276 new varieties of carnations were registered in 1960. The Pattens patented and distributed William Sim, which has produced 55 registered sports. New Varieties Day, established in 1938 by the New England Carnation Society, has been held nearly every year at Tewksbury. Its purpose is to stimulate interest in hybridizing "the divine flower."

The Pattens follow carefully the results of research at the University of Massachusetts and cooperate with the Extension Service in conducting demonstrations of the use of cultured cuttings to improve quality and quantity; weed control; improvement of soil structure to increase drainage and aeration; a liquid-feeding program; automatic heating valves and ventilators to reduce labor; the construction of temporary plastic greenhouses for starting young plants; and installation of a mist system for the propagation of cuttings.

Richard Patten, of Massachusetts.   *Harold J. Patten, of Massachusetts.*

Although red tart cherry trees grow in countless backyards across the United States, more than 60 percent of the commercial trees are grown on rolling land on the western side of the lower peninsula of Michigan. There, under the tempering influence of Lake Michigan, more than 4 million red tart cherry trees annually produce 85 thousand tons of the fruit.

Typical of the many Old Mission farmers who depend on cherries for a livelihood is Bruce Lyon, a third-generation grower and lifetime resident of the peninsula. He and his father, Charles Lyon, farm 180 acres of two farms in a partnership; 95 of those acres were cleared by Bruce's grandfather. The Lyons annually produce about 750 thousand pounds of cherries. Most are red tarts, but 40 acres are planted to sweet cherries. Charles Lyon recalls early cherry harvests, when each cherry was clipped from the trees because the fruit would keep longer with stems on. Although cherries are still picked by hand on the Lyon farms, mechanical pickers were being tried out in 1962. The Lyons, quick to adopt the latest production methods, now use water handling. The rest of the handling is almost entirely mechanized. Mr. Charles Lyon lives on the old homestead. Bruce lives on a farm a few miles down the peninsula with his wife, Eleanor, and their two sons and daughter.

Late-summer picking, year-round pruning and replanting, and spring spraying make a full-time job for him, but he has time for community and producer activities. He is a director and treasurer of Great Lakes Cherry Producers, Inc., a cooperative whose members in 5 States grow 50 percent of the red tart tonnage. The Lyons do most of the work on their acreages except during the short summer harvest. Hard work over the years has boosted the value of the farms. Bruce says that neither farm would be sold today for 100 thousand dollars. Expenses are high. About 60 thousand dollars have gone into tractors, trucks, sprayers, and pruning, picking, and other equipment. The payroll for 200 pickers may be as high as 25 thousand dollars.

Bruce Lyon, of Michigan.

David and Maurice Nystuen, of Minnesota.

Maurice Nystuen operates a general farm of 480 acres near Kenyon, Goodhue County, Minn. He has 60 registered Southdown ewes and 70 lambs, 32 registered Hampshire hogs, 40 head of feeder cattle, and 80 Hereford cows and calves, most of them registered. His son David has a 5-percent ownership in the livestock. David showed a heifer, 12 sheep, and 12 hogs at the Minnesota State Fair in 1961, when he was 15 and a sophomore in Kenyon High School. He won 16 ribbons.

James Skelton, of Mississippi.

James Skelton cultivates 650 acres near Cleveland, Miss. He owns 80 acres and rents the rest. His farm, which he acquired in 1949, reflects the emphasis in Mississippi on highly efficient production of cotton and the growing interest in good beef cattle. His operation includes cotton, 195 acres; soybeans, 375 acres; corn, 40 acres; improved permanent pasture, 25 acres; and hay, 15 acres. Oats are double cropped on 90 acres. He has raised the yield of cotton to about one-half bale above the average of the Delta region by controlling insects better, using preemergence chemicals on all day-labor cotton to cut in half the bill for hoeing, applying anhydrous ammonia at the same time that he prepares his cotton land in March or early April, irrigating as needed, skip row planting—plant four, skip four—on part of his crop, and studying every cut of cotton and using subsoiling, liming, and other special practices where needed.

He built a grain storage in 1959. It measures 49 by 50 feet. Its capacity is 10 thousand bushels. Thus he is sure of having storage space. When the time comes to sell the stored grain, he makes sure of getting the best price by asking prospective buyers to take samples and submit bids. He may decide to feed some of the grain to his own livestock rather than to sell it. He has had good experience with feeder pigs. He keeps about 20 Hereford brood cows of good type. Creep feeding saves labor in this cattle operation. Mr. Skelton irrigates cotton, soybeans, and corn. He tries small acreages of new varieties as they become available. He is active in the Bolivar County Livestock Association and the Bolivar County 4-H Advisory Council. Mrs. Skelton understands farm planning and management and helps to run the farm.

Mr. and Mrs. William H. Holtcamp and their family started farming in Audrain County, Mo., in 1922. Their first farm they purchased from his grandfather with borrowed money. As members of an Extension-sponsored balanced farming program, they made a plan for their farm and family living in 1947 and have followed it closely. It has helped them gain financial security, a pride in seeing their livestock top the markets, and a new home. Livestock improvement has been a major feature. The herd comprises 32 cows, 14 heifers, 22 steers, 25 calves, and an Angus bull. Their 106 ewes in 1961 produced 110 lambs, which topped the market when shipped. The first 300-acre farm that Mr. Holtcamp bought is operated in partnership with his son, Bud. Mr. and Mrs. Holtcamp moved to a 240-acre farm near Mexico, Mo., in 1953. The entire farm is in pasture. Two ponds are for livestock watering and for recreation. One is stocked with bass and bluegill. Mr. and Mrs. Holtcamp have been active in the Agricultural Extension Council, Balanced Farming Association, Farm Bureau, the Missouri Farmers Association, and their church. They are the parents of two sons and one daughter, all of whom have families. Both sons farm nearby. The Holtcamps believe that recreation and vacations are important to a successful and happy life. They have nine fox hounds. They enjoy local and State fox hunts, camping weekends with children and grandchildren, card parties with friends, and vacations in distant places.

The Holtcamps, of Missouri.

A native Montanan and ranch reared, Wallace Thompson operates a combination livestock and grain ranch of 9,360 acres in Stillwater County, in south-central Montana. His layout includes 6 thousand acres of deeded land. The rest is leased. It is a typical mountain foothill ranch. In the distance are the lofty summits of the Beartooth Mountains. With his wife, Virginia, and their son, Tim, Mr. Thompson lives in a modern home, whose picture windows overlook his lush hay bottoms along the Stillwater River. Their nearest community is Absarokee, a picturesque town about 7 miles down the river from the ranch. Mr. Thompson's main enterprise is raising cattle. His basic herd is 250 Aberdeen Angus cows. He raises 500 sheep. On a dryland bench above the river, he has about 500 acres of wheat, half of which is in summer fallow each year. He also has 400 acres of hay, barley, and oats. Mr. Thompson grew up on his parents' ranch in the Stillwater Valley and attended the School of Forestry at Montana State University. During the war, he served in the European theater with an army tank outfit. After the war he decided on ranching as a career, starting out on a small scale. Mr. Thompson is president of the Stillwater Wool Growers Association, which operates the largest wool pool in Montana. He is chairman of the board of supervisors of his Soil Conservation District. He rides with the Black Horse Patrol of Al Bedoo Shrine of Billings, a riding unit that has given exhibitions in many cities.

Wallace Thompson, of Montana.

Edward W. Simonson, of New Jersey.

Edward W. Simonson and Raymond G. Simonson farm 600 acres in Middlesex County, N.J. The brothers have been farming since 1933. They grow 280 acres of potatoes, 115 of wheat, and 60 of rye. They planted 80 acres of Christmas trees in 1951. The trees, in fields not suited to cropping, fit well in their program. The potato fields are irrigated. The harvest must be spread over a long period of time. The Simonson farm can store 400 thousand pounds of potatoes. Most of the crop is shipped in consumer packs. Edward is a member of the New Jersey White Potato Council and a director of the New Jersey Potato Association. Ray is on the Executive Committee of the Middlesex County Board of Agriculture and represents Middlesex County on the Freehold Soil Conservation District. Both are high school graduates. Their hobbies are hunting and fishing.

83

John K. Clayshulte, of New Mexico.

John K. Clayshulte, Mesilla, N. Mex., is a beekeeper. His bees, whose average annual production is 100 thousand pounds of honey, are stationed in 30 yards, or locations, the entire length of the irrigated Rio Grande Valley in Dona Ana County—but not too close to the industrial smog from El Paso and not too close together, for an area can be overstocked with bees, just as a section of rangeland may be overstocked with cattle. In his bee yard at Mesilla Dam, for example, Mr. Clayshulte has 58 stands of bees, with 4 boxes to the stand, and 8 frames or combs to the box— nearly 4.5 million bees in the Mesilla Dam yard alone. He also places bees in the Hondo and Mimbres Valleys when the apples are in blossom. He extracts honey three times a year. The extracted honey is strained to eliminate wax and is stored in 5-gallon cans, weighing 60 pounds each, for sale to large honey processors. He retails strained honey at his farm at 15 cents a pound. Comb honey retails at 20 cents a pound. Many buyers prefer light-colored honey, he says, "but a dark-colored honey has more vitamins and minerals; dark honey is filtered to lighten it." Beeswax is an important by-product of the honey business. It is used for candles, cosmetics, waterproofing, grafting trees, medicines, and many other things. One pound of beeswax is produced for every 60 pounds of honey. Beeswax sells at 50 cents a pound.

Each stand has one queen bee and thousands of worker bees and drones—males. The drones serve little purpose except to fertilize the queen in the first few days of her life. From this fertilization she will produce hundreds of thousands of eggs for the 2 to 3 years of her life. She can produce drones or workers at will and is the mother of all the bees in the stand. The sexless worker bees, whose lifespan is about 6 weeks, are the driving force of the hive. They gather the nectar and pollen from the fields and store them as carbohydrate and protein, respectively. A stand of bees will work only one crop at a time and will not mix types of honey in the same comb. Bees produce honey from mid-May to mid-September in most years. They gather mesquite nectar early in the season, then switch to alfalfa, and wind up on cotton from mid-July on. Mr. Clayshulte leaves 50 pounds of honey for food in each stand at the close of the season and starts checking the stands in March to make sure the bees have enough to eat.

Bee scouts discover new fields of nectar and pollen and come back to the stand to report the location to the other workers by means of the bee dance, by which they give directions to the fields and information about the type of crop. Bees carry nectar in special sacs in their bodies and pollen in "baskets" on their legs. They turn over these supplies to younger workers, who act as housekeepers and store the pollen and nectar. Nectar, the secretion of blossoms, is 88 percent water, and the bees evaporate the moisture until honey has only 10 to 12 percent water by fanning the breeze. That is, the bees vibrate their wings so as to set up an air current within the stand and thus cause evaporation. Honey will sour if the moisture content exceeds 18.6 percent, but this excess moisture is not a problem in the dry Southwest.

Bees need lots of water and can often be observed drinking along river banks or irrigation ditches. They never sleep. Only worker bees sting people—and then only when they are disturbed or excited. Mr. Clayshulte has been stung so many times he hardly notices a sting. All of his bees are of the Italian variety. Other common varieties are the Caucasian and Carniolan, as well as hybrids. Mr. Clayshulte is a graduate in civil engineering of New Mexico State University. He took over the beekeeping business from his father after he returned from service in the war. He is one of about a dozen commercial beekeepers in New Mexico and one of a thousand in the United States who depend on bees for a livelihood. Like other beekeepers throughout the country, he has lost many hives because of insecticides sprayed on farm fields and orchards and because of industrial smog. During the spring of 1961, industrial smog coming up the Mesilla Valley from El Paso killed 800 of his 1,400 stands. Greater understanding of bees and their values is needed, Mr. Clayshulte says: "Protecting bees is good business for farmers, because bees are important in the production of field crops and fruit. Cotton is a self-pollinating plant, but experiments have shown that bees can increase long-staple production 10 to 15 percent if they cross-pollinate the cotton. They are also essential in the production of alfalfa seed and melons in Mesilla Valley."

Ray Moore, of North Carolina.

Ray Moore farms 77 acres near Winston-Salem, N.C. He was born on a farm in 1906 and was reared on a farm. He and Mrs. Moore have six sons and a daughter. He completed the sixth grade, and he has taken advantage of many of the programs for adults in his and nearby communities. His program of general farming includes tobacco on 4.2 acres, small grain on 7 acres, corn on 10, truck crops on 3, 9 acres in permanent pasture, 3 cows, 7 hogs, and some chickens. Mr. Moore is active in his church and community organizations. His success in farming, he says, is due to hard work and the help given him in State and Federal farm programs.

Nathan Little Soldier, of North Dakota.

Nathan Little Soldier runs 150 cows on his ranch unit of 1,800 acres north of Golden Valley in Mercer County in North Dakota. He raises some corn, oats, and alfalfa, but everything else is in grass. A fullblooded Indian, he is in the south segment of the Fort Berthold Indian Reservation. He has served as a member of the tribal council, a Soil Conservation District supervisor, and an officer in the Beulah Post of Veterans of Foreign Wars. He has been an active rodeo performer and announcer for a number of years. He helped start the State High School Championship Rodeo in Beulah in 1950. Mr. Little Soldier was reared in Mercer County and attended school in Wahpeton, N. Dak. He and Mrs. Little Soldier have two sons—Arby, at home, and Dale, a college student—and a daughter.

The Baileys of Belmont County, Ohio, are known as Ohio's Jersey pioneers. The first was L. P. Bailey, who moved to a 252-acre farm near Tacoma in 1881. His three Jerseys were the progeny of animals brought from Rhode Island in 1867, the first to cross the Allegheny Mountains. He became an outstanding dairy leader. Convinced that dairying had a bright future, he traveled east in the early 1880's to import more Jerseys to Belmont County. He returned with 30 head and almost immediately sold them to farmers in the community. The success of this first trip encouraged him to make others. He established an outstanding herd of his own. He won more than 100 medals at State and national dairy expositions. Two of his four sons remained on the farm and devoted their energies and enthusiasm to the improvement of the herd of Jerseys. Lester Bailey is a third-generation Jersey man. He was graduated in 1939 from Ohio State University with a major in dairy husbandry. In 1943 he bought his uncle's interest in the farm and herd and he and his father, Jesse, formed a father-son partnership. Lester Bailey has been president of the Belmont County Jersey Cattle Club and a director of the Ohio Jersey Breeders' Association, the county dairy service cooperative, and the Barnesville Cooperative Milk Marketing Association. He and Mrs. Bailey have served many years as 4-H leaders. Their three daughters have been active in the 4-H Club.

The Bailey Jersey herd has numbered nearly 100 head since 1915. The 50 milk cows are housed in a stanchion barn. Calves and yearlings and the two herd sires are kept in an adjoining barn that was hand hewn and built in 1856. The herd averages nearly 400 pounds of butterfat.

Lester Bailey, of Ohio.

The Oliver Ranch near John Day, Oregon.

Bernard Keim, of Pennsylvania.

Bernard Keim, his father, George, and his brother, George, Jr., operate the largest maple sugar producing farm in Pennsylvania at West Salisbury, Somerset County. They have thousands of sugar maples on their extensive acreage and hang the equivalent of more than 8 thousand sap buckets each year. Instead of buckets for collecting sap, the Keims use plastic tubing. The sap from several trees flows through a tube into a collection tank. Thus they save much of the work of picking up buckets from each tree in all kinds of weather. They turn out more than 2 thousand gallons of sirup in their processing plant on the farm. Maple sugar products are also made and sold at retail on the farm. Some of their products are sold in restaurants along the Pennsylvania Turnpike. Besides the home farm of 225 acres, the Keims own three other farms. To bring sap from the outlying farms, they use a tank truck. They also have a Brown Swiss dairy herd of 110 head. The Somerset farms of the Keims have been in the family for four generations.

Ramiro Colon has a diversified program, including coffee, a fruit grove, and 1,500 laying hens, on his hilly farm in the municipality of Jayuya, P.R. Chickens do well in the cool climate. The commercial production of poultry has grown in Puerto Rico into a major farm enterprise, worth more than 28 million dollars. Changes in raising poultry include the use of productive disease-resistant breeds adapted to the conditions of the Island, improvements in feeding practices and control of parasites and diseases, and the improved marketing of poultry products.

Ramiro Colon, of Puerto Rico.

There are almost 400 dairy farms in Rhode Island. Many of them are family-type operations. One is Wemacs Farm in the town of Exeter. Stuart MacDonald, its owner, is a native of Cranston. He attended public schools in Scituate, worked for the Lippitt Ayrshire Farm in Hope, and was foreman of the dairy farm of the University of Rhode Island until 1950, when he bought Wemacs (so named because "we Macs run it"). It has 150 acres and 74 head of registered Ayrshires. Mr. MacDonald puts corn in his two silos. He buys hay, and the animals, being barnfed, see very little pasture. His herd test average for 1960 was 10,024 pounds of milk, 4.5 percent test and 406 pounds of fat. He was the State winner in the New England Green Pastures Contest in 1961. He and Mrs. Mac-Donald sing in their church choir. She is secretary of the Southern Rhode Island Farm Bureau. He is a director of the Rhode Island Ayrshire Club. Their daughter, Synthia Jean, is a student in the College of Home Economics at the University of Rhode Island. Two other daughters and a son are married and have left the farm.

Stuart and Synthia Jean MacDonald, of Rhode Island.

W. N. ("Will") Henderson and W. N. ("Fred") Henderson, Jr. operate Broad Acre Farm, Ninety Six, S.C. They are widely known for their country hams. The father began the business in the twenties. Fred took over most of the responsibility for curing the hams in 1949, and Mr. Will assumed the work of buying hogs and managing the farm. The Hendersons grow some of the hogs but do not produce enough to fill all requirements. Equipment and buildings used in slaughtering, butchering, curing, and ripening are modern and efficient, but they still have the 110-year-old smokehouse, nailed together many years ago with homemade nails. All the Hendersons' meats are smoked over burning hickory wood. They sell hams, sausage, bacon, liver pudding, lard, and chittlings to grocery stores and individual customers. Killing is done on mornings after the night temperature has gone below 32° F. After the hogs are dressed, the carcasses are pushed into the cooler, where they are chilled overnight. The next day, the carcasses are cut up for sausage, bacon, lard, or ham. The hams are trimmed and rubbed with salt, saltpeter, and sugar. Then they are stacked in a cooler. The hams are taken out after 3 days and again after 10 days and are rubbed again and restacked. Later, they get a soaking in warm water, are allowed to dry, and are hung in the old smokehouse. After smoking, the hams are hung on hooks in the ripening room, where they remain for a year to age. Then they are ready to eat. Fred grows about 100 acres of cotton annually, half of it irrigated. He also grows some truck crops. Mr. Will takes care of 250 acres of grain and looks after a beef herd and the swine. The ham business helps them to better utilize their labor in the off-season.

W. N. Henderson, Jr., of South Carolina.

James Sutton, Jr., of South Dakota.

James Sutton, Jr., of Onida, Sully County, S. Dak., knew from the day he started college that he would be going back to the ranch. He did so after his graduation from South Dakota State College in 1957 with a major in animal husbandry and after 6 months in the service. The ranch operation of which he is a part is so large that each man has a specialty. His involves rodeo stock and training horses. The ranch is on the Missouri River west and north of Onida. He is one of eight brothers and sons who operate the Sutton Brothers Ranch. His grandfather raised draft horses, beef cattle, and buffalo and expanded his operations when his three sons grew up. Now five of their sons take an active part in the ranching. They own and lease about 80 thousand acres. They have a loose partnership arrangement; each family owns land and buildings separately, but the livestock is owned jointly. An exception is a large acreage recently purchased, which has been incorporated. The stock includes 3,500 Hereford cows, 450 registered bulls, 300 yearling steers, 100 buffalo, and 400 horses. There are 3,500 acres of corn, 800 of oats, 800 of wheat, and 400 of alfalfa. Care of the livestock requires employment of 15 men, and the crops are custom farmed. Three sales take place on the ranch each year. In the spring, 200 registered 2-year-old Hereford bulls are sold. Then in October comes the sale of 75 Quarter Horse colts and 25 mares. The November sale includes 300 to 500 registered and commercial cows, 15 buffalo calves, and 25 horses for rodeo stock.

Jim's main job is to take care of the amateur rodeo stock and to train and show their registered Quarter Horses. A new sale-training barn is located at the ranch on which Jim and his family live. He supplies horses, Brahman bulls, roping calves, and dogging steers for the rodeos that abound throughout the summer. The Suttons raise the horses on the ranch and buy the other stock—Brahman bulls wherever they hear of some that sound as though they would make good rodeo material, roping calves in Cheyenne, and dogging steers in Mexico. Jim, a member of the South Dakota Rodeo Association since 1957, started rodeoing when he was in the seventh grade. Almost every weekend from May through September, Jim and his family—his wife, Julie; daughter, Teri, 7; and son, Steve, 4—are off to a rodeo.

Harold Ranzau was reared on the 1,845-acre Kendall County ranch in southwestern Texas that he runs in partnership with his father, Paul Ranzau. The two families live in homes built side-by-side under spreading liveoak trees. Cattle, sheep, and goats have provided the chief cash income for the families. The depression brought the need for more diversified sources, and production of hatching eggs was added to the ranching activities. Leasing wildlife privileges to hunters was added later, and a wildlife program was established. There is little competition for forage among cattle, sheep, and goats, and the Ranzau families have managed their ranching operations to make the most of their livestock resources. There is no inclination to want more land; they want to make more efficient use of the resources they now possess. Mr. and Mrs. Harold Ranzau and their two children are active in community and Extension work.

Harold Ranzau, of Texas.

Harry R. Varney, Jr., of Vermont.

Harry R. Varney, Jr., began farming in 1953, when he was 22 years old and had a bachelor's degree from the University of Vermont and a master's degree from Purdue University. His dairy farm is just south of the village of Shelburne, Vt. From his front window, he has a view of the Green Mountains. Looking the other way, past his barn, Varney can see Lake Champlain. His 60-cow, 285-acre farm represents an investment of 80 thousand dollars. His herd produced 600 thousand pounds of milk in 1960. He tries constantly to improve and enlarge the herd and to find quicker, better ways of doing things. He reads a number of farm publications and keeps in contact with specialists at the College of Agriculture of the University of Vermont. As a man who lists his goals as rearing his family of four girls and a boy and providing security, he is active in church and community activities. The Varneys live in a lovely white frame house near busy Route 7. Like many farmers, Mr. Varney finds the pace speeding up: "It seems like we're all racing. A fellow has to go faster all the time just to keep up. Gains in efficiency don't pay off as much as they used to. And yet if we don't keep increasing our efficiency, we're not going to stay in business long."

The Tanakas, of Washington.

Hand labor is not altogether a thing of the past in American farming, particularly truck gardening. Vegetable crops seem to appreciate special attention, and Mrs. Ito Tanaka and her sons, Harry and Joe, make sure they get it. They farm just south of Spokane, Wash. Mrs. Tanaka came from Japan with her husband, who has since passed away. Five acres support the three families. To make it pay, they farm every square inch. They have to crop their land hard. They raise onions, cauliflower, radishes, lettuce, cabbage, and turnips. Most home gardeners are happy to get one crop of vegetables from their gardens, but the Tanaka family harvests two crops of lettuce, onions, and cabbage and five to six crops of radishes in a growing season that is not especially long. In the early spring they cover their land with barnyard manure, which they buy from stockyards. At intervals during the summer, they apply commercial fertilizer. Planting is done with a push-type garden planter. Crops like lettuce are planted thick. The seedlings are thinned by hand. Some weeding also is done by hand. Chemical weedkillers are used, too. The family does the harvesting. The Tanakas see no need for hiring help when by working extra hours they can do it themselves and do it the way they want it done. The vegetables are sold to store owners at the Spokane produce market. Within a few hours of harvesting, their produce is in grocery stores throughout the city.

Richard E. Strom leases 2,500 acres in Albany County, Wyo., from his father. He has 400 head of Rambouillet sheep, and by selective breeding he strives to improve the breed, with emphasis on larger size, open faces, and freedom from wrinkles. At shed-lambing time he records the dam's number and the lamb's number, sex, size, and birth date. He weighs all lambs at weaning and scores them for open face, wrinkles, body conformation, fleece grade, density, and uniformity. These factors he combines into an index score, which tends to balance the factors of wool and lamb production. The weaning weights are corrected for age with a nomograph and further corrected for sex and maturity of ewes. His tools include an adding machine, slide rule, fleece squeezing machine to estimate clean weight, fleece sample book, record forms, aluminum sheep holders, scales, and a branding board. Aside from attacks of enterotoxemia before the lambs are old enough to vaccinate, occasional killings by dogs, and disappearance of a sheep now and then, he has few problems that good management cannot solve. He began working with sheep on his father's ranch when he was 12. He began managing the ranch in 1957, when he was 30 years old. He received a degree in agriculture from the University of Wyoming in 1950. In Laramie High School he was active in 4-H and FFA. Mr. and Mrs. Strom have two sons and a daughter. He cooperates with the Wyoming Agricultural Experiment Station in experiments in sheep coating, nose branding, dust branding, and vaccination for immunity to enterotoxemia.

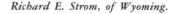

Richard E. Strom, of Wyoming.

Plants

The Greatest Service

FRANK NICHOLAS MEYER sailed for China in 1905. He died there in 1918. In those 13 years of search for plants and seeds for his adopted United States, he achieved what few men have achieved: "The greatest service which can be rendered to any country" (as Thomas Jefferson wrote in 1790) "is to add a useful plant to its culture."

The search was hard. The young man, who was born in Holland in 1875 and trained there in horticulture, had a wide assignment from the Department of Agriculture to look at and send back every fruit, nut, and vegetable that he thought would have value in this country and to learn all he could about Chinese methods of cultivating plants. He smelled and tasted produce in the markets of Peking and then went to the places the fruit grew, and so got seeds of persimmons, grapes, apricots, cherries. He went to gardens of monasteries and temples and found, among others, a valuable pistachio tree. He walked through central China to find strains of cabbage, rice, and soybeans, which he sent to Washington. Then he set off for Manchuria, Korea, and Siberia. He walked 1,800 miles in the next few months over mountains, hillsides, plains, collecting seeds of onions, peppers, pumpkins, and many more, 680 varieties in all.

He spent 2 years in Turkestan, Siberia, and the Caucasus. In 1916, ill and tired, he was trapped by a Chinese revolution. He wrote to his anxious coworkers in Washington: "I have not received mail now for many months. Travel is nearly impossible. Food supplies are running low." He disappeared from a steamer on the Yangtze River on June 2, 1918. The American Consul later found his body in a village, where some Chinese had buried it. It now rests in Shanghai. His will left a bequest to his associates, and they decided to have a medal struck in his honor, to be awarded each year for outstanding efforts in plant introduction. It shows the first recorded plant exploration, that of the Egyptian Queen Hatshepsut's expedition to the Land of Punt for the incense tree in 1500 B.C.

Frank Nicholas Meyer's service was greater than he knew, for he saw growing in this country only a few of the treasures he sent back. It was a great service in a great tradition. The Department of Agriculture since 1898 has had a formal organization whose main

Frank N. Meyer's cart in Turkestan in 1911.

P. H. Dorsett's pack train in China in 1924.

Howard S. Gentry, agricultural explorer, in 1961.

concern is the exploration for useful plants, their introduction and evaluation for crop potentials, and the preservation of breeding stocks of value in American agriculture. Department explorers have collected more than 275 thousand introductions from all parts of the world. Early plant explorers, like Frank Nicholas Meyer, traveled by primitive means. They spent much of their time just getting to the field and returning their collections. Plant explorers today use airplanes and heavy field trucks to accomplish their missions faster and more successfully. Their greater knowledge of the global distribution of plants also has helped them. Shipping methods have changed from the cumbersome Wardian case designed to protect soil-grown plants during ocean voyages to the growing of plants in sphagnum moss, wrapped in plastic film, and packed in light cartons for shipment by air.

The testing of the plant introductions formerly was done at Federal Plant Introduction Stations at Chico, Calif., Miami, Fla., Savannah, Ga., and Glenn Dale, Md. Four more stations have been established at Experiment, Ga., Ames, Iowa, Geneva, N.Y., and Pullman, Wash. Today testing of plant introductions is a precise, coordinated effort by research groups in Federal and State agricultural experiment stations so that the best of the plant immigrants are quickly incorporated into our crop varieties. Seeds of the introductions and breeding lines that are believed to be essential for the needs of crop breeders in generations to come are preserved in the National Seed Storage Laboratory, Fort Collins, Colo.

The Meyer Medal.

Plants shipped in a Wardian case in 1914.

Plants packed for overseas shipment in 1954.

Gerald Seaton (left) and John L. Creech prepare cuttings of plants from Portugal for propagation at Glenn Dale, Md.

Scientists examine wild collections of vine crops at Geneva, N.Y.

Plant introduction encompasses the study of innumerable plants, not all of which have become important to us. Our modern wheats, rice, potatoes, and many other crops may be said to derive from the germ plasm provided by plant introductions. Our success with soybeans has grown out of the collections of two plant explorers, P. H. Dorsett and W. J. Morse. Today the search is equally hard, despite modern conveniences, and the role of the Department's explorer remains unchanged. He is still essentially a one-man team, who depends on his knowledge of plants and his curiosity to find plants growing wild in near or remote regions that will fill the needs of agriculture and industry for more plants for new uses. In Meyer's day, the emphasis was on cereals, vegetables, and forage plants; the explorers now seek species useful to scientists in their search for new industrial components, constituents that may have value in medicine, sources of paper pulp, and other plants that may diversify our agriculture and be useful to gardeners and nurserymen.

One of them is Howard Scott Gentry, a senior plant explorer of the Department of Agriculture. He has traveled the world over— the Alps of southern Europe for legumes and grasses, the hill country of Afghanistan and India for forages and food crops, the deserts of Mexico and our Southwest for drug and industrial plants, and South Africa for new oilseeds. He has made 9,500 collections. Tomorrow somebody may be sent to Mexico or Ethiopia, or Japan. The names of the explorers and the places may be different, but the search will continue, and more new and useful plants will enrich our agriculture. *(John L. Creech)*

Valuable seeds are kept at the National Seed Storage Laboratory, Fort Collins, Colo.

Hybrid Corn

ABOUT 95 percent of our corn acreage now is planted to hybrid corn. We produce at least 20 percent more corn on 25 percent fewer acres than in 1930, when seed of hybrid corn became available in quantity to American farmers. From the time of the first settlers, who obtained corn from the Indians, farmers selected seed ears from the standing stalk or from the crib. They entered the best ears of these open-pollinated varieties in fairs and shows, and people thought the prizewinners would pass on their superiority to their progeny and so improve yields. It did not turn out that way.

G. H. Shull, a geneticist at Cold Spring Harbor, N.Y., started experiments in 1906 on inheritance in corn. From them came important observations on the reduction in vigor on inbreeding and the restoration of vigor on crossing. They provided the basis for hybrid corn. Studies of inbreeding were made at other experiment stations. The general opinion was that hybrid corn was not feasible because of the poor vigor of the inbred parents. Open-pollinated varieties are maintained by mass selection. Windborne pollen effects fertilization, and there is no control of the male parentage. Inbred lines are developed by a combination of inbreeding and selection. Inbreeding involves the transfer of pollen from an individual plant to the silks of the same plant. This process is repeated for several generations until the strain becomes stable, or true breeding. Selection is practiced in each generation to maintain only the superior types. Crossbreeding involves the crossing of selected parents. Single crosses are produced by crossing two inbred lines. Double crosses are produced by crossing two different single crosses.

D. F. Jones, who was in charge of research on corn at the Connecticut Agricultural Experiment Station, suggested in 1918 the double-cross hybrids involving four inbred parents, which partly removed the limitation imposed by poor vigor of the inbred parents. The use of this system of crossing made hybrid corn commercially feasible. The first commercial double-cross hybrid, Burr-Leaming, was released and recommended by the Connecticut station in 1921. Many of the State and Federal inbreeding and hybridization programs were started in the early twenties. Basic genetic theory was inadequate to serve as a guide. New procedures were required. Many persons contributed to this phase of the development. Hundreds of inbred lines were isolated, and these were evaluated in

106

thousands of crosses. When the best of them became commercially available, some farmers were reluctant to adopt them, but demonstration plantings and field observations proved the worth of the hybrids. The demand for hybrid seed in 1935 in the Corn Belt exceeded production, and the hybrid seed industry developed rapidly.

The production of hybrid seed requires careful control of the parents. During the experimental phases of developing inbred lines and hybrids, this control is accomplished by covering the ear shoots and tassels with bags and transferring pollen of the desired type by hand. In commercial seed production, control is achieved by the isolation of the seed fields and by the removal of tassels, before shedding of the pollen begins, from the rows to be used as female parents. Detasseling originally was done by crews walking through the field pulling tassels before the pollen was shed. Machines were developed later to carry the workers through the seed fields. Still later, cytoplasmic-sterile stocks and fertility-restoration genes were discovered and incorporated into the more widely used inbred parents. Stocks carrying cytoplasmic sterility shed no pollen. Cytoplasmic sterility is transmitted only through the female parent and results in the absence of fertile pollen. In effect, the strain is male sterile. Fertility restoration is conditioned by genes having the ability to restore male fertility to otherwise cytoplasmic male-sterile lines. The proper manipulation of these two traits completely avoids the necessity for detasseling but assures full fertility in the farmer's field.

Besides an increase in production, other benefits have been achieved by the use of hybrid seed. Hybrids make more efficient use of applied fertilizer. Progress has been made in developing hybrids resistant to some insects and diseases; the result is a product of higher quality and a more stable yearly production. Because of their greater uniformity in maturity and resistance to lodging, the hybrids have helped make large-scale mechanization possible. *(G. F. Sprague)*

Controlled hand pollination of corn.

The Improvement of Wheat

THE STORY of the improvement of wheat has no beginning and no ending. Improvements are made every year.

Half of the total crop production of the United States, measured in dollars, comes from plants first used by the Indians, but wheat, our leading food grain, is not among them. It came to us from half-way around the world as food for colonists in the New World or in the luggage of immigrants, who knew its worth. The introduction of wheat from many lands provided an array of varieties and kinds for colonists to try. Many kinds failed because they were not suited to the soil and climate in the places they were planted, and they were replaced by seed from varieties that did succeed. Wheat became established by this process along the Atlantic coast before 1800. The process was repeated as settlers moved westward. Wheat was beginning to look like a native in America by 1859. Now it is grown regularly in 44 States.

The expansion of wheat production in new areas seems at first to have been a simple matter of migration, but success was possible only because of the special adaptation of a few of the introduced varieties. Another factor has been the availability of a broad base of germ plasm, the hereditary material. Foresighted early workers systematically assembled and preserved valuable wheat germ plasm to form the world collection of wheats in the Department of Agriculture. It now comprises about 16 thousand accessions. In it are maintained wheats from every continent and every major geographical area and every pool of breeding stocks for the use of breeders and geneticists. This work became a regular function of the Department in 1897. Mark Alfred Carleton, one of the early research men, conducted a vigorous program of exploration, introduction, and evaluation of wheat between 1894 and 1918. Through his efforts, hard red winter and durum wheats became widely accepted. Other scientists have bred varieties for every section and have developed plants that surpass the older types in yield, resistance to diseases and insects, and quality.

Besides introducing new varieties from other countries, they have done pedigree selection, hybridization, and backcrossing, a system of crossbreeding in which one parent is used repeatedly for several generations while selection is made to retain the desired trait or traits of the nonrecurring parent. In 1934, 32 varieties were grown that were

108

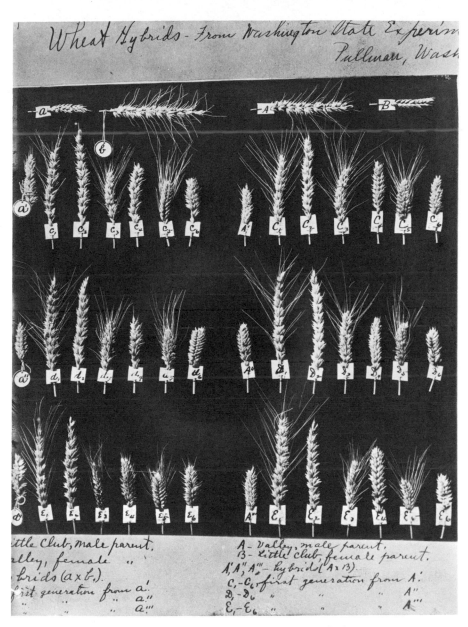

An old picture of W. J. Spillman's crosses of wheat.

originated by private breeders; only two of them were originated by hybridization. Also, in 1934, 100 varieties were grown that originated at agricultural experiment stations; 30 of them were bred by hybridization, 59 by selection, and 11 by introduction from other countries. The acreage sown to varieties produced at the experiment stations in 1959 accounted for 99 percent of the acreage in the hard red spring wheat, 100 percent of the durum, 77 percent of the hard red winter, 93 percent of the soft red winter, and 99 percent of the white wheat acreage. Planned breeding by scientific methods thus has become almost universal.

Rust is one of several diseases that must be controlled. Farmers in New England more than 200 years ago thought the barberry was responsible for the rust that often blasted their crops. Laws provided for its eradication. Many persons have worked hard since 1918 to rid all sections of the plants. Native and vulgaris barberries have nearly been eradicated from the 10 North Central States where rust is most feared; millions of bushes have been destroyed in 9 other States, but more work is needed to finish the job. More than a million square miles of land formerly infested now require only enough attention to maintain the barberry-free condition. Nurserymen in the rust area sell only barberries that are resistant to rust. Barberries are beautiful ornamental shrubs, but resistant forms only should be planted. The infected barberry is the source of early-season epidemics of stem rust and the important source of new races, of which more than 300 different ones have been identified. Wind can carry the wheat-infecting rust spores hundreds of miles. The red stage of stem rust survives the winter on wheat and susceptible grasses in the South and Mexico, and spores may be blown northward in quantity to infect the wheat in a series of leaps along the continuous belt of wheat that extends from Texas to North Dakota and Canada.

The use of resistant varieties of wheat has been the most effective means of breaking the rust chain, a point that has been emphasized anew in each major epidemic. Breeding wheats that withstand rust has been a long, hard struggle. It is not finished and may never be. Dr. Carleton tested hundreds of varieties for resistance. W. J. Spillman, a wheat breeder in Washington before he joined the Department of Agriculture, in a work on crossbreeding published in 1901 opened a new epoch in plant improvement. His results established that by hybridization predictable recombinations of parental traits could be bred. The valuable emmer-common crosses by E. S. McFadden in South Dakota and durum-common crosses made in Minnesota ushered in the longest (1938–1949) stabilized rust-free situation in the United States. There followed a host of improved varieties of spring wheat resistant to stem rust, including Thatcher, Pilot, Rushmore, Mida, and Lee. Pathologists nevertheless had warned about a new race of rust, labeled 15B, that had been found near barberries a few times. This rust, they said, would thrive on all these highly bred, hitherto resistant wheats. As insurance against the worst, breeders made crosses with a few resistant varieties from East Africa and other places.

110

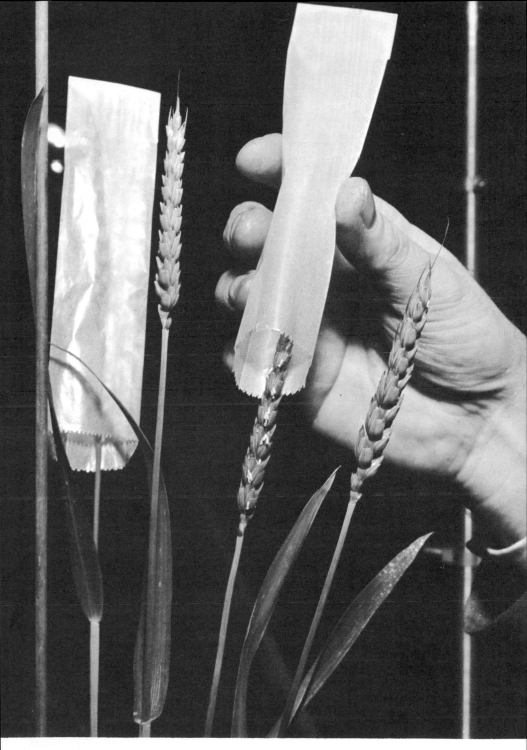

New varieties start from single flowers. The covered spike at the left has been crossed with another variety. The empty anthers of the spike whose cover is partly lifted show it has already pollinated itself.

111

Anthers are removed to prevent inbreeding, and the spike later is covered to prevent stray pollen from contaminating the crosses.

Stems of wheat infected with black stem rust cannot nourish the developing kernels in the head. The smooth stem is of a resistant variety.

What they feared happened. One-third of the durum crop in Minnesota and one-fifth of the crop in North Dakota were lost in 1950. Losses in North Dakota, South Dakota, and Minnesota reached 80 percent on durum wheats and 35 percent on common wheats in

Barberry bushes are killed with herbicides.

the following years. Breeders went to work in earnest in the fall of 1950 to meet what was now a known threat to the wheat crop of the North Central States. They planted the new selections and promising varieties at experiment stations near Brawley, Calif., and Ciudad Obregon, Mexico, so as to have two crops a year. They organized an international rust nursery so they could test promising selections at many places in 30 countries where diverse kinds of rust, including 15B, were known to occur. They exposed test plots in Puerto Rico and the Virgin Islands with specific new races of rust. Meanwhile, they evaluated most of the world collection and an equal number of breeders' lines for reaction to specific cultures of stem rust. Useful commercial varieties resulted. The crosses and pedigrees of the varieties they produced are complex, indeed.

Practically all the durum acreage in the black rust area and 88 percent of the durum acreage in the United States were seeded to varieties resistant to the 15B rust by 1959, and 55 percent of the spring wheat acreage was sown to resistant varieties. A new period of stabilized low rust losses began in 1956. Will it last? Probably not, but no one knows. We know of rust cultures that attack our best wheats. Better tools are available to combat the rust, however. Chemicals for control are in the offing. The susceptible barberry is about gone. Even wider crosses and mutations are being utilized experimentally because colchicine, X-rays, and other aids to breeders have been discovered.

Other diseases attack wheat. We need not go into detail about them; the work with rust illustrates the many facets of research we must explore to get effective results. Some of the other important diseases of wheat include two entirely different rusts (orange leaf and stripe rust); three smuts (stinking, loose, and flag smut); powdery mildew; scab; two septoria blotches; four virus diseases (streak mosaic, soilborne mosaic, false-stripe, and barley yellow dwarf); and several root and foot rots. To control them, our goal has been to develop resistant varieties. For several, no other means of control is known. For some, no effective control of any kind is known. In the control of stinking smut, crop and soil management, the use of resistant varieties, and chemicals may separately be of value; together, they may curb the disease. Combining resistance with good chemicals has brought the incidence of common stinking smut to the lowest point in 50 years all across the Nation. Dwarf bunt will be harder to control.

Another aspect of improving varieties of wheat has to do with quality. Our grain and milling trade always has demanded the best quality. The marketing of grain was unsettled as to grades and inspection until 1916, when the Congress adopted the United States Grain Standards Act to set up a system of uniform grading of wheat under Federal supervision. This system has provided a common

Mechanization and heavy fertilization require short- and stiff-strawed wheats.

A combined harvester-thresher in a field near Alliance, Nebr.

language of trading, given a dependable and uniform description of certain factors of quality, provided the basis for accurate market reports, and facilitated storage, credit, and future delivery transactions. Standards of market acceptability were fixed soon after 1910 around a few wheat varieties—Turkey hard winter, Fultz and Fulcaster soft winter, Marquis hard red spring, Kubanka and Mindum durum, Hybrid 128 club, and a few others. Breeders have adhered to them as minimum levels and in many respects have improved on them in newly bred varieties. The breeding job is only half done until appropriate quality is obtained.

Whether higher yields affect the quality of flour produced from the grain depends on the use to be made of the flour. Wheat whose protein is less than 10 percent of the wheat kernel is preferred for pastries. Wheat of a higher content of protein is preferred in bread and macaroni. Impressive gains in yields are evident in records dating from 1866. The yield per harvested acre in the 1920's was about 13 bushels; in the 1940's, 15 bushels. Between 1919 and 1952 average yields (adjusted for weather) increased by 3.8 bushels in North Dakota and by 3.3 bushels in Kansas, or about 25 percent. Contributing to the climb in yields have been improvements in quality of seed; better adapted varieties; proper and timely tillage operations; better control of diseases, weeds, and insects; increased use of fertilizer; and improved management. Higher yields since 1953 have been influenced by favorable growing conditions, more use of fallow, and the selection by farmers of their better land for seeding to wheat, which has been possible under the acreage allotment program of the Agricultural Adjustment Act of 1938, as amended. An exceptional yield in 1958 was also due in part to a minimum of diseases and insects. Compared with the average yield of 17.2 bushels per harvested acre in 1951–1953, yields 40 percent above this seem attainable if the same base acreage of 67 million is assumed.

Heavy applications of fertilizer to wheat tend to cause varieties to go to straw and lodge. Research has been meeting the problem to a degree with new varieties that have stiff straw and tolerate fertilizer better. Monon, a soft wheat bred in Indiana, has short straw and stands under fertilization. Shortness and stiff straw have contributed to the high yields and popularity of Pawnee and Triumph, hard winter wheats, in parts of the Great Plains. The new durum wheats, Wells and Lakota, average 10 to 14 inches shorter than old varieties. New semidwarf selections in the Pacific Northwest are 35 to 50 percent shorter than normal varieties and are the most fertilizer-tolerant of all. Earliness of grain formation has been of great importance in breeding higher yielding winter wheats for a part of the Plains area. There each day of earlier maturity, on the average, means an increased yield of a bushel an acre, especially in varieties that head 1 to 10 days earlier than the Turkey type. *(L. P. Reitz)*

Plants and Light

Two MEN in the United States Department of Agriculture in 1918 set themselves the task of finding a way to make a certain tobacco plant flower. Most tobacco plants flower without any prompting, but this particular plant was different. It arose as a mutation and had great promise for commercial use if only seed could be produced. But seeds come from flowers, and plants like this one, seen occasionally in previous years, had always been killed by frost before they could flower. As autumn approached in 1918 and no flowers were evident, the men moved the plant into a greenhouse so it could continue to grow. The plant flowered about Christmastime and produced seed. The immediate problem thus was solved.

This event attracted little attention at the moment because only a few persons were aware of it and understood its significance. But to W. W. Garner and H. A. Allard, the two men with the problem, the production of those tobacco flowers opened up an entirely new area of plant science. They had discovered the fundamental principle that the relative length of day and night controls flowering. They named the phenomenon photoperiodism. They tested the principle of photoperiodism on several other plants and found it worked on many. Some kinds, the "short-day" plants, like the tobacco, they learned, flower when days are short and nights are long, but do not flower under other conditions of daylength. Other plants, the "long-day" ones, such as spinach, flower only when the days are long and nights are short. Still others, "day-neutral" ones, have no preference as to daylength.

When that one tobacco plant flowered in 1918, probably even Garner and Allard did not appreciate the impact their discovery would presently have on agriculture and on scientific understanding of the growth and development of plants. It led to the essential knowledge on which the multimillion-dollar industry of year-round production of blooms of chrysanthemums was founded. It gave the wheat breeder a tool that permitted three times the former rate of progress in producing disease-resistant strains, a tool that was used when strain 15B of stem rust threatened ruination of the country's wheat production. It opened the door to understanding many problems of plant production not outwardly related to flowering. It prepared the way for basic investigations of the response of plants to environment. Research on photoperiodism at an ever-increasing rate

Dark houses at Arlington Farm in 1940.

Harry A. Borthwick and H. A. Allard.

is creating a backlog of knowledge useful in new ways to improve further our agricultural efficiency and contribute to our enjoyment of flowering plants.

The story of the further development of our knowledge of the control of flowering by daylength is the story of how a single biochemical reaction of plants to light not only controls flowering but also prepares trees and other plants of temperate climates for the onset of cold weather; causes seeds of some crops and many kinds of weeds to germinate; controls the coloring of apples, tomatoes, and other fruits; and brings about other plant responses. The discovery of photoperiodism was turned immediately to practical use — for example, in the control of time of flowering in commercial production of chrysanthemums. Garner and Allard found chrysanthemums to be short-day plants in their original experiments. Artificial light added to the end of short autumn or winter days to make the days long and the nights short delayed blooming until later, more desirable dates. Conversely, shortening the exposure to light and lengthening the dark periods artificially in the summer induced early, out-of-season blooming.

Extensive use of light control in the production of chrysanthemums did not follow that discovery at once, however, because the amount of artificial light used made the method expensive. Presently scientists studied the mechanism by which daylength controls flowering. Did the short days make chrysanthemums flower, or was it the long nights? The investigators put a short period of darkness in the middle of the long day to make two short days of it, but that had no visible effect on the plants; they flowered at the usual time. Then they put a short light period in the middle of the long night to make two short nights, and that had a profound effect. It prevented flowering. This short-day plant apparently carried on reactions in the dark that led to flowering only if not interrupted by light. The dark-period interruption pointed the way to an effective and less expensive way to use artificial light for control of flowering. The present practice with chrysanthemums is based on this discovery. Three or 4 hours of light in the middle of the night delay flowering as effectively as do 6 or 8 hours from sundown to midnight and costs less for electricity.

Scientists have wondered, however, why chrysanthemums require an interruption of darkness of as much as 3 or 4 hours while the soybean, another short-day plant, requires only 3 or 4 minutes to prevent flowering. We now have the answer. Chrysanthemums do not require 3 or 4 hours of light. They can be kept from flowering by much less than 3 or 4 hours if the light is divided into short periods and distributed throughout 3 or 4 hours near the middle of the night. For instance, 18 minutes of continuous light given at midnight does not prevent flowering; but if it is divided into nine

2-minute exposures at 30-minute intervals throughout a 4-hour period in the middle of the night, the total of 18 minutes is as effective as continuous light for 4 hours. Other equally effective lighting schedules have been found, and better ones may be possible.

This method of cyclic lighting during a part of the night was just being developed when this was written. It has promise of profitable application by the grower because it permits him to use a limited amount of power for lighting a large area. By lighting each of several small areas briefly, in succession, instead of a big area continuously for a long period, he greatly reduces both the demand charge for service and the actual amount of current he uses. Progress in applying light to chrysanthemums since 1925 has come largely as a byproduct of fundamental studies of the action of light on plants in general. One of the first underlying facts scientists discovered about photoperiodism was that red light is more effective than that of any other color when used as a dark-period interruption to control flowering. This discovery has obvious practical importance; it indicates the best kind of lamps to use. Lamps giving light that is rich in the red are more efficient than those giving light that is poor in red.

A second major discovery was that the action of red light on flowering is nullified by light having somewhat longer wavelengths in the near infrared, the so-called far red. Thus, after one exposes a soybean to enough red light in the middle of the night to prevent flowering, the capacity to flower is easily restored by an exposure to far red immediately afterward. This discovery was very important, because these red and far-red wavelengths of light also caused peculiar reversals of the ability of certain seeds to germinate. Some kinds of seeds must have light to germinate, and the kind they need is red light. After they receive the red light, however, the seeds can be kept from germinating by promptly giving them far red. Since the same wavelengths of red and far-red light, respectively, control both seed germination and flowering in the same reversible way, these two plant processes must be set in action by the same basic light reaction. This is startling, because germination of seeds and flowering are so different in appearance as to seem quite unrelated.

The occurrence of reversibility in the ability of seeds to germinate and of plants to flower suggested the possibility that such photo-reversibility might also occur in other plant responses. A careful survey revealed that it is, in fact, involved in several other phenomena. It has much to do with the regulation of length of stems and the size of leaves and with the pigmentation of fruits and other plant parts. It probably is responsible for many other responses not yet demonstrated. Discovery of the effectiveness of red light and the reversal of its action by far red led to a further step in the knowledge of how light affects plants. Red light obviously causes effects that other visible wavelengths either do not cause or cause far less effectively than red. The energy of light, of course, must be absorbed to induce these effects. Absorption of red in preference to light of other colors requires the presence of an absorbing compound, a pigment that is blue. We therefore look for such a blue compound in plants. Most plants are green, however; even albino plants are white, not blue. Either there is no blue pigment in certain plant parts, or so little is present that we cannot see it.

Fortunately, a more sensitive instrument than the human eye can be used to search for such a hypothetical pigment. With a spectrophotometer of special sensitivity, scientists detected the unseen blue pigment in the living plant. Moreover, they have extracted the pigment without destroying its action. By keeping track of the pigment with the spectrophotometer, they have separated it from other constituents of the plant and thus partly purified it. We do not yet know what the compound is nor do we know what it does chemically. For convenience, the substance is called phytochrome. This no longer hypothetical pigment exists in two forms. One results from the action of red light. The other results from the action of far red. The two forms are repeatedly interconvertible by red and far red applied in alternating sequence. One form of the pigment, the one that absorbs far red, is believed to be an enzyme. This enzyme causes various actions, such as prevention of flowering of the chrysanthemum, germination of seeds, inhibition of stem elongation, and coloration of fruits and other plant parts.

One characteristic of the pigment in the live plant is that it undergoes gradual change in darkness from the far-red-absorbing form to the red-absorbing form. It is because of this change that plants exhibit response to daylength. The pigment is changed to the active, flowering-inhibiting form during the daytime. When darkness comes, the pigment begins to change back. If the dark period is short, the short-day plant remains vegetative because sufficient pigment remains in the flower-inhibiting form to keep it from flowering. If the dark period is long, however, more of the pigment changes back, and its level falls below the minimum required for flower inhibition; therefore the plant flowers.

Where do these studies of the light reactions lead? The answer in part comes from looking backward. As recently as 1951 we did not know that the photoperiodic reaction was reversible by light. We knew that a pigment was involved, but we did not know about its change of form in darkness. Extraction of the pigment had not been undertaken at the time. Control of many different kinds of plant response by a single reversible photochemical reaction was not even imagined in 1951. An obvious answer to the question is that we cannot predict where the results of this work will lead in the next few years. We can give assurance, however, that the work will

Controlled-environment room at Belts-
ville for studying effects of light on plants.

A forester examines young cedars that get
artificial light at night.

lead to more complete understanding of how plants are influenced by their environment and will enable farmers and gardeners to grow and use plants to better advantage.

Exactly how results of this kind of work may contribute in the future to more efficient agriculture is also difficult to predict. Looking backward again, we see many practical applications already made and many opportunities not yet realized. Plant breeders use daylength control to make potential parent plants flower at the time desired so they can be hybridized. They grow the progenies on day lengths favorable to flowering and thus shorten the time to maturity and increase the number of generations they can grow in a given time. Physiologists know that plants in different stages of development do not always give the same response to herbicides. Daylength treatments are used therefore to produce plants in vegetative and reproductive states for experimental purposes.

Many kinds of woody plants normally become dormant in winter even though they stay in a warm greenhouse, but they will continue to grow throughout the winter if a little light is given during a part of the night. Light for forcing growth of such woody plants has important practical applications, but it has been little used. Light greatly stimulates the rooting of some kinds of leafy cuttings, but here, too, practical application has not kept pace with scientific discovery. Garden areas in suburban shopping plazas are certain to present the gardener and nurserymen with photoperiodic problems caused by bright lighting at night. The increasing daily duration of darkness in late summer and early fall naturally conditions plants in preparation for cold weather. Prolonged artificial light prevents such

121

conditioning of many plants that are accordingly caught in an unhardened, actively growing condition by the first frost and killed back. The gardener must devise ways to meet this problem, either by selection of plants that are less sensitive to light or by proper placement of lamps and manipulation of light.

The regulatory effect of light on seed germination is widely seen but seldom appreciated. The admonition to plant certain kinds of small seeds almost on the surface of the soil is a wise one taught by experience, but the reason given is rarely correct. It is often said that such seeds are so small that if planted deep, the seedlings could not possibly reach the surface. Actually, reaching the surface is not the problem, because the seeds do not germinate even if they are covered with only a little soil. The same effect of depth of soil cover is exhibited by most weed seeds. The soil is populated by tremendous numbers of seeds that remain ungerminated for years. The process of cultivation, one objective of which is to destroy weeds, in one sense defeats its own purpose because cultivation brings more seeds to the surface, where they receive the light required for their germination. Methods of using preemergence herbicides depend largely for their success on the requirement of seeds for light. Seedlings from seeds at or near the surface are destroyed by the herbicide. Seeds below the reach of the herbicide remain ungerminated as long as they are not brought to the light. This is the basic reason for the recommendation that the field remain uncultivated after a pre-emergence herbicide is used.

Still another illustration of the action of light on seeds comes from experiments in burying seeds. Seeds mixed with moist sand in an unstoppered bottle were buried 3 feet deep in the soil. The bottle was inverted so as not to accumulate any standing water and left for 80 years. Some of the seeds promptly germinated when they were dug up. How could they remain viable so long? Why did they not germinate earlier? They were moist, had presumably adequate aeration, and surely must have encountered temperatures favorable to germination many times in the 80 years. Then one wonders why they germinated as soon as they were taken from the soil and placed in a seed germinator. It seems that they did not germinate for 80 years because they were in the dark. In the process of being dug up, they received light and germinated immediately.

Examples of how light affects plant growth are almost inexhaustible. Those I have given are merely selected illustrations of rather commonplace ways in which light affects our lives through its influence on the plants or plant products that we eat, wear, burn, or admire. Only enough is told of the direction in which the research is currently leading to indicate its rapid change. An advance in understanding of flowering pointed the way to a new approach to germination of seeds. Progress in extraction and study of the light-

122

Spruce after 36 weeks of growth on natural days (left) and interrupted nights (right).

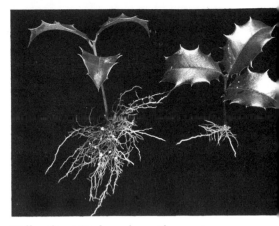

Holly after 118 days of growth on natural daylengths plus 3 hours of supplemental light (left) and interrupted nights (right).

Three pinto bean plants that received, respectively (left to right), 8 hours daily of fluorescent light supplemented on the 10th, 11th, 12th, and 13th days by no radiation; 5 minutes of far red; and 5 minutes of far red, followed by 5 minutes of red.

Lepidium seeds sown on surface of soil (left) all germinated; seeds covered with one-fourth inch of soil (center) failed to germinate except where exposed to light along a cut made in the soil; and seeds covered with one-fourth inch of soil (right) remained viable but ungerminated because they were in dark.

absorbing pigment confirmed the conclusions previously reached from physiological studies and provided the basis on which new experiments were designed. In research of this kind there is no new frontier. The ever-advancing old frontier, however, changes so fast that it always seems new and filled with promise. *(Harry A. Borthwick)*

Weeds

MANY TROUBLESOME weeds came from other countries, usually mixed with crop seeds. A report in 1860 said 70 thousand weed seeds were counted in 2 pints of clover seeds shipped from England. Purslane, common milkweed, St.-Johns-wort, nutgrass, johnsongrass, bullthistle, sowthistle, mayweed, hedge bindweed, jimsonweed, and dock were among the introduced weeds. Some plants, like oxeye-daisy, wild onion, chicory, purslane, cornflower, morningglory, and wild carrot, were brought in to flavor foods or beautify settlers' yards. Some got out of hand. Earthen ballast from sailing ships was dumped near eastern ports. It contained weed seeds, which grew into plants that were spread by wind, water, and man. The 1895 Yearbook of Agriculture listed 200 weeds that were serious obstacles to agriculture in the United States; 108 of them came from abroad.

Weeds cause losses of millions of dollars to American agriculture, because they reduce yields of crops and prevent the efficient use of land. Some people are allergic to the pollen of some weeds. Poison-ivy causes discomfort to many persons. Weeds harbor insects and disease-producing organisms that attack crop plants. They steal water and nutrients from valuable plants. They increase costs of labor and equipment and reduce land values. Thorny weeds discourage hand harvesting. Weeds clog harvesting equipment and prevent recovery of full harvest. Weeds clog up irrigation and drainage canals. Weeds interfere with swimming, boating, and fishing. They are costly to control in rights-of-way and lawns.

Farmers used the hoe, hand pulling, tillage, mowing, burning, smother crops, and crop rotation to control weeds. They came to know the importance of preventing annual weeds from producing seeds and of mowing the tops and cultivating crops to starve roots of perennial weeds. Nevertheless, weeds continued to spread. Long ago men knew it was futile for one farmer to control weeds on his land while a nearby farmer allowed them to grow. The Federal Government recognized more than 100 years ago the need for preventing the spread of weeds from one farm to another. Many States penalized farmers who permitted certain kinds of weeds to grow. Legislation was passed to prevent the sale of crop seeds containing seeds of noxious weeds. It was the forerunner of the Federal Seed Act and State laws designed to tighten the control over the sale

124

Seeds of dodder, johnsongrass, bull paspalum, and rough buttonweed were sorted out from the lespedeza seeds that surround them.

of crop seeds contaminated with weed seeds. A century ago salt was poured on cut stubs of thistles to prevent their regrowth. Salt and ashes were placed along roadsides and fence rows where it was desirable to kill all vegetation. Europeans who used copper salts on grain to control fungus diseases noticed that the chemicals killed certain broad-leaved weeds but did not injure the grain. This amounted to what is now known as selective weed control, which was possible only on a limited scale until the 1940's.

The tract on the right was sprayed twice with 2,4-D. The buckbrush on the left was not.

Then scientists in the Department of Agriculture discovered that 2,4-D, an organic chemical, could kill weeds in a way different from that of such inorganic compounds as copper and iron sulfate and sodium arsenite, which scorched the weeds and killed only the parts they touched. Leaves, stems, or roots of weeds absorb 2,4-D. Once inside susceptible plants, it moves to all other parts and kills the entire plant, even though at first it touches only a limited area.

Nonproductive brush and scrub trees infest millions of once-productive acres.

Dense oak brush was treated with 2,4,5-T, and the land returned to a good volunteer stand of grasses.

A weedkiller was applied at planting time to all but one strip of a field of sugarbeets.

Applying chemicals to control weeds.

Following the introduction of 2,4-D in 1944, there was a phenomenal growth in production of selective herbicides by the United States chemical industry. Several dozen effective and safe selective organic herbicides are available now to farmers and homeowners. Among them are 2,4,5-T, MCPA, silvex (phenoxy compounds); DNBP (a substituted phenol); TBA (a substituted benzoic acid); IPC, CIPC, EPTC (carbamates); monuron, diuron, fenuron (substituted phenylureas); TCA; dalapon; and simazine and atrazine (triazines).

They are effective against weeds in row crops, pastures and rangeland, drainage ditches and irrigation systems, lawns, and gardens, under powerlines, and along railroads and highways. They are used against ragweed, poison-ivy, and unsightly weeds in many cities. Weedkillers can be applied before the crop plant comes above the soil or even before the seeds are planted. Small amounts of liquid containing a herbicide can be sprayed over a wide area. Herbicides in granules are useful. Sometimes herbicides are placed near the root zone to kill young weeds as they begin to grow. The chemicals have useful characteristics. Some evaporate. Some dissolve in water, and others do not. Some can be dissolved in oil. Some remain a long time when mixed with soil. Research workers take advantage of such characteristics. They use herbicides that break down in the soil and become harmless before the crop seeds are planted. They use persistent chemicals when they want to keep land free of weeds for a long time—for example, along railroads. They use oil-soluble herbicides to kill brush and trees. The oil penetrates crevices in the bark and helps the weedkiller to penetrate the plant. Thus they fit the herbicide to the need at hand. Effective machines have been developed and airplanes have been adapted for applying the chemicals. Chemical weedkillers are used on more than 53 million acres of cropland. Some plants change certain inactive chemicals into herbicidally active ones. Corn changes the herbicide simazine into inactive components. Because most weeds are unable to do so, they die when a cornfield is sprayed with this chemical, but the corn lives. Thus the physiological characteristics of the weeds themselves provide a basis for selective weed control. Weedkillers, correctly used, leave no residues in plants, soils, and water that may harm man and animals.

An example of biological weed control is a beetle that has been used to control selectively St.-Johns-wort on western ranges. This insect, *Chrysolina quadrigemina,* feeds on the weed but does not eat grass or other valuable plants. Rangeland that was almost worthless for grazing because of this weed has been made useful again. Some insects have been introduced from abroad to control such weeds as gorse, tansy-ragwort, Scotch-broom, and puncture vine in the Western States. *(W. B. Ennis, Jr.)*

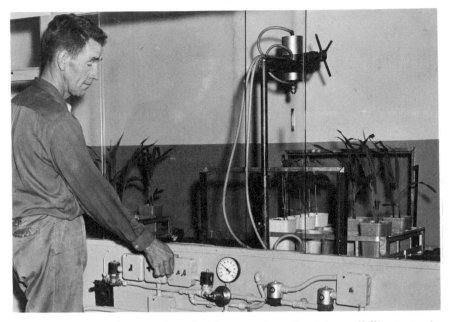

Hundreds of chemicals are evaluated each year to determine their weedkilling properties and effects on crop plants.

Simazine applied at planting time kept a cornfield free of weeds. It produced 106 bushels an acre.

An uncultivated, untreated cornfield yielded 45 bushels an acre and nearly 2 tons dry weight of weeds.

Potatoes

AMERICAN farmers 100 years ago got an average of about 80 bushels of potatoes an acre. The average was 100 bushels 50 years ago and 120 bushels 25 years ago. Then, beginning in 1940, yields shot up to about 300 bushels. What happened? What happened to potatoes is an example of what happened to a number of our vegetable crops.

The varieties grown in the 1860's were unattractive, not very productive, and highly susceptible to diseases. Private breeders introduced some attractive and potentially productive varieties between 1860 and 1910. A few had fine quality, but diseases finished off most of them. Yields remained low for a long time because of the diseases and insects and for other reasons. Bordeaux mixture, which came into use as a fungicide about 1887, helped to control late blight, but heavy losses from late blight and other diseases continued. Varieties "ran out" for unknown reasons. The Colorado potato beetle spread over the country about a century ago. Farmers waged a losing battle against it and leafhoppers, aphids, and other insects. They had no effective insecticides. They had limited supplies of commercial fertilizers and knowledge of how to use them. Varieties developed in 1862-1912 produced little more than the earlier ones, and most of those "ran out" too. Production methods for that half century remained rather primitive. Then plant pathologists discovered that viruses caused "running out." The viruses were found to be transmitted from year to year by the seed potatoes. Insects spread many of the viruses through the fields each year. The investigators of plant diseases found that virus-free potatoes were much more productive than virus-infected ones. Specialists in Wisconsin in 1913 devised a scheme for producing, under State certification, seed potatoes relatively free of virus infection. As more was learned about the viruses, their effects, and control, the production of certified seed was undertaken in many States. From 1920 on, the increase in the use of certified seed has increased greatly the yields and quality of potatoes.

Systematic and scientific breeding of potatoes was started by the Department of Agriculture and by a few State agencies during 1910-1920. A comprehensive cooperative breeding program was organized by Federal and many State scientists in 1930 to give greater impetus and effectiveness to their efforts. That successful program has stressed the breeding of higher yielding, disease-resistant varieties of good quality. More than half the potatoes grown in this country in 1962 were varieties produced by the Federal-State breeding work and unknown 30 years earlier. These new varieties, most of which have some resistance to disease, have helped push up the yields since 1930. The commercial production and purposeful use of insecticides also got underway during 1910–1920. Calcium arsenate was among the first chemicals prepared especially for use as an insecticide. Potato growers were among the first to use it extensively. Many other phases of research and development began expanding at an increasing rate—soil science; plant nutrition, physiology, and pathology; breeding; the study of insects; applications of motorized power and mechanization; and improved methods of making fertilizers, including fixation of nitrogen from the air. All these helped to increase yields and the efficiency of production. Average yields

Potato flowers.

Potato fruits ("seed balls").

In research in Maine on virus diseases, potatoes are grown in insect-proof cages.

inched up to about 120 bushels an acre during 1935–1940. Under the heavy pressures for more food during the war years, 1941–1945, growers did a progressively better job of applying existing methods and knowledge. Yields of potatoes rose gradually to about 155 bushels an acre in 1945.

The results of public and private research and development in many fields of science and industry during the Second World War became available for application in agriculture when the war ended. Remarkable new insecticides, chlorinated hydrocarbons (such as DDT) and organic phosphorus compounds (such as parathion), improved kinds of fungicides (such as the dithiocarbamates), greatly increased supplies of synthetic nitrogen and other fertilizers, more certified seed, and more efficient machines appeared, year after year. Many new varieties with resistance and even immunity to viruses, blight, and scab were introduced. Yields of potatoes in the 5 years after the war increased more than in the preceding 75 years. Other factors that have helped to improve average yields since 1945 are greater use of supplemental irrigation in the humid parts of the country and the shift of some potato acreage to more productive soils.

The war also stimulated advances in the preservation and preparation of food. Each year an increasing proportion of our crop of potatoes goes through a processing plant of some kind before it reaches the consumer. About 30 percent of the crop in 1962 was processed into dozens of canned, dried, and frozen items. Americans seem to have had progressively less need for energy-producing foods in the past 40 years—especially the carbohydrates, including starches—because many of them now do less manual work. Their average annual consumption of potatoes has declined therefore from 152 pounds in 1920–1924 to 103 pounds in 1955–1959. There it seems to be leveling off. As a matter of fact, the potato itself is not "fattening," as some people believe it to be, because its water content is relatively high. Frying or adding excessive amounts of fat-rich sauces to potatoes, however, can result in a product or a dish that has a much higher energy value than the potato alone.

Growers and processors still have production problems, and consumers want even higher quality in potatoes. The new varieties and methods of growing that have increased yields so greatly have not always increased the quality of the product. Requirements as to quality of potatoes for manufacture are even more exacting than those for the fresh market. Artificial controls of diseases and insects are expensive and need to be replaced by biological methods, including additional varietal resistance. The problem is how to produce potatoes of better eating quality and suitability for specific manufacturing processes without a marked increase in cost. (*Victor R. Boswell*)

Crops for Our Grasslands

WE NOW grow grass and forage on a billion acres. We set a value of 5 billion dollars a year on this enterprise, but we have no good way to measure its great value in conserving soil, stabilizing agriculture, and lining up better the production of other crops with our need for them. Grassland agriculture, as we call it, is a major new development.

Somewhere or other on the grasslands are grown more than 125 different species of forage grasses and legumes. Most of them grow well over large areas. A few have special requirements as to soil, climate, and environment and can be grown in only a few States. Alfalfa can be grown with some success in all States. Generally speaking, we have enlarged the areas of adaptation of most of the species by developing improved varieties of them. A few grasses are native to the Great Plains, but most of our main forage crops have come from other countries. Early settlers brought in the clovers, alfalfas, timothy, orchardgrass, bermudagrass, and many other grasses. The Department of Agriculture began in 1898 to distribute seeds from abroad to farmers so as to find out how well they grew on different soils and in different climates. The first step in improving them was to collect ecotypes—the ones that developed in one place or another through survival of the fittest. Several generations of seeds generally were required in the self-sorting that leads to suitable ecotypes. Today the breeding and improvement of grass and forage plants involve studies of adaptation and genetics and selection and breeding of the best strains.

We know all too well that diseases, insects, and other hazards begin to take their toll as an introduced crop comes into extensive use. If the crop is to survive as a useful species, it has to be improved by developing varieties that resist the hazards. Tests of varieties and strains help us find lines or individual plants that tolerate or resist the hazards. Such tests must be supplemented with fundamental research designed to provide knowledge that will help us if we encounter any blocks to further improvement. Basic research, for example, led to the development of the extensive use of inbreeding, hybrid vigor, male sterility, and plant-to-plant transfer of the genes that contribute to resistance to diseases and insects and to other desirable characteristics.

We have to remember that with our present knowledge and

Grass-breeding nursery at the Northern Great Plains Field Station, Mandan, N. Dak.

Coastal bermudagrass grown in Georgia in studies of the effect of shading on forage crops.

methods we cannot create at will new, superior genes, the carriers of heredity. Plant breeders therefore are limited to the genes present in existing plants. In many species there are no known desirable genes for certain essential plant traits, but such genes may be found in related and often unimportant species. To obtain resistance to ergot in dallisgrass, for instance, this species was hybridized with another species of *Paspalum* that had limited value as a forage crop. Perennial forage sorghums have been developed by crossing annual types with johnsongrass, a perennial and weedy species. We have begun to use similar methods of hybridization among species with fescue and ryegrass.

Wendelin Grimm, a farmer who emigrated from Germany to Minnesota in 1857, brought with him seeds of alfalfa and used improvement by selection of ecotypes to develop the outstanding crop we know as Grimm alfalfa. Each year he planted the seeds of plants that had not winterkilled and so finally got an ecotype that would survive the northern winters. This ecotype, named Grimm, continued as an important variety in the Northern States for a long time. It and other ecotypes of alfalfa are being replaced by improved varieties. The parentage of the improved varieties includes much germ plasm from these early ecotypes. Other plants from abroad that have contributed significantly to our grassland agriculture include alfalfa, which was brought from South America to California about 1850. Crested wheatgrass was introduced in 1898 as a dryland grass for the Northern Great Plains, but it was unknown to most farmers until 1915. Ladino clover was introduced in 1900 and became important 30 years later. Sudangrass, introduced in 1909, is grown in nearly all States. Korean lespedeza grew on more than 50 million acres 40 years after its introduction. Most of these crops underwent extensive improvement during the periods of expanding use.

A serious problem arose in the 1920's. Varieties of alfalfa that

134

had been known to persist with good stands and vigorous growth for a decade or more began to die out a few years after planting. The cause was found to be bacterial wilt, a crown and root disease that in early stages causes plants to look wilted even when soil moisture is abundant. We began research in 1926 on the spread of the bacteria that causes the disease and its development in the alfalfa plant. Breeding for resistance began in 1927. Ranger, the first resistant variety that came out of these studies, was released in 1942. Five more varieties resistant to bacterial wilt had been released by 1959—Buffalo, Caliverde, Vernal, Lahontan, and Cody. They were grown on more than half of the 28.5 million acres devoted to alfalfa and alfalfa-grass mixtures in 1961. The spotted alfalfa aphid appeared in New Mexico in 1954. It had spread into 30 States by 1956 and was causing an estimated annual loss of more than 40 million dollars. From research designed to meet this problem came four varieties with resistance to the aphid. These varieties, Lahontan, Moapa, Zia, and Cody, have different regions of adaptation and meet the needs of most farmers in the southwestern quarter of the United States.

Many farmers were surprised when we began work to improve bermudagrass because it had become a serious weed in cotton and cornfields. When they saw the superior traits of the new hybrid Coastal bermudagrass, they recognized it as a promising pasture and hay grass. It was released in 1939 and was a cross between a strain discovered in an old cottonfield in Georgia and an introduction of bermudagrass from South Africa. Its propagation is entirely by rhizomes and stolons. The few seed heads it produces rarely contain viable seeds. Seeds of this grass therefore are not carried or spread by livestock to cultivated lands where bermudagrass is unwanted. Coastal bermudagrass is tall, vigorous, and immune to root knot

Hybrid millet at Tifton, Ga.

nematodes. It excels common bermudagrass in resistance to helminthosporium leafspot, tolerance to frost, and growth in the fall. While its primary importance is for pasture, its erect, leafy growth makes it a desirable perennial hay and silage crop. Within 20 years after release, 3 million acres of this new grass had been planted in the South. This acreage of Coastal bermudagrass is said to have an annual value of more than 50 million dollars above what could be realized from an equivalent acreage of common bermudagrass. Coastal bermudagrass continues to be widely used as pasture and hay for dairy and beef cattle in the Southeastern States; it encouraged a shift from row-crop farming to livestock farming.

The development of hybrid pasture grasses propagated by seeds is a major forward step in the development of improved varieties of forage crops. The first such hybrid developed is Gahi 1 pearl millet, a summer annual pasture grass that is superior to Starr and common pearl millets in rate of establishment, speed of recovery following grazing, length of seasonal growth for pasturage, and total forage production.

Common sweetclover is used widely for pasture, hay, and soil improvement, although it contains coumarin, a bitter substance that makes it unpalatable to grazing animals and gives rise to a product in spoiled sweetclover hay that is responsible for bleeding disease in livestock. Denta white sweetclover was bred to have a low amount of coumarin. We hope it will provide forage and hay in which there is no danger of the disease.

Improved varieties of forage crops were disappointing for many years because of the slowness with which they replaced old varieties inferior in adaptation and performance. The main reason was largely lack of enough seeds. We knew that to solve this problem special arrangements would have to be made to assure the production of a large volume of seeds in a way that would maintain genetic superiority. Early attempts to do that were by seed certification. Rules and regulations governing the growing and certification of grass and legume seeds both inside and outside the region of adaptation of a variety gave good protection against genetic shifts, but seed production of these varieties continued to be far short of national needs. The Department of Agriculture organized the National Foundation Seed Project in 1948 to assist the States in the rapid buildup and maintenance of foundation seed supplies of improved varieties. An index of the success of this program is that 470 million pounds of certified seed of six improved varieties of alfalfa—Atlantic, Buffalo, Dupuits, Narragansett, Ranger, and Vernal—were produced in 1958 in the United States. Eighty-five percent of this production was outside the regions of adaptation. More than 50 percent of our alfalfa acreage grown for hay is planted to these varieties. *(Hugo O. Graumann and Mason A. Hein)*

Chemicals and Plant Growth

EVER SINCE Percy W. Zimmerman discovered that certain chemicals can change the growth of plants in one way or another, we have had a succession of developments that have given us better apples, larger prunes, potatoes that store better, ways to kill weeds in grainfields without injuring the crop, and a broadened knowledge of plant science. Dr. Zimmerman was born in Manito, Ill., in 1884. He was a plant physiologist at the Boyce Thompson Institute from 1925 until his death in 1958. In his discovery of the first use for plant-regulating chemicals, he used indoleacetic acid to induce stems to develop roots. The reproduction of many kinds of valuable plants thus was made easier. Only three chemical regulators were known at first, and they were scarce and expensive. More than a thousand organic compounds have been used since in experiments to control the growth and behavior of crop plants. New ones are discovered each year.

Chemists can readily make practically all of these compounds, only a few of which are found in plants. The chemical regulators can be absorbed by leaves, stems, flowers, and roots. Only minute amounts are needed—a few grams, for example, are enough to prevent fruit from dropping in an acre of orchard. The compounds act somewhat as animal hormones control the growth and development of animals. Fertilizer chemicals are different, because they furnish some of the building blocks of which plants are made. Regulating chemicals determine to some extent when and how the building blocks are used.

Plants can be made to behave in widely different ways with regulating chemicals. The buttons on the end of lemons can be made to remain attached during storage and thus protect the fruit from rot. Some fruit, such as bananas, can be made to ripen rapidly and develop better flavor than untreated ones. Malt production can be improved. The cost of thinning crops such as apples can be reduced. Properly used, the substances increase the size of some fruit, such as blackberry and prune. Some kinds of valuable plants cannot readily be propagated vegetatively. The Dr. Dresselhuys and E. S. Rand varieties of rhododendron are such plants, but small amounts of 2,4,5-T, a chemical used to kill some weeds, cause cuttings from them to root readily. Commercial preparations for stimulating roots on cuttings usually are available where garden supplies are sold.

Cuttings produce roots more readily when soaked in water containing indolebutyric acid.

Some farmers use regulating compounds on early clusters of tomato flowers, which otherwise often fail to produce a full set of fruit, especially during cool, cloudy weather. Tomato plants in a greenhouse may not produce good pollen during cloudy days of winter. A spray containing beta-naphthoxyacetic acid or another appropriate regulating chemical can be used to increase the productivity. Under some conditions, however, fruits from certain varieties of greenhouse tomatoes, such as Globe, produced with chemical regulators, fail to keep as long in storage as do those grown from pollinated flowers.

Some fruit, particularly apples, may fall from the trees before harvesttime. They may thus be bruised and of lower quality. The formation of an abscission layer, which weakens the stem, can be retarded with a minute amount of a regulating substance, such as naphthaleneacetic acid. Stems of pears can be strengthened similarly. Regulating chemicals are sprayed on thousands of acres of orchards each fall as an aid in harvesting the crops. Because the chemicals practically eliminate the premature falling of the fruit, some growers tend to delay harvest too long, and the fruit may become overripe on the tree. The improper use of the chemicals can result in crop loss. Apples sprayed improperly to prevent drop may cling to the tree so tightly that they may be hard to pick. The proper chemical, dosage, and time of application must be considered for maximum benefit.

Regulating chemicals to be effective must be absorbed by plants and be translocated readily from one part of the plant to another.

138

Indoleacetic acid, rubbed on the stem of this plant, caused it to produce roots. This was the first response to growth regulators found to be generally useful.

Plants can absorb many kinds of chemicals into their roots and then move the substances upward through their stems into the leaves along with the water, which is moved in the same direction. Plants can move some regulating substances, such as 2,4-D, from a leaf downward to the stem and then upward to the tip of the plant. The total distance covered may be as much as several feet. That discovery led in part to use of the substances as herbicides. A little 2,4-D, placed on a few leaves, eventually reaches the growing tip of the plant and sometimes reaches the roots. Excessive amounts of 2,4-D reduce or prevent growth, and often the plant is killed. The use of 2,4-D as a weedkiller followed research on regulating chemicals.

Even some closely related plants respond differently to the same regulating chemical. We can use 2,4-D to retard the drop of Stayman Winesap apples, but it is not effective in retarding drop of McIntosh apples. The difference in sensitivity is thought to be due

Stem curvatures are a means of finding new chemical regulators. The new chemical is rubbed on stems to make the test.

The rate of water loss of harvested snap bean pods can be slowed down by treatment with the chemical parachlorophenoxyacetic acid.

partly to a difference in the rate that the plant breaks down the compound and inactivates it once it is inside the plant. Such a difference may also account in part for the differential effects obtained with selective herbicides of the regulator type. Because the most effective regulators often are those that the plant can readily absorb and translocate, we have tried to learn how to increase the ability of plants to take up and translocate them.

A way has been found to change the molecular structure of some regulating chemicals so that plants are better able to absorb and translocate them. Some regulators are translocated from leaves to

140

The potatoes on the right were dipped in a chemical regulator that kept them from sprouting during storage.

In experiments, 2,4-D reduced growth of sprouts on stored turnips.

Ryegrass is a quick test for the presence of very small amounts of potato sprout inhibitor.

A scientist tests the strength of the stem of an apple on a tree sprayed with naphthaleneacetic acid. The chemical makes the fruit remain attached to the tree until harvesttime. The large pile of apples at the right fell from the nearby unsprayed tree.

142

the roots, from which enough is exuded into the soil to bring about growth responses in nearby plants. An understanding of how the chemicals ooze from roots may be useful in developing compounds that protect plants from disease organisms that attack the roots. Many kinds of regulators have been tagged with radioactive elements, such as carbon and iodine, so that we can trace their movement through plants. We can follow their absorption and translocation and their metabolism as they are changed by the plant or broken down into other substances. Naphthalenelactamide, for example, was absorbed by bean leaves, metabolized, or converted to another compound. Then a second metabolite was detected as the compound moved from the leaf to the stem. Still other metabolites were made by the plant after the growth regulator had reached the stem. Much is yet to be learned about movement and metabolism of regulators by plants, and radioactivity will no doubt help us gain this information.

Gibberellic acid has accelerated the growth of some kinds of plants by increasing the rate at which they assimilate carbon and build up solid matter. This regulator has been used experimentally to bring about many different responses, including rapid elongation of stems of slow-growing trees, production of flowers in a year on plants that usually require 2 years, and improved quality of flowers for display. Gibberellic acid has been used commercially in only a few ways. Its use has led to improved production of Thompson's seedless grapes.

A new family of regulating chemicals retard rather than stimulate plant growth. Some kinds of plants, such as chrysanthemum and azalea, can be dwarfed in a way that is often beneficial, since the plants take up less space, require less pruning, and develop a usually pleasing foliage. The use of regulating chemicals in developing plants with hybrid vigor is a new step. Male-sterile cotton plants have been produced experimentally with a chemical spray, a response that may be helpful in the production of improved cotton. We expect that other valuable responses in crop plants will be developed. For example, seasonal low temperatures limit the places where many plants, such as citrus, peach, and azalea, can be grown. We need a chemical method of increasing the resistance of plants to low temperatures; some progress has been made. We may sometime increase the resistance of some kinds of plants to drought or to a high salt content of the soil with retardant chemicals. We can speed up the rate that fruits ripen, but we need a safe chemical means of retarding ripening that will help to reduce the refrigeration now required.

It may be possible with chemical regulators to improve the palatability and nutritive value of some plants used as food. Regulators are used to improve the storage quality of some vegetables, but we

The first experiment showing that 2,4-D killed dandelions in a lawn without injuring grass.

Aeration apparatus used to study the movement of chemical regulators out of the roots of plants.

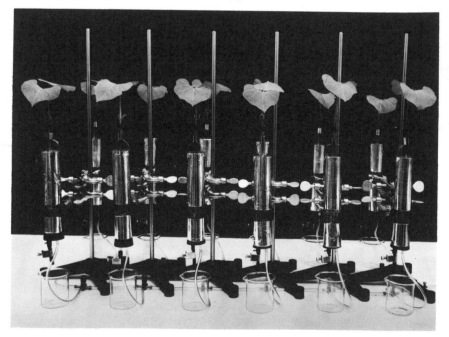

144

John W. Mitchell shows how the chemical retardant Amo–1618 regulates the height of sunflowers when applied to leaves of the young plants.

still need more effective chemicals for the purpose. Retardant chemicals may be used in the future to limit the growth of undesirable plants and to slow down the growth of plants used as ground cover so they will require less care. The overall growth and to some extent the chemical composition of some forage crops may eventually be controlled with chemical regulators. *(John W. Mitchell* and *Paul C. Marth)*

One way to follow the movement of a regulator in a plant is to tag the chemical regulator with a radioisotope such as C^{14}. A picture showing movement of the chemical regulator is made by placing a film close to the plant for exposure to the radioactivity.

Kentucky Wonder and other varieties of pole beans can be experimentally made to grow as a bush-type bean when treated with the retardant Amo–1618.

Elongation of young wheat plants can be retarded and tillering can be increased experimentally by the use of a chemical retardant.

X-Disease and Other Viruses

MORE THAN 400 viruses infect plants. More than 150 viruses infect animals. Among them are the ones that cause rabies, hog cholera, and influenza. Among the 65 that can infect man are those that cause smallpox, poliomyelitis, measles, mumps, influenza, the common cold, shingles, and warts. A virus may be regarded as a minute parasitic organism that infects, grows, and multiplies within and at the expense of living hosts. They resemble bacteria, but they are unlike bacteria in that (as far as we know) they cannot grow or multiply outside their living hosts. Many bacteria live their whole lives on dead and decaying matter.

Viruses are too small to be seen under an ordinary light microscope. The largest viruses are smaller than the smallest bacteria. The smaller viruses range down the scale to only slightly larger than the largest molecules of their hosts; 100 thousand particles of the poliomyelitis virus put side by side would reach across the head of an ordinary pin. Some viruses are spheres, ovals, and rods. Some are cubes or shaped like tadpoles. Differences in their chemical makeup no doubt determine the range of host plants in which they can grow. Once inside a living host cell, a virus particle may multiply rapidly, and the new virus particles may pass to other cells and thus cause a systemic infection. Some viruses appear to produce toxins, which act like poisons and cause the host to turn yellow and die. Some cause only local areas to die. Still others interfere with the development of normal green color and cause patterns of green and yellow. The symptoms include witches brooms, stunting or excessively lush growth, galls, nutritional unbalance, and failure of seeds to form or mature. Plant viruses are thought to interfere with the normal enzyme reactions or with growth regulator systems necessary for normal growth. They may also rob a plant of some of its self-developed protein building blocks. Most viruses invade all the living tissues of their hosts, even big trees. Some move slowly and may invade only parts of their hosts.

Viruses do not arise out of nowhere. Some apparently were present in native plants and spread to crop plants when the areas became cultivated. An example is peach yellows. It is known only in America and existed in native plums, from which it spread to the peaches that were brought in from Europe by early settlers. It causes little damage to native plums but kills peaches. Other viruses have been brought into new areas in nursery stocks, cuttings, bulbs, and tubers. A few have been distributed in seeds. Once in an area, a virus may be found by a vector, a natural carrier that can move the virus from diseased to healthy trees. Insects are the commonest vectors. They acquire virus-bearing juice from infected plants and leave a little of it when they feed on healthy plants. Many plant viruses have no insect vectors—or at least none in the areas where they are known. Some of these, however, have been spread by man in his quest for better sorts through propagation of infected trees, budwood, tubers, and other propagating materials. Such transport in most instances has been in dormant material, in which the presence of the virus was not evident, or in material from tolerant hosts, plants that show few or no symptoms.

More than 40 virus diseases affect stone fruits, and half that many affect pome fruits. The X-disease of stone fruits illustrates how a virus disease affects a crop. It was described as a disease of peach in 1933. Because it could not be identified with any other virus disease of peaches, it was given the designation "X," to represent an unknown quantity. Use has now firmly fixed this character in the name X-disease. A virus disease of sweet cherries—termed "buckskin," because of the leathery appearance it gave to the surface of affected fruits—was described in 1931 and is now believed generally to be caused by the same virus that causes X-disease. X-disease has occurred widely across the northern half of the United States and in southern Canada. It has wiped out whole orchards in some places in Washington and Oregon, southern Idaho, and Utah. In the Eastern States and Canada, X-disease was restricted to areas in which the chokecherry was native, and it was related to a red leaf disease that killed the chokecherry. In the West, X-disease was associated with chokecherries; it was found also in places where peaches and cherries are distant from chokecherries. It was thought to be distinct from the eastern form and was named western X-disease.

Several diseases are now believed to be caused by the X-disease virus: Red leaf disease of chokecherry, small bitter cherry of British Columbia, western X little cherry and western X wilt and decline in Utah, western X-disease of peach, buckskin of cherry and leaf casting yellow of peach in California, yellow red virosis of peach in New York, and yellow leaf roll of peach in California. There are a number of strains of the causal virus, and some of them cause more severe symptoms on the same host than do others. X-disease virus is sensitive to environment, particularly to temperature; it is worst in warm, dry years and in the warmer fruit-growing areas.

Diseased peach trees, except for dead arms in advanced cases, appear normal in the spring. Leaves look normal until 6 to 8 weeks after foliation, when symptoms may appear suddenly. Initial infections in orchard trees are usually limited to single twigs or branches

148

Western X-disease on peach leaves.

Montmorency sour cherries: Right, normal fruit without stipules; left, immature fruit, some with stipules, from an X-diseased tree.

on one or more arms. Often symptoms are seen first on rapidly growing sucker or water shoots. The virus continues to spread slowly from infection points to other arms, until eventually whole trees are enveloped. Severely affected twigs and branches commonly die during the first winter, and later growth tends to cause trees to develop a one-sided, scraggly appearance. Orchard trees seldom are killed by X-disease but become unproductive and may be so weakened that they are killed by pests or die from winter injury.

Initial symptoms on peach leaves appear as irregular, pale-green areas in the leaf blade. The affected parts appear to shrink and often form a line of cleavage at their borders. Affected leaves tend to become rolled upward from the midrib. As the disease progresses, the oldest leaves tend to drop, and the bare twigs have a tuft of yellow leaves at the top. Fruits on affected branches develop normally until symptoms appear in the leaves, when they turn pale, shrivel, and drop. Seeds do not develop in affected fruit, and the pits do not harden as in normal fruits.

The virus of X-disease can infect most of the stone fruits besides the peach, including sweet and sour cherries, almonds, wildgoose plum, chokecherry, sandcherry, Japanese cherry, Manchu cherry, and various plums. Tomato, carrot, parsley, and periwinkle have been infected in experiments. Chokecherry is naturally infected, and the native thickets are bridging hosts, through which the virus can travel across the country. On chokecherry the disease is characterized by stunted growth, often with brilliant red coloring. Diseased chokecherries set few fruits after the first year of infection, and these remain salmon pink to dull red, as contrasted to the larger shiny, dark-red, and black fruits on normal plants. The chokecherry is prized as a jelly fruit and has been planted for purposes of soil conservation. Its usefulness, however, is outweighed by the fact that it serves as a host reservoir of the X-virus, and near orchards it should be regarded as a noxious weed. Some new brushkillers eliminate chokecherries.

Sweet and sour cherries are susceptible to X-disease virus. Sweet cherries on mahaleb rootstock often wilt and die rapidly or suffer serious decline when they become infected. Trees on mazzard rootstock do not wilt and show no tree decline but develop abnormal leaves, fruit, and twigs. The wilt type of symptoms are similar to those caused by any injury that causes quick killing of the tree roots. Affected trees commonly die so quickly that leaves remain attached and dry while still yellowish green. Leaves on the declined trees turn yellowish green or yellow and drop before normal leaf fall. Such trees generally die during the ensuing winter. The most striking symptom of X-disease on cherry trees on mazzard rootstock is the production of small fruits, which fail to color and mature at the normal time. The affected fruits of the Napoleon variety remain dull white; those of Montmorency are pink to light red, and darker colored fruits become darker red. The affected fruits may be on only a few spurs on one or two arms the first year a tree is affected; rarely are all fruits affected, even on trees diseased for several years. Failure of fruit to reach proper size can result from other causes, but in such cases affected and normal fruits are not usually interspersed. X-diseased trees on mazzard cherry rootstocks develop other symptoms which aid in diagnosis. Stipules at the bases of leaf petioles become enlarged and resemble small leaves.

The natural spread of X-disease to orchard trees in the Eastern States is generally limited to places where orchards are near diseased chokecherries. Very little, if any, spread occurs from diseased to healthy trees within the orchard. Spread can be stopped merely by removal of the chokecherries. The natural vector, a small leafhopper *(Colladonus clitellarius),* flourishes on chokecherries. It flies from them to orchard trees, carrying the X-virus with it. It apparently does not reproduce on cultivated varieties of fruit trees. A number of leafhoppers can carry the X-virus in the Western States. One is the *Colladonus geminatus.* It breeds primarily on weeds, alfalfa, and herbaceous plants, but as these dry up it migrates to fruit trees.

The control of X-disease in the Eastern States consists in elimination of chokecherries near fruit orchards. In the Western States this is not enough. New orchards should be as far from old orchards as possible. Otherwise, diseased trees should be rogued promptly when they appear within the orchard and in plantings around it. The general use of new insecticides, especially in sprayers that also cover weeds and cover crops, has helped, probably by reducing the numbers of vectors. *(L. C. Cochran)*

Conservation

Ill Fared the Land

A HUNDRED years ago there was an average of about 60 acres of land for every man, woman, and child counted in the 1860 Census. These acres included fertile valleys, virgin forests, rolling prairies, short-grass plains, mountains, and deserts. But the original forests of the East gave way before ax, fire, and plow. The prairie grasslands withered through overstocking and breaking the sod where rainfall is low. Erosion by water in the East was matched by erosion by wind and water in the West. Floods increased as the land was cleared. That was the only water problem then; scarcity of water became serious first in the low-rainfall areas of the West.

Our land problems have varied from one region to another, but one pattern has been common: A single-resource approach to development, a single-practice approach to problems, and exploitation of resources for immediate gain. In the Southeast the period of exploitation began more than 100 years ago—in the cotton country when the cotton gin changed the way of life of a people as have few inventions in history. Many farmers began to expand their operations; commercial agriculture based on cotton began. Farmers cleared the slopes farther and farther up the hillsides to plant more cotton. It mattered little to an individual if he got only a few crops before the topsoil was washed away: Two or three crops would pay for the land, and there were always more acres to be brought into production with ax, fire, and plow. Tobacco, not cotton, was the principal cash crop in some sections. The effect on the land was the same. Both crops were planted in rows and were clean tilled to keep down weeds. The upright-growing cotton and tobacco plants gave little protection to the land against runoff water during heavy rains. This attitude toward the land was natural among the pioneers who settled on a new continent with a lot of land. Many of them were not interested in a permanent agriculture. Adventure, wealth, and freedom were among the settlers' goals. This disregard for natural resources was carried westward by men of later generations.

The damage increased as steeper land was brought into cultivation. After the crops were harvested, the land was bare and exposed to the elements. On sloping land during a single rain, an inch of topsoil might be washed into the river below. Stream channels made shallower by accumulating sediment caused the water to spread more readily over the bottom lands during heavy rains. Swamped-out areas developed along the streams. Floodwaters moved out more slowly and prolonged the flood damage. Streams ran red with sediment. Game fish disappeared from many rivers. Sand and other inert materials were deposited on fertile bottom lands. Ponds, created by damming streams, provided the source of power for many of the early cotton mills in the Southern Piedmont. Later hydroelectric reservoirs were built on available damsites along the streams. Most of these reservoirs, small or large, filled with sediment and became useless in time.

The economic life of the South depended on cotton for more than a century. It was the one crop admirably suited to economic and climatic conditions. There was always a market for it. If the price was down, the crop could be stored without much damage. Bank loans could be obtained on it. Even after the First World War, cotton continued to dominate nearly every act of southern people. Through war and peace, drought and flood, slavery and freedom, panic and prosperity, the production of cotton continued. The price of cotton affected the lives of everybody in the South during these long and often lean years. Fluctuations of a fraction of a cent a pound on the New York market were felt in the lives of the people of every community throughout King Cotton's empire. Under those conditions, the cotton farmer followed what seemed his only hope. He planted cotton and more cotton. When the price dropped to 5 cents a pound and when the boll weevil threatened destruction, he plowed more land and cultivated steeper slopes.

The cotton farmer was not alone in his predicament. His was not unlike the situation faced by the rancher and the wheatgrower of

The Missouri River in flood in Iowa.

the West, when the destruction of the lush native grass of the plains spawned the duststorms of the 1930's. Seven hundred million acres of grass west of the Mississippi River were depleted or destroyed within 50 years after pioneers moved into the area late in the 19th century. Oversized herds of cattle, sheep, and horses made waste of Nature's bounty.

The damage of the Western Plains reached a peak during the First World War, when opportunists plowed up great tracts of marginal land for a few crops of wheat or cotton. The boom burst when prices went down after the war. The land was abandoned, and no protective cover was planted. The dry years came. From the bare, abandoned land, from abused pastures, and from fields unwisely maintained in cultivation in the High Plains, there arose billowing clouds of dust that hid the midday sun in many parts of the country. The evidence of the destructive processes was everywhere, but for a long time no one seemed to see it. Some accepted erosion as a natural consequence—something men would have to learn to live with.

In 1900 the total United States population had passed 75 million, but even then there was no shortage of land. There was still an average of 25 acres to supply the food, fiber, and other needs of each person. The per capita acreage of land had shrunk to 15.5 by 1930, a reduction of 40 percent in three decades. By then the evidence of what was happening was clear. The University of Missouri was the first to establish experimental plots to determine the effect of slope, ground cover, soil type, and tillage methods on the rate of runoff and soil removal. The early activities of the Extension Service in soil and water conservation emphasized terracing, and county agents throughout the Southeast labored with improvised equipment to help farmers construct terraces.

A Federal appropriation was made in 1929 to study the effects of erosion and ways to control it. Eight erosion-control experiment stations were set up in representative areas. The Soil Erosion Service was created in 1933 as an emergency agency. Watershed demonstrations on 25 thousand to 100 thousand acres were established by the Service in strategic locations. The Soil Conservation Service was established in 1935 as a permanent agency. The number of watershed demonstrations increased to serve all of the country's major problem areas. Members of the Civilian Conservation Corps were assigned to work on them and elsewhere to demonstrate methods of erosion control and conservation. The outstanding accomplishment was to bring all appropriate sciences to bear upon the problem of proper use of land. Agricultural engineers, foresters, agronomists, biologists, soil scientists, economists, and others contributed

An abandoned farm in Oklahoma.

to the program. The viewpoint developed that each acre of land should be properly used and treated by methods that were coordinated with the needs of the land and needs of the owner.

It became apparent by 1937 that conservation must be undertaken not alone by a bureau or department of the Government but by the people themselves. That year soil conservation districts began to come into existence as result of the passage of permissive legislation in a number of States. New action programs took shape across the Nation. Today 96 percent of our farms and ranches—more than 1.6 billion acres—are included within the limits of legally constituted, locally governed soil conservation districts. A total of 1,887,091 cooperators operating more than 594 million acres were cooperating with their local districts in 1961. More than 700 million acres of land have been mapped by the Soil Survey. Almost 99 million acres are in conservation cropping systems. Crop residues are being properly used on 68 million acres. Thirty million acres of woodland have protection. More than 4 million acres of wildlife areas have been developed. A million acres of waterways have been grassed. A million ponds have been constructed. More than a million miles of terraces have been built, and 23 million acres of drainage improvements have been carried out. Six million acres of land have been leveled for more efficient use.

Millions of acres of land have been shifted from cotton, corn, and other row crops in the Southeast to pastures for dairy and beef cattle. The acreage of improved pastures in a number of Southeastern States is greater than that of cotton. One has to know the deep-seated antipathy of cotton farmers toward grass—it was something they fought for generations every summer day—to appreciate the significance of this change. Modern farmers of the South are using more lime and fertilizer on their pastureland than they ever thought of using on cotton and other cash crops in years past. New grasses and combinations of grasses and legumes are making it possible for southeastern farmers to pasture cattle almost all winter.

Similar changes have occurred elsewhere. In the plains of the West, where wind erosion was a menace a few decades ago, good grazing exists in increasing abundance. Abused lands in the dry plains have been planted as suitable grasses were found and identified, adequate seed sources and harvesting methods were developed, and planters capable of handling mixtures of the light and chaffy seed were designed and built. Ranchers have learned that denuded land can be returned to profitable pasture by planting the right grasses and that depleted range can be returned to vigorous stands of lush grasses with rest and proper stocking. The Nation today has a clearer picture of its available resources and a more scientific basis on which to make its present and future plans for wise use of resources than ever before. *(T. S. Buie)*

An overgrazed range in New Mexico.

Improper logging destroyed vegetation on a hillside in Oregon.

Conservation in Knox County

THERE WERE good reasons why the people of Knox County, in Indiana, should have stayed home the night of January 5, 1940. The thermometer was well below zero. Snow and ice made the roads almost impassable. Nevertheless, 70 citizens drove to the county building in Vincennes for a hearing on a petition to form a soil conservation district.

One after another they outlined their concerns. J. R. Coan, of Washington Township, said: "Sheet erosion is severe. Eight hundred acres were taken out of cropland last year, and 1,200 acres the year before because of silted up ditches and eroded areas. Ditches silt up before the original ditch is paid for." Clarence McCormick, a farmer in Johnson Township, said: "In some places in Knox County 90 to 100 percent of the land is being ruined by erosion. The topsoil is gone. We can't make enough to keep a good standard of living. The soil conservation district and soil technicians and engineers will help us do better than we have been doing." Edgar Haskins, who also owns land in Johnson Township, said: "It cost me 200 dollars to move my neighbor's farm out of my pond." H. S. Benson, who was county agent from 1930 through 1945 and who had worked unceasingly for a long-range soil conservation plan for Knox County, said: "We have reached the point where only the best of management and wise use will guarantee prosperity of those to follow as operators of our lands. We must fight to stop the forces of destruction that have allowed fertility to be washed away. Records show that 800 acres within our county have been destroyed in just one year. In Knox County the conservation of agricultural resources depends first of all on the efforts of our farmers." He made an urgent plea that farmers be given an opportunity to vote on whether they wanted a district.

There were other comments and a summary of the situation: Nearly 5 years earlier, the Congress had approved the Soil Conservation Act, and under it 22 States had approved legislation giving farmers and ranchers authority to organize districts for conserving soil and water resources. Soil conservation districts are legally constituted units or instrumentalities of State government created to administer soil and water conservation work within their boundaries. They are not branches or agencies of any Federal Department. Each district is autonomous and self-governed. It has authority to enter into working agreements with other governmental agencies and with private concerns to carry out its purposes. Through such working agreements with the individual districts, the Soil Conservation Service and other agencies of the United States Department of Agriculture provide assistance to farmers, ranchers, watershed associations, and others. Each district is created by legal procedures under authority of State law. In most States, each district is created after petition, public hearings, and a referendum show that landowners and operators want such a local agency to deal with their conservation problems. Once established, a soil conservation district is legally responsible for soil and water conservation within its territory, much as a county is responsible for roads or a school district for education.

Each soil conservation district is governed by a board of local people, usually resident landowners or operators, elected or locally designated. Members of the governing board are called supervisors, directors, or commissioners. The board decides upon a districtwide program and plan of action. It then arranges for assistance from public or private sources to put the program into effect. It directs the use of this assistance to help farmers and ranchers further their individual conservation plans. A State soil conservation committee established by the State soil conservation law has general direction of district activities in each State. This body acts for the State government in creating new districts. It consults with and advises district supervisors and facilitates their local operations. It manages the State funds made available for district operation.

The chairman of the hearing, T. E. Coleman, Director of the Agricultural Extension Service at Purdue University and acting chairman of the State Soil Conservation Committee, then asked: "Is anyone opposed to this movement? If there is, let him speak up." There was no opposition. He concluded the hearing by saying, "We are making a favorable report of this hearing to the State committee for their further action on the petition you have presented." One month after the hearing, a referendum showed opinion overwhelmingly in favor of a district. A governing body was elected, and the Knox County Soil Conservation District was formally organized on June 19. That day the governing body signed a memorandum of understanding, which provided for assistance from the United States Department of Agriculture in achieving erosion control and soil conservation.

The first farmer in Knox County to sign a cooperative agreement with the district was Clair Dean of Bicknell, whose Plan Number One, dated September 4, 1940, is still in effect. By the end of 1941, 127 other Knox County farmers had requested technical help on 19,320 acres of land. In the years since then, the Knox County Soil Conservation District has averaged one new cooperator every week; 1,034 of the county's 1,542 operating farm units (154,173 acres)

Uncontrolled runoff from 55 acres made this gully on Herman Small's farm in Knox County, Ind.

The gully was filled, and a waterway was developed.

Eugene Leedy, a conservationist, and Herman Small (right), on a grassed waterway, discuss details of Mr. Small's farm plan.

The new waterway stopped erosion and made it possible for Mr. Small to rearrange field boundaries.

Mr. Carnahan's farm in 1961 had 7 miles of terracing.

An aerial photograph made in 1940 of the Boyer farm (owned by Lowell Carnahan in 1961) near Vincennes, Ind.

Farmers of Knox County, Ind., see a demonstration of land forming arranged by the district board.

The Knox County Soil Conservation District, in cooperation with Kiwanis Club members, sponsored a terracing contest in 1945.

were under agreement in 1962 to carry out soil and water conservation programs. John Wolfe, Lester Williams, Charles Stevens, N. Y. Yates, and Ivol Myers, farmers and leaders, made up the first governing body. The program they initiated and directed has gone a long way toward halting further loss of Knox County's topsoil and restoring the vitality of the county's agriculture and business life.

Knox County is the oldest of Indiana's 92 counties and the first county formed out of the Old Northwest Territory. It is in southwestern Indiana in the pocket formed by the junction of the White and Wabash Rivers. In the early days, Knox County included all of what is now Indiana and parts of what is now Ohio, Illinois, Michigan, Wisconsin, and Minnesota. Settlement of the county began about 1796. It is still predominately agricultural. The soil has been used for cash-grain farming a long time, and there have been severe, widespread, and costly losses of the highly erosive wind-blown soils. Corn has occupied a larger acreage than any other crop in the county since 1889. Knox County's farmland also grows the largest wheat acreage of any Indiana county and a substantial acreage of forage crops. Large acreages are devoted to potatoes, sweetpotatoes, vegetables, melons, and nursery stock. Farmers often say the soil melts away like sugar during a rainstorm. Rainfall of

The farm of Curtis G. Shake in Palmyra Township, Ind.

The pond on John Newton's farm in Knox County has a surface area of 3.5 acres, a depth of 18 feet, and a drainage area of 40 acres. It is stocked with bass and blue-gill. The fenced area around it is seeded to tall fescue.

about an inch a week during the winter and frequent freezing and thawing, with readings above freezing on all but 20 days or so, create conditions that favor severe soil losses.

The governing body in their report for 1941 said interest in the district program was growing as a result of an educational program that the district sponsored and almost every organized group partici-pated in. Bankers provided prizes for a county terracing contest held on Clinton Powell's farm. The district was host to the first Indi-ana terracing contest, which was on Judge Curtis G. Shake's farm. One bank sponsored a contest, in which farmers were judged on how fast and well they established their farm conservation plans. To give people a chance to see what had been done and what still needed doing, the governing body arranged for air tours for more than 200 persons. Fifteen planes put in a full day giving farmers and members of their families a bird's-eye view of their own farms, of the ravages of soil erosion, and of the measures that are being used to combat it. Prospective buyers of Knox County farms often consult the district office to get information on the land's potential under conservation treatment. Buyers want to know about erosion on the land in which they are interested, drainage conditions, the degree of slope, soil type, the fertility level, the prospects for prof-itable production, and so on. Because so many farms have conser-vation plans that include a farm map, the questions usually can be answered in detail.

A contoured peach orchard, planted in 1947, of the Dixie Orchard Co. near Vincennes.

Members of the governing body carry on a continuous program to encourage adoption of soil and water conservation. Their own farming plans are examples. Mr. Yates, a commercial peachgrower, for example, was the first in Knox County to plant peaches on the contour. Knox County orchardists have since planted more than a thousand acres on the contour. The governing body arranged a tour for veterans in farming classes to an experiment station to see the results of conservation work and a similar tour for businessmen to see the soil- and water-saving practices in use locally. They engaged an irrigation engineer to discuss ways to meet the county's water needs. They investigated the feasibility of developing the Mariah Creek Watershed under Public Law 566, for which their application was approved. They solicited financial support for district activities. They sponsored pasture-improvement contests. They encouraged the making of 600 farm ponds. For such efforts and others, the governing body won the first nationwide soil conservation contest, which a rubber company sponsored.

Farmers have adopted a number of conservation measures. Farming around the hill has become accepted practice. They recognize terraces as a good way to keep soil at home. Good grass-legume mixtures are replacing straight red clover or lespedeza seedings. Pastures are being renovated. Adequate stock water supplies are being developed. An example is the farm of 394 acres Woodrow Boyer bought in 1945. The land, almost all tillable loess, had been mismanaged and was badly eroded. Mr. Boyer, city reared, became a

Terraces on Paul Utley's farm in Knox County stopped serious erosion and the deposition of silt in a roadside ditch.

Before this land was terraced, topsoil washed onto the road created a maintenance problem after every heavy rain.

soil conservation district cooperator. As soon as he bought the farm he requested help in developing a conservation plan, which he put into effect as soon as he could. He took out some of the fences, changed his field layout, developed a water disposal system that included terraces and grassed waterways, and revised his crop plans to include more good pasture and hay crops. The farm soon took on a new look. Further soil waste was stopped, crop yields increased, livestock flourished, and the farm began to make money for its new owner. Mr. Boyer remodeled his buildings, built a new house, and saw his equity grow. So effective was the conservation plan that when he sold the farm it brought four times more than he had paid for it 12 years earlier. There was inflation in land prices during the decade, but it is more than likely that half of the appreciation in value can be credited to the conservation program he carried out.

Another example: Bert Shake in the 1940's bought 150 acres. Two-thirds of the land was so badly gullied it could not be farmed. He decided on a conservation plan that included terracing some slopes and contour stripcropping some. He was able then to raise 40 to 50 bushels of wheat an acre. When Mr. Shake was the county highway supervisor, he had to hire men and equipment each spring to remove 500 cubic yards of topsoil that washed from a sloping field onto an 80-rod piece of road. He advised the owner of the land that terraces would prevent further loss of topsoil from the field. The district's work unit conservationist staked them out. Shake used road-building equipment to build the terraces. In 2 days and for a labor cost of 60 dollars, Mr. Shake corrected a situation that had been costing the county about 500 dollars a year. Another example: George Kerns bought 175 acres in 1946. The land was so run down it would not support the 11 cows he then had. He became a district cooperator and made a plan for rebuilding the soil. He qualified for a loan to begin a general improvement program. Mr. Kerns in 1962 owned 99 dairy cows. He has a new home, barn, silos, three tractors, silo filler, and chopper. Without his conservation plan, he said, his land would look like that of a neighbor who was having trouble paying taxes.

Now, in 1962, the work to safeguard Knox County's soil, to rebuild its fertility, and control its water supply is still going forward actively. In the years since the district was formed, much progress has been made, but the work is not finished. More than half of the cropland acreage needs further treatment for improvement and protection against erosion by wind and water. Only about one-half of the woodland improvement job has been done. Not until every acre is used according to its capability and treated according to its needs will Knox County's land be safe from further damage. (*M. M. Merritt* and *Milton E. Bliss*)

The Small Watershed

THE SCIENTIFIC management of rainfall on small watersheds has yielded invaluable endowments for many communities, for good water from protected watersheds is a resource that is growing in importance and value everywhere as an asset in industrial development, recreational facilities, a stable rural population, and higher farm income.

As proof thereof I cite one watershed, where all interests in a community worked together to solve a problem. Three new industries have located near it, because the community was able to guarantee an adequate supply of water. They employ about a thousand workers, and their payrolls are a sizable stimulant to what was a lagging economy. The basis for the work is the Pilot Watershed Program, the forerunner of the Watershed Protection and Flood Prevention Act of 1954. Under this authorization (Public Law 566 as amended), local people initiate and administer watershed treatment with Federal help—not a Federal project with local help. The Federal Government provides technical aid and pays all of the construction costs applicable to flood prevention. Local people must administer the program, arrange for easements and rights-of-way to permit installation of works of improvement, contract for construction work, and provide adequate maintenance for all installations. The costs of related measures that have agricultural and recreational benefits, such as drainage or wildlife facilities, which enhance local values and have flood-prevention features, are shared by local interests and the Federal Government. The costs of projects of municipal and industrial benefit, such as additional water storage in a flood-prevention structure, are assumed by local beneficiaries.

My example is the Six Mile Creek Watershed in west-central Arkansas. The creek drains some 165 thousand acres of land directly into the Arkansas River. The topography ranges from mountainous to gently sloping valley land. The soils are derived mainly from sandstone and shale, vary in depth from more than 20 inches to less than 10 inches, are generally light colored, and are well drained to very slowly permeable. Erosion has affected most of the sloping, open land. Most of the soils that have been farmed are in poor physical condition and have a fair to poor cover of vegetation. Early settlers found fertile soils, abundant water, and an excellent cover of native grass and trees. Dating from 1825, the early resi-

Six Mile Creek in Logan County in Arkansas after a week of heavy rainfall.

A sign of improper use of resources.

Six Mile Creek in 1955 before improvements were started.

The same place in 1960.

After channel improvements, Six Mile Creek flows at full capacity after a 6-inch rain.

Pines were planted to protect the Six Mile Creek Watershed near Paris, Ark.

171

dents established farms, built schools and churches, and developed a flourishing agricultural economy. Some 3 thousand farm families lived and enjoyed a high standard of living there. Eight banks, 50 churches, 30 rural schools, and many stores served the area at its peak of prosperity. Problems developed. The prevailing custom was to farm too intensively. Unwise use of the land, failure to maintain fertility and control erosion, and strong economic pressures on the farmers between 1920 and 1940 accelerated the deterioration of the fertile uplands. As crop yields and farm income declined, the land-owners farmed even more intensively and cleared more acres of marginal, shallow soils for crops. They got lower yields, sold their products on a declining market, and lived at progressively lower standards.

Silt and debris moved downhill into the stream channels. Further neglect reduced their capacity to carry water, and damaging over-flows became more frequent. Farm operations on the bottom lands became limited. People were forced to leave the farms because of continued crop losses and the locality because jobs were not available in nearby towns. The number of farms declined from about 3 thousand to about 1 thousand. Churches and schools closed. Many thriving community centers were abandoned.

The opportunity to reverse the trend came when the Congress authorized the establishment of 65 small watershed projects to demonstrate the feasibility of combining soil conservation measures with upstream detention structures to reduce frequent flooding. Officials of the Soil Conservation Service of the Department of Agriculture, who were assigned leadership in the small watersheds program, considered favorably the Six Mile Creek Watershed as a good location to demonstrate complete watershed treatment. The success of such an undertaking depends on the attitude of the people. Did the people of Six Mile Creek want to help themselves?

To get an answer, the boards of supervisors of the Magazine and the Franklin County Soil Conservation Districts, in which the Six Mile Creek Watershed is located, arranged a public meeting at the Logan County courthouse in Paris on September 22, 1953. About 150 landowners and business and professional men attended. The State Conservationist, Hollis R. Williams, explained the nature and scope of the Pilot Watershed Program. He answered many questions. A typical reaction was that of John Williams, a Booneville banker and landowner: "I have always gone along with the Magazine Soil Conservation District and the Soil Conservation Service and will continue to go along with the district in sponsoring this watershed project. If any of the works of improvement are located

Native grasses return in a field after brush was killed by aerial spraying of 2,4,5-T in oil.

A floodwater-retarding structure on Six Mile Creek.

in the Booneville trade territory, I will assure the project sponsors that easements will be donated. The Bank of Booneville will also make a cash donation to procure easements elsewhere in the watershed." Tommy Raney, a druggist in Paris, offered office space to the planning party free of cost. Jeta Taylor, Ozark attorney and operator of a 1,200-acre farm in the watershed, said that he would be delighted to participate in such an undertaking. He made the motion that this group go on record as urging the two soil conservation district boards of supervisors to sponsor the watershed project and that this group offer full cooperation to the sponsors in discharging non-Federal obligations. The motion carried unanimously. The people in the Six Mile Creek Watershed thus gave the Soil Conservation Service the answer about their active interest in watershed treatment. The supervisors of the two districts formally assumed responsibilities of sponsorship.

Once they realized that watershed treatment was within reach, all wanted to help. Newspapers and radio stations informed the public. County agents and teachers of vocational agriculture talked with landowners. Chambers of commerce donated money. County and city governments lent a helping hand to the sponsors. Men of the Soil Conservation Service and the Forest Service worked for 5 months on a tentative work plan, which the local people accepted. They organized to complete it in 5 years. Procurement of easements and rights-of-way were the first prime non-Federal responsibility of the sponsors. Civic clubs, chambers of commerce, farm organiza-

Soil Conservation Service technicians helped a farmer construct this drainage ditch in Logan County.

tions, county officials, newspapers, and other interested citizens gave their time and resources to help with this first job. Works of improvement could not start until landowners, public utility companies, railroads, and highway departments had dedicated the necessary easements to the local sponsoring soil conservation districts.

Installation of the works of improvement started on six flood-detention structures by June 1954, some 8 months after Six Mile Creek Watershed was designated as a project; 24 in all were built. One, for example, is designed to store temporarily 5 inches of run-off from 1,800 acres of drainage area above it, where silt and debris had reduced the capacity of the channel of Six Mile Creek to practically nothing in places. Twenty-nine miles of channel improvement work have been completed. County and State highway ditches were the major silt-producing areas in the watershed. Arkansas State Highway Department crews stabilized the ditches with bermuda-grass sod. Since 1,338,000 dollars of Federal funds were expended to pay the construction costs of the works of improvement relating to flood prevention, the local sponsors set a policy of annual inspection of each site to determine maintenance needs. The 29 miles of channel were sprayed for brush control in 1959.

Landowners completed 95 percent of their responsibility for establishing the land treatment measures at the end of the 5-year installation period. Measures to cost an estimated 1,300,000 dollars were needed for 20 thousand acres of cropland, 34 thousand acres of woodland, and 110 thousand acres of grasslands. Some 1,028 of the 1,039 landowners have developed basic soil and water conservation cooperative agreements with the two soil conservation districts. These conservation farm plans are based on soil surveys, which catalog soil depth, erosion, use hazards, and land capabilities. Land treatment on cultivated land includes the planting of 15 thousand acres of cover crops, the construction of 105 miles of terraces, and contour tillage of 1,500 acres. Some 50 thousand acres of tame pastures have been seeded, fertilized, or improved, and 62 thousand acres of native grasslands are under good range management. To obtain proper grazing distribution on grassland areas, 775 farm ponds have been constructed. Treatment measures on farm woodlands include tree planting, fire protection, stand improvement, and fencing for grazing control. Some 1,200 acres have been planted in pine. Some 12 thousand acres of land, largely idle cropland, have been retired from intensive use and established in permanent pasture.

Technicians of the Soil Conservation Service evaluated the damage and measured the effectiveness of the works of improvement after a heavy rainstorm in 1957 when project installation was incomplete. They set the total damage at 10,185 dollars. Without watershed treatment, they thought the total damage would have been about 18,010 dollars. If all works of improvement had been in place, the damage would have been around 6,305 dollars. The sediment pools of the flood-prevention structures have other uses. One such site holds enough water to fill the supplementary needs of a new factory in the town of Booneville. Another factory was built near Ratcliff, when a flood-prevention structure gave assurance its need for large quantities of water for sewage, fire protection, and air-conditioning purposes would be met. The new lakes have added recreational facilities. They have been stocked with fish.

Visitors from Japan, southeastern Asia, and other places have come to observe the results of the project on a field, farm, and watershed test basis. Neighboring communities have shown interest in undertaking similar work to protect watersheds. Another result is that the Six Mile Creek has become a sort of laboratory for later work. Full hydrologic, hydraulic, and economic information relative to small watersheds was not available when the Six Mile work plan was begun, but men of the Geological Survey, Department of Agriculture, and the Weather Bureau have undertaken an intensive evaluation and instrumentation program to appraise the costs and benefits of the watershed protection and flood-prevention measures in both physical and economic terms. Fifty-four rain gages, five stream gages, and four reservoir gages have been placed strategically to gather information that will guide watershed planning on future projects. *(Wm. B. Davey)*

What People Are Doing in Nebraska

FROM A small beginning in the 1930's, the work of conserving soil and water in Nebraska has grown into a far-reaching undertaking of people and Government working together in a voluntary, democratic way to accomplish a vital and beneficial result. When the soil conservation movement started, landowners and operators needed the help of technicians. The 74th Congress enacted Public Law 46 in 1935 to meet the need. Because of the costs involved and because we all recognized the national interest in maintaining the Nation's resources of soil and water, the Federal Government offered cost-sharing assistance and credit facilities for conservation measures.

The Nebraska Legislature enacted in 1937 the first of a series of laws, which specified, in part: "It is hereby declared to be the policy of the Legislature to provide for the conservation of the soil and water resources, rainfall, and soil moisture of this state, and for the control of soil erosion, and thereby to preserve natural resources, control floods, prevent impairment of dams and reservoirs, preserve wildlife, protect the tax base, and protect and promote the health, safety, and general welfare of the people of this state." The law permitted the creation of soil and water conservation districts and established a State Soil Conservation Committee, which gives guidance and direction to the soil conservation districts and has the central responsibility for the State's program of conservation. The committee devoted most of its efforts in its first 10 years to forming soil and water conservation districts, getting them in operation, and informing the agricultural landowners of the State as to the aims of the districts. By the end of the second 10 years, all farmland of Nebraska was in soil and water conservation districts. State appropriations at first were about 4 thousand dollars a year and by 1955 were 25 thousand dollars a year. The 87 district boards of supervisors needed more help in operating and managing their affairs than the part-time State Committee could provide. The committee employed a full-time executive secretary. Each year the number of landowners applying conservation measures to their lands was increasing and so was the demand for technical assistance. Technicians provided some of this help when they were freed of record-keeping and other office work. The Legislature increased the State conservation appropriation to 100 thousand dollars for the 1957–1959 biennium to permit the hiring of clerical help.

As the program progressed, it became apparent to landowners, conservationists, and others that measures applied on individual farms and fields would not solve all conservation problems. Something more was needed to correct situations affecting the lands of groups of landowners. The Congress therefore enacted the Watershed Protection and Flood Prevention Program in 1955, which provides a way and means for landowners to develop and carry out a more complete conservation program in small watersheds. The local sponsors receive technical assistance from the Federal Government in planning watershed projects and financial help for building flood-prevention structures. The people of Nebraska promptly accepted this creek-size watershed program and started to make use of it. Under this program, local interests must provide land, easements,

A crew checking terraces in Kimball County, Nebr., includes an instrument man paid from Federal funds, a notekeeper paid by the contractor, a rodman paid from county funds, and a chainman paid from State funds. The contractor and equipment operator are at the right.

and rights-of-way for flood-prevention structures. Many farmers and ranchers cooperated by providing lands for some sites without cost, but funds were needed in many cases to buy valuable farmlands that were involved. The Nebraska Legislature amended the Soil and Water Conservation Districts Law in 1957 to permit the creation of Watershed Conservancy Districts, which are empowered to raise funds through taxation of lands within the district. This provides money to purchase lands, easements, and rights-of-way; administer construction contracts; and operate and maintain structures built under the Watershed Protection and Flood Prevention Program. The watershed program then expanded rapidly. Federal resources for planning assistance could not keep pace with the mounting demands. At the same time, the need for still more technical help for individual landowners was increasing. Once again the district supervisors, the State Soil Conservation Committee, and others took action to meet these needs. They presented their problems in 1959 to the Legislature, which increased the appropriation for conservation work to 150 thousand dollars a year.

In 1961 the Legislature further increased State appropriations to 230 thousand dollars a year. These actions enabled the State committee to add State money to Federal resources for watershed planning work. It also allowed the committee to provide funds to soil conservation districts for part-time technical help to assist the landowners in the district. These State employees work with and under the technical direction of the Soil Conservation Service. The district supervisors and the State committee also set out to bring county governments more actively into the soil conservation program. County governments already had authority to levy taxes for flood control. During the 1961 session of the Legislature this authority was broadened to permit counties to contract with the Federal Government to maintain, keep in repair, and operate flood control works or other similar projects, furnish all necessary lands, rights-of-way, and easements, appropriate funds to develop, plan, and carry out a coordinated program of flood control or soil and water resource development and make an annual tax levy of not to exceed one-fourth mill on the dollar upon the assessed value of all the taxable property in such county, except intangible property, in addition to all other levies authorized or limited by law. Only a few counties at first offered this type of help in conservation. The number had been increased to about two-thirds of the counties by 1962. The contribution by county governments for this activity was about 100 thousand dollars in 1962.

Additional needs have developed through the years. District supervisors and the State Soil and Water Conservation Committee have been successful in getting assistance from still other agencies having some responsibility in soil and water conservation—the

Federal Extension Service, the State Game Forestation and Parks Commission, and the Nebraska Agricultural Experiment Station. Other problems were developing in some localities. Much conservation work requires large earthmoving equipment. Contractors and others owning such equipment were not always available to serve the demands. Boards of supervisors of soil conservation districts usually met this need by purchasing and operating equipment. As contractors were able to fill this breach, soil conservation districts ceased to operate equipment. Today only a few districts in Nebraska do this type of work. There has been, however, a need for such special equipment as grass seed drills and tree planters. Ordinarily, individual landowners would not have the volume of this work that would warrant their owning equipment. Some Nebraska soil conservation districts own and operate this specialized equipment on a rental basis. County governments have made another major contribution to the program by cooperating with landowners and soil conservation districts. There are numerous instances where erosion and flood control problems affect county roads as well as agricultural land. Solution usually involves construction of dams. Through the cooperation of the landowner, soil conservation districts, and county officials, many such dams can be built on the county road and the cost is borne by the county or jointly by landowner and county. Such a structure may eliminate an expensive bridge or culvert which, in addition to the original cost, is costly to the county to maintain.

In Washington County, more than 100 of these structures have replaced insufficient and inadequate bridges. Dollar savings to the county have been substantial. The elimination of more than 150 bridges from the county road system reduced maintenance costs about 10 thousand dollars annually. Landowners have benefited from this program. Gully erosion which was destroying valuable farmland has been controlled. The first generation to become deeply involved in the conservation of soil and water resources has made amazing progress. The terraces on the agricultural land of Nebraska would circle the earth four times at the equator; about 2 thousand square miles of land have been seeded to grass; nearly one-fourth of the irrigated land of the State has been shaped and leveled to reduce erosion; and over 2 thousand miles of irrigation pipelines and concrete ditches installed to conserve water. In Nebraska, as in other States, however, the greater part of the job—and possibly the hardest part—is still to be done. With completion of any segment of soil conservation, there naturally follows the responsibility for maintaining the work and for making any needed improvements as experience and new techniques point the way. This means unending opportunity for further and greater contributions from all sources. (C. Dale Jaedicke)

Water

THE 49'ERS and gold rush prospectors who went west cursed the streams they had to ford and hated the snows that blocked their trails. A hundred years later the streams and snow transmute desert valleys into a prosperous region that produces farm goods of greater value each year than the total value of all the gold extracted from the mines since the first gold nugget was found.

Irrigation in the West has been practiced for centuries. The canal-building Hohokam Indians of the Southwest had built canals to irrigate their crops in the Salt River Valley as early as 600 A.D. Later the Spanish settlers established modest irrigation works. Some 250 thousand acres of land had been put under irrigation by 1890. Other places in the West were developed for agriculture by cooperative irrigation enterprises, until by 1900 some 7 million acres were under cultivation. Today more than 30 million acres of land are watered by manmade devices.

The water supply of our Western States is not great. It must be carefully developed and equitably divided so as to serve all the needs. Only when two or three farmers join together can they successfully divert a stream. Only when a large group of farmers organize into an irrigation or water district can they successfully build storage reservoirs. Only when districts join are they strong enough to transport water great distances in aqueducts and canals. The storage, diversion, conveyance, and application of water demand high skills in engineering and agriculture.

The source of the water is snow high up on the rim of the watershed or basin. The prevailing westerly winds blow moisture-laden air off the Pacific Ocean. The air is cooled as it crosses eastward and is forced upward by the mountains. The resulting precipitation falls as rain or snow. The Department of Agriculture has been a pioneer in snow surveying. Technicians often go into the mountains to record snowfall at representative locations, called snow courses. They observe the depth, weight, and moisture of snow and so forecast how much runoff will occur from this snowmelt. Spring runoff is captured in large reservoirs, where it is held for use in summer.

A major part of all irrigation systems is adequate storage facilities. In a large one, like the Salt River Project, there may be enough storage dams to control nearly all the runoff of the river system.

Snow surveyors in Idaho and Nevada.

Water impounded by Coolidge Dam on the Gila River in Arizona is a key to the agricultural enterprise of the Salt River Valley.

An overnight storage reservoir near Weston, Idaho.

Lining with concrete the main canal of the Columbia Basin Project in Washington.

Water from mountain snow irrigates potatoes near Teton, Idaho.

Silt is always a menace to the useful life of a reservoir. The Department of Agriculture and the State agricultural experiment stations have carried on a great deal of research on upstream watershed management. Revegetation, selective logging, controlled grazing, terracing, stripcropping, and other management practices have been developed to control erosion and lower the silt hazard. Some dams act merely as a means for creating holding reservoirs. Other dams function to divert the water into canals and aqueducts.

An estimated half of all water diverted for irrigation purposes is lost in transit to the place of use. The Department of Agriculture and the Utah Agricultural Experiment Station have carried on investigations on the hydraulics of canals and conducted a program of test and analysis of canal linings, including clay, concrete, asphalt, bituminous fiber, and plastic membranes. Agricultural engineers and technicians have surveyed and redesigned thousands of lineal miles of canals and farm lateral irrigation systems. Irrigation practice and water management have been advanced to a high degree. Early irrigation practices were mostly wild flooding over the lands. Water was wasted, and the distribution of moisture to the root zone of the plants was uneven. The texture and water-holding capacity of

In studies in Arizona of evaporation losses from reservoirs, a hexadecanol raft applies a chemical film to the water surface to suppress evaporation.

soil, land slope, type of crop, root depth, and length of furrow enter into the design of a good irrigation system. Large earthmoving machines now make it possible to level the irrigated land to almost any reasonable slope. Technicians of the Department have surveyed millions of acres and have provided the technical knowledge necessary to level the land to the proper grade and to design the irrigation systems to fit the land. It has been estimated that nearly one-fourth of all water in storage is lost by evaporation. Extensive research has begun on ways to reduce evaporation. Chemical films, which float on the water surface, can cut evaporation losses greatly. The investment in irrigation systems and devices has exceeded half a billion dollars each year since 1945. This money has been spent for land leveling; underground irrigation pipe systems; slip-form concrete head ditches; aluminum, canvas, rubber, and plastic pipe systems; sprinklers, valves, and automatic controls; check dams; holding reservoirs; and siphons, gates, gages, and meters. Any device that will save water and make its use and management more efficient is welcome because, the farmer knows, west of the 100th Meridian water is as precious as gold. *(William W. Donnan* and *A. L. Sharp)*

The Soil Survey

THE PEOPLE who came to be known as Americans took over the soils of a great continent. They worked hard. They dreamed of good homes and security. The soils on which they based their dreams they took mostly for granted even when the soils behaved badly. They had during the first half of the 19th century a respectable body of writings about soils. One writer was Edmund Ruffin, a Virginia patriot and farmer who tried to promote a scientific approach to the problem of declining yields. He emphasized that Americans could not follow European practices too closely—the soils were not the same. E. W. Hilgard, who became a great scholar in soil science, printed his first book on the soils of Mississippi in 1860. Most of his principles were soon forgotten, however, and had to be relearned near the end of the century.

The great rush to the West was on after the Civil War. Although it was hard to reach the Great Plains and beyond, it was easier to make cropland from grassland than from the forest lands of the East. *Hurry, hurry, hurry; the dream is just before us!*—that was the spirit of the times. Many realized their dreams. Many failed. Some lacked courage and industry. Some had bad luck. Settlers took any kind of soil. They scarcely knew one from the other. Although 160 acres of good soil might be enough for a farm family in Ohio or Iowa, it was not enough in the Great Plains. Enormous acreages were turned over for crops.

Then around 1890 people began once more to look at the soil resources themselves. Many farm families had failed. Was this necessary? The serious students of the problem said "No." So the Soil Survey began in 1899 on this basis: People can be helped in the selection of farmland and the kinds of crops their soils can support and in the management of the soils to bring out their potential abundance and to have them remain productive year after year. These objectives, broadened, guide the Soil Survey today. From the start the work has been cooperative between the Department of Agriculture and the land-grant colleges and universities. Other Federal, State, and local agencies share a part of the cost in many soil surveys. The program is known now as the National Cooperative Soil Survey.

In his first report of field operations of the Soil Survey, Milton Whitney, as Chief of the Division of Soils, wrote: "During the sea-

Early soil scientists at work with "the most modern equipment."

son of 1899 three well-organized parties were in the field from 6 to 8 months each, equipped according to the most modern methods for surveying, investigation, and mapping of soils of several important agricultural districts." An optimistic statement, that. Actually they had no accepted methods for such research at that time, beyond the field methods of geology and the laboratory methods of chemistry and physics. Maps were drawn at 1 inch to the mile on heavy drawing paper, which was mounted on a drawing board that had a built-in compass and was supported by a tripod. A device counted the turns of a buggy wheel to record distances. Now soil maps are drawn on high-quality aerial photographs at 4 to 8 inches to the mile. Maps in 1899 were made of some 720 thousand acres and showed about 20 kinds of soil. More than 55 million acres were mapped in 1961. Now some 70 thousand kinds of soil, each with unique potentialities for use, are recognized in our system of soil classification. The main effort of the Soil Survey from the start has been on detailed surveys that can carry specific suggestions for the individual farm. By the present standards, the early ones seem very general. That they were, for technology cannot get much ahead of basic science; soil science had to come before good, detailed soil surveys.

A "double" soil in Kansas: An old soil was covered with alluvium long ago and a new soil now lies above it.

Profile of a gravelly soil in Washington.

A wooded Podzol soil in Maine that has an organic mat at the surface; a leached, white, acid layer; and iron, with some clay and fine organic matter, is concentrated beneath.

Sandsage roots go deeply into this sandy loam soil in Texas—an indicator of its value for irrigation.

The soil scientist begins by describing the color and other features of each layer. On such descriptions the classifications shown on soil maps are based.

Soil scientists must have deep pits in representative areas to study soils in depth.

Most people in 1899 looked at soil as primarily finely divided rock, more or less darkened with the remains of organic matter. Although the problem of salty soils, which baffled western farmers, was known to exist largely in dry regions, we had yet to learn of the great effects of vegetation and climate on soil properties, which Hilgard had explained earlier. A few soil scientists suggested this relationship quite early, but it was not generally known and accepted until a decade after the Soil Survey began. On similar glacial formations in northern Maine and eastern Montana, for example, the properties of the soils and the adapted crops and the methods to produce them are highly contrasting because of the great differences in native plants and climate. We had to learn to look at the soils themselves. This sounds obvious, but for generations people did not do that. They did not dig holes. They tried to find a direct relationship between the soil and the rocks or the vegetation or the climate. One reads in the old writings such expressions as "granite soils," "glacial soils," and "pine soils," none of which means anything except in strictly local comparisons.

We can say that five factors produce soils: The *climate* and the *vegetation,* acting on the *parent material,* as conditioned by *relief,* over periods of *time.* Until we actually looked at the soil carefully, we could not tell how the factors combined to produce a unique kind of soil. The study had to be done across the continent. The local observer sees only how soils differ. Their common characteristics he unconsciously takes for granted. Since the differences in soils between one field and the adjoining field appear to be related to relief and geology, he assumes that these are the causal factors, but actually the most important characteristics of the two soils are due more likely to the longtime influence of the climate and the original vegetation. To make accurate predictions of soil behavior, we must take all the characteristics of the soils into account, for the combination of characteristics controls the behavior of the soil. We can say very little about soils that are sandy, those that are hilly, those that are high in organic matter, and so on, because each characteristic influences the behavior of the others in the combination.

The time required to produce a soil is a misunderstood factor. A deep, potentially productive soil may form in a single day with a deposit of a new alluvial terrace along a river or with a new shower of volcanic ash. It may take millions of years to produce a soil on the rocky face of a dry mountainside. If we avoid these extremes and dig a hole into an ordinary soil under its natural vegetation, we find that it consists of a series of contrasting soil layers, called soil horizons, down to the not-soil beneath. The horizons collectively make up the soil profile. Soil study begins with a full description of the thickness and the physical, chemical, mineralogical, and biological properties of the horizons of the profile and of the mate-

A power auger is used to get at the deeper layers of soil that influence the planning of irrigation.

A soil map is being made in a semidesert area to learn its potential for irrigation.

A soil scientist in Oklahoma has determined the kinds of soils and is sketching their boundaries on an aerial photograph.

rials beneath that influence its moistening, drying, and stability. The soil scientist prepares this description partly from his observations in the field and partly from those made with special apparatus in the laboratory on samples of the horizons. This fully described profile reflects the full integrated effect of all these factors and thus the history of the formation of the soil. At the same time, to the extent the soil scientist does his work well, it forecasts the future behavior of the soil under various treatments.

Besides depth, the soil has breadth. One can walk over it. One can find the boundaries between a soil and the next one to it with different properties. These boundaries, which are the sides of the soils, come where there is a change in one or more of the factors responsible for soil formation. Thus a soil is a three-dimensional piece of the landscape. Some are mere spots of a few square feet. Others are more than a square mile. Some are only a few inches thick. Others are 5 feet thick or more. Some are nearly flat. Others are strongly sloping. When the boundaries are plotted on maps, we find almost every conceivable shape of area from roundish spots to narrow, winding strips. Each of these landscapes is an individual soil. We have millions of them. They are what the soil scientists study and classify and what people use. Those that are alike in the characteristics that we think reflect their genesis and determine their behavior we call a kind of soil. As we learn more about them, we can determine more precisely just which combinations of characteristics are most revealing about their genesis and their probable behavior when they are used. Based on field studies, the boundaries of each soil are shown on a map (or air photograph) with a unique symbol for each kind. The description of each is based on all we have learned about it.

Thus as our basic soil science develops, the classification of soils improves, and predictions based on the classification become more precise. The more we study soils in the field, classify them, map them, and observe their behavior under use and in experimental plots, the more we know about the soils of the United States. Thus has the Soil Survey and our knowledge of the soils of America developed. The process is never ending. People often ask me, "When will the Soil Survey cease changing the descriptions, interpretations, and names of the soils?" I answer: "When we cease to learn more about soil genesis and behavior; when we cease developing new technology for soil use; and when farmers, ranchers, foresters, gardeners, and builders on soil cease to have new problems."

The soil classification and the soil maps are a bridge between research and specific tracts of land. The experience of one user is a guide to another only if the soils are alike. By locating a specific tract on the detailed soil map, we can find the names of the soils that compose it. Then we have the accumulated knowledge from

A device for determining how fast water enters the soil. This knowledge is necessary for planning irrigation or terraces.

decades of research and experience for planning its use. What is a good practice on one field may be ruinous on another with different kinds of soil. Some soils require the periodic growing of deeply rooted legumes and legume-grass mixtures to remain open to water and air in the rooting zone. On others, one can grow corn or cotton continuously with an appropriate set of practices.

Today's Soil Survey makes possible a host of predictions: The crops that can be grown and by what methods; the yields of these crops under the principal alternative combination of practices; the practices to control runoff and erosion; and the kind of arable soil that results from combinations of drainage, irrigation, land leveling, fertilization, liming, cropping, and so on. From the Soil Survey we also learn what wild plants are most likely to take over after cultivation has been given up; the suitability of the soil for forest trees and their rates of growth; and the suitability of the soil for grasses and their rates of growth. We can learn how well each soil can support a highway or a building. The soil map, and our knowledge of how each soil responds to management, is the best basis for farm planning, as already demonstrated, on at least 2 million American farms and ranches. It is the best basis for planning communities, including those in the urban fringe. It gives the land appraiser a clear statement of the potential productivity of soils for use.

As we increase our technology in farming, the correctness of fit between the soil and its management becomes ever more critical. Farmers have substituted city labor in the form of machines, chemicals, fuel, and other materials for direct farm labor. Production expenses per acre steadily increase, and so do yields, where the fit between the kinds of soil and the practices is correct, whether by

Modern, detailed soil maps are plotted on aerial photographs.

design or accident. The development of fertilizers to build up the fertility of the soil nearly parallels the history of the National Cooperative Soil Survey in the United States. Although few may have realized it, each depended on the other. Few soils in the world have enough plant nutrients naturally to support efficient production for more than a few years at best. About the same time that the Soil Survey began, scientists in Europe learned how to make nitrogen fertilizer chemically from the nitrogen of the air. Before that, farmers had only natural forms, which were so low in total nitrogen that they were bulky to ship and thus expensive. During the First World War, the chemical processes were greatly improved and the costs to farmers were sharply reduced. Further improvements came later.

England had commercial phosphatic fertilizers by 1850. Later they were made in the United States. They improved only gradually, and the concentrated sorts were relatively scarce until after the Tennessee Valley Authority took hold of the problem in 1933. The use of potash fertilizer came along with the use of nitrogen and phos-

Here one goes from the soil symbol on the map to the basic soil description in the text of the published soil survey.

phorus. As all three increased, we learned to use the secondary nutrients—magnesium, boron, zinc, and the others. Few farm managers on reasonably good soils now need to let soil fertility be a limiting factor. Knowledge of how the soils respond and chemical tests for current nutrient status are generally well established as the basis for recommendations. Thus has the fertilizer industry expanded and contributed to the labor efficiency of farm people. We now use about five times as much fertilizer as we did in 1935. On lime to correct soil acidity, the story is about the same, but slower. Lime was used in England during Roman times. Edmund Ruffin had demonstrated its use in Virginia in the 1820's. Both his theory and his practice were sound. Progress on farms has been slower. Probably even now farmers use more nearly the fertilizers they should than the lime they should.

After 1899, scientific study was undertaken of soil erosion and of the movement of the soil by wind—the basic principles of the processes of erosion and methods for controlling them. America was becoming conscious of her soils, forests, and waters. Yet homesteading continued on drier and drier lands. The 160-acre tracts could not stand. Shortly after settlement, many were starved out to make room for a few. Some of the settlers found opportunities in irrigated sections. These farmers, too, had new kinds of problems, along with many of the old ones. These had to be solved to make a soil productive enough, and to keep it so, for them to have a reasonable return for their labor. Opportunities for new settlement nearly ceased about 1910. Farming was spread over a larger surface than was really needed. Much of this was on unresponsive soils that had to be abandoned. In fact, a gradual adjustment in land use to get crops off the poor soils and on to the good ones was essential and inevitable under the American rules of competition.

Since soil resources were abundant and wages high, the successful farmer had to have a high output per man-day. This might be had with high yields per acre, but it could be had with low yields if the hours per acre were few enough. Thus American farmers have always been eager for machines so that more could be done by each man per day. The adjustment in soil use that should have started in 1912 did not happen. Instead, even more poor soil came into use. With the great demands and the prices of the First World War, even poor managers on poor soils could make ends meet. But the reckoning came with the end of the war. Farm abandonment became serious in many parts of the country. American industry was still growing in the twenties, so that new and different opportunities were available in the cities. Then came the depression of the early thirties; it reduced farm and city opportunities. By the mid-twenties, this whole problem of land abandonment, stranded agricultural communities, low farm prices, and soil depletion was forced on the attention of the public. Many little things were tried, and they might have worked if the general economy could have remained strong. It did not. Then, with the coming of the New Deal in the midst of the depression, programs were initiated to deal with these problems of agricultural adjustment. The soil conservation work was

Soil surveys, as shown here in Kansas, help engineers plan routes of new highways.

Soil maps are an aid in planning suburban development. Some soils may be all right for cropping but too ill drained or unstable for houses.

enormously emphasized. Gradually farming conditions improved. In this improvement, the good managers fared well and the poor managers fared badly. As more and more technology is used in agriculture, the premium for good management over poor management gets higher and higher.

Up until the midthirties, not much of the improved soil use showed up in higher average yields. In the latter part of the 1930's, great changes were initiated. We learned how to fit practices together. Agricultural science itself had been highly specialized, as it must be to advance in research. Recommendations in bulletins and talks for farmers had also been specialized, which they cannot be in application. That is, one can rarely make a great improvement in farming by adopting just one specialized practice. Each practice influences the others. We can say that every acre of soils in the world that has a good harvest has an appropriate combination of soil fertility, soil water when the plants need it, variety of crop, and plant protection. The only way to make irrigation pay for example, is to do a good job of irrigation without waterlogging, eliminate nutrient deficiencies of the soil, grow a variety with the genetic ability to respond to a good environment, and then protect the crop. This interrelation among practices is an example of the principle of interactions, and each kind of soil has its unique potentiality for specific combinations of practices.

It was the discovery of the importance of this principle and its use by commercial farmers that made possible the fantastic growth in the efficiency of agriculture. During 1939–1959, production per man-hour went up threefold. Farm production increased about 2 percent a year, and we used fewer acres and fewer people to get it. This did not come about in an orderly way. Many soils are still being used for crops that should not be but that could produce good forests or good pastures. We still have serious problems of erosion and waste of water. We should be able to look forward to the elimination of these wastes. Actually, we have only begun to apply science to agriculture. We have great unused resources of scientific skill. With what we know now we could expand our crop acreage by another 150 million or 200 million acres. We should not do so until we have made the best of what we are now using. We should leave that for our great-grandchildren so they can have some room to expand.

We still have a great abundance of soil resources for all our uses—for crops, trees, and grass, for play, and for living space. Fortunately, we have a wide variety of kinds of soil. These vary enormously in their suitability for these uses. We know how to classify them, we know how to identify them on maps, and we know a great deal about how to use them. People make the best use of their labor and the capital when they apply them to the soils that respond most. This applies to cropland, on which we still have great unrealized potentials for greater efficiency. It applies also to rangeland and to forest land. We have much to gain by being more selective of where we put our work and money for growing trees.

This same principle also applies in the growth of our cities. Millions of dollars are being lost each year around each of our great cities by the use of soils for houses that will not support them. This, too, we can prevent. We have plenty of soil suitable for building houses on. Yet some built in the past few years have become useless now because they were put on the wrong kind of

A soil scientist in Rockville, Md., explains to community leaders the characteristics and behavior of the kinds of soil shown on his map.

soil. So many people have been hurt by this process that we are beginning to learn to adapt our city planning to the soil pattern as the farmer has had to learn by experience, with all its wastes and sorrows. Through soil study and the use of soil maps we have the chance to eliminate both urban and rural slums without waste. Some of the country can be brought into the expanding urban fringes on soils best suited to farming, forestry, and parks. Homes need not be built on soils unsuited to them. In the process, we can bring some of the city to the country, where resources are available to support industry and urban services. Everybody gains thereby. Each group has the advantages of the others. We will all know one another better. We will be using our soils in the best way. *(Charles E. Kellogg)*

A farmer in Oregon watches as a soil scientist sketches the boundaries of soils he has studied.

Salt in Soil

A POTTED plant has a lovely color and is growing vigorously when one brings it home from the florist's shop. In a few weeks or months it may have stopped growing, and its leaves are dropping off. Very likely it is an example of what happens when soluble salts accumulate in the soil, a problem mainly in arid regions where irrigation is required to produce crops. Water used for drinking or irrigation contains more or less dissolved salt, such as common table salt. Each cup of water supplied to the potted plant adds a certain amount of salt to the soil. The water evaporates from the plant leaves and from the soil surface, but nearly all the salt remains behind. Some of the salt may appear as a white crust on the soil surface. As each cup of water is added, the amount of salt in the soil increases until finally the plant can no longer grow.

Soil salinity usually can be corrected. The treatment for a potted plant is the same as for agricultural crops in the field. If water is caused to move through the soil, it will dissolve and leach out the excess soluble salts. A potted plant that has become affected by salt can be placed in a sink with the faucet dripping fast enough to maintain a layer of water over the soil. The water draining from the opening in the bottom of the pot will soon carry away the excess salt, and the plant will recover. Because the leaching will also remove soluble nutrients, recovery will be more rapid if fertilizer is added after leaching.

The United States Salinity Laboratory at Riverside, Calif., has developed a simplified test for salinity. A sample of soil from the root zone, whether from a potted plant, a greenhouse bench, or an irrigated field, is placed in a cup and mixed to a saturated paste by adding distilled water while stirring. The paste is then placed in a vacuum filter, and the salt content of the solution removed from the paste is measured with an electrical conductivity bridge. The bridge can also be used to test the salt content of irrigation water.

The management of irrigation water for a potted plant is similar in many ways to water management for irrigated farms. The water that drains into the saucer under the pot contains more salt than the irrigation water, but this saline water moves back into the root zone if it is not discarded. Potted plants often are subirrigated by supplying water to the saucer and allowing it to move up into the soil. This same process occurs in fields when a water table exists

202

Cotton on nonsaline soil in California has a uniform stand and growth.

Cotton on saline soil has an irregular stand and growth.

close to the soil surface. This is hazardous in arid climates because the ground water contains salt and the root zone becomes salinized. The water table should be kept below the root zone in irrigated land. This occurs naturally in some places, but often one has to provide artificial drainage for lowering the water table. A grid of

Testing soil for salinity.

deep ditches along the boundaries of fields often is provided. Sometimes tile lines are laid in the field to collect ground water and convey it to a collector ditch.

Roots absorb the water applied to soil but exclude most of the salt. To prevent the soil from becoming saline, some of the applied irrigation water has to leach through the root zone and be discarded as drainage water, in which the amount of salt removed should equal the amount added in the irrigation water. The fraction of the irrigation water that must be removed as drainage water is called the leaching requirement. Its value depends on the salt content of the irrigation water and the tolerance of the particular crop to salinity. If soil to be put under irrigation is naturally saline or if irrigated soil becomes saline because of improper water management, the whole field often is leached until it is essentially free of soluble salts. That is done by ponding water on the surface; the ponding is done by building a network of contour dikes. Plants vary in their tolerance to soil salinity. Many fruit and vegetable crops suffer if only a small amount of soluble salt is present in the soil. Certain field crops, such as sugarbeets, alfalfa, and cotton, can tolerate larger amounts and still produce profitable yields. The reduction in yield of crops caused by various kinds and amounts of soluble salts is determined by controlled experiments at agricultural research stations.

We grow different kinds of plants under controlled saline conditions at the Salinity Laboratory. The roots of the plants are supported in clean, coarse sand. Beneath the sand is a reservoir of solution that contains all the essential mineral nutrients. In addition, the solutions in the various cultures contain different salts that cause soil salinity. Periodically a timeclock operates a pump,

204

The tile outlet into a drainage ditch.

Leaching of soil by ponding water on the surface.

Sand cultures for testing the salt tolerance of plants.

Small plots for testing the salt tolerance of plants at the United States Salinity Laboratory, Riverside, Calif.

An apparatus for studying water retention by soils.

Dr. L. A. Richards of the Salinity Laboratory uses psychrometers to measure the relative humidity of water in soil.

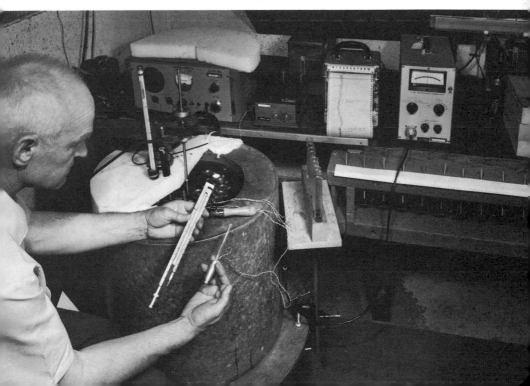

A house plant suffers when salts accumulate in its soil.

which floods the solution in the reservoir over the surface of the sand. The excess solution drains back into the reservoir. Thus the salt solution surrounding the plant root is controlled. The tolerances of various species and varieties of plants also are tested in small field plots. We irrigate the plots with water to which measured amounts of different salts have been added. The tolerance of crops to salinity is usually expressed in terms of the amount of salt in the soil solution that reduces the yield to half of that obtained when the crop is grown in nonsaline soil. Information on the tolerance of various crops to salinity is given in agricultural handbooks. We have developed a pressure membrane apparatus for measuring the relation between the water content and the tenacity with which water is retained by soil. This apparatus is used in laboratories around the world for classifying soils and for determining irrigation practices.

The purpose of irrigation is to maintain water conditions in the soil that are favorable for plant growth. Because soils are porous and fine grained, the total surface area of the particles is enormous. For example, the total surface area of the particles in a vial of clay soil amounts to 1 acre. The surfaces of soil particles adsorb and retain water as a film. As soil dries, the water films on the surfaces become thinner and are held more tightly. The result is that plant roots, in effect, must exert increasing suction to obtain water from the soil. As the suction required to obtain water increases, the growth of the plant diminishes. When the amount of soil in the vial has its water depleted to the volume represented by the colored liquid in an adjacent vial, crops in this soil wilt and stop growing. This is one of the determinations made with the membrane apparatus. *(L. A. Richards* and *C. A. Bower)*

Forests

Research and Wood

WOOD comes from organisms that live and die, from trees that grow in many sizes and shapes. Wood has as many differences in strength, machinability, resistance to decay, gluability, and so on as there are species of trees. To determine the properties of the various woods and to investigate the multitude of problems of wood utilization were the tasks assigned the Forest Products Laboratory when it was founded in 1910. From a half century of research at the Laboratory in Madison, Wis., has come knowledge that makes the mature timbers from commercial species of North American trees true engineering materials. Their strength properties and reactions to stress have been determined. Applications for wood undreamed of in 1910 now form the bases for a range of expanding industries. Yet each scientific advance opens up new avenues of thought and creates new challenges. Ahead lie expanding opportunities for the wiser use of our forest resources. Although our annual per capita consumption of lumber has declined slowly since 1900, markets for other wood and wood-based products have increased greatly our total demand for wood.

Paper is an example. About 450 pounds of paper are used annually per capita. In the early days, only a few long-fibered species— primarily the spruces and hemlock—were considered suitable for pulping. The southern yellow pines were too resinous. The hardwoods, which were already contributing a large part of our total forest growth, were too short fibered to yield acceptable pulp by conventional pulping methods; many of them were also too low in quality to have significant value as lumber. Modifications of the kraft pulping process brought the southern pines into the acceptable category for paper. The hardwoods remained a problem.

Chemists developed a promising new pulping process in the mid-twenties, a process in which hardwood chips are softened by cooking in a chemical solution and then reduced mechanically to fibers. It is called the neutral sulfite semichemical process. It received its first commercial trial in a scheme to utilize chestnut wood chips left as a residue after the extraction of tannins for tanning leather. The success of the trial launched the process into industrial application. The new semichemical process has two advantages over its completely chemical predecessors. The yield of pulp from a given weight of wood is much higher. It has unlocked the door to vast areas of low-grade hardwood forests and made them available as a raw material for a paper industry hard pressed to find enough wood. Some 50 mills use the neutral sulfite semichemical process or the newer cold soda chemimechanical processes, developed later at the Laboratory. The cold soda process requires less capital investment and gives even higher yields with the hardwoods. Aspen, once considered to be a weed tree, has risen in popularity to a point where it is the leading pulpwood species in the Lake States.

Chemists have believed that the less desirable trees should be worth harvesting solely for the value of the organic chemicals in them. The chemical utilization of wood was not economically feasible in the United States under normal conditions. Fundamental and applied data have been gathered, however, to the point where a chemical industry based on wood could now be an economic success. Chemicals worth some 60 million dollars annually are produced from wood, but they are largely secondary operations that rely on residues from a primary operation for raw material. A sound chemical conversion plant will probably have to make use of all three major fractions of wood, the lignin, cellulose, and hemicellulose.

Wood is approximately two-thirds fiber and one-third binder. The binder, lignin, has a complex organic structure that someday may become even more valuable than the fiber portion as a source of industrial chemicals. The fiber fraction is much more orderly and can be separated into two carbohydrate fractions. The most easily obtained fraction, the hemicellulose, consists largely of sugars that can be converted economically to furfural and other polymer-forming chemicals used in the production of nylon and similar synthetic fibers and resins. It is probable that a growing part of our production of organic chemicals will be based on these sugars from low-grade hardwoods. The cellulose fraction, more difficult to obtain in pure form, is the primary constituent of paper. Purified, it is reformed in high tonnage as rayon for tire cord and textiles.

Glucose is the sugar that can be obtained from the pure cellulose in wood. Since food sugars are available at low cost from other natural sources, research on glucose from wood has been primarily to establish the optimum reaction conditions for its conversion to promising industrial-type organic chemicals, such as hydroxymethyl-furfural and levulinic acid. Glucose also can be fermented biochemically to glycerin, various alcohols, and food yeast. The yeast is high in protein and vitamins and could be useful in countries that rely heavily on a carbohydrate diet.

Our total wood supply can be conserved and used more wisely if we can modify individual pieces to make them last longer. Wood will last indefinitely if it is properly seasoned to remove its natural moisture and is then kept dry. A few years ago, for instance, archeologists found sound wood beams in the tomb of King Gordius,

Improved gluing technology enabled engineers to extend the use of wood as an engineering material, like these huge laminated members.

Engineers at the Forest Products Laboratory use a machine that can exert a million pounds of force to test prototypes of laminated arches.

Technicians at the laboratory in Madison, Wis., establish the cutting and gluing characteristics of wood to be used for veneers.

Technicians make paper so as to study in finished-products form the characteristics of experimental pulps.

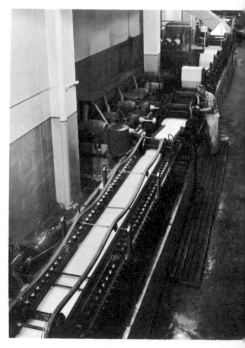

a king who reigned some 2,700 years ago in what now is Turkey. A few houses of wood built in New England in the 1630's still stand. Only exterior items, such as siding, have had to be replaced because of the gradual eroding effects of weather.

In many of its normal uses, however, wood cannot remain sufficiently dry. When it reaches a moisture content much above 20 percent, it becomes susceptible to damage by decay fungi or other wood-destroying micro-organisms. Window sills, posts, poles, railroad ties, and such other items in contact with the soil should be given added protection against decay and destructive insects. Creosote is still a standard preservative for piles, railroad ties, and such uses, but for uses where odor, appearance, or paintability are critical, only the newer preservatives are acceptable. Pentachlorophenol, a result of research at the Laboratory, is among the leaders in this class. It is a solid preservative that must be dissolved in a solvent. It is used at the rate of 11 million pounds a year, more than all other solid preservatives together. In a new approach to preservation, scientists at the Laboratory are attempting to avoid the costly deposition of quantities of toxic chemicals in wood to kill invading fungi. Their goal is to modify the cellulose in wood inexpensively so that fungi cannot digest it or possibly to destroy certain vitamins and other chemical compounds present only in trace amounts but necessary if fungi are to survive. Similarly, they are looking for ways to modify some one or more of the several stages in the combustion of wood so that the wood will not actually burn and contribute fuel to a fire.

As the new, young forests replaced the old, virgin stands of timber in this country, research workers had to find new ways of combining the smaller sizes of available timber. The research engineers found that modern adhesives are more efficient than the typical mechanical fastener, the nail. It was the beginning of a range of new structural products. Efficient gluing and techniques of cutting veneers made possible today's plywood industry. Nearly 8 billion square feet of softwood construction-grade plywood was produced in the western softwood region in 1960. Completely waterproof synthetic adhesives made it possible to make plywood for exterior and marine use. The first building with exterior siding of plywood, built in 1934, stands on the grounds of the Forest Products Laboratory and houses its facilities for research on packaging. It is the first structure in the United States built with glue-laminated arches. Through laminating, wood has become a truly beautiful, engineered structural material. You see it in modern churches, sports arenas, and gymnasiums, which must have a large, unobstructed floor space.

Although man for centuries has been building with wood, many of the crafts that rely on wood were not based thoroughly on a sound, technical understanding of its strengths and limitations. The

Moisture meters developed at the Forest Products Laboratory make it possible to determine whether lumber has been seasoned properly.

conventional homebuilding industry is typical. To meet the housing needs of the Nation efficiently and inexpensively during the early thirties, engineers at the Laboratory adapted the principles of wood aircraft design to the factory production of houses. Called the stressed-skin principle, the design involved the gluing of plywood or other sheet material to light framing members, so that all parts contributed to the strength of the unit. The units, which had a high strength-to-weight ratio, were then used for walls, floors, and roofs. Today, when more than a million houses are built every year, nearly 13 percent of new houses are factory built. Most of them are based on the original stressed-skin principle.

Supply problems in wartime gave impetus to research in packaging. Shipping space and the amount of lumber used had to be kept low, yet the packaged goods, from aircraft engines to combat clothing, had to withstand the violence of winter gales on the North Atlantic and the rain, waves, and tropical humidity of the South Pacific. Some 1,500 packaging specifications had been completed at the Laboratory by 1945 for the Ordnance Department and the Air Force, 16 thousand persons from privates to generals had been trained in techniques of efficient packaging, and four ships were moving the cargo that in 1941 had required five ships.

Because wood is a structural material of many uses, yet is organic in nature, research on forest products enters many fields of natural and applied sciences. The chemist, physicist, engineer, wood technologist, mathematician—each must have the support and ideas of the others if his research is to be fruitful. So, research men from several universities went to work in the Laboratory when it opened for business in 1910 with a staff of 45. Wood research was barely hitting its stride when the United States was confronted for the

Tests of preservatives and treating methods and conditions indicate the ability of wood to withstand severe exposure to insects and fungi.

first time with the logistics problem of long-distance war. Wood of the best quality was gravely needed in 1917 for gunstocks, truck bodies, aircraft propellers, and barracks.

Because time was so precious, probably the most valuable of these inspired efforts culminated in Harry Tiemann's design of a radical water-spray kiln. This device kept the surface of lumber from getting too dry while the moisture within was being removed rapidly without warping, twisting, and general degrading of the lumber. His kiln eliminated months of air seasoning between the sawmill and the manufacturing plant. By the thirties, a great variety of projects had produced a wealth of information for industry and had indicated an even greater need for research. An expanded program was begun in 1932. Soon came technical publications on preservative treatment, painting, prefabricating, machining, laminating, plywood, and chemical products, all eagerly sought by industries.

Another war brought more problems and answers in such fields as packaging, stabilizing dimensions of wood, industrial chemicals, waterproof plywood, and sandwich-type construction, an improvement on the stressed-skin principle, to name a few. Successes brought new industries and new research ideas for the postwar years. But still there are products to be improved, processes to be developed, chemical mysteries to be unraveled. The research has a monetary value now. It is laying the groundwork for developments that may determine whether future generations will continue to have the abundance of forest products that we have. *(Edward G. Locke)*

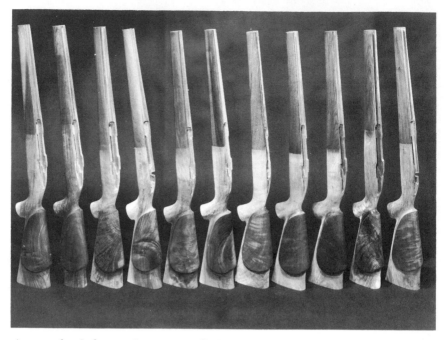

A new chemical seasoning process eliminates drying checks and splits and adds dimensional stability in these walnut gunstocks.

Scraps from nine species of hardwoods, salvaged from a residue pile, were bonded and glued directly to a concrete subfloor for this office floor at the Forest Products Laboratory.

Farm Woodlands

SMALL FAMILY forests offer a double opportunity: A good chance of growing money on trees and the certainty that the owner is adding something of value to his community. They range from 3 acres to 5 thousand acres and average 59 acres. They make up 265 million acres and are owned by 4.5 million individuals, more than half of whom are farmers. The lands are as different in composition, age, and capabilities as are their owners. They exist everywhere that forest-type trees grow naturally, but most are east of the Great Plains.

Most farmers own their woodlands as a part of the farm, usually as a back forty or a hilly tract too steep to cultivate. Nonfarmers own woodlands for many reasons—for hunting and fishing, other recreation, pride of ownership, speculation, or investment. The possibility of making money is the primary motive of many owners, but fewer than half of them have done anything about management; they seem to think that growing timber is different from other enterprises in that Nature will take care of it. When an owner asks a forester, "What are my chances of making money in timber?", the forester probably will ask, "Are you interested in speculation or in management?" If the answer is speculation, the forester may show little interest, for he knows that almost anything bought cheap and sold high can yield a profit. He also knows that if all the timber is cut at once the owner might just as well sell both trees and land and get out of the business. If the owner is interested in managing now and in the future, the forester will be anxious to help him. Forestry is generally a long-term business, and quick profits are rare.

The small woodland can be a source of profitable self-employment. A woodland owner can save money by producing posts, poles, and construction materials. Sometimes he can produce maple sirup, fish from his pond or stream, and wild game for his table and have recreation for himself and his family. He may be able to lease for profit the fishing and hunting rights in his woodland or he may rent out campsites. With trees he can heal the scars of erosion. He can protect his fields, cattle, and homesite from the wind and extremes of heat or cold. The prospective timber owner will find opportunities almost everywhere, but some places are better than others. Technical assistance is more readily available in

A fine stand of mixed hardwoods in North Carolina.

218

some counties. Some sections have excellent publicly financed organizations for protection from fire; in others, the owner must fight fire alone. Opportunities for profitable management are possible only under favorable conditions. One of the most important is that the owner have full control of the land—by living on it himself or having someone live on it who will protect the woodland from fire, animals, insects, diseases, and thieves.

In many places an owner can hire a consulting forester for a daily fee or a percentage of the income from timber sales. Some manufacturers, like the big paper and lumber companies, may offer some free technical forestry assistance. Most States provide the services of a forester free or at a nominal charge to help small owners get started in management and to check on the operations.

Markets vary from place to place and are never static, but timber does not have to be harvested every month or every year. Generally it will keep on increasing in size and value if it cannot be sold profitably this year or next, but harvesting cannot be deferred indefinitely. The sale must be made before decay and other risks become excessive or the owner will lose money.

Good roads and railroads or water transportation are essential to the economical movement of forest products, which are generally bulky and heavy. Also to be taken into account are soil and water. A pine tree or an oak is as responsive to good soil and moisture as a cornstalk. The local tax situation also has a bearing on the purchase of a woodland. In one place, woodland worth 50 dollars an acre may be taxed at 10 to 20 cents; in another place, woodland worth 10 dollars an acre may be taxed 2 dollars a year.

How to start depends a great deal on the resources one has. With respect to the timber, most owners have a small amount of mature salable timber; some good, immature timber, which will yield future harvests; a large number of cull trees, which must be gotten rid of; and some bare or poorly stocked land in need of planting or seeding. Good, growing stock trees of the right species, quality, and sizes, well spaced over the land, are an asset in managing timber. Stocking land with good trees, like developing a fine herd of cattle, cannot be done in a day or a year. Many small woodlands are so choked with cull or scrub trees that good growing stock can be developed only by clearing, followed by planting or seeding. Also to be considered are the owner's physical, financial, and managerial capabilities. A man who can do his own work often can earn a good wage in addition to the stumpage value of the trees to be harvested. An owner who is financially secure can forego limited immediate profits and wait for favorable prices.

Quicker profits can be expected by starting with growing stock at or below harvest size and managing it for a few years, rather than buying bare land and planting it. Price is important. The

Pruning ponderosa pine in California to grow good, knotfree sawlogs and veneer.

initial cost plus carrying charges (including taxes and interest), and costs of protection, development, and administration can add up to a large total expenditure. Unless returns are frequent and sizable there will be no profit. Land with scrubby growth that must be cleared and planted may have a negative value while land supporting a stand of pole-size yellow poplar trees which in a few years will make good sawlogs and then later valuable veneer may yield a profit even if the purchase price is high. Over the long term, good timberland and growing stock generally are more profitable than are poor land and poor growing stock. The owner of a small woodland cannot expect to become an experienced forester overnight. He must have technical help to inventory what he has, determine its capabilities, and make the right steps in planting, thinning, pruning, release cutting, protection, road development, sale, and harvest. Plans and decisions must be made on the basis of facts, good judgment, and experience. *(Arthur R. Spillers)*

This stand of scrub oak has many trees of poor quality and must be improved if it is to be profitable.

The slash pine being planted in this old field in Georgia in time will be a profitable woodland like the one in the background.

The Forest Ranger

THE FOREST RANGER'S work used to be to protect the National Forests from fire, squatters, and timber thieves and to plant and harvest trees. His visitors usually were sportsmen. In later years the work of management, conservation, and administration has changed and grown, as many more people have discovered the values and pleasures of the National Forests. There were 800 forest rangers on the 155 National Forests in 1962.

I visited one of them, Theodore S. Seely, who has been an employee of the Forest Service since 1933 and a ranger since 1939. He is a graduate of the College of Forestry, Syracuse University. His first assignment as a junior forester took him to the Pisgah National Forest in North Carolina. He later was a wildlife management specialist and ranger on several forests before he became ranger of the Pisgah Ranger District in 1952. He received the Superior Service Award of the Department of Agriculture in 1960 for his outstanding work.

I had met Mr. Seely one morning at the district work center. Nineteen men went about their tasks in preparation for the day. Three workmen selected plumbing tools to clear a clogged water system on one of the 13 public recreation areas. Two others put cans on a truck to collect trash and garbage at picnic and camping areas. Seven loaded materials for the construction of campsites in the Coontree recreation area. A construction foreman, a workman, and an engineer from the North Carolina supervisor's office in Asheville prepared to relocate a section of road destroyed by rock slides. Assistant Ranger Harry McCutcheon and three other foresters picked up paint supplies to mark timber soon to be sold. Mr. Seely saw to the organization of the day's work; then we drove to his headquarters.

His office is a neat, white building, nestled against steep banks of white pine, hemlock, and hardwoods southwest of Asheville, N.C. A few hundred feet to the south across the valley flows Davidson River, its clear waters filtered from steep mountain slopes by thick, healthy stands of trees. The place looks like a secluded vacation cottage. A sign on the front of the building reads, "Pisgah Ranger Office, Pisgah National Forest." From there the ranger administers 160 thousand acres of mountain forest lands. The clerk at headquarters, Anita Macfie, is the radio operator, receptionist,

Theodore S. Seely, ranger, and Anita Macfie, clerk, of the Pisgah Ranger District in North Carolina.

Mr. Seely and Dixie Howell, assistant supervisor of the North Carolina National Forests, inspect plantings that stabilize roadbanks.

223

Training sessions of Pisgah Ranger District personnel include talks on safety.

Mr. Seely checks the work of a road maintenance crew.

stenographer, filing clerk, and general factotum when Mr. Seely is working outside.

"I always like to start the day with the crews," the ranger said. "Even though their work is laid out in annual, monthly, and weekly work plans, we depend on the experienced foremen and forestry aids to direct much of the work on the ground, and some of the men have been with us many years. Still I like to keep in close touch with them."

He told me about the Pisgah district, from which comes the water supply of three nearby towns—a daily average of 100 million gallons. Three major industries came to the area principally because there is clean water. Traffic counters tallied 1,700,000 visits to recreation areas in 1961. Many more drove through just to look at the mountain scenery and were not counted. Permits to hunt totaled 14,600; to fish, 15,400. The ranger staff maintains seven game protection stations used by personnel of the North Carolina Wildlife Resources Commission during managed hunts. Timber sales include some 7 million board feet of sawtimber and pulpwood annually. Pulpwood sales in 1961 were 8 thousand cords, which kept about 75 family wage earners busy in the woods. There are 120 special-use permits for powerline and road rights-of-way, television tower sites, scout camps, trails, one church and so on. Some 154 miles of permanent forest roads are maintained, besides temporary logging routes and 130 miles of foot trails. Mr. Seely's crews planted 140 thousand seedlings of forest trees in 1961. Work varies with the seasons. Winter is a time of trail maintenance and timber sales work. Spring brings tree planting, fire control, preparation for recreation visitors, heavy fishing, and much of the road construction and maintenance. Summer is a time for cleaning up recreation areas, maintaining recreation facilities, and establishing new units. Organized hunts, timber stand improvement, and fire-control duties take place in autumn. Timber sales go on all year, and so do educational programs with organizations and schools, the many jobs involving public contacts, and planning.

For a look at the district, around midmorning we drove westward along Davidson River. Healthy, vigorous trees line both sides of the paved road and extend up steep slopes of the valley edge. Near the river are recreation areas—Coontree, White Pines, Looking Glass Falls, Sliding Rock Falls, and Pink Beds—for picnicking and camping. The ranger pointed out that the grass cover planted along roadbanks to prevent erosion and be supplemental food plots for wildlife also kept the roads from looking like ugly scars. Zones along roads, highways, and trails are left in near-natural condition. Trout streams and recreation areas are managed to preserve tree cover for shade and beauty. Particular attention is paid to the overlooks on the mountain. We toured the trout hatchery of the United

States Fish and Wildlife Service, where thousands of fingerlings are hatched each year for stocking as adult fish in the National Forest streams. The ranger, the Fish and Wildlife Service, and the North Carolina Wildlife Resources Commission cooperate in wildlife and fisheries programs.

As we continued up the river, messages came over Mr. Seely's shortwave radio. One crew reported they found the mutilated carcass of a doe deer killed out of season. Seely informed the State game protectors immediately so that they might start the necessary investigations; such day-to-day cooperation between the ranger and State game personnel is routine under cooperative agreements between the State and National Forest supervisor. A fire towerman in a remote area reported conditions of wind, weather, and vegetation. Seely checked with Mrs. Macfie at headquarters after we had been away from the radio. All are mindful always of the danger of fire, even on a day like this when, Mr. Seely said, the vegetation had greened up enough to shade the ground and wind and moisture were such that fire danger was low.

We stopped at the site of the first forestry school in the United States. Here Gifford Pinchot managed the first tract of timber ever to receive intensive management in this country according to modern concepts. George Vanderbilt began the development of an estate in the western North Carolina highlands in 1889. He purchased 100 thousand acres of forest land and constructed a mansion in what he called Biltmore Estate. Pinchot became director of Vanderbilt's forest. Before the purchase of the land, most of the tracts were small ownerships that had been farmed, cut over, or burned so cattle could graze there. The stands of trees had deteriorated. Soil fertility had suffered because of the fires. Interest in forest conservation heightened with Pinchot's work, and citizens in western North Carolina advocated that the lands be brought into public ownership.

Recreation areas are kept neat and clean.

Looking Glass Falls.

Wildlife openings contain food plantings.

Pinchot in 1905 became the first Chief of the newly created United States Forest Service. Carl Alwin Schenck, a German forester who came to North Carolina in 1895, succeeded Pinchot as manager of the Vanderbilt Forest. The Biltmore Forest School, established in 1898, grew out of the work. The Vanderbilts in 1916 sold 86,700 acres of the estate to the Forest Service, with the stipulation that it be known as Pisgah National Forest. Under terms of the Weeks Law of 1911, Pisgah became the first National Forest in the Eastern States. The Pisgah Ranger District came into being at the same time. Other lands were added later by purchase to bring the district to its present size. It is one of the 5 districts on the Pisgah National Forest and one of the 11 districts in the National Forests in North Carolina.

"Our management is according to multiple-use principles conceived here by Pinchot more than half a century ago," Mr. Seely said as we drove on. "Water conservation on the Pisgah District is a part of all activities. If too many recreationists trample the earth, grasses and other small plants die, and tree roots are exposed above the ground. The soil loses its ability to absorb and slowly discharge maximum quantities of water. To avoid this, recreation use must be regulated and play areas must be continually repaired. Timber operations—selective cutting, planting, and improvement of timber stands—are conducted so that there is always vegetative cover on the land. Logging is done in a way that protects the earth's surface and its water-bearing qualities. Skid roads are located where they will do the least damage and are grassed after logging is finished."

Wildlife populations are controlled by managed hunts for both doe and buck deer. The Pisgah has some overpopulations of deer, and their range has deteriorated. Now, however, State and Forest Service technicians manage timber and other vegetation to improve habitat and the annual hunts to increase the harvest and to balance deer populations with the habitat. Surplus deer trapped here have been stocked throughout the South to start new herds. As we reached the ridge at the edge of Mr. Seely's district, we drove along a section of Blue Ridge Parkway, a place of spectacular beauty that draws thousands of visitors annually. Here the National Forest and National Park programs blend to provide visitors with scenery and places for picnicking, camping, hiking, swimming, and fishing.

The drive up Davidson River and along a part of the parkway covered less than one-fourth of Mr. Seely's district, but it was enough to indicate the scope of his work and responsibility and those of other forest rangers. Uses and public demands vary, but the forest ranger, wherever he is, carries out and coordinates the production, use, and complex management of the resources of large tracts of valuable land that belong to the American people. *(George M. Kyle)*

Forests for the Future

WE IN the United States now grow more wood of all kinds than is being cut, but the growth is not enough to replace the kinds most in demand. Moreover, estimates of the growth of population and economic expansion up to the start of the new century indicate a need for a nationwide forestry effort far more intensive than we have known in the past.

To early settlers, America's virgin forests were vast and stubborn obstacles to be hacked, burned, and uprooted until the land was bared for the plow. Through the years this huge supply of wood became fuel, lumber, and other products needed by an expanding Nation. Forests were used as if the supply were limitless. As a result of clearing land, lumbering, and uncontrolled fires, an estimated billion acres of forest was reduced by one-third between 1620 and 1900.

The situation changed in the past several decades. Large reservations of public forests starting in 1891 and extensive repurchase of lands in the 1930's formed our system of National Forests, which now cover 181 million acres and include 16 percent of the commercial forest land. Organized fire protection of timberlands on a cooperative Federal-State basis began in 1911, and fire control has been extended to nearly all forest lands. Strong State departments of forestry have been established in most States to help carry out various programs of aid to private forest owners. Forest industries have adopted intensive forestry programs. Comprehensive programs of forestry research have been developed. Education in forestry has expanded, and 40 institutions train professional foresters to manage public and private forest lands and timber operations. The downward trends in forest resources have been arrested and reversed as a result of such efforts by public and private groups and a general change in public attitudes toward natural resources.

The total area of forest in the United States in 1962 was about 770 million acres, or one-third the land area. Some 530 million acres are commercial timberlands, managed for or capable of yielding such industrial wood as sawlogs and pulpwood and not reserved from cutting. The other 240 million acres are too unproductive to manage for wood production (although they are useful for watersheds, grazing, and other purposes) or are productive but reserved for parks or other special purposes. About 70 percent of our timber-

lands is privately owned by some 4.5 million owners. About 36 percent of the remaining commercial forests is in the South, 33 percent in the North, and 31 percent in the West. The volume of wood in trees more than 5 inches in diameter is 550 billion cubic feet; nearly half is in the four Pacific Coast States; more than half is privately owned. There are 2 thousand billion board feet of sawtimber—enough, if converted to 1-inch boards, to make a platform 8 feet wide between the Earth and Mars. Three-fourths of this sawtimber is softwood.

The Nation's inventory of forest capital has been increasing in volume, particularly on public and large industrial forest holdings, where management efforts have been greatest. The total annual growth of all sizes of trees, amounting to 14 billion cubic feet, now exceeds the annual harvest. The yearly lumber cut is enough to provide homes for a city of 11 million Americans, and the total annual cut of all timber products would form a woodpile 9 feet wide and 9 feet high stretching around the world.

Although quantities of timber supplies have been increasing, the picture is not so bright in other respects. The more valuable grades of lumber and other products and such preferred species as white pine, walnut, sugar maple, and yellow birch are increasingly in short supply. Moreover, costs of harvesting timber have been rising steadily as loggers reach farther for timber and mills are forced to process poorer logs. Much progress has been made in the use of residues from logging and milling (particularly by large operations that produce a variety of forest products), but nearly a fourth of the volume of felled timber is still not used. Most of the waste is in the woods on sawlog operations. Natural enemies of the forest still take a heavy toll despite great progress in controlling the destructive agents. The losses from fires, insects, and diseases each year, in outright kill of trees and slowdown in growth, are estimated to approximate the volume removed from the forest by lumbering.

National demands for wood are expected to increase greatly during the next several decades. Projections made by the Forest Service indicate that by the year 2000 annual demands for timber products might be as much as twice the present level of demand. Present prospective growth, however, would not supply such an expansion of markets. Pressures on forest resources are being intensified by growing competition for a limited supply of land. Although possibly 50 million acres of land once in crops and pasture have reverted to forest in the past several decades, a growing population will require much of our present forest land area for other uses—suburbs, in-

Forests cover one-third of the United States, but their pattern (as in Centre County in Pennsylvania) is broken by clearings for various uses.

231

Areas with malformed and inferior trees need to be restored to a productive condition. (Sumter National Forest in South Carolina.)

dustrial sites, highways, reservoirs, airports, parks, and more crop and pasture lands. To meet prospective demands for wood products from a forest area that may shrink significantly requires major efforts in reforestation beyond the current rate of 2 million acres of planting a year; in improved cutting to promote growth of desirable trees, particularly on the several million poorly managed small forest holdings that comprise more than half our timberlands; in control of fire and forest pests; and in more efficient use of the timber cut. By such means, more abundant supplies of timber can be assured, but we cannot put them into practice in a day. Trees take a long time to grow. *(H. R. Josephson* and *R. C. Wilson)*

Timberlands must produce new crops of desirable trees to fill the gaps left by harvest cuttings. (Jefferson National Forest in Virginia.)

Hybrid Trees

NEW TREES have come from research by forest geneticists, who by careful selection and controlled breeding have incorporated desirable characters in trees of hybrid origin. The wonder is not that it is possible—the science of genetics tells us that living organisms can be modified in total character by controlled breeding—but the vision and perseverance of the geneticist who works with plants whose life cycle is so long that he may see only two or three generations of trees during his life as a research worker.

Work like this is done at the Western Institute of Forest Genetics at Placerville, Calif., a part of the Pacific Southwest Forest and Range Experiment Station. James G. Eddy, a lumberman, started the Institute in the twenties with his own funds to develop superior forest trees, particularly pines. He deeded it in 1935 to the United States Government for operation by the Forest Service. During the early days, scientists at the institute developed techniques for producing hybrid trees that are now used around the world.

Producing a hybrid pine requires a series of steps spread out over a period of about a year and a half. The forest geneticist or forest tree breeder first selects the parent trees. Because he usually knows nothing about their genotype, or ability to transmit characters, he must select them on the basis of their phenotype, or their apparent characteristics in the conditions under which they grow. Then he must climb the tree in the spring to find out whether the trees will bear female flowers or male flowers. (These structures in the conifers technically are not truly flowers but are so termed for convenience.) The female flower, or conelet, develops into the cone, which bears the seed. The male flower, or catkin, produces the pollen. Before the conelet is developed and ready to be pollinated, the geneticist places a bag of cloth or plastic over it to shield it from contaminating pollen. Meanwhile he has collected the catkins from the father tree, dried them, and extracted the pollen.

When the conelet is ready to receive the pollen, he injects a syringe filled with the pollen into the bag and dusts the developing conelet thoroughly with the pollen. He may remove the bag in several weeks, after the danger of contamination by other pollen has passed. In the pines, about 18 months must pass before the seeds are mature and the cones are harvested. Only after seedlings are grown will the geneticist know if he has created a hybrid.

O. O. Wells, a forester at the Western Institute of Forest Genetics at Placerville, Calif., collects pollen from a western white pine to start the process of creating a hybrid.

From this research have come some remarkable and valuable new trees. One is the hybrid between knobcone pine *(Pinus attenuata)* and Monterey pine *(P. radiata)*. Knobcone pine survives under such adverse conditions as warm, dry, rocky hillsides or cold mountain flats. Monterey pine, on the other hand, grows along the central California coast in a moderate climate, where fog is common and frosts are rare. It is one of the world's fastest growing pines and is planted extensively in New Zealand, Australia, and South Africa. It has been planted rarely in the United States, its home, because of its climatic requirements.

This pine hybrid, the first manmade hybrid between two species of pine, has many desirable characteristics. Because it is hardier than its Monterey pine parent, the forester can plant it in colder or drier sites than this parent. The hybrid grows fast—27-year-old trees at Placerville were 80 feet tall. It grows rapidly when small, so that it can keep ahead of brush. The hybrid is being produced for planting in National Forests in California.

A hybrid forest tree resistant to a destructive forest insect pest is

234

Female flowers of a western white pine are dusted with pollen.

This western white pine in Idaho is resistant to blister rust. It is the mother tree in the production of resistant progeny. The bags forestall pollination with unwanted pollen.

This small-limbed pine in Georgia came from small-limbed parents.

This bushy pine came from bushy-crowned parents.

the one that results from the cross between Jeffrey pine *(P. jeffreyi)* and Coulter pine *(P. coulteri)*. It, too, was developed at Placerville. Jeffrey pine, a commercial forest tree, grows in the high mountains and plateaus of California and southern Oregon. It was planted extensively in northern California, but often a weevil killed or damaged the young trees. Coulter pine is a tree of intermediate altitudes in central and southern California, outside the commercial timber belt. It grows rapidly when young but has not been used for reforestation. The hybrid between these two pines is generally resistant to the weevil and grows fast when young. It is produced on a large scale for planting in the National Forests.

Another hybrid pine of promise in the South is one between the popular and fast-growing slash pine *(P. elliottii)* and shortleaf pine *(P. echinata)*. More slash pine trees are planted in the United States than any other species, all in the South. This pine grows well, is suitable for lumber or pulp, and also yields resin for the naval

In Olustee Experimental Forest in Florida, slash pines selected for high yield of naval stores gum are control-pollinated to produce superior trees.

stores industry. But it is severely damaged by fusiform rust in parts of the South. Shortleaf pine, however, is resistant to this rust. Although it does not grow so fast as slash pine, it is an acceptable timber species. The hybrid from these two species is resistant to a satisfactory degree and appears to have a good rate of growth. This hybrid can be useful in places where the disease is serious.

Not all superior forest trees have resulted from crosses between two species. Some were selected in the natural forest. This was the procedure in Idaho, where thousands of white pine trees were examined for presence or absence of the blister rust disease. A few disease-free trees were found. By controlled breeding among the disease-free trees, the tree breeders determined that some of the trees did have the ability to transmit resistance to their progeny. These resistant trees, plus others that may be found, will be used in seed orchards to produce seed for pines resistant to blister rust. By a similar procedure, forest geneticists in Florida discovered slash pines that yielded much more resin than the average. Among 100 thousand trees being tapped for resin, they found a few that yielded twice as much as the average. They studied their yield and determined that some did have the ability to produce much more resin. By careful selection, they have found some which may yield twice as much as the average. Progeny of these will be used in seed orchards to produce seed for future plantations of high-yielding pines.

The Forest Service has established other institutes of forest genetics at Rhinelander, Wis., and Gulfport, Miss. There and at Placerville are being tackled some of the more basic problems of forest genetics, such as studies of the extent of variation within a tree species, the determination as to whether characters are inherited and how strongly, or the pattern of crossability among tree species. The Forest Service conducts research in tree improvement at a number of other locations, where problems of more local nature are studied. For example, at Burlington, Vt., foresters are looking for maple trees that produce more sugar; at Lake City, Fla., for pines that yield more resin; at Lincoln, Nebr., for full-crowned trees for better windbreaks; and at Corvallis, Oreg., for small-crowned trees.

Nature has given the breeder of forest trees abundant material with which to work. For example, in the genus *Pinus* are 90 or more species that are native around the world in the Northern Hemisphere. They grow from the Arctic Circle to the Equator at sea level and at an elevation of at least 10 thousand feet. They grow in regions with only 15 to 20 inches of precipitation a year and in humid regions where precipitation exceeds 100 inches annually. Some are tall, and some are short. Some are long lived, and some are not. Some have soft, light wood. Others have dense wood. This great genetic diversity provides the basic material from which foresters can make a new tree. *(H. A. Fowells)*

Fighting Forest Fires

ABOUT 12 thousand fires burn an average of 200 thousand acres of the National Forests each year. Many more start, but all but one in a hundred are put out before they can do much damage. To protect the forests, we have a highly skilled organization of many men, the experience of six decades, and the newest techniques.

The smokejumpers' part is the most glamorous and dangerous. Usually they are college students who are carefully chosen for these summer jobs. They undergo 4 weeks of grueling training in how to fight fires, take care of themselves in the woods, and jump from an airplane and land safely in whatever kind of wooded, rocky, mountainous, remote terrain a fire might start. In minutes they can reach, fight, and put out a fire that a ranger with burro and pack used to take days to get to. In 20 years, 4,529 smokejumpers have made 21 thousand jumps. Each jumper has dropped to him fire-fighting tools, such as shovel and ax, and often a radio, so he can report to the plane that dropped him. He also gets rations and a bedroll. The firefighting organization also includes men in high, strategic lookout towers, who are on guard 24 hours a day. When they sight a wisp of smoke, they telephone or radio to the ranger station. Dispatchers plot the fire on a map with readings provided by several lookouts and order the jumpers out. The pilots of the smokejumpers' planes circle the fire, and the spotter who is the boss of the jumpers selects a spot for the men to try for. Test parachutes are dropped to determine wind drift. At the correct time, the spotter tells them when to jump.

Air tankers dropped 124 thousand gallons of water and retardant on 24 fires in 1956 and nearly 6 million gallons on 1,050 fires in the severe 1960 season. The use of smokejumpers has risen rapidly, too, from 27 jumps on 9 fires in 1940, the first year of operational use, to 2,559 jumps and 673 fires in 1960. The firefighters already have a body of tradition: The flights in 1919 of Major Hap Arnold's "air force" enlisted to help the Forest Service spot fires; the first jump on a real fire in 1939 by Francis Lufkin; the first use of a bulldozer tractor and of fire plows on fires; and the first dropping of cargo and the first use of a helicopter to transport men from one spot in rugged terrain to another spot thousands of feet up or down the steep mountainside.

Fire control has become safer, more scientific, and more depend-

This observer on the Mount Hood National Forest in Oregon is ever alert for signs of fire.

A tractor makes a fire lane near the edge of a fire on the Boise National Forest in Idaho.

A smokejumper nears his landing spot on the Lolo National Forest in Montana.

ent on machinery. Firefighters turn more and more to the air for help rather than depend on hard work to dig a fire trench with a shovel or an ax and grubhoe. They look more to airtankers to cascade chemicals mixed in water to stop or slow down a fire, although the man on the ground with handtools may have to follow in quickly and hold the advantage gained by fast air attack. Besides 200 privately owned and contracted air tankers and 400 smokejumpers, the Forest Service air attack forces include many small, well-equipped "helitack" crews, who go by helicopters. Tankers, helipumpers—small waterpump tanks and accessories—and hoselaying helicopters are used widely. We expect to have self-guided, retardant-carrying bombs or missiles to carry more powerful suppressants and better chemicals, pushbutton controls to send them on their way, and computing machines to determine fire-burning conditions based on weather measurements.

Newer developments include fireproof clothing for firefighters, an aluminized fabric shelter for emergency protection of men caught in a fire, new pumps and mixers for chemicals, a new handheld burning torch for widening the fireline, new and larger maneuverable parachutes, new accessories for helicopter, and a wind machine to blow chemicals on the fire. Tests were made of a new trencher, or

A TBM plane drops borate slurry on the hot edge of a fire in Bitterroot National Forest in Montana.

line digger, which is a motor with flails on a stick. Forest Service men are continuing their search for a better retardant chemical and methods of dropping retardants that would permit air tankers to fly higher on their drops and thus be safer. The increased dependence on aircraft and ground line-building machines has given new importance to the skill and technical knowledge of the fire bosses. Their training program has developed to include national training in air operations, fire behavior, and fire generalship. A special training project, directed at finding better methods for teaching fire and air jobs, uses training machines and includes problems much like those encountered in real fires. Many Forest Service men devote their lifework to fire control; for others, it is only a part of their assignment. Many are seasonal employees hired as fire crewmen and lookouts. They must be trained quickly and well, even though they may be called on in only a few emergencies, or none at all. Firemen believe great changes in methods will come. Missiles, rockets, or similar devices may be used to carry chemicals to slow down and put out fires. Firemen some day may go to fires in one-man helicopters or large ones that carry an entire crew. Television and infrared detectors, possibly in balloons or satellites, will discover fires almost as soon as they start. Research discoveries on the effects of weather, fuel, slope, and other factors in a fire, and fast computers will decide the action to be taken and automatically set into motion the whole complex firefighting operation. *(Merle S. Lowden)*

A fire crewman jumps from a helicopter in the San Gabriel Mountains, Angeles National Forest, California.

Large fans have been used experimentally to control fires in heavy brush.

Help for the Forest Owner

A FARMER had some wornout acres on which big gullies were forming. Encouraged by a neighbor, who had planted a windbreak on the advice of the local farm forester, he decided to put the idle land into timber. He invited the farm forester to look it over and tell him about trees that were best suited to his land; when, where, and how to order them; and how to plant them. The farmer got an application form from the county agent and sent it to the State nursery. His seedlings were delivered to a central point in the county, where he picked them up. Because planting by hand required more time and help than he had, he had a contractor with a planting machine do it for him. The farm forester, a State employee in a cooperative program with the Forest Service, gave the farmer advice on how to care for and protect the seedlings. He also advised him of the help he could get under the Agricultural Conservation Program and referred him to the county office for more information. Had the farmer's land been eroded so seriously that it had too much runoff and sediment during heavy rains, he could have got help under the Cooperative Watershed Protection and Flood Prevention Program. Measures to retard waterflow and stabilize soil would have been applied with the cost shared by the farmer, the State, and the Federal Government. The forester decided that tree planting was enough.

The importance of this cooperative effort is that about 70 million acres of non-Federal land need reforestation and an additional million acres could be planted to windbreaks. Under Section 4 of the Clarke-McNary Act, which has been in effect since 1924, the States are responsible for producing, or acquiring, and distributing trees to those who want to reforest their lands. The Forest Service reimburses the State in part with funds furnished under this act for any loss it may have incurred in these operations. The Forest Service also furnishes technical advice and guidance to the State nurseries. Under this cooperative plan, known as C–M 4, nearly a billion trees were distributed in 1960 by 48 States and Puerto Rico. More than 7 billion trees were so distributed in 1926–1960. Arizona and Alaska were not participating States in 1962.

The farmer's next step was to consult the State Forester about how to protect the seedlings from fire, insects, and disease. The State Forester told him that the State would do everything possible to protect his forest land against these dangers. More than 400 million acres of non-Federal forest and watershed lands in all States except Arizona, in fact, were protected against fire in 1962 through the cooperative activities of the Federal and State governments and private efforts. Section 2 of the Clarke-McNary Act makes this cooperation possible on all forest land, potential forest land, and non-forest watershed lands. Not all such lands are under organized cooperative protection as yet, but as more funds and facilities become available the States will extend this protection to many more millions of acres. The State forest organizations are equipped and ready to meet fire emergencies. Several States may have an arrangement by which they provide mutual assistance during critical fire periods. Farmers help a lot in fire-prevention efforts by being careful with brush burning and cleanup fires, but about 100 thousand fires each year burn over 4 million acres. The Secretary of Agriculture is authorized by law to cooperate with States and local groups to suppress or control insects and diseases on all forest lands, regardless of ownership—the country cannot afford to have bugs and fungi kill more than 7 billion board feet of timber every year. Thirty-eight States in 1962 had laws for the control of forest pests.

The farmer's trees flourished, and once again he went for advice to the farm forester on the best way to manage a growing forest. The forester pointed out that through the Cooperative Forest Management Act of 1950, the State forestry departments of all States except Arizona and Hawaii cooperate with the Federal Government

A farmer in New York and a forester from the State Forester's office plan the management of a small woodlot.

A forester from the State Forester's office in Rhode Island and a landowner discuss the removal of a merchantable red oak.

to bring improved management to small woodland owners, and to help timber operators and small sawmill operators to improve manufacturing techniques and plant efficiency.

The Agricultural Conservation Program (ACP) of the Department of Agriculture, begun in 1936, was set up to help defray costs of planting trees, thinning crowded stands, pruning young stands, eliminating weed trees, and practicing other good forestry methods on farmland. A farmer can get in touch with his local Agricultural Stabilization and Conservation Committee and work out a program of forest improvement in keeping with the standards of the committee. Federal payments of 50 to 80 percent of the cost would follow satisfactory completion of his work.

Twenty years after he had put out the seedlings, the farmer had a fine stand of trees that adds to the beauty of his farm, checks erosion, attracts wildlife, and provides a steady income. He can use the Naval Stores Conservation Program, which gives cost-sharing benefits to those who use improved naval stores conservation and forestry practices; this is an income in addition to that received from other forest products. What did it cost him? The price of the seedlings and planting and the care that is required to bring to maturity any valuable farm crop. *(William J. Stahl)*

245

More Water from the Mountains

THE FARMS, ranches, industries, and cities on the plains in Colorado get most of their water from the high mountains that hold ice and snow in cold storage until the time of greatest need. Water always has been scarce there. The first settlers claimed water as property, knowing that without it their land was worthless. Never has there been enough water on these lands to match man's dreams. Men have led water through the passes and through tunnels under the mountains. They have stored it in reservoirs. Yet always there is a need for more water. We continue to study Nature and search for new ideas in the hope that her methods can be improved. The Fraser Experimental Forest is one place where these new ideas are born and tested by the Forest Service, the custodian and manager for most of the Rocky Mountain watershed. These lands provide timber, forage, wildlife habitat, and recreation, but water receives major emphasis in the research at Fraser. Its 36-square-mile mountain watershed is a field laboratory for land managers. It is divided into smaller tributary watersheds that reach from the lodgepole pines at 9,000-feet elevation up through the spruce-fir forest to the windswept, treeless alpine zone above 11,000 feet.

Researchers began work at Fraser just before the Second World War. Their first assignment was to see how trees affected the accumulation and melting of snow. Observers had often noted that trees affect the snowpack in contrasting ways. A favorable effect is that trees protect snow from sun and wind. An unfavorable effect is the trapping of falling snow on limbs and branches, where much of it evaporates without reaching the ground. Measurements were started to determine the magnitudes of these different influences. All during the winter months, the depth and water content of snow were measured at many places under different kinds and arrangements of trees and in different sizes of openings. This was done by pushing a tube with a special cutting bit through the snow to the soil beneath. The tube and the snow within it were then weighed to determine how much water the snow contained. From hundreds of such measurements, the amount of snow that did reach the ground was determined. Most snow was found under aspen trees, a little less in the open, and much less under dense lodgepole pine.

Evaporation rates also were studied. Many difficulties have been encountered in this work, and we have no satisfactory comparisons yet of evaporation from snow in different situations, but by combining various methods with a little guessing we have been able to make estimates. On this basis, evaporation was believed to be about four times greater in the open than under a dense stand of pine trees. This difference in evaporation is too small to offset the amount of snow held by the dense pine foliage and evaporated there. Observations on melting confirmed the belief that snow melted much earlier in the open than under the shade of dense trees. There are even more spectacular differences between north and south slopes and with elevation. The influence of tree cover on melt rate has yet to receive full attention at Fraser. The total quantity of melt water was considered to be of first importance.

These and other observations brought out the danger of clearing all trees from a large area. This would cause the fierce mountain winds to tumble snow completely out of unprotected openings. Here again, researchers are not fully satisfied with present knowledge and available test methods. A complex of factors, including wind, exposure to the sun, topography, elevation, and climate, are involved. As soon as an opening is large enough for wind to funnel into it, the snow is moved to some protected area, which usually is a patch of trees. Evidence gathered so far indicates that an opening is most efficient as a snow trap if it is at least twice as wide as the height of surrounding trees. The maximum permissible size depends on the exposure and on whether drifted snow will be trapped nearby. Openings should not be more than 10 tree heights wide unless it can be readily demonstrated that larger openings will hold snow or that it will be blown to a spot where it is needed.

Testing the first results on plots was the next step. In dense stands of lodgepole pine saplings, we reduced the number of trees by one-half. This gave a 20-percent increase in accumulated snow water. In mature lodgepole pine, plots 8 acres in area (about 600 feet square) were laid out. All merchantable trees were cut on some; on others, cutting removed one-fourth, one-half, and three-fourths of the trees. No cutting was done on check plots. The increase in snowpack was 29 percent where all trees were cut. The increase on the intermediate degrees of cut was in proportion to the amount cut. For example, where half the trees were cut, the increase was 13 percent—just about one-half the 29-percent increase where all trees were taken. Other plots were laid out to test the results of strip and other cutting patterns. The general conclusion was that, under Fraser conditions and with cut areas protected by surrounding forest, the proportion of tree cover removed—not the pattern of cutting—was the determining factor in the accumulation of snow. Opening the canopy did increase the rate of melting. In fact, it was increased so much that snow disappeared at the same time on cut and uncut plots. This indicated that the possible in-

crease to streamflow from opening the forest canopy would be produced during the spring freshet and not later in the season.

With this knowledge, the Forest Service was ready to see what happened when the timber on one of the smaller Fraser watersheds was harvested. The cutting system chosen was alternate-strip clear-cutting, favored by foresters because it provides for regenerating subalpine forests. The watershed specialists like the method because it results in a pattern of protected openings. In this system, clear-cut strips alternate with uncut strips to form a checkerboard pattern. The trees on the uncut strips are not logged until new tree growth is established on the strips first cut. This perpetuates the checkerboard arrangement. The watershed chosen was 714 acres in size. Streamflow had been measured for this and a neighboring watershed for several years. The flow from the two areas was so closely comparable that one could be used as a control to determine the effect of timber harvest on the other.

Cutting on the test area was completed between 1954 and 1956. Widths of cut and uncut strips ranged from 30 to 400 feet (from one-half tree height to seven times tree height). No trees were cut within 90 feet of the stream. All live trees larger than 4 inches in diameter on cut strips were made into logs, poles, mine props, and pulpwood. Slash was lopped and scattered. There were 550 acres of merchantable forest on the watershed, of which 55 percent was lodgepole pine and the remainder was spruce-fir. The trees cut on the strips and in the clearing for roads amounted to half of the total timber volume. Water yield after cutting was increased. In 5 years, 1956–1960, the streamflow would have been 11.4, 19.6, 11.4, 10.5, and 11.1 area inches, respectively, if there had been no cutting. The increases as a result of cutting were 4.2, 3.4, 2.1, 3.1, and 3.9, respectively. Nearly all of the increased flow takes place during the spring melting period of May and June. In places where the snowpack is deeper than in the central Rockies, it is probable that timber harvest might have more effect on the timing of water yield. These possibilities are being investigated in the California Sierras. Two different approaches toward timing have been taken at Fraser. One, in recognition of the need for regulation of flow by reservoirs, has been to improve the accuracy of forecasting the streamflow. The other is research in the alpine snowfields to add more usable water to this important source of late-season streamflow.

Reliable forecasting of streamflow from snow-fed streams is not easy. Because of the winter cold storage, there is little flow until spring. Then it comes off in a rush. Three-fourths of the year's

Fraser Experimental Forest in Colorado is a rugged chunk of the central Rocky Mountains. Its peaks extend above 12 thousand feet and reach above timberline. The forest belt has lodgepole pine, Engelmann spruce, and alpine fir.

A 714-acre watershed has a pattern of alternate cut and uncut strips—a way to harvest timber and improve water yields. An air traveler approaching Denver from the west sees this checkerboard.

From the ground one sees an attractive landscape of intermingled trees and openings. Such an arrangement traps snow and protects it from sun and wind. Abundant browse and shelter favor mule deer.

The forest in early summer. Fierce winds scour the snow from exposed areas and pile it in protected places. Thus late summer flow is enhanced, for the snow would melt faster if it were evenly distributed.

flow may leave in 30 days. To add to the difficulties, snow melts during the day and freezes at night; each day the flow fluctuates from flood to dribble. Reservoir operators want to fill their reservoirs, regulate diversions efficiently, make all the electricity they can, and prevent floods downstream. This cannot be done without forecasting peak flows, daily runoff, and total flow for weeks, months, and seasons. Many schemes were tried, but forecasting daily total flows and peaks continued to be a difficult problem on snow-fed streams. At Fraser, the Forest Service and the Bureau of Reclamation collaborated to develop ways of predicting amounts and timing of snowmelt. With this pooling of skills and with the past information collected at Fraser, rapid progress has been made. The results obtained, which are now in routine use in operation of reservoirs,

Measurements of evaporation on a summer snowfield. A plastic tank is set with its top level with the surrounding snow. A false bottom allows melt water to flow out of the snow. Repeated weighings give the loss by evaporation or gain by condensation.

Probing in a fence-test area to measure the depth of trapped snow. Drifted snow packs to a higher density than freshly fallen snow.

have paid off by saving water and preventing property damage downstream.

The alpine snowpack is receiving increasing attention. If efficient ways can be found to increase snow storage in the deep drifts of the mountaintops, late-season streamflows can be improved. Fortunately, the snow above timberline is not evenly distributed. If it were, it would all melt early in the year. Instead, it accumulates into deep drifts, some more than 40 feet deep. These drifts prolong the melt period. Some of them melt out completely only in the warmest and driest years. The scientists decided to examine this system, too. The first question to be answered involved a controversy. Some people said that at these high elevations evaporation disposed of most of the snow. Others said that the mountain snowfields were the key to late-season flow. This question was not hard to answer. Rather simple evaporation measurements and climatic observations showed that evaporation from summer snow was insignificant. In fact, it was often completely offset by condensation. When moist air was present, water condensed on the snow just as it does on a cold windowpane. The next step was to see how much water might be derived from the snowfields. The melting rate turned out to be amazingly constant. During summer months, it is just about 2 feet of snow depth per week. The summer snow is more than one-half water by volume. Each week's melt produces a little more than 1 acre-foot of water per acre of snow surface. Thus, a drift 10 feet deep on July 1 will last until early August, and each acre will yield 5 acre-feet of streamflow.

Tests have begun to show more about snowdrifting, terrain, and season. Various kinds, heights, and arrangements of snow fences are being tried. Another approach is to use surface coatings and chemicals to regulate melt rates. Often it would help if early season melting could be held back. Sometimes it might be beneficial to speed up melt. A few simple trials indicated that there are indeed possibilities. Melt rates were cut in half by a coating of sawdust and were increased by thin layers of lampblack. More effective kinds of substances remain to be tried.

Research at Fraser is far from finished. A great deal has been learned and put into practice, but much remains to be learned. The Fraser Experimental Forest is just one of the watershed research areas of the Forest Service. It is a small part of a nationwide research program aimed at developing methods for rehabilitating damaged watersheds; protecting soil and water while the land is also being used for timber production, grazing, wildlife habitat, and recreation; and increasing water yields and improving seasonal distribution of streamflow. This coordinated effort is required if our wildland watersheds are to meet the growing demands for their resources. (*Marvin D. Hoover* and *Elmer W. Shaw*)

Snoqualmie

A LEGEND of the Snoqualmie Indians is that the inhabitants of the moon came to earth, settled in and near what is now the Snoqualmie National Forest of Washington, and founded the Snoqualmie Tribe. The moon voyagers could scarcely have picked a more bountiful and beautiful land. Other wanderers in the course of time came to know the open, semiarid country on the east side and the dense, unbroken forests on the west side of the mountains that cut through this country. Indians, trappers, prospectors, immigrants, and soldiers moved about the Cascade Range, which was home to some, possible treasure trove to others, and an obstacle to many whose sights were farther west to Puget Sound.

The Snoqualmie National Forest now encompasses much of this land of historic interest, scenic beauty, and economic value. Snoqualmie, almost as large as Delaware, is one of 155 National Forests, which cover more than 181 million acres. It is representative of the other National Forests not necessarily in terrain, size, or vegetation, but in the scope of activities and the policies that govern their administration. Snoqualmie is divided into six ranger districts. Its operations are directed from Seattle, Wash., by the forest supervisor and his staff. From there the line of authority extends to the regional forester's office in Portland, Oreg., and then to the office of the Chief Forester in Washington, D.C. Like most other National Forests, Snoqualmie is a major water producer for industry, agriculture, and homes in and near the cities of Everett, Tacoma, Yakima, and Seattle and many smaller communities whose existence also depends on adequate water supplies. Industry east of the Cascades and agriculture on both sides of that range—especially in the irrigated Yakima Valley, with its tremendous investments in fruit groves—have heavy stakes in this water resource. The forest is managed to extract the fullest use from it.

Also important is Snoqualmie's store of renewable, merchantable timber. More than 20 billion board feet of Douglas-fir, western hemlock, ponderosa pine, and other forest trees clothe the slopes and valleys of the Cascades. The application of the sustained-yield principle to timber production on the forest—by which the amount of timber taken out is balanced by the amount of new growth—assures industry of a continuous supply of wood. Timber harvesting is an all-year activity on Snoqualmie. Mature trees selected by for-

Goat Rocks Primitive Area, Snoqualmie National Forest, Washington.

esters in accordance with scientific plans of management are advertised and sold to the highest bidder and logged according to Forest Service specifications. Proceeds from timber sales, which in 1961 amounted to more than 2 million dollars, go to the United States Treasury after 25 percent has been earmarked for State distribution to the counties from which the resource came and 10 percent is made available to the Forest Service for roads and trails. The counties use their part of the money for schools and roads.

More and more people each year discover the magnificent opportunities for sport and relaxation on Snoqualmie. There are picnic areas for one-day outings, campgrounds for family campers, the Cascade Crest Trail for hikers and horsemen, the Goat Rocks Wild Area for the lover of the wilderness, and organization camps for youngsters. In summer, an outing in the Forest offers relief from the heat of Yakima Valley. In winter, ski enthusiasts are drawn to Snoqualmie Pass and White Pass, areas developed and operated privately under permit from the Forest Service. As host to people who use Snoqualmie's 250 campgrounds and more than 250 thousand acres specially designated for recreation, the Forest Service extends a cordial welcome. All it asks of forest visitors is that they keep the campgrounds clean and be careful with fire.

This is Federal property, but State fish and game laws apply, and forest officers cooperate with the State in their enforcement. In managing wildlife, the Forest Service tries to maintain always a balance between the numbers of wildlife and the capacity of the forest environment to support them. Thus, hunting is more than

254

Mountain goats on the Snoqualmie.

Water from Snoqualmie flows to orchards in the Naches Valley.

A good stand of young trees assures sustained yields of timber.

just sport; it is a way of harvesting animals that otherwise could build up in numbers to the point that they would starve or cause unnecessary damage to the Forest through overbrowsing. On this, as on most National Forests, timber harvests and other special practices are timed to produce favorable food and cover conditions for wildlife. Grazing by domestic livestock, by permit, is another forest use on Snoqualmie. Forage types, extensive enough to support these animals, grow on two ranger districts east of the Cascades, the Naches and the Tieton. Here, continuing a land use which started before Snoqualmie was established, the Forest Service manages the range resource. This involves controlling the numbers of grazing livestock and seasons of grassland use, increasing production of forage, and generally improving the range conditions.

Through fire-prevention programs, research into better ways of fighting fires, early detection, and trained crews, the foresters in charge of Snoqualmie have been effective in reducing the number of man-caused fires and in limiting the number of acres burned each year. Research, detection, and control are also required for the constant struggle against insects and disease. The struggle is worth it: As lands of work and play, beauty and practical usefulness, prime necessities and intangible values, the National Forests are precious possessions. *(Morris Mash)*

From Ox to Helitug

THE LOGGER'S main aim a hundred years ago was to deliver logs to the millpond at least cost and with little attention to the remaining trees, fire hazard, and the slopes he left naked. Now we are concerned about sustained yield, soil erosion, and water yield. Logging therefore has changed. Logging has several operations. A tree is felled, the process of separating it from its stump. It is limbed and bucked, operations that include removing limbs and cutting the tree into logs or bolts. Logs or bolts are then yarded or skidded to the mill or to a transportation route. A hundred years ago driving logs, or transport by water, was in common use to carry logs long distances to the millsite. Later railroad logging was introduced. Then huge trucks became the main method of transport. Some methods of the past are still used, but most logging operations are now highly mechanized.

The virgin forests a century ago were logged by rugged, reckless men. They used the ax and crosscut saw for felling, limbing, and bucking, which now are done largely with chainsaws powered by gasoline or electricity, but still with the help of the ax. Logging once depended on horse and oxen as motive power for skidding logs. To reduce ground friction, the logging wheel, a forerunner of the present logging arch, was invented. The horse and oxen eventually gave way to steam-driven cable skidders. Ground skidding was improved by the invention of high-lead and high-line skidding, whereby the logs were partly or wholly raised off the ground. Then, as the centers of logging moved to the West and South, came the gasoline- and diesel-driven engines for skidders and tractors. The logging arch replaced the logging wheel. The use of chokers or cable loops with special quick-coupling devices were used to bunch logs for skidding. Another means used then and now to carry logs to main transport routes is the timber flume, which usually is V-shaped in cross section. Water is used to lubricate the flume. Flumes may be hundreds to thousands of feet long.

Oldtimers used cant hooks and peavies for rolling logs and guiding logs in the water. Brute strength gave way to levers and winches for hoisting logs. The parbuckle and crosshaul for loading logs has given way to mechanized loaders for handling logs or bunches of logs. Truck loaders today may be self-loaders or expensive but highly efficient individual loading units. The long haul

Felling a tamarack with a powersaw on Flathead National Forest in Montana.

Bucking a Sitka spruce on Tongass National Forest in Alaska.

Ground skidding Douglas-fir with a steam donkey in Oregon in 1918.

Skidding with a skyline crane in Colorado in 1955.

River drivers use peavies to break a logjam at Carrick Pitch in Maine.

from woods and mill has evolved from sled or wagon to water transport, to railroads, and to trucks as main vehicles. Even yet all of these methods are used. The white-water boys were one of the first of the special breed of men, the loggers. They decked logs at stream edge and then discharged or rolled them into the stream when waterflows were adequate. Flash-dams sometimes were constructed to back water for release during drives. Stream driving was hazardous. Nimble-footed men with pikes or peavies guided the flow and broke up logjams. This process has not changed much over the years, except that the safety helmet and life preserver have been introduced, symbolic of present-day concern for personal safety.

Railroad logging was introduced as the center of logging moved westward and southward from New England. Logs were skidded to railside by cable skidders and loaded on rail cars. Hundreds of miles of roadbed and wooden trestles were built. Specially designed steam engines were built to give traction. Log hauling is different from other transport in that the uphill pull is usually empty. In mountain country, curves were made sharp to cut down cost of roadbed and to help in braking trains on steep grades. The modern era of logging is characterized by a movement to log hauling by truck or truck and trailer. Special roads and trucks are used in many off-highway hauls to handle loads up to 125 tons gross vehicle weight. One operation uses trucks with bunks 16 feet wide and an empty weight greater than is allowed on highways in most States. Main-haul logging roads often are built to higher load capacity than main transcontinental highways.

New cable systems are being introduced to handle logging on steep mountains. Helicopters are being built to handle high-capacity loads. Lighter-than-air craft have been proposed. Pulp chips may be transported by pipelines from forest to mill. Helitug logging is being considered—the use of helicopter to tow balloon-lofted logs from stump to mill. The future may be symbolized by the distance we have progressed from the era when boards and timbers were pit sawn or hewn and carried by hand to place of use. Today automation is a word of hope to the timber industry.   *(J. J. Byrne)*

Loading lodgepole pine pulpwood bolts, Targhee National Forest, Idaho.

Silent Killers of the Forest

THE MAN with a hard hat and a backpack tank sprayed an oily mist on a young western white pine. An airplane flew overhead, depositing a cloud of the same oily mist on the tops of a growing pine forest. Both were using antibiotic drugs against blister rust, the white pine's worst enemy. Millions of these prime lumber trees in the West have been killed by blister rust. The economic drain and loss of timber have been enormous. Up to now, control meant toil and sweat and slow progress. It was literally a digging process—digging out gooseberry and currant bushes, host plants from which the spores of blister rust spread to nearby pines. Now the antibiotic fungicides, cycloheximide and phytoactin, are used, mixed in fuel oil. They were developed by scientists of the Forest Service and industry. Like the history-making achievements of penicillin in human therapy, antibiotic fungicides usher in a new era of disease control in forestry—an era that could mark the beginning of the end for many tree diseases besides white pine blister rust.

Plenty of insects and blights remain to worry the forest manager, although antibiotics are indicative of the headway being made against a multitude of pests. Insects kill more trees and diseases reduce the growth of our forests more severely than all other destructive agents combined, fire included. Trees killed each year by them contain enough wood to have built 730 thousand houses. The wood never produced or made useless because of their activity would have built 2 million more. The combined losses are about equal to the Nation's timber cut in 1962. Insects and diseases, furthermore, lower the quality of much of the wood that is produced and harvested by creating defects in the trunks of trees. They deform and weaken trees. They delay regeneration by destroying cones, seeds, and seedlings. Hundreds of forest pests—insects, fungi, bacteria, viruses, and nematodes—are responsible for this loss of forest productivity. Trees are susceptible throughout their lives. No species of tree or any of its parts—fruits, foliage, twigs, branches, bark, stems, and roots—are immune. Most of these pests have been with us always. The bark beetles, the dwarf-mistletoes, and the heart rots are examples. Some of the more destructive ones, like white pine blister rust, the gypsy moth, chestnut blight, balsam woolly aphid, and European pine shoot moth came from abroad. Not all insects and diseases should be blanketed in one indictment, for many are harmless or

Ranger Joe Gjertson checking on budworms on Umatilla National Forest in Oregon.

Spraying ribes in Franklin County, New York.

actually essential to forest vigor. By their activities they reincorporate dead trunks, limbs, leaves, and other litter into the forest soil. They are scavengers that convert wastes to useful purposes. Some insects and diseases prey on insects and diseases of diseases, all of which help to maintain Nature's biological balance.

Control projects are not launched just because there may be an insect or disease loose in the forest. The problem first must be defined, its present and potential threat evaluated, the values at stake appraised, and a biologically sound method of attack developed. Which insects or diseases are beneficial, which harmless, and which destructive? The identities of the destructive ones must be determined for all their various stages and their life histories worked out so points of weakness can be found. Next to be determined is where and at what stage does pest activity result in damage and how the forest environment, in turn, affects the activity of the pests. Still another step must be taken before control is started. We must

A mist blower is used to control insects in a young plantation of red pine in Michigan.

determine precisely where and when to attack a troublesome pest. Surveys and biological appraisals answer these questions. Unlike fire, where the smallest blaze is a threat to an entire forest, insect and disease outbreaks tend to develop slowly and insidiously. Often they never reach significant levels. They may develop for years before they are noticed by any but the experienced eye. Early detection favors early control, however, or at least opportunity to appraise the situation and determine whether any great damage would be done if Nature was left to follow her course unmolested. Again, as with fire, prevention often is more effective and cheaper in the long run than control. If we know which insects and diseases will be destructive in a favorable environment and the details of their life histories and modes of damage, often we can introduce preventive measures in our everyday forest management practices.

Sometimes there is no effective indirect approach to control, or indirect measures fail to check pest activity. More drastic action has to be taken then. At other times, opportunity for preventive action already has passed, and we must use a direct attack by chemical means. At still other times, direct control is more effective and cheaper than any other. The control of white pine blister rust by spraying trunks or needles of infected trees with antibiotics from the ground or from the air is an example. The use of DDT applied by aircraft has been the most reliable means of reducing epidemics of defoliating insects. Better chemicals are being developed almost daily, and insect predators and diseases having excellent promise of biological control are being found and introduced from abroad.

Time was when losses from insects and diseases could be tolerated because our forests seemed inexhaustible. Today most of our virgin forests have been cut over and the larger demands for forest products mean that we can no longer accept these losses. Better forest management will help to close the production gap. More access roads will make salvage and risk cuttings possible (so that killed trees and those too weakened by pests to survive until harvesttime can be utilized) and will permit more intensive cultural operations (so that we can keep our forests more sanitary, more vigorous, and hence more resistant to pests). Intensified management may also call for artificial regeneration, extensive plantings of single species, and sometimes a wholly unnatural forest environment— developments that could mean new pests or more serious epidemics. Furthermore, the dollar values at stake will be higher than in present and past natural stands. Fortunately, however, people have become more aware of the seriousness of the problem; we have more efficient detection systems and more effective means for combating the pests; and higher forest values will make it possible to incorporate more intensive control practices in everyday management. (*Warren V. Benedict*)

Forest in Winter

THE COLD COMES. The forest changes to a place of sunny splendor or howling mountain blizzard or white, sparkling serenity.

It rests, for another spring is not far behind; as for all vibrant life, the rest builds reserves for the demands of the summer.

The forest in winter is a place to play; a place where wild creatures hibernate or search for food; where tomorrow's homes stand in tall, straight trees; where next summer's water is stored in deep-packed snow; where rangelands sleep in repose; where the hunter tramps with gun, and the forester tends his domain; a place of work and thought and measuring things.

A place to play: Millions of citizens come now to the National Forests for hunting, skiing, skating, tobogganing, snowshoeing, and ice fishing.

A place for animals: They are part of Nature's world. They have their reasons, too, for being, and for them man must protect and care for the forest if the animals are to flourish.

A factory for men's homes: From the forests comes the material to build chairs, tables, houses, barns, a thousand things. It is a factory that need never shut down if we keep it in repair.

A source of water: When spring winds warm the mountainside and melt the snow, the water flows to cities and farms on the plains below. Without that water there would be no cities and farms.

A place of grass on valley ranges and meadows and hillsides: It is next summer's food for grazing herds. The grass has withdrawn into its subterranean vitality, to emerge on the first invitation from spring.

Many faces has the forest in winter—a world of changing lights and weathers. While serving man in practical ways, it lifts his senses to the sublime.

Throughout our history, America's forests in winter—in all seasons—have been a great storehouse of resources, bountiful blessings to a favored country and a birthright to each American.

Now that there are many more millions of us, and more of us in crowded cities, each can but enlarge himself by knowing the forest better.

As William Wordsworth wrote, "One impulse from a vernal wood, may teach you more of man, of moral evil and of good, than all the sages can." *(Clifford D. Owsley)*

266

White Mountain National Forest in New Hampshire.

Green Mountain National Forest in Vermont.

San Isabel National Forest in Colorado.

Manti-LaSal National Forest in Utah.

Whitman National Forest in Oregon.

Coconino National Forest in Arizona.

Wasatch National Forest in Utah.

The World of Wild Things

IN A SMALL PATCH and in a vast wilderness there is a wonderful, intricate world of wild creatures. A beneficial kinship exists between man's dominion and Nature's and between wildlife and its home. This is especially true in this age when more and more people are intruding on Nature's world of wild things. We have gained much knowledge about this world and thereby a deeper appreciation and understanding of its scope.

Hunting and fishing may appear cruel to some, but is it not cruel to let an animal starve for lack of food later in the year? The legal, proper hunting of some game animals is a necessary way of helping Nature keep a balance between animals and available food. While man kills some animals and catches some fish, he also carefully tends the homes of others, and makes it possible for them to live, reproduce, and enjoy their wild freedom.

Creatures of the wild are a natural part of their environment; they are as much a part of the forest as the trees. The forest and its wild animals are inseparable, because the forest provides them with their daily and yearlong needs. There is cover for escape, hiding, rearing young, and for loafing. The forest provides many kinds of food. There is foliage from herbs and shrubs for the plant eaters and berries, nuts, and other fruits. The yield of seeds, acorns, hickory nuts, and other mast may equal several hundred pounds an acre.

A dense forest can be a poor home for some kinds of forest animals. Plants are shaded out, and there are no stands of wild shrubs or even young trees that may serve as food or cover for wildlife. Conversely, wherever a large tree falls or the forest is otherwise opened to the sun, the ground becomes covered with many kinds of vegetation. Wildlife tends to concentrate therefore along these edges of the forest where food and cover requirements are in relative abundance. A deer or a turkey can feed in the opening, yet scamper to dense forest for protection when it is alarmed. Foresters and wildlife managers understand these relationships and make use of this knowledge to improve the food and cover conditions. This management of habitat is carried on by creating openings, planting food, developing water sources for the forest animals, and harvesting timber.

Many forest areas are adapted to grazing by cattle, which tends to favor woody and forb species over the preferred grasses. This, in turn, tends to improve the habitat for deer and some other wildlife. Fire has a tremendous effect on habitat; it can change the environment to the benefit of some wildlife species and to the detriment of others.

Fish life in the streams is affected by the surrounding forest. Good forest cover prevents silting of water courses. Trout particularly need clean, pure water and continuing flows. Trees and decaying plant matter on the forest floor break up the impact of raindrops and filter the water into the soil and the underground reservoirs. Streambanks on well regulated streams are covered with vegetation, which provides shade to cool the water and cover, under which fish can rest.

In every animal community are many species that live by tooth and claw. They depend primarily on the prey species for their food; they, too, need cover and a place to rest. They usually are preyed on in turn by other predators, but ordinarily the total number of animals surviving from one breeding season to the next is not greatly affected by these natural relationships. *(Lloyd W. Swift)*

Young elk on the Bitterroot National Forest in Montana.

Hunting the javelina with bow and arrow on the Coronado National Forest in Arizona.

Wildlife openings and fringe plantings of pine on the Monongahela National Forest in West Virginia.

Deer in a wildlife management area, Nantahala National Forest in North Carolina.

Black bear cub in Glacier National Park in Montana.

Shiras moose in Hoodoo Lake, Lolo National Forest in Idaho.

The National Arboretum

THE UNITED STATES National Arboretum occupies 415 scenic acres in the Mount Hamilton section of the District of Columbia. Its higher hills overlook the Capitol and the Washington Monument to the south and, in the east, break in sudden drops to the Anacostia River. It is an educational institution. It is an outdoor museum, in which one can study many kinds of trees, shrubs, and other plants, which are arranged in pleasing patterns. The slopes of Mount Hamilton are color painted in April with 70 thousand azaleas of more than a thousand varieties. Several hundred camellias flower earlier in the month or again in November. There is a demonstration planting of street trees; 300 or more varieties of crabapples; 700 kinds of holly; collections of dogwood, magnolia, firethorn, viburnum, crapemyrtle; a garden of boxwood, peonies, daylilies; and so on. It is a research institution. The Arboretum uses such plants as these for cultural observation and in breeding and testing programs. It names new productions, and through the New Crops Research Branch of the Department of Agriculture it cooperates in the introduction of new plants and seeds from foreign countries and in their multiplication and dissemination to other botanic gardens of this country. It maintains collections of living and dried plants for the study of plant relationships and the identification of specimens from homeowners and nurserymen. It publishes research findings and provides leaflets for its visitors.

It is a place for recreation. It is not a picnic area and is not a park in the usual sense, but the Arboretum offers opportunity for the diversions of observation and study and walking its many trails among planted displays and stream-edged woodlands. When the azaleas are in bloom, 20 thousand persons may visit the Arboretum in a day. Volunteer guides assist with the tours of scheduled horticultural groups. At all seasons there is a steady flow of callers — tourists, scientists, gardeners, and schoolchildren. The Arboretum may be visited free of charge Monday through Friday from 8:00 a.m. to 4:30 p.m. throughout the year and on Saturdays and Sundays during the principal display periods of April–May and October–November. It is open to car traffic, and the main gates are readily approached via Maryland Avenue from downtown Washington.

A century ago a few persons dreamed of an arboretum in the National Capital that would be in its field what the Smithsonian

Among the azaleas at the National Arboretum in Washington, D.C.

Naturalistic plantings in Fern Valley.

Camellia Trail at the Arboretum.

The architect's model of the new laboratory-administration building.

Institution and the National Zoological Park are in theirs and that would take a place among the world's national botanic gardens, which long have been noted for their contributions to botany, agriculture, and the general sciences no less than for their public services in pleasurable education and recreation. The first attempt to transform this dream to reality was in a plan developed in 1901 by a commission, which later became the National Commission of Fine Arts, for a combined botanic garden-arboretum in the Washington area. With the support of the Department of Agriculture, the Congress in 1927 approved a bill that directed the Secretary of Agriculture "to establish and maintain a national arboretum for purposes of research and education concerning tree and plant life." The acquisition of land and early planning were directed by F. V. Coville and B. Y. Morrison, within the Division of Plant Exploration and Introduction. Dr. Coville was principal botanist of the Department of Agriculture. Mr. Morrison was principal horticulturist and head of the division before he became the first director of the Arboretum in 1951. The National Arboretum now is administered by the Crops Research Division of the Agricultural Research Service. The development of operational and research facilities has accelerated since 1950. Such facilities include a stone gatehouse, brick-faced service buildings, more than 9 miles of paved access roads, three imposing gateways, two service residences, a range of five 100-foot greenhouses, and a new headquarters-laboratory building, which provides office space, laboratories, an auditorium-exhibit hall for public use, a library, and a modern herbarium. *(Henry T. Skinner)*

274

Animals

New Breeds and Types

LIVESTOCK on American farms a century ago were mostly the descendents of nonpedigree types brought from Europe by settlers, who usually were too busy subduing a new land to put much effort into improvement of animals. By 1862, though, the Spanish Merino was well established in the United States and had been extensively modified by breeders here. Trial importations of several European breeds of sheep and other species had been made. Development was well along on native strains, which would emerge shortly as the American breeds of swine. The establishment of these breeds and the extensive importation of purebred cattle and sheep from Europe were well along by 1900. Imported breeds today dominate many sectors of our livestock production, but efforts of our scientists and the genius of American breeders have brought about the development of new breeds at perhaps a more rapid pace than at any time in history. Some of them have a commanding place in an industry. Some fit special niches or overcome specific conditions to which no existing breed was adapted.

The traditional American breeds of swine—Duroc, Poland China, Spotted (or Spotted Poland China), Chester White, and others less numerous—can be considered new, because none was established firmly a century ago. All were developed by private American breeders from foundation stocks based on crosses and the intermingling of older types imported from many parts of the world. The Hampshire usually is included in this group, although its origin is obscure. It may have descended entirely from an English breed of a similar color pattern. In any event, it has been greatly modified by American breeders. Intense selection in all these breeds for meat-type—that is, a high proportion of lean cuts and a minimum of fat—has resulted in a great modification, as compared to the older lard-type, which was favored when lard was a more valuable product.

The Department of Agriculture and the Iowa Agricultural Experiment Station in 1934 imported a number of Danish Landrace hogs, a breed developed in Denmark with intense selection for both performance and the production of high-quality bacon carcasses. Crosses of American breeds with the Landrace and subsequent intermating of the cross-progeny gave rise to several new, mildly inbred lines, several of which can be termed breeds. These include (with the foundation breeds and developing institution in parentheses): The

LORD WENLOCK.

Suffolk Boar, imported by Col. Lewis G. Morris, of Fordham, N. Y.

A drawing in the "Report of the Commissioner of Agriculture for the Year 1863."

Minnesota No. 1 (Landrace-Tamworth; Minnesota Agricultural Experiment Station); Beltsville No. 1 (Landrace-Poland China; the Department of Agriculture); Montana No. 1 (Landrace-Hampshire; the Department of Agriculture and Montana Agricultural Experiment Station); Palouse (Landrace-Chester White; Washington Agricultural Experiment Station); and Maryland No. 1 (Landrace-Berkshire; Maryland Agricultural Experiment Station and the Department of Agriculture). Other lines developed with none or only a little Landrace blood include the Minnesota No. 2 (Yorkshire-Poland China; Minnesota Agricultural Experiment Station); and Beltsville No. 2 (principally Yorkshire and Hampshire with a little Duroc and Landrace; the Department of Agriculture). These new strains have been used commercially and are recommended principally for crossing with other lines or breeds in systematic programs. Under terms of the original Landrace importation, pure Landrace swine could not be released for general use in the United States. This provision was later modified, and private breeders have established the American Landrace on the basis of purebred animals of the original importation and animals carrying a small proportion (one-sixteenth to one sixty-fourth) of Poland China blood. Subsequent importations of Landrace swine from Norway and Sweden also have been incorporated into the breed, which has become the third ranking breed in terms of numbers registered.

The Western sheep industry had a problem. The Rambouillet and Merino are fine-wool breeds that are vigorous and hardy, flock well, and produce wool of fine quality. They tend, however, to be deficient in size and in quality of meat. British medium- and long-wool breeds are excellent in meat qualities, but they tend to be deficient in characteristics in which the fine-wool breeds excel. Recog-

A Palouse gilt.

A young Spotted boar. The breed formerly was known as Spotted Poland China.

nizing these problems, scientists in the Department of Agriculture in 1912 made initial crosses between a long-wool mutton breed, the Lincoln, and fine-wool Rambouillets to investigate the feasibility of combining the good qualities of both in a new breed. Subsequent intermating and selection within the crossbreds led to a

278

Somebody in the 1860's considered this to be the ideal type of Shorthorn bull.

Polled Shorthorn.

new breed, the Columbia, which has had a large influence on the western sheep industry directly and through the stimulation of the production of this type of sheep by breeders. The Targhee is another new breed developed by the Department on a foundation similar to that of the Columbia; it has a higher proportion of Rambouillet inheritance. Private breeders in the United States have utilized the Corridale, a breed developed in New Zealand in the 19th century from crosses of the fine-wool Merino and the Lincoln and Leicester long-wool breeds. Private breeders also have been active in the development of breeds and have produced the Panama, Romeldale, Debouillet, and Montadale—all based on crossbred foundations—and a few other strains that have had only limited distribution.

The breeds of beef cattle that were imported from the British Isles dominate the industry in most parts of the country. More than 95 percent of total registrations are of these breeds. They did not prove satisfactory to many cattlemen in the South, however, apparently because they lacked resistance to heat and insects, and fared poorly on coarse, tropical-type forages. Zebu-type cattle introduced from India tolerate heat and insects better, but they did not meet requirements as to carcass and were deficient in reproduction and rate of growth in many places in the South. The American Brahman was created by breeders in this country from an amalgamation of several Indian Zebu breeds. In a sense, it is itself a new creation. Observations on crossbreds of British and Zebu breeds indicated that for many areas they met needs better than purebreds of either type. Decisions therefore were made to interbreed the crossbreds with the purpose of founding new breeds. The first such attempt was by the King Ranch of Texas, where crossing of the Brahman and Shorthorn breeds culminated in the development of the Santa Gertrudis, which has become popular in many parts of the United States and in several other countries.

After observing results of crossing the Angus and Brahman breeds by the Department of Agriculture and the Louisiana Agricultural Experiment Station at Jeanerette, La., Frank Buttram and Raymond Pope of Oklahoma undertook the development of a new breed, the Brangus, based on such a crossbred foundation. Other breeds or strains developed on similar foundations include the Beefmaster, which was developed on a Brahman-Shorthorn-Hereford foundation by the Lasater Ranch in Texas and Colorado, and the Charbray, developed from crosses of the Brahman and the Charolais, a French breed. The development of polled types within existing breeds, Hereford and Shorthorn, since 1900 has been an outstanding achievement of private American breeders with both the Hereford and Shorthorn breeds. About one-third of all Herefords and Shorthorns now are of the polled type. *(Everett J. Warwick)*

American Brahman. This breed was developed in the United States. Animals of this type have served as one foundation of several other new breeds.

Santa Gertrudis.

Feeding Livestock

CHEMISTS years ago developed methods by which they could analyze feeds and have the constituents sum to 100 percent. Chemists and physiologists concluded therefrom that protein, fats, carbohydrates, and certain mineral elements were the only nutrients animals required. Data from experiments made it clear, however, that the quality of the ration and its ability to promote growth could not be predicted accurately on the basis of its chemical composition. Animal husbandmen then began to speak of "specific effects of nutrients" to account for improved results when certain foods were included in the ration. Chemical studies later showed that proteins of different sources yielded different proportions of amino acids, the building blocks of proteins. It also became known that the different proteins varied in quality or biological value, an expression of efficiency for maintenance and growth of animal life, depending on the combination of specific amino acids. The amino acids subsequently were grouped as essential and nonessential. We now know the amino acid composition of proteins as determined chemically and microbiologically, and we can supplement deficient proteins with specific amino acids or with other proteins rich in the needed amino acids. The latter method is commonly used today in the feeding of livestock.

The quality of protein or its biological value is not an important consideration in terms of the ruminant because the proteins largely are broken down and resynthesized into bacterial protein by the bacteria in the rumen. The bacterial protein is then utilized by the ruminant. Thus, if an essential amino acid is missing in the original protein, it will be synthesized by the rumen bacteria and thus become available to the ruminant. Even synthetically produced urea, a nonprotein source of nitrogen that contains no amino acids, can be utilized by the rumen bacteria to synthesize amino acids and bacterial protein. The use of urea as a substitute for part of the "protein source" for ruminants has been one of the important advances of the century in animal feeding.

Recognition of the importance of calcium and phosphorus for bone formation and of common salt in the diet of animals dates back many years, but the real needs and functions of calcium, phosphorus, sodium, and chlorine began to be understood less than 100 years ago. Then came the recognition of the essential nature of other elements, such as magnesium, sulfur, potassium, iron, and iodine. There followed a series of discoveries on trace minerals that have added copper, cobalt, manganese, fluorine, zinc, and selenium to the list. Iron, copper, and cobalt were found to be essential for the formation of blood hemoglobin. All classes of livestock require all the essential mineral elements, but the actual needs vary with the state of development and function. The likelihood of deficiencies in farm animals varies widely, depending on the feed supplies, their restrictions in use, and the effects of local deficiencies in soils and plants.

Especially dramatic have been discoveries of local deficiencies in phosphorus and cobalt that affected cattle and sheep. Another example is the development of corrective measures for iodine deficiency associated with goiter in the Great Lakes region, the Dakotas, and Montana. Confinement feeding of swine and poultry has led to development of abnormalities that have produced discoveries of mineral deficiencies, such as manganese in poultry and zinc in swine. Much interest has centered in the role of selenium as a required nutrient, especially in calves and lambs. We now recognize fine distinctions between excesses of certain elements that produce toxic effects and amounts too low to meet essential body needs. An example is selenium. Certain areas became recognized as unhealthy for raising livestock, and the trouble was identified as excess of selenium in the forage and grain crops. The reverse has been found to be true in other sections. Research since 1920 has clarified problems of too little phosphorus, copper, cobalt, and iodine and too much fluorine, selenium, and molybdenum. Research continues on interrelations of some of these and other mineral elements. Quantitative requirements of cattle, sheep, swine, and poultry have been established for most of those elements, so that feeding practices now have eliminated many of the obscure livestock disorders.

An outstanding development in the nutrition of farm animals was the discovery and identification of the vitamins. Research since 1920 has helped us identify many abnormal conditions as due to a deficiency of one or more factors. The vitamin requirements of ruminants are quite simple, since many of the vitamins, especially the water-soluble ones, are synthesized through bacterial action in the rumen. As far as we know, only three are required by ruminants— the fat-soluble vitamins A, D, and E. Good farm rations usually furnish enough of them, with the exception of vitamin D, which is derived largely from sunshine. Good forage is the primary source of carotene, or provitamin A. Some vitamin D is likewise contained in forages, sun-cured hays being richer than the growing plants. Vitamin E is in concentrates and forages. The single-stomach animals, such as pigs and chickens, depend on their feed for other vitamins, besides A, D, and E. Swine require also thiamine, riboflavin, niacin, pantothenic acid, choline, pyridoxine, pteroylglutamic acid, biotin, and cobalamin. Requirements for some are very low, and natural feeds contain more than enough to meet the needs. The important factors from a possible deficiency standpoint are vitamin A, vitamin D, riboflavin, niacin, pantothenic acid, and cobalamin. Some other factors for swine and chickens still are incompletely identified and may be required. The vitamins required by chickens include A, D, E, K, thiamine, riboflavin, pantothenic acid, niacin, pyridoxine, biotin, choline, pteroylglutamic acid, and cobalamin. Turkeys require essentially the same vitamins as chickens.

Hormones, antibiotics, enzymes, arsenicals, and other chemicals distinct from the usual nutrient substances often are added now to livestock rations. Many have been tested, but only a few have been put to practical farm use. Some raise the rates of growth and efficiency in the use of feed by growing animals. Some have increased production of milk and eggs. The antibiotics particularly have found wide practical use since their effect on growth was found out in 1949. The mode of action still is not clearly understood, but we attach importance to the beneficial effects they have in controlling unfavorable micro-organisms in the alimentary tract. The antibiotics have been most useful in the rearing of young pigs and calves and in the production of broilers, presumably by lowering such stress factors as disease organisms.

The important functions of hormones in growth and reproduction have prompted investigators to determine the possible additive or counteractive effects of supplying hormone or hormonelike chemicals to animals through the diet or by implantation under the skin. Feedstuffs, such as certain legume forages, contain substances that have hormonal properties, sometimes in sufficient amounts to affect the animals that eat them. Stilbestrol, a hormonelike chemical, has had wide use in the fattening of beef cattle in feedlots. Here there has been a material advantage in rate of gain and efficiency of feed utilization without attendant danger of residues of the drug in the meat under prescribed conditions of use. The use of stilbestrol is also regulated for the fattening of lambs. Of the several other classes of feed additives, the arsenicals have probably shown more consistent promise of benefit than the others. Fowler's solution once was widely used as a tonic for livestock, but now we are more interested in organic arsenicals. Tranquilizers have been tested in feeding, but the benefits have been small.

By combining the required nutrients, protein, energy, vitamins, and minerals in proper amounts in relation to each other, we have developed balanced rations that animals utilize to a maximum extent with a minimum of wastage of the nutrients. The greatest possible amount of meat, milk, and wool thus is produced per pound of feed. Too much or too little of any particular nutrient

284

make an imbalance, and the feed is not used efficiently. An animal usually eats more of a ration balanced in every respect than one that is not balanced. This effect contributes greatly toward efficient production, since body maintenance is the first charge against the day's intake of feed, and all nutrients above maintenance in the balanced ration go into the production of meat, wool, and milk.

The pattern of feeding dairy cattle in the past has been to obtain 75 to 80 percent of the required nutrients from forages, including pasture. Considerable emphasis has been placed therefore on the quality of the forage—that is, harvesting the forage at an early stage of maturity and utilizing methods that retain the leaves and reduce weather damage during curing. Such high-quality forage retains its green color, is high in digestibility, is acceptable to the animal, and has high nutritive value. The first cutting of hay crops declines in digestibility at the rate of 0.05 percent for each day it is delayed after the vegetative stage of growth. Thus the date of cutting is important, but it varies in different parts of the country, depending on weather. Services have been set up in some States to make chemical analyses for certain constituents, such as protein and crude fiber, and to determine the dry matter in the forage. Such guides are useful in feeding programs. Scientists have turned their attention toward developing artificial rumen techniques, which will determine indirectly the digestibility of forages. An artificial rumen, set up in the laboratory, uses rumen bacteria and glass containers to simulate the conditions in the rumen. A certain amount of forage is introduced into the device, which ferments and digests for several hours. We determine the indigestible residues and from them calculate the digestibility of the forage. The procedure, if it is refined, should help plant geneticists in testing strains or species of grasses or legumes.

There has been a trend toward feeding more concentrates to dairy herds. Each cow in 1942 received 1,365 pounds of concentrates; she received 2,050 pounds in 1959—a reason for the increased average

In this farm feedlot in Nebraska, cattle are fattened for market.

level of milk produced per cow. More than 32 percent of the concentrates fed to dairy cattle are commercially mixed feeds, which are carefully compounded and take into account comparative costs of the individual feeds in order to produce the most economical ration.

Among beef cattle, the age at which steers are marketed has trended downward from 3-4 years to 15-27 months. Feeding and management have been prime factors. Young cattle once were wintered through the first, second, and even third year on low planes of quantity and quality of feed. Now they are kept almost continuously on good to high levels of feeding. Some of the acceleration in growth rate has been achieved through the use of stilbestrol and other feed additives. The improvement in quality of feed is to be found in better forages, protein supplementation, sources of vitamin A and required minerals, and more adequate energy feeds. This is a reflection of the development and use of feeding standards and tables of nutrient requirements. More of the beef we eat today comes from animals finished in feedlots. The quality, or grade, of the carcass averages higher. Feedlot operations have expanded over the West, especially in large enterprises that market thousands of head yearly on a continuing basis. Rations are better balanced. The preparation and distribution of the feed are highly mechanized. Great progress has been made in elimination of nutritional deficiencies.

The self-feeder for hogs was developed when better balanced diets in terms of protein and mineral improvements were coming into widespread use. Feed grade tankage and then fishmeals were used. More and more oilseed meals suited for feeding hogs also became available. Soybean meal eventually headed the list of protein feeds. Old practices of feeding hogs on ear corn shoveled out from the corncribs or of slop-feeding ground grains soaked in skim milk, whey, or buttermilk gave way to self-feeding of corn, protein, and mineral supplements. Self-feeding saved labor and helped to pave the way for improvements in formulation of diets. Better breeding, management, and protection of health to utilize the full potentials of good nutrition cut in half the time a pig needs to reach marketing weight. The hog of today produces 100 pounds of gain on two-thirds of the feed a hog did in 1900.

The production of sheep in the United States has declined since 1940. Changes in feeding practices therefore have been less dramatic. Better nutrition has been achieved, nevertheless. Developments in the correction of nutrient deficiencies have aided the sheep farmer. An appreciation of the values of good forages through rumen research has helped. Feedlot diseases have been brought under control. Pelleted diets high in good quality forage are used widely. Accelerated feedlot gains have helped to reduce the length of the fattening period. *(N. R. Ellis* and *L. A. Moore)*

286

The Reticulo-Rumen

CATTLE, sheep, goats, camels, reindeer, and buffalo are ruminants. Their digestive systems include four-compartment stomachs. The largest is the rumen, from which the term "ruminant" is derived. The other compartments are the reticulum, omasum, and abomasum. The reticulum and rumen are referred to as the reticulo-rumen. Ruminants can convert coarse, fibrous feedstuffs, unsuited for simple-stomach animals, into meat, milk, fiber, and energy. Ruminants can thrive on feeds that are high in fiber and deficient in essential amino acids and B vitamins because of their unique digestive system. The reticulo-rumen provides a suitable environment for the growth and development of bacteria that break down complex carbohydrates, change and synthesize proteins, synthesize vitamins of the B complex, and alter fats. The bacterial fermentation is carried out anterior to the true stomach (abomasum) and small intestine. This seems to be an efficient arrangement for the digestion and utilization of cellulose and provides for digestion of microbial products in the true stomach. Most forage-consuming animals, such as horses and rabbits, have a reverse arrangement.

The number of ruminal bacteria per milliliter (one-thousandth liter) of rumen contents seems to be about 10 billion to 100 billion. There may be approximately 1 million protozoa per milliliter. The capacity of the rumen is in the range of 4 to 10 liters in adult sheep and 100 to 300 liters in adult cattle; the total number of ruminal micro-organisms in an animal therefore is phenomenal. A number of types of ruminal bacteria have been isolated and classified; among them are streptococci, lactobacilli, and selenomonads. Others have been classified into general types, such as cellulolytic bacteria and lactate fermenters. Several others have been described but not completely classified. The isolation and study of the ruminal protozoa is much more difficult, and their exact role in the rumen has not been established. They probably contribute toward the digestion of cellulose and other complex carbohydrates and proteins and store carbohydrates and proteins for later metabolism by the ruminant.

Marked differences exist between ruminants and monogastric—simple stomach—animals in their metabolism of carbohydrates. Carbohydrates are broken down to the simple sugars and absorbed as such from the alimentary tract by monogastric animals, but only small amounts of carbohydrates are handled in a similar manner by

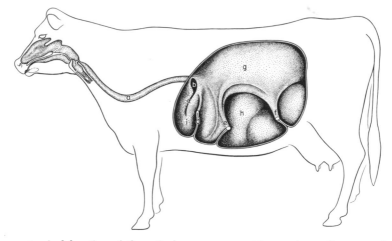

The anatomical location of the reticulo-rumen: a, esophagus; b, cardia; c, esophageal groove; d, rumino-reticular fold; e, anterior pillar of rumen; f, posterior pillar of rumen; g, dorsal sac of rumen; h, vertical sac of rumen; i, reticulum.

ruminants. Most of the carbohydrates, complex and simple, in the diet of ruminants are fermented by bacteria in the rumen to volatile fatty acids (VFAs). At least 600 to 1,200 Calories of energy are absorbed as VFAs from the rumen of sheep every 24 hours. Likewise, some 6 thousand to 12 thousand Calories of energy are liberated in the form of VFAs each day in the rumen of cattle. Thus the VFAs supply a major portion of the energy requirements of the ruminants.

Acetic acid usually is the predominant VFA produced by ruminal fermentation. Propionic and butyric acids are next. Small amounts of valeric acid and branched-chain isomers of butyric and valeric acid also occur usually in rumen contents. Proportions of the VFAs vary with the type of diet and level of feeding. Diets high in soluble or readily fermented carbohydrates favor the production of propionic acid. Diets high in cellulose and a low level of feeding favor the production of acetic acid. Very likely the production of acetic acid in the rumen is correlated positively with the production of butterfat by lactating cows. Propionic acid may be concerned with other processes, such as the production of milk solids. Some VFAs also may be utilized more efficiently than others for fattening of animals.

The quality of protein is important for monogastric animals, and a number of essential amino acids must be supplied by ingested proteins. A considerable portion of the ingested proteins in ruminants, however, is subjected to degradation and alteration by the ruminal micro-organisms during their own metabolism and growth. Urea and other nonprotein nitrogen substances apparently can be used to a certain extent by the micro-organisms in the synthesis of their body proteins. About half of the protein in the rumen contents of hay-fed sheep may be in the form of microbial protein. A considerable amount of the protein requirements of ruminants is thus met by micro-organisms, which are digested in the abomasum in much the same manner that protein is digested by monogastric animals. Enough vitamins of the B complex and vitamin K normally are synthesized in the rumen of adult ruminants to meet their requirements. Vitamins A, D, and E are not synthesized and must be supplied through dietary or other means.

Fat is another major dietary nutrient. Body fats of cattle and sheep (tallow and mutton suet) have relatively high melting points and chemical stability compared with fats from nonruminants. The melting point and chemical stability of fats are correlated positively with the degree of saturation of the fatty acids—that is, tallow contains a relatively high amount of saturated fatty acids compared with lard. Dietary fats fed to swine also have a pronounced effect on the body fat (lard). Dietary fats with low melting point give rise to soft fat. Feeding experiments with ruminants, however, have shown that dietary fat has little, if any, effect on body fat. Other experiments have demonstrated that unsaturated fatty acids are partly or completely hydrogenated (saturated) by contents of the rumen. These observations appear to be definitely related, and we can conclude that micro-organisms in the rumen affect all major nutrients, other than minerals, consumed by ruminants.

Complex movements of the reticulum and rumen keep the ruminal contents in perpetual movement and are associated with chewing the cud and belching—eructation. Average frequencies of ruminal contractions in cows have been reported to be 168 an hour during eating, 138 an hour during rumination, and 108 during rest. During the process of cud chewing, or rumination, coarse particles of food are passed up through the esophagus from the rumen to the mouth, where the material is remasticated, mixed with saliva, and again swallowed. The total time spent in rumination varies with different diets, but dairy cattle on normal diets spend from about 7 to 10 hours a day in rumination. A. F. Schalk and R. S. Amadon, of the North Dakota Agricultural Experiment Station, described regurgitation (passing of the cud) as resulting from a systemic succession of events that was initiated by a complex reflex mechanism. The reflex—not under voluntary control of the animal—depends on proper stimuli, the kind and amount of food, and rather definite moisture requirements. The reflex appears to be stimulated by the presence of coarse materials in the reticulum. The mechanical events of regurgitation, set in motion by the reflex, include an extra contraction of the reticulum, a contraction of the diaphragm, and reverse motility of the esophagus. The entry of the material into the esophagus also is aided by increased pressure within the rumen, together with decreased pressure within the esophagus.

Ruminants have to belch. Large volumes of carbon dioxide and methane and lesser amounts of other gases are formed during active fermentation in the rumen. The gases must be expelled, or the ruminant will succumb to bloat. R. W. Dougherty and his coworkers of the New York State Veterinary College and other scientists in several countries have conducted extensive studies of eructation since 1950. They have used various techniques, including X-ray movies of the rumen, reticulum, and esophagus during eructation. Eructation, like regurgitation, is a reflex and not a voluntary act. The stimulus

The gross structure of the recticulo-rumen from a sheep. The muscular structure in the lower center is the anterior pillar; just above it is the most heavily papillated area of the rumen. The recticulum is at the top.

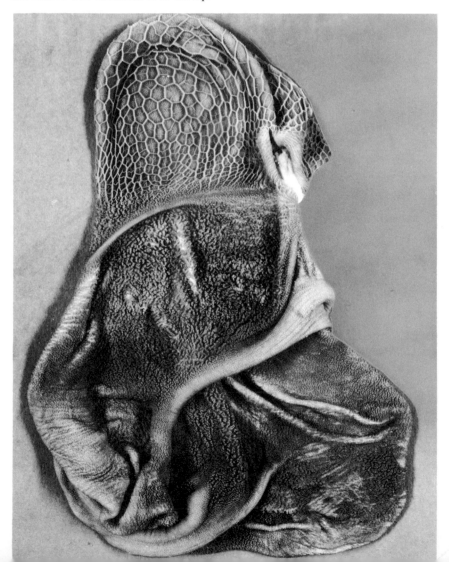

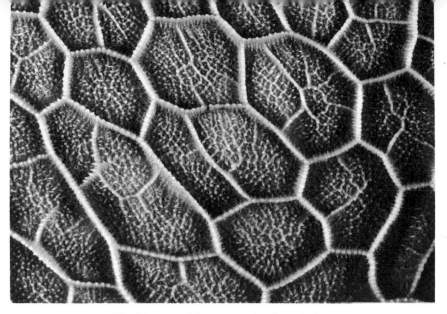

The "honeycomb" structure in the reticulum.

for the eructation reflex is gas pressure in the area around the cardia the opening of the esophagus into the rumen. The eructation reflex also is complex and apparently is controlled by both initiator and inhibitor components. Dr. Dougherty has shown that eructation can be initiated by applying gas pressure to the area around the cardia and also that eructation can be blocked by applying fluid pressure to the same area. The presence of reflex receptors that are sensitive to gas pressure and not to fluid pressure explains why ruminants belch gas and not fluid, although the cardia is often covered by fluid. The cardia normally is alternately covered and uncovered by fluid as a result of relaxation and contraction of the reticulo-rumen. Eructation also is coordinated with complex movements of the reticulum, rumen, esophagus, and other organs.

Bacteriologists, biochemists, and physiologists have given us some information as to why eructation fails when ruminants are consuming certain feeds, such as lush legumes. Under some conditions, the gas bubbles are trapped within the fluids in the rumen instead of rising to the surface. When that occurs, the rumen contents become frothy and cover the cardia so that it cannot be cleared by the rumen contractions. Eructation then is prevented. We do not know exactly why the gas bubbles are trapped within the rumen contents, but it appears that a number of interacting factors are responsible. Future work will involve research on all phases of ruminal microbiology and physiology. From it we can expect greater understanding of an important class of animals and basic knowledge applicable to other phases of life. *(Ivan L. Lindahl)*

Hormones

ALMOST every function of the animal organism is influenced by hormones produced within the body. Hormones act together; the secretion from one gland often affects the secretion of another gland. Hormones are the major chemical integrators of the many reactions involved in growth and development; the production of meat, milk, and eggs; and reproduction. Scientists have made many studies of the role of hormones in reproductive processes and control, the growth of the udder and lactation, and the growth and fattening of livestock. The function of certain organs, notably the thyroid gland, the ovaries and testes, and the pancreas, as sources of substances that produce profound physiological effects was known in the latter part of the 19th century, but most of our information about them has accumulated since 1910. Nine have been identified as endocrine organs, some of which produce more than one hormone. The pituitary gland, for example, produces eight separate and distinct hormones. Several substances of differing chemical composition but of similar functions may be produced within a gland. The substances that have hormone activity thus are more numerous than the glands that produce them. Most of the hormones have been isolated in pure form, and most of the steroid hormones can now be synthesized in the laboratory. Most nonsteroid hormones are obtained by extracting tissues obtained at slaughter, but thyroxine may be produced by laboratory procedures. Chemists have likewise synthesized a number of compounds—stilbestrol, hexestrol, and dienestrol—which are unrelated chemically to estrogenic hormones but have similar actions to the naturally occurring estrogens.

The hormones produced by the ovary—estrogens and progesterone—cause the udder to develop from simple ducts or tubes to a complex duct-secreting cell system capable of secreting milk. The pituitary gland hormones also participate in this development, but they are concerned more directly with the initiation and stimulation of lactation in the fully developed udder. The use of hormones now makes it possible to grow udders and induce lactation in nonpregnant cattle and goats. Some lactations, comparable to those that may be expected naturally, have resulted, but they have not been obtained consistently. Until more consistency is obtained, such results are primarily of experimental interest.

The anterior pituitary hormone, prolactin, promotes the secretion of milk from a fully developed udder. Growth hormone, another anterior pituitary hormone, increases yields of milk and the percentage of fat in milk. Thyroxine and thyroprotein, the latter an iodinated casein product that contains thyroxine, also have been used to stimulate the production of milk. While daily milk yields are increased for some time when thyroprotein is fed, the total production for the whole lactation seldom has been increased. Efficiency of production is not increased, and increases in consumption of feed are required to provide for the thyroprotein-stimulated increase in yield. Oxytocin, a posterior-pituitary hormone, is concerned in the milk letdown process. Its secretion causes milk to be squeezed from the depths of the udder into the milk cisterns and facilitates the removal of milk from the udder. Interference with the letdown process makes rapid milking difficult. Nervous reactions control the secretion of oxytocin. Proper preparation of the udder at milking, regular milking, and avoidance of fright or unusual situations at milking time facilitate the letdown.

The practical application of the use of the hormones probably will remain limited because of the expense of the hormonal preparations, the limited supply of pituitary hormone substances, and the lack of effectiveness of some of the material when given by mouth. The application of hormones to increase milk production is a useful research technique to study the endocrine processes involved in normal development of the mammary gland and lactation.

Research relating to reproduction in livestock has centered around a determination of the role of hormones in controlling the estrus—heat—cycle of mammals and the egg-laying cycle in birds. The use of hormones to manipulate the heat cycle, to increase production of germ cells, and to treat reproductive abnormalities has been studied extensively. Early work was concerned with use of the chick in hormone assays, the occurrence of prolactin in the pituitary glands of

This calf resulted from an ovum that was produced and fertilized in another cow and then transplanted into the cow shown here.

fowl, and the effectiveness of posterior pituitary preparations in causing hens to lay their eggs prematurely. Work at Beltsville has stressed the processes controlling ovulation in the hen. Ovulation is the shedding of the yolk from the ovarian follicle, within which it developed. Ovulation was known to be induced in mammals by a hormone (luteinizing hormone, which is secreted by the anterior pituitary gland) for some years before the same fact was established experimentally in 1942 for birds. As in mammals, ovulation was induced most effectively by preparations containing the luteinizing hormone.

Soon after these basic relationships had been established, it was discovered that progesterone, a hormone long thought not to occur in birds, is effective in causing premature ovulation in the hen. The substance (or substances with similar physiological properties) later was found to be present in the blood of chickens. Scientists succeeded in identifying progesterone itself in extracts of ovarian follicles and in blood. The essential pituitary and ovarian hormones therefore may be much the same in birds and mammals, however different their reproductive processes may be.

The use of supplemental lights to control seasonal egg production of chickens and turkeys is well established. The importance of the central nervous system and the hypothalamus in transmitting the effects of light to the pituitary and thus to the ovary has long been recognized. Newer investigations have been directed toward the elucidation of nervous pathways in the hen's brain. Small lesions in certain regions of the hypothalamus—the paraventricular nucleus, for example—prevent nervous stimulation of the pituitary and thus prevent the secretion of hormones for growth of ovarian follicles and their ovulation. Such lesions also prevent the ovulation-inducing action of progesterone systemically administered, an indication that this steroid acts over nervous pathways. The injection of minute amounts of progesterone directly into the same sites of the brain as were the lesions induces ovulation, but injection into some other regions of the brain are likewise effective, and the actual nervous mechanism of progesterone action is unknown.

Similar physiologic work with the larger farm animals has been extended in several directions. Now we can control several phases of the reproductive process experimentally with the aid of hormones. Hormones can be used to treat certain reproductive disorders, such as nymphomania due to cystic ovaries. They can be injected or fed to stimulate various phases of reproductive function or to slow down reproductive activity for a desired length of time. For example, heat in farm animals can be controlled to a high degree of predictability. Feeding certain substances similar to the natural hormone progesterone, which maintains pregnancy, results in cessation of the heat cycle. If a large number of animals in various stages of the estrus cycle are fed the proper hormone for a time, usually about 2 weeks, no heats will be observed until about 4 days after the hormone feeding is stopped. By this procedure, a whole herd of cattle could be brought into heat on the same day. This technique would be an advantage to many animal breeders, particularly ranchers. Artificial insemination often becomes more practicable when a large number of animals can be expected in heat on a certain day. More efficient use could often be made of outstanding sires owned by breeders; semen could be collected, diluted, and used to inseminate several times the number of animals that could be bred naturally. Parturition occurring over a relatively restricted period may be an advantage of breeding a large number of animals in a similarly short period. Fertility at these controlled heats is high in sheep and swine. Breeding these species under controlled conditions may become common. Fertility at the induced heat in beef and dairy cattle is rather low, but perhaps it can be improved by further research.

Transplantation of fertilized ova—eggs—from one female to another is a possible means of improving production rapidly through control of reproductive processes. A female of high-producing ability can be made to shed large numbers of ova at one time by the use of hormones to stimulate development and rupture of follicles. Insemination results in fertilization of nearly all the ova. Each ova transplanted into another female, in which the embryo and fetus develop, retains the genetic characteristics of its donor dam. A high-producing female thus could have hundreds of offspring if her ova could be readily collected and transplanted into other animals. Before these techniques can be used efficiently, a method for collecting ova from live females and a method of transplanting the ova into recipient animals without surgery must be developed. By using these rather cumbersome techniques, scientists have transplanted ova in sheep and rabbits. We know of only one instance in which the transplanting of an egg resulted in the birth of a live calf. An interesting application of this technique has been accomplished by British scientists. They transported fertilized sheep ova in the body cavity of rabbits overseas, where the sheep ova were transplanted into native sheep, which became foster mothers to sheep of quite different ancestry. The procedure saved the costs of shipping the sheep if they had been born in England.

Scientists have tried to regulate growth and fattening in livestock and poultry by administering the thyroid hormone or by reducing the activity of the animal's own thyroid gland by feeding goitrogenic substances. The results have been disappointing in cattle and sheep. In swine and poultry, small doses of thyroid hormone have increased the rate of gain at certain periods of the growth phase. Thereafter the use of goitrogens has increased the degree of fattening, but that frequently has been at the expense of gain in weight. At present, the use of these substances does not seem practical for use in livestock production. Some studies have shown that variation in the thyroid hormone status of animals may affect feather growth in birds, rate and quality of wool growth, and quality of fur in mink. Growth hormone from the anterior pituitary gland has been administered to pigs and cattle and has resulted in increased growth and increases in feed efficiency. Chickens have not shown growth responses to growth hormone of mammalian origin. The use of growth hormone is limited because of the expense of hormones and the small supply.

The most consistent results in the use of hormones to regulate growth and fattening have been obtained with the sex hormones. The synthetic estrogens, stilbestrol, hexestrol, and dienestrol, have been used. These substances, implanted in birds, improve carcass quality and fattening, but increases in rate of gain or in feed efficiency were not observed. Such implants were commonly employed in the poultry industry, but the presence of estrogen residues in tissues led to a discontinuation of the practice. These substances are still being used for cattle in the feedlot. Tissue residues do not seem to be a potential problem here. The implantation or feeding of stilbestrol is used extensively and results in increased rates of gain and increased feed efficiency. Androgenic hormones—for example, testosterone—and progesterone have likewise been tested. The results have been somewhat variable, and the hormones are not in general use. Sheep show similar responses to these substances as cattle. Rates of gain and feed efficiency are increased, although to a less extent. Carcass quality is reduced in some instances, particularly if estrogens are administered without administration of testosterone or progesterone at the same time. The practice of hormone fattening is less extensive for sheep than it is for cattle. The use of sex hormones has not yielded favorable results with swine.

Two other applications of endocrinology to problems of production deserve attention. Ketosis, a common disease of cattle and sheep, frequently causes marked decreases in production and loss of animals. Research has shown that the pituitary gland and the adrenal cortex are involved in the incidence of ketosis. The pituitary hormone, ACTH, and cortical hormones are commonly used in the treatment of the disease. Milk fever, a common disease of dairy cattle, is considered to be due to the inability of the parathyroid glands to maintain sufficiently high levels of blood calcium. The use of high doses of vitamin D to control this condition is reasonably successful and appears to function through stimulation of the parathyroid glands. A similar response of the parathyroid glands may also be involved in the use of the special low-calcium diets that have been proposed for treating milk fever. *(Joseph F. Sykes)*

296

Artificial Insemination

A GROUP of dairymen in New Jersey organized in 1938 the first cooperative in the United States for the artificial insemination of their cows. This method of serving females without natural mating has since become one of the most significant programs for livestock improvement in the history of American agriculture.

A great deal of research has been done on all phases. A basic contribution was the invention of the artificial vagina, by which semen is obtained directly from the bull without contamination. After that came the development of the rectovaginal insemination technique, which permits the placement of semen in the cow's cervix or uterus and improves the conception rate. The development of the yolk-phosphate diluent made it possible for the first time to store semen for as long as 2 days without seriously affecting its fertilizing ability. The addition of antibiotics to diluted semen improves breeding efficiency and helps to prevent the transmission of certain reproductive diseases. Adoption of the photoelectric colorimeter for determining sperm concentration permits maximum dilution of semen without lowering breeding efficiency. One of the newest developments, the freezing of semen, makes it possible to store diluted semen for indefinite periods. Improvements in semen diluents, methods of handling semen, and insemination techniques have enabled most studs to maintain breeding efficiency equal to or slightly higher than natural service.

A shortcoming of artificial insemination used to be that a sire could be made available to dairymen only about 2 days each week. Semen was collected from a bull at weekly intervals, and satisfactory fertilizing capacity could not be maintained for more than 2 days. We have learned how to freeze bull semen without destroying its fertilizing capacity. By adding glycerol as a protective agent, then freezing and storing diluted semen at extremely low temperatures ($-110°$ F. with dry ice or $-320°$ with liquid nitrogen), fertility can be maintained for several years. The use of frozen semen makes it possible to have semen from each sire available every day. It facilitates the long-distance transportation of semen. It permits more cows to be bred to some bulls, as a "bank" of semen can be accumulated during periods of light demand. Cows can be mated to a bull during extended periods of sexual inactivity or after the bull is dead. Thirteen studs were using frozen semen for their entire oper-

The Dairy Breeding Research Center, The Pennsylvania State University.

ation in 1960, and at least 46 others were using it on a limited basis. An estimated 40 percent of all artificial inseminations in the United States in 1961 were with frozen semen. Many of the advantages of frozen semen are realized only in organizations that breed large numbers of cows or cover large geographical areas. Smaller studs can make each of their sires available every day with liquid semen by using improved diluents and following a twice-weekly schedule of semen collection. Lower costs and a higher breeding efficiency result.

Artificial insemination—sometimes shortened to "A.I."—offers great opportunities for improving dairy cattle if only the best bulls are used, but great harm could be done by using inferior bulls. A bull can produce enough sperm in a year to inseminate 100 thousand or more cows. No doubt the trend toward fewer bulls and more services per bull will continue. In 1960, 24 bulls sired 11.4 percent of all registered Holsteins. Improvement in the dairy industry therefore may well be in the hands of those who select bulls for use in the program.

Progeny testing is the most accurate method of measuring a bull's breeding value. Since the performance of dairy cows is influenced by feeding and management, it is difficult to measure transmitting ability even though a bull has daughters in production, particularly if all his daughters are in one herd. Many geneticists agree that a sire selection program based on the development of A.I.-proved sires

298

As many as 275 calls a day for service are received at the Lancaster office, one of 10 service offices of the Southeastern Pennsylvania Artificial Breeding Cooperative. From this office, 16 technicians breed about 40 thousand cows a year on more than 2 thousand farms. Each member's farm is marked on a wall map, and a small map is used to route the technicians.

offers the greatest opportunity to improve dairy cattle. Under this plan, carefully selected bulls are placed in service when they are about a year old. Each is mated to enough cows to insure that at least 50 of his daughters will complete lactations on a recognized production testing program. Ideally, the bull is then removed from service until production and type information is available for his daughters. Thus he becomes an A.I.-proved sire. If the average level of production among his daughters is satisfactory, he can be used intensively with reasonable assurance that his future daughters will produce at a level indicated by the A.I. proof.

A relatively new method of measuring a sire's breeding value is the herdmate comparison. Production of each daughter of a particular bull is compared with the production of other cows freshening in the same herd during the same calving period. Effects of management and feeding upon differences in production thus are minimized. It is highly desirable to measure the breeding value of a bull at an early age in order to lengthen his useful life in the stud. In Pennsylvania, where 18 percent of the cows are enrolled in Dairy Herd Improvement Associations, breeding 2,500 cows to a

American Breeders Service transports frozen semen to technicians in liquid-nitrogen refrigerators, each with a capacity of 50 thousand ampules. They normally have about 1 million ampules in storage and as many as 50 thousand from one bull.

Recharging a technician's refrigerator with liquid nitrogen at a distribution point. The small refrigerator holds about 500 ampules of semen and enough liquid nitrogen for 2 weeks' storage. Frozen semen permits more efficient utilization of semen.

young sire provides enough records to appraise his breeding value. All D.H.I.A. records in the State are processed by means of electronic data-processing equipment, and records completed by A.I. daughters are reported promptly to the studs.

Scientists at the Dairy Breeding Research Center of The Pennsylvania State University have made several contributions to the A.I. program—coloring semen to identify the semen of bulls of different breeds; the use of penicillin and streptomycin to improve fertility of semen; the development of milk diluents; the management of bulls to increase their production of sperm; and the use of glycerol in liquid diluents to extend effective storage time. This research has enabled the five cooperative studs in Pennsylvania to offer service to each bull every day at a net cost of less than 5 dollars per first service. Lauxmont Admiral Lucifer is an example of a bull that was proved in natural service and then made an outstanding contribution to the A.I. program in Pennsylvania. His 50 "natural" daughters averaged 12,454 pounds of milk and 475 pounds of fat. His A.I. daughters in 1961 had completed 3,835 records, which average 12,806 pounds of milk and 481 pounds of fat. Lucifer had been mated to 45,190 first-service cows when he died at the age of 17 years and 4 months. Another outstanding bull, Spruceleigh Monogram Rag Apple (Expectation), was bought as a calf by the Western Pennsylvania Artificial Breeding Cooperative and placed in service when he was a year old. In 2 years he had been mated to 1,655 first-service cows—fewer than 2 percent of all Holstein services during this time. As his first A.I. daughters completed lactations, it became apparent he was transmitting outstanding production and desirable type. During 1958–1960, he was mated to almost 55 thousand cows—24 percent of the Holstein services. In the herdmate comparison, 315 of Expectation's daughters averaged 12,455 pounds of milk and 480 pounds of fat—495 pounds of milk and 31 pounds of fat more than their herdmates. The increased production for the first lactations of the 315 daughters had a value of more than 7 thousand dollars. As of June 1, 1961, Expectation had been mated to more than 81 thousand first-service cows. It was estimated that 28 thousand daughters would result from those services and complete at least one lactation. If these daughters perform as well as the herdmate comparison suggests, their combined superiority will be worth more than 600 thousand dollars per lactation. An average of three lactations per daughter would boost this value to almost 2 million dollars.

Artificial insemination has been practiced with all species of farm animals, but extensive application in the United States has been limited to dairy cattle. Some of the reasons are that management practices may make the detection of heat and insemination difficult, as in beef cattle and sheep; breed registry organizations may restrict the registration of offspring resulting from artificial insemination, as in beef cattle and horses; and satisfactory diluents and insemination techniques may be lacking, as in poultry, horses, and swine. Most of these problems may be solved by research, but it is unlikely that artificial insemination will be used extensively as a means of improving livestock other than dairy cattle, beef cattle, and swine.

It is hard to predict possible developments for a program that has been changing so fast, but it seems likely that emphasis will be put on ways to get earlier and more accurate methods of evaluating sires. Longtime storage of semen at room temperature may become a reality through the use of metabolic inhibitors, freeze-drying, or other means. Control of sex in dairy cattle, longtime storage of fertilized ova, and fertilization in a test tube may become feasible. Scientists have attempted to alter the normal sex ratio by destroying the fertilizing capacity of spermatozoa that carry one of sex-determining chromosomes or by separating the two types of spermatozoa in an electric field. Limited success has been achieved with laboratory animals. A cow's ovaries can be stimulated by injections of hormones to produce several eggs during each estrus cycle. These eggs can be fertilized by the usual insemination technique or they can be removed from the oviduct and fertilized in vitro. Each fertilized egg can then be placed in the uterus of a host cow, where it develops. Although maintaining pregnancy in the host cow is difficult and expensive, this may become a way to increase the influence of genetically superior females. *(Harvey E. Shaffer)*

Expectation, an outstanding A.I.-proved sire.

Five of Expectation's daughters in the herd of Ray Simpson, Butler, Pa.

The herd of A. S. Hallock Estate, Laceyville, Pa., illustrates the results that can be achieved when A.I. service to outstanding sires is combined with good feeding and management. Since 1950, all of the cows in this herd have been sired by bulls in the Nepa Artificial Breeding Cooperative. The D.H.I.A. herd average has exceeded 13 thousand pounds of milk and 500 pounds of fat each year since 1950, and the 10-year average is 14,265 pounds of milk and 569 pounds of fat. The 18 cows classified in 1961 were sired by 13 bulls and had an average score of 81.5.

This calf was born in the herd of John Melchor, Easton, Pa., more than 5 years after her sire, Lauxmont Admiral Lucifer, had died. Frozen semen was used.

A Broiler Any Day

KEEPING CHICKENS used to be one of the housewife's duties. Nearly every household that had a backyard kept a few chickens to supply the family with eggs, mostly in the spring, and an occasional stewing chicken for Sunday dinner. A few fryers could be sacrificed for a family treat in summer from the extra cockerels the broody hens had raised. That old index of well-being, "a chicken in the pot every Sunday," has come true beyond expectation for any day of the week, for raising poultry has become an industry that grosses 3.5 billion dollars a year, a fast-growing business that grabs up new research findings almost before they can be published. Industrial techniques and assembly-line methods are utilized in hatching millions of baby chicks, feeding and watering the growing and laying flocks, and speeding the eggs and the broilers through the processing plants to the consumer.

A few years ago the producer of broilers expected to take 13 weeks to grow a 3-pound bird. Now he can market his flock at 3.5 pounds in only 9 weeks plus 2 or 3 days. Instead of requiring 4.5 pounds of feed per pound of broiler produced, less than 2.5 pounds is needed. The national average egg production was 134 eggs per hen in 1940 and more than 200 in 1962. It used to take about 7 pounds of feed per dozen eggs; 4.5 pounds is enough today. Many commercial flocks average more than 250 eggs per hen on little more than 4 pounds of feed per dozen eggs. Turkeys a few years ago required 4.5 pounds of feed per pound of gain to 24 weeks of age; they need little more than 3.5 pounds of feed per pound of gain now.

Making all this possible was the invention of the forced-draft incubator, the large models of which can incubate more than 50 thousand eggs at a time. The poultryman is relieved of the restrictive capacity of the broody hen; selective breeding has nearly eliminated the broody hen. The art of breeding has become the science of genetics. The trap nest came into use at the turn of the century. Accurate records of egg production and pedigree information provided the tools the poultry breeder needed. To these have been added electronic data-processing methods, made necessary by the size and complexity of today's breeding programs. Nearly all commercial chickens produced take advantage of the gains to be made through the utilization of hybrid vigor. Various breeding systems

In the old days, flocks were produced by broody hens, usually in stolen nests.

have been devised to accomplish this purpose. Some involve the crossing of inbred lines, as for hybrid corn; others involve crossing different strains or stocks of the same breed or different breeds. The outstanding characteristics of stocks of different genetic origin are combined upon crossing, and often more is achieved than was expected because of hybrid vigor.

The typical broiler of today is the result of crossing a male line that has outstanding growth rate, meat quality, and dominant white feather color with a female line that has outstanding growth rate, hatchability, and reasonable egg production. Breeding parent stock of broilers has become so specialized that some breeders have tended to concentrate on the development of male lines, while others have concentrated on female lines. In an effort to reach the ultimate in perfection, the breeders of both male lines and female lines have resorted to crossing two or more strains. To be most competitive, a breeder of either a male or a female line must produce a bird that "nicks"—crosses well—with the opposite sex supplied by other breeders. Breeders of stock for egg production operate somewhat differently. They almost invariably breed both the male and female breeders used in the production of the commercial pullet chicks. These breeders select for many desirable traits, but emphasize egg production, livability, feed efficiency, and size and quality of eggs.

The first major contribution of nutritional science to poultry production was the discovery and use of vitamin D in the feed. Poultry flocks that got enough vitamin D could be confined indoors, where the efficiencies of industrial methods could be applied to their feeding and management. Vitamins A, E, K, and the water-soluble vitamins of the B complex have come to be important in formulating poultry rations. Scientists continue to improve poultry diets through knowledge gained about essential amino acids, energy, minerals, and the relationships between them and other dietary constituents. Poultrymen and consumers owe much to the nutritionists for the great gains made in efficiency in feeding. High-producing flocks have greater requirements for es-

Incubators like this produce 22 thousand chicks per hatch.

An assembly line for cage layers.

Chicks of several breeds, varieties, and strains often are started together to provide genetic evaluations under uniform conditions.

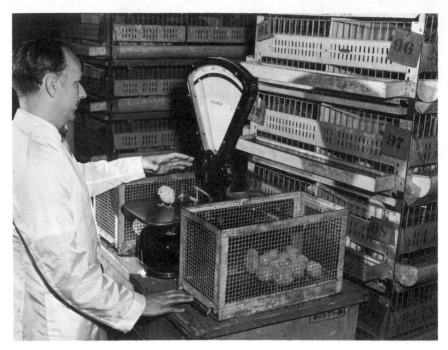

Perry F. Twining, a nutritionist at the Agricultural Research Center, checks the growth rate of chicks in comparisons of diets.

Radioactive nutrients are injected into eggs to learn whether they affect the hatchability of eggs and development of chicks.

Edward C. Miller records results from a proportional flow counter at Beltsville to determine how birds metabolize certain nutrients that have been tagged with radioisotopes.

The thickness of shells is measured as part of the work of developing strains that will lay eggs whose shells are strong enough to withstand handling in marketing.

sential nutrients, some of which ordinary feedstuffs may lack. A basic diet of corn and soybean oilmeal can be supplemented to give a high-energy feed that is low in cost but gives fast growth and high egg production. Poultry feeds are quite specialized. Separate diets are compounded for starting the chicks or turkeys during the first few weeks, for growing them to maturity, and for feeding during the laying period. Breeders get a ration different from the rations of flocks for market eggs. Diets for chickens, ducks, and turkeys differ with species, age, and purpose of the flock.

It takes more than just feed and water to have a profitable flock. Baby chicks, poults, or ducklings need a warm place to stay. It cannot be too hot or too cold; it must be just right for their comfort and health. Later on, summer temperatures can get too high for the laying flocks unless cooling, water, and ventilation are handled properly. It can get too cold, also. If the combs and wattles of the hens or roosters freeze, their reproductive performance is affected adversely. Light has a great influence on the reproductive performance of birds. Poultrymen used to think that supplying extra light artificially during the short winter days enabled the pullets to eat more and thus lay more eggs. It turns out that light affects the pituitary gland, which in turn stimulates the ovary, causing the ova to mature. In the same way, the cockerel's testes are stimulated, so that the eggs can be fertilized during the breeding season. Many other factors are important for rapid growth or high egg production. Clean, fresh water is required. A hen drinks about 25 gallons during her laying year. Adequate housing space, room to take her place at the waterer or feeder, freedom from insects, parasites, and various bacterial or virus diseases are all important. Vaccinations are as necessary to poultry flocks as they are to our children these days. (Steven C. King)

Parasites in Livestock and Poultry

A NUMBER of serious diseases beset American livestock at the time the Department of Agriculture was established. Some were caused by parasites, whose nature was not understood or against which effective measures had not been developed or put into general practice. Texas fever was causing losses among northern cattle that came in contact with apparently healthy cattle driven northward from the South. Sheep scabies was damaging flocks on western ranges and spreading to feeding centers farther east. Because the disease was highly contagious, sheep could not be exported. Cattle scabies, lice, and grubs were serious problems. Parasites of the flesh of swine, known as trichinae, were regarded as exceedingly dangerous because of their possible harmful effects on human beings. Several countries in Europe put an embargo on American pork, and an inquiry was started to find the means of eliminating this hazard to human health.

These were among the main problems in parasitisms. Little was known about the kinds of parasites in livestock and poultry and the diseases they caused. The Congress established in 1886 in the Bureau of Animal Industry a Zoological Division for the study of parasitisms. It is now the Beltsville Parasitological Laboratory of the Animal Disease and Parasite Research Division, Agricultural Research Service. The work on parasitisms had modest beginnings. A rented building housed a small laboratory and a library. Here in 1891 began a research collection of preserved "type specimens" of parasites and the indexing of the world's parasitological literature. Five parasitologists were at work by 1912. Today the Beltsville Parasitological Laboratory houses 34 parasitologists, the parasite collection, and the index of parasitological literature, both many times their original size. Scientists from all over the world come to utilize the index and study the collection. Technical studies at the laboratory are supported by pasture investigations and other studies and by work at four smaller laboratories in important farming areas.

The parasitological work has contributed to public health and to livestock hygiene. The discovery that a new hookworm was the cause of anemia of man in the South was the beginning of public health activities to control it. The discovery that trichinae in pork and larval tapeworms in beef may be destroyed at relatively low temperatures and by curing procedures formed the basis for meat inspection regulations covering the processing of those meat products, which are customarily eaten without cooking, to insure safety from trichinae and tapeworm infections in man. The discovery that carbon tetrachloride and tetrachlorethylene are effective against hookworms of dogs led public health workers to the discovery that these drugs are effective against hookworms in human beings. The use of the drugs throughout the world has saved the lives of thousands of persons that might otherwise have died from hookworm disease. The discovery that the causative parasite of Texas fever is transmitted by a tick opened the way to the discovery of the transmission of malaria by mosquitoes and the transmission by insects of other parasitic diseases.

The scientists have studied treatments; methods of herd, flock, and pasture management to break the life cycle of parasites; and methods of immunization against parasites and the effects thereof. From their work have come important advances. Development of

The parasite collection of the Beltsville Parasitological Laboratory.

the so-called critical test for evaluating worm treatments led to the discarding of ineffectual ones and the development of new, effective ones. Examples are phenothiazine for controlling worm parasites in all kinds of farm animals, including poultry; sodium fluoride for removing large roundworms from swine; carbon disulfide for horse bots; barium antimonyl tartrate dusts for poultry gapeworms; sulfaguanadine for poultry coccidiosis; hexachlorethane drenches for liver flukes in cattle: derris and cube dips for sheep ticks; and systemic drugs, particularly organophosphates, for nose bots of sheep.

Elucidation of the life history of the sheep stomach worm provided a basis for determining the life histories of roundworm parasites of livestock and poultry. The McLean County system of swine sanitation permits the raising of pigs free or nearly free from the destructive effects of roundworms and reduces losses from filthborne diseases. Another discovery was that bovine venereal trichomoniasis, a breeding disease, can be controlled by a system of hygienic herd management. The development of the portable pen program reduced mortality of dairy calves due to parasitisms.

These are only a few examples of the accomplishments. Problems in parasitisms may be increasing, however. The more livestock and poultry are crowded together, the more prevalent and serious parasites tend to become. Changing agricultural practices, such as grassland conversion, irrigation, free movement of stock, geographical relocations within industry and expanding urban development, both of which remove lands from agricultural activities, and increasingly concentrated production of stock and poultry all mean that more and more animals and birds are raised on fewer acres. Under such conditions, parasites tend to surmount the barriers erected against them and adjust themselves to changing conditions. In this they have had centuries of successful experience. Some parasites probably are as old as the animals in which they now live. Some organisms living free in nature may now be acquiring parasitic habits. New types are developing, particularly among the intestinal roundworms. The annual cost of parasitisms to the producer of livestock and poultry, estimated at about a billion dollars, may be expected to increase with the concentration of agricultural practices. Moreover, some important parasites are becoming resistant to drugs and chemicals used against them. Some effective drugs and chemicals can no longer be used as treatments, because residues thereof become lodged in the flesh and organs of treated animals and may create hazards to the person consuming the tissues. Problems facing the parasitologist today are therefore more complex, more difficult of solution, more urgent, and more demanding of an infinitely wider variety of skills and aptitudes than a century ago. Many of the easier problems have been solved. The harder ones are still unsolved. *(Lloyd A. Spindler)*

Eradication of Animal Diseases

HOUR AFTER HOUR, year in and year out, an unceasing battle is waged between man and disease. We have learned much about the hidden agents of disease and how they live, multiply, and attack, but at the same time they fight for survival and change when confronted by new conditions we develop to combat them. We have on our side a number of natural defenses against diseases. We are isolated from all but two other countries by expanses of water. Because many of the diseases of livestock affect only one species, the problem of controlling them is less complex than it otherwise would be. Wildlife has never posed the problem in the United States that it has in many countries, since we have relatively few species in comparison with the world total and many of our wild animals are kept in confinement or are isolated by their native surroundings. The freezing temperatures that occur in much of the country in winter kill certain species of arthropods known to be vectors of many foreign animal diseases. These natural barriers still exist, but faster transportation and more travel and trade make it imperative that we learn more about the causes, spread, and control of livestock diseases. Only when we consider them in terms of the tremendous variations that exist among these factors from one disease to another can we understand the true importance of the problem. We cite a few examples.

Before contagious bovine pleuropneumonia was eradicated in 1892, research had shown that the major method of spread was by means of inhalation. When an infected animal coughed, bacteria became airborne, and healthy animals became infected when they breathed in the bacteria. Man understood that when one animal coughed directly into the face of another, it could spread disease, but he was not aware that an invisible mist associated with the cough covered a much greater area and that this mist carried droplets containing the infective agent. The isolation and slaughter of infected animals and herds led to the eventual eradication of the disease, even though the organism could live in affected parts of the lung for several months, and carriers could harbor the disease for 2 or 3 years. Thus the first animal disease of bacterial origin in this country was eliminated when all of the agent's means of perpetuation were attacked.

Foot-and-mouth disease gained entry into the United States for the sixth time in 1914 and spread rapidly to 22 States and the District of Columbia. It took 20 months of intensive efforts to eliminate it. That was during the horse and buggy era. The disease probably would spread ever so much faster in this country today if the virus of FMD, one of the smallest known animal viruses, leaked through our defenses, because millions of susceptible animals pass through our 2,500 markets and terminal stockyards every week. The disease has gained entry into the United States nine times, but it has never become established. The last case occurred in 1924–1929 in California. Canadian officials in 1952 promptly stamped out Canada's only outbreak. Mexico eradicated its first outbreak in 1926–1927. The United States and Mexico joined forces to stamp out the disease during an extensive campaign in central Mexico in 1947–1954. The disease spread over 16 Mexican States and the Federal District and involved more than 17 million susceptible animals. The successful program cost about 135 million dollars and is without parallel in international efforts to eradicate disease. The stamping-out—or slaughter—method of eradication is used to combat the disease in the United States. This entails prompt and effective quarantines, the immediate establishment of inspection procedures to

Federal inspectors examine cattle at a public stockyard.

Pens are thoroughly cleaned and disinfected.

A plan for testing market cattle for brucellosis includes tagging animals to identify their State, county, and herd.

315

check all possibly exposed herds, quick disposal of infected and exposed animals and material, and thorough cleaning and disinfection of the affected premises. Strict regulations govern the entry of animals and products that may introduce the disease from other countries. Soon after the outbreak in Mexico in 1946, advisory committees of scientists and representatives of the livestock industry were appointed by the Department. The research advisory committee recommended a two-way approach. One led to cooperative agreements with established laboratories in Europe. In accordance with the second, the Congress authorized construction of a laboratory in the United States for research, stipulating that it should be located on a coastal island owned by the Federal Government. Plum Island, off the coasts of Long Island, N.Y., and Connecticut, was selected as the site. The Plum Island Animal Disease Laboratory was dedicated in 1954. Men there have made substantial contributions to knowledge of FMD and other foreign plagues that threaten our livestock industry, including contagious bovine pleuropneumonia, fowl plague, rinderpest, Teschen disease, vesicular exanthema of swine, which was declared eradicated from the United States in 1959, and African swine fever, which closely resembles hog cholera. Research on African swine fever has been done chiefly through a cooperative agreement in Kenya. Development and maintenance of necessary biological materials and capability for accurate diagnosis of the exotic, or foreign, diseases in general have been a major objective of the laboratory. All work with foreign infectious diseases at the laboratory is conducted in plain but solidly constructed, tightly enclosed buildings specially constructed for work with such dangerous disease agents. The precautions are complete as anyone can devise. All animal carcasses and solid wastes are incinerated in special facilities. Sewage is decontaminated by heat before being discharged into the sea. Outgoing air is filtered through special filters. Workers change into laboratory clothing when they enter the buildings and must take shower baths before they leave. Only authorized and essential official visitors may land on the island. Other measures limit possibilities of escape of infectious materials from the laboratories or from the island.

Fowl plague, a highly fatal virus disease of chickens, turkeys, and pheasants, was introduced in 1923 by a laboratory worker who illegally brought the disease agent with him. It killed 500 thousand birds in the New York poultry market area in a short time. We do not know the exact mode of transmission, but histories where outbreaks have occurred indicate that new birds have been introduced into a flock, the birds had contact with neighboring flocks that were sick, a poultry buyer brought in dirty poultry crates, a dead bird from some other source was found on the premises, or poultry offal was fed to the flock. Experimentally, the disease can

The National Animal Disease Laboratory of the Department of Agriculture at Ames, Iowa, was dedicated in December 1961. It cost 16.5 million dollars and has 33 buildings, in which scientists seek ways to eradicate livestock and poultry diseases that cause losses of 1.4 billion dollars a year. The photograph was taken in May 1961.

be transmitted by most any route. The challenge before eradication authorities was: Can you successfully eradicate a poultry disease that is highly contagious? This outbreak and one that occurred in 1929 were eradicated. Newcastle disease, a serious disease of chickens and turkeys, has been recognized in the United States since 1944. From California it spread rapidly to many of the poultry-growing States in the East in 1945 and 1946 and to the rest of the country by the end of 1947. Presently the disease follows chronic respiratory disease and leucosis in economic importance to the poultry industry. The facility with which research on Newcastle virus can be accomplished led to the development and widespread use of live-virus vaccines soon after the disease became widespread. The gradual development of an effective killed vaccine gives hope for its eventual eradication.

Dourine, a disease of horses, is spread during mating. It is caused by a Trypanosoma, a parasite that multiplies in the blood and is present in serous discharges from lesions. The disease was eradicated in 1934. Glanders, one of the oldest of the bacterial diseases, presented a transmission problem like that in contagious pleuropneumonia. Skin lesions were present, however, and discharges from them carried the infectious agent and thus were a means of contaminating premises and facilities. It is contagious to man. Scientists were helped in their battle against it when automobiles and tractors replaced many horses. It was eradicated in 1942.

317

Piroplasmosis, a disease that mysteriously killed cattle in the South, was found to be caused by a protozoa, a blood parasite. A notable discovery in medical science was achieved in 1889 when it was learned this disease was spread by a tick. The solution of this enigma led to the eradication of the disease in 1943. Vesicular exanthema, another virus disease, spreads mainly through infected pork scraps fed to pigs in garbage. It was eradicated in 1959. This agent produced at least 11 types of the virus during its existence in this country.

The magnitude of the problems created by variations in the cause, spread, and control of diseases is apparent in the diseases we now are fighting. The battle against bovine tuberculosis has gone on since 1917, but much remains to be learned about it. Avian and human tuberculosis and an intestinal type of infection called Johne's disease all tend to camouflage the bovine tuberculosis organism itself and thus make true identification and eradication difficult. In some herds, more than 100 factors must be evaluated before we can determine the course of action that leads to elimination of tuberculosis from the herd. Brucellosis, a disease of cattle, swine, and sheep, as well as man, has been drastically reduced. This disease, which is spread in cattle mainly by the aborted fetus and discharges from the vagina, presents another route of transmission that must be attacked in order to bring it under control.

Studies of scrapie, a disease involving the central nervous system of sheep, indicate that its transmission may be by a viral agent linked to certain genetic factors. The problem of tracing possible exposures and establishing the presence of infection is made difficult by the fact that the incubation period for the disease averages 42 months. Bluetongue, another viral disease of sheep, is under study in several countries. A gnat is the vector responsible for the spread of the only type of the disease known in the United States, but 19 strains of the disease have been isolated in South Africa. Although vaccination is presently being used to bring bluetongue under control, the ability of this and other disease agents to develop new strains that can survive the effects of vaccine only serves to emphasize the need for constant research.

Extensive studies have been made to determine how the disease known as vesicular stomatitis is perpetuated in certain sections of the United States. The studies have shown that practically every species of animal, as well as human beings, has been exposed. The disease ceases to occur after the first frost, and nothing is known of the method by which the agent itself overwinters.

Scientists have been aware for some time that young animals often gain passive immunity to some diseases through the colostrum, or first milk, from their mothers. It is also realized that exposure to their mothers has been the cause of some diseases being

Even books and papers are treated overnight in a pass-clave before they are circulated from one unit to another at the laboratory, an example of the precautions to insure safety of the workers, eliminate contamination of research projects, and prevent the escape of disease agents.

A room in the animal-isolation building at the laboratory at Ames.

A research team at work in one of the 32 isolated laboratory units of the laboratory.

introduced into them. Scientists have developed a different approach to the problem of protecting newborn animals from disease. This method involves performing a hysterectomy to remove baby pigs from the sow and keeping them isolated from all other swine. It has been used to prevent such diseases as virus pig pneumonia, transmissible gastroenteritis, and atrophic rhinitis. It is being put to practical use in the production of what are known as specific pathogen-free pigs. Our knowledge relative to how diseases are spread and our attempts to control and at times eradicate them has provided us with experience to combat new diseases as they appear. However, there are diseases present whose method of transmission and manner of control are not understood and it will take outstanding perseverance and competence on the part of our scientists to find the answers.

Vaccine as a way to prevent disease and treatment with biologicals, antibiotics, and other pharmaceutical products have contributed greatly to the efforts to prevent, control, and eradicate disease, but we need to look for other weapons. One of them may be based on the knowledge that under certain conditions agents can be introduced individually into an animal's body without harmful effects, but disease is produced when the agents are introduced in combination. Another may come from studies of genetic factors that may be responsible for the perpetuation of diseases and their relationship to inherited resistance and susceptibility. It may be possible to produce safer vaccines by splitting a disease-producing agent into its component parts so that the disease-producing portion can be separated from the part that produces immunity. *(F. J. Mulhern, L. O. Mott, M. S. Shahan, and R. J. Anderson)*

Clean, Wholesome Meat

FROM COLONIAL days to the opening of the Union Stock Yards in Chicago in 1865, the production of livestock and the processing of meat were small, local businesses. Systems for inspecting the meat were local, too, and as varied as the many towns that had such service. The Congress in 1890 passed the first Federal meat inspection law providing for an inspection of meats for exportation. In 1906 the Congress adopted the Food and Drug Act to cover foods other than meat and a law under which the current Federal meat inspection program was organized. The Federal Meat Inspection Act makes it illegal to ship meat from cattle, calves, sheep, swine, and goats in interstate or foreign commerce unless it has been federally inspected and so marked. To be marked "U.S. Inspected and Passed," meat must have been prepared in a packing plant that operates under Federal meat inspection control and found to be clean, sound, wholesome, free from adulteration, and truthfully labeled. The granting of Federal inspection to meat processors is based on their willingness to meet and maintain standards of plant construction and sanitation. Veterinarians employed by the Government and their trained assistants are present whenever meat preparations are underway. Federal inspection of meat for export was being conducted in 1906 in 163 establishments in 58 cities; in 1962, in nearly 1,500 establishments in more than 600 cities. They were granted Federal inspection in much the same manner as the following example.

Management at Jones Packing Co., Payette, Idaho, wanted to expand their business by selling meat products in Utah and California. The operation included slaughter of cattle, sheep, and swine and making, canning, curing, and smoking sausage. An application for Federal inspection was filed. Blueprints of the existing building, equipment, and intended expansion, prepared by an architect, were forwarded to the Meat Inspection Division in Washington, whose staff specialists reviewed the plant layout and checked standards proposed for sanitation and inspection, efficient lighting, good drainage and ventilation, ample hot water under pressure, and convenient places for sterilizing instruments and for workers to keep clean. Nontoxic, easily cleaned construction materials for floors, walls, ceilings, and all working surfaces were approved. Placement of equipment, designed for efficiency, control of inspection, and ease of

A Department veterinarian examines swine before slaughter.

cleaning were specified. A rate of operation based on plant capacity was recommended.

Using the blueprints approved by the Meat Inspection Division, Jones Packing Co. let contracts for building and remodeling their plant. The completion of the job was estimated at 10 months. During this time Dr. George A. Brown, Inspector in Charge from Nampa, Idaho, who has responsibility for the area, made frequent checks on the building and equipment to assure agreement between approved drawings and actual construction. Looking to the day when inspection would be granted, the company designed labels for use on meats prepared under inspection. They were reviewed by Dr. Brown and approved by the Meat Inspection Division. Eligible

Approved blueprints are compared with actual construction in the lard rendering department of a packing company.

Tests to assure that federally inspected meat does not contain harmful residues are made in this laboratory at Beltsville.

labels pass through accuracy tests to be sure that words and pictures describe the contents exactly. The statement on each can, wrapper, or other container, "U.S. Inspected and Passed by U.S. Department of Agriculture," indicates approval of the contents. When inspection is inaugurated, inspectors are on hand to assure that the labels are used only as approved. He also got assurances from State public health officials of a potable water supply and adequate facilities for waste disposal and sewage. On the inspector's recommendations, the Director of the Meat Inspection Division granted Federal inspection to Establishment 38, the Jones Packing Co. Each establishment is given an identifying number. With the assignment of trained inspectors, the new establishment was ready to operate.

Inspection of meat at Establishment 38 and all other slaughtering establishments under Federal supervision begins with the examination of live animals in holding pens in the company yards. An inspector picks out any animal that looks abnormal. He ear-tags such animals either with "U.S. Condemned" or "U.S. Suspect." The condemned animals are destroyed. A suspected animal is slaughtered separately, and the carcass is given special examination before it is passed or rejected. Postslaughter inspection is made of every carcass. Inspectors examine the glands and organs as well as the carcass and give special attention to parts in which abnormalities are likely to make their first appearance. This system of detailed inspection makes it possible to trace diseases directly back to the herds from which they come. Steps can then be taken by disease-control officials to stamp out sources of infection. Condemned carcasses or parts of carcasses are kept under the inspector's control. Such meat is held under Federal lock or seal until it is processed for fertilizer or inedible grease. Salvage of unfit meat combines practical thrift with safe disposal.

The round, purple stamp that denotes completion of inspection and wholesomeness of product is placed on each inspected and passed carcass and cut. The preparation of cured and smoked meats, sausage, and canned products at Establishment 38 has the constant attention of inspectors. Since meat is perishable, it must be reinspected for wholesomeness at every step of its preparation. Other ingredients, such as spices, extracts, sugar, and salt, must meet exacting requirements before their use is permitted. Processing procedures, time and temperature controls, and formulas must be followed as specified with each label approval.

Before any meat may be offered for importation, the Meat Inspection Division must have recognized the inspection system of the country of origin as being comparable to our own. As each shipment is received at an entry port, inspectors sample and examine it for soundness, wholesomeness, and proper labeling. Thus any meat of foreign origin passed at time of entry may be used as an ingredient of prepared items. Packaged or canned meats may be sold in their original containers.

Under Federal inspection, Establishment 38 may take into its premises only the domestically prepared meats that have been inspected and passed at other federally inspected establishments. From time to time, inspectors at Establishment 38 draw samples of finished products and other materials. They send the samples to one of the seven chemical control laboratories maintained by the Division for chemical analysis or other tests. The laboratories test composition of the product as an aid to the inspector on the job by giving additional assurance that formulation and label requirements are followed. The laboratories test operational equipment and materials, such as cleaning solutions or paint used in the plant, to make sure such materials will in no way contaminate the meat. Biological control laboratories also are provided to give the inspector whatever service he needs. Recent developments in chemicals, drugs, and growth-promoting substances in agriculture and the presence of radiological materials have given the inspectors and chemists in the Division additional responsibilities. Regular sampling of meat products from federally inspected plants are drawn for detection of these substances. Cooperation with producers and other Government and State agencies has helped to keep the levels of such substances in meat products well within safe limits.

The Jones Packing Co. sells some of its products to the Veterans Administration Hospital in Salt Lake City. Since the Federal humane slaughter law, which became fully effective September 1, 1960, requires that all Federal purchases of meat be from companies that slaughter all species humanely, this company adopted officially approved methods for rendering all animals insensible to pain before slaughter. In contracting for meat products, the Veterans Administration, Army, Department of Agriculture, and other Federal agencies often request the Division to act as their agent in guaranteeing compliance with contract specifications.

Federally inspected establishments in the United States prepare more than 80 percent of the commercially slaughtered meat in the United States. Only they may use the purple stamp that indicates Federal approval. They account for the slaughter of more than 100 million meat animals a year and the processing of many billions of pounds of processed product. Americans consume more than 160 pounds of meat per capita annually. They have confidence in the wholesomeness and truthful labeling of the meats they buy. The protection given consumers costs the public only about 1 cent a person a month, which is nothing compared to the cost in money and health of one purchase of adulterated or tainted food. *(C. H. Pals* and *K. F. Johnson)*

Inspection and Quarantine

THE ANIMAL Inspection and Quarantine Division of the Department of Agriculture directs two programs that protect the Nation's livestock and poultry. One involves inspection of animals and animal products for import and export. The other involves the control of veterinary biologicals.

The Division prevents the entry of foreign animal diseases into the United States through its inspection of imported animals, poultry, and byproducts. Animal quarantine regulations in force in 1962 covered imported cattle, horses, sheep, swine, poultry, and wild ruminants for exhibition in zoos. The use or disposal of animal products and related materials—meat, bones, blood, glands, manure, hides, and skins—also is controlled. To make sure that only healthy livestock and poultry are imported, the Division requires a Department of Agriculture import permit, indicating that disease incidence and control procedures in the exporting country are satisfactory and describing specific conditions under which the importation may be made. Also required is a certificate of health from an official veterinarian in the country of origin, indicating freedom from communicable diseases and from exposure to such diseases.

An animal or bird upon arrival in this country is inspected by a Department veterinarian, who uses tests, quarantines, or treatments to make sure that it will not bring a foreign disease into the United States. Imported animal byproducts may enter this country with a certificate from the government of the country of origin. This certificate must show that the products came from healthy animals. Uncertified products are held under Government seal until the potential danger to animal health has been removed by treatment and reprocessing or until the product is safely destroyed. Animal quarantine—originally the responsibility of the Secretary of the Treasury—was transferred to the Department of Agriculture in 1884. An effective system of animal inspection and quarantine was developed by 1890. Regulations have been revised periodically as animal diseases have appeared or been eradicated in other parts of the world. Today the animal inspection and quarantine system of the United States is internationally recognized for its efficiency.

The Division also inspects and certifies livestock and poultry and animal byproducts for export. Only healthy animals and safe byproducts are certified to move in international trade. The need for

American inspection and certification of live domestic animals intended for export arose from English embargoes on American cattle in 1879 and from other foreign restrictions. Inspection and certification have been expanded to cover animal byproducts processed in the United States for export. Until the Department of Agriculture offered these services, many foreign markets were closed to American hides for tanning, inedible tallow for soaps and lubricants, and meat meal for animal feeds.

Veterinary biologicals and the establishments in which they are produced are licensed and inspected by the Department to assure the American stockman and poultryman safe, pure, and effective products for the prevention, control, or diagnosis of livestock and poultry diseases. Department scientists developed an effective serum for hog cholera in 1907. Limited production by the Government could not satisfy the demand that resulted during widespread outbreaks, and worthless or harmful commercial serum flooded the markets and discredited the worth of all disease-control products. To restore farmers' confidence in American biologicals, the Virus-Serum-Toxin Act of 1913 set up standards, which insure the reliability, purity, potency, and safety of biological products. Serum shortages during later outbreaks of hog cholera caused disastrous losses. The lack of sufficient reserves prompted Federal regulation of the supply of the serum and hog cholera virus. No nationwide outbreaks of hog cholera have occurred since Federal controls were imposed on supplies of serum and viruses. The Department's supervision of anti-hog-cholera products insures the swine producer of an adequate supply at reasonable cost. The serum industry is required to maintain reserve stocks of serum, which are available whenever they are needed. The animal quarantine law of 1903 placed Federal controls on organisms and vectors that cause animal and poultry diseases. The controls were later extended to cover all foreign veterinary biologicals after foot-and-mouth disease was brought into the United States in contaminated smallpox vaccine.

Veterinarians in the Division review all applications to bring animal disease organisms and vectors into the United States or to move them interstate. Before permission is granted, the research agency that wishes to use the materials must show that its use of the organism will not endanger American livestock and poultry. The research scientist is responsible for using and disposing of the organism safely. Some dangerous disease-producing agents—such as the viruses of rinderpest and foot-and-mouth disease—are prohibited from the United States and its possessions, except at the Plum Island Animal Disease Laboratory. This control of disease organisms and vectors from abroad allows important research to continue but prevents the introduction of disease. *(Harold A. Waters* and *L. C. Heemstra)*

Quality and Efficiency

QUALITY fetches a premium in the marketplace. Quality makes us well nourished as well as well fed. Quality is what we like. Livestock producers are increasingly conscious of the need to meet quality standards, especially of uniformly good quality—no runts, no culls, no cracked or misshaped eggs, no barebacked broilers, no milk of high bacterial count. Quality is determined by breeding, environment, age and sex, nutrition, health. Research has determined many of the causal relationships and developed means of producing animal products of the desired quality.

Most people prefer white-shelled eggs. This preference was (and is) easily met by using Leghorns as layers, but it posed a problem for breeders of hybrid chickens, for most crosses of inbred Leghorn strains with non-Leghorn inbred strains lay tinted eggs. Non-Leghorn inbreds that laid chalk-white eggs had to be developed. Probably some Leghorn inbreds have also been used in producing commercial hybrids that combined with one another with a high degree of heterosis—hybrid vigor. Brown eggs are equal in nutritive value to white eggs. Most strain crosses and hybrids that produce brown-shelled eggs are larger and eat more feed than Leghorns. These larger hens are used as breeder stock for broilers and only to a limited and diminishing extent as producers of commercial eggs. Interior quality of eggs—firm, upstanding whites and spherical, golden, unblemished yolks—depends partly on genetic capacity of the hen (firmness of white in the fresh egg and freedom from blood spots) and partly on controlled nutrition (color of yolk). It also depends heavily on the proper temperature at which eggs are held, treatment of shells, and age of the egg. The content of linoleic acid, vitamins, and iodine depends on diet, too, but eggs in commerce are not likely to be deficient in those constituents. Before the discovery of vitamin D in 1922 and the need for it in egg production, fresh eggs were highly seasonal—abundant in spring and scarce in winter. Feeding cod-liver oil was a major factor in achieving abundant supplies of high-quality eggs the year around. The later discovery that irradiated 7-dehydrocholesterol could supply the vitamin D needs of chickens assured winter supplies of eggs when cod-liver oil became scarce in wartime. Feeding vitamin D made possible the production of hatching eggs in winter and a yearlong supply of broilers.

Broilers of good quality have plump breasts and few and white pinfeathers. Even more, broilers must be uniformly well fleshed, healthy, free from defects, and heavy for their age. Quality in broilers means quality under conditions of mass production, with ever greater efficiency in converting feed to flesh. Quality is essential, but it must be economical. Quality in broilers depends on genetic capacity for growth, fleshing, light-colored and rapid feathering, abundant health, and optimal nutrition and well controlled environment. Quality must be protected by isolation from diseases and parasites and immunization and prophylaxis against them.

Quality in beef depends on age, sex, nutrition, and inheritance. Carcass quality is highly heritable; so is the quality of preferred cuts. Tenderness, whiteness or yellowness of fat, size of the porterhouse that can be cut from a carcass of given weight, and distribution of fat all depend in part on the breeding of the slaughter animal. The tenderness and size of the retail cut are also affected by age. Grass feeding as well as Jersey or Guernsey ancestry will produce yellow fat. The amount of fat is a function of age and nutrition. A large and increasing proportion of our beef is from feedlot animals fed to a uniform weight and degree of fatness to reach the most widely accepted quality. Feedlot beef will reach acceptable quality and weight about a year younger than the grass-finished animals. Best beef for frankfurters comes from well-fleshed, mature bulls, because their flesh binds water and fat more firmly than other beef in the making and during cooking of this type of sausage. Older animals generally yield tougher meat than younger ones, although filet mignon may come from the tenderloin of old cows and yet be tender. Color of flesh darkens with age of animal. It is generally darker in bull flesh and may result in any animal from overexcitement before slaughter. We eat beef bred and fed for that one end. It is excellent beef. People in Australia, Argentina, New Zealand, Uruguay, and the United Kingdom also eat beef bred for beef. Most other countries eat beef that is principally a byproduct of the dairy industry. We eat that kind of beef, too, principally as sausage and hamburgers.

Producing pork of high quality means producing pigs quickly and efficiently that yield a high proportion of lean hams, shoulders, and loins of good quality. Our pigs are the principal consumers of our corn crops. It is easy to fatten pigs on corn. It is equally easy to grow meaty pigs by adequately supplementing the corn with protein, vitamins, and minerals if we use pigs that are selectively bred for meat type. Crossbreeding unrelated strains of meat-type pigs is the surest way of getting the fecundity essential to economical production. Meat type can be produced in any breed or combination through effective selective breeding. We are a long way from our goal, but we are making progress. A few years ago, only 20 per-

cent of our slaughter pigs were of the meat type; current estimates exceed 35 percent. Pork fat can be modified quite readily in quality as well as quantity by diet, in contrast to beef, which is readily amenable only to dietary control in quantity. The amount of linoleic acid in pork fat normally is substantial—about one-fourth the amount of the saturated fatty acids. The linoleic acid content can be increased if research in human nutrition demonstrates that it need be.

Milk may be golden, from Jerseys and Guernseys, or white, from Holstein, Ayrshire, Shorthorn, and Brown Swiss. White milk and golden milk may be equally good sources of vitamin A (or its carotene precursor) and both may be relatively high or low in butterfat. The golden milk usually is higher in butterfat and in nonfat milk solids than the white milk. Breeding in the future may increase the proportion of protein to butterfat. This remains to be demonstrated through research. Less likely is the possibility that the proportion of linoleic acid in butterfat may be increased through breeding, feeding, or physiological control—less likely because the end products of the digestion of carbohydrate and fat by the microflora in the rumen in the cow are short-chain fatty acids, which generally are reconstituted into characteristic hard or saturated beef fats, regardless of the nature of the carbohydrate or fat fed. High-quality milk comes from healthy cows kept in clean quarters and milked in a sanitary manner.

Now let us consider efficiency. Efficiency of production may be measured in terms of feed conversion and productivity per breeding unit or in terms of other inputs, combinations of inputs, or of total inputs. Feed is the principal cost in the production of livestock and livestock products. Feeds adequate in protein, energy, vitamins, and minerals are much more efficient than feeds inadequate in any or all of these dietary essentials.

It used to require 20 bushels of corn to feed a pig from weaning to 225 pounds live weight and take 8 to 10 months if it got only corn and water. Some of the pigs developed niacin deficiency on such a diet. Necrotic enteritis used to be common in hogs in the Corn Belt if they got little besides corn. Twelve bushels of corn equivalent will now do the job and do it much faster. Crossbred or hybrid pigs generally grow faster than their parental purebreds. Crossbred and hybrid sows generally wean larger litters than their purebred ancestors. Since the sow requires about 1,200 pounds of feed during gestation and lactation, each pig of a litter of 8 weaned represents a cost of 150 pounds of feed, while each pig of a litter of 7 represents 171 pounds. We have increased the live weight of hogs per litter marketed by 450 pounds, or about 2 pigs, in the past 30 years. Breeding, feeding, management, and disease and parasite control have all helped. I must emphasize that the savings in feed that are realizable through superior production stock and feeding methods are not wholly realized in practice. When farmers have abundant feed supplies, they tend to use them lavishly, and pigs are pigs—they waste a lot of feed.

Our national dairy herd is apparently holding its own in efficiency of feed conversion. Our milking cows since 1945 have received about 31 pounds of concentrate per 100 pounds of milk they produce. Milk production per cow increased by 1,650 pounds from 1945 to 1958. Obviously, grain feeding increased enough to account for the increase in milk, although skillful feeding of more and better forage might have achieved the same increase at lower cost. The steady increase in milk production per cow from about 4,200 pounds per cow in 1924 to more than 6,400 pounds in 1959 reflects improvement in genetic capacity. Breeders and dairymen cooperating in Dairy Herd Improvement Associations, many of them using sires proved by daughters' records to be superior, have had a major role. The average production of cows in D.H.I.A. herds in 1959 was more than 10,300 pounds of milk. The increased use of artificial insemination has become a major factor in increasing the use of superior dairy sires.

In the production of broilers, outstanding increases of feed efficiency have been realized in practice. Research on nutrition, genetic management, and control of diseases made it possible. We estimate that 4.6 pounds of feed units (corn equivalent) were needed in 1945 and only 3 pounds in 1958. Egg production per hen has increased steadily since 1910—especially since 1935, when the results of research on breeding and nutrition began to be applied at an accelerated rate. Adequate formulated feeds have replaced the grain and scavenged feeds that sustained the farm flocks of 50 or more years ago. Vitamin D in these formulated feeds assures winter egg production in spring-hatched pullets that are given extra artificial light to lengthen the short winter days. Selective breeding and hybrid breeding have increased greatly the genetic capacity of our layers to produce eggs. Egg production per average layer was probably about 100 eggs in 1910, 122 eggs in 1935, and 206 eggs in 1959.

Beef production per cow has increased rapidly since 1925. It reflects an increase in our national herd of beef cows from about 11 million in 1925 to more than 27 million in 1959, while the number of cows kept for milk dropped from about 22.5 million in 1925 to 21.3 million in 1959. Milk cows when culled, dairy bulls, culled heifers, most of our veal calves, and a few dairy heifers and steers are used for meat, but the yield on per-cow basis is small compared to that from feedlot steers and heifers and culled beef cows and bulls.

The production of meat from ruminants requires about twice as much feed per pound of live weight produced as is required per pound of meat or eggs by nonruminants. This wide difference reflects the relatively low fecundity of the ruminants, which at best produce a single calf or a pair of lambs each season. We market about 1,450 pounds of live pigs from each sow farrowing; thus each sow farrowing results in live weight production about 4 times her body weight, while each cow produces only about 0.6 times hers. Since feed consumed by the dam is also a charge against feed cost, each 400 pounds per calf at weaning represents about 10 pounds of corn-equivalent feed units per pound of live weight, while each 35-pound pig at weaning may represent only about 5 pounds of corn-equivalent feed units per pound of its live weight. Poultry species also carry a feed cost for reproduction of stock often not included in estimates of the efficiency of turkeys and broilers grown for market. Each poult at hatching may represent 2 pounds corn-equivalent feed units and each broiler chick about 1.

331

Realized feed efficiencies lag behind those that have been demonstrated to be feasible. Our national dairy herd eats enough concentrates to account for all the milk produced, assuming only that pasture and harvested roughage is sufficient for maintenance and reproduction costs. Our eggs are estimated to cost 6 pounds corn-equivalent feed units in spite of the fact that healthy, well-managed laying flocks, for which careful records have been kept, produce eggs at a cost of 4.5 pounds of corn-equivalent feed units.

There are other and inherent limitations on efficiency. Energy required for maintenance varies with surface rather than the weight of the animal—weight increases in proportion to the cube of height and surface in proportion to the square, so that small animals, like hens, have a much higher energy requirement per pound of body weight for maintenance than large animals, such as cows. The efficiency of feed conversion of all well-fed, healthy young animals is relatively high. In the laboratory, young chicks, up to 4 or 5 weeks of age, often have produced a pound of gain in live weight on less than 2 pounds of dry feed. Equivalent efficiencies have been demonstrated for pigs and calves of the same age. Pigs under carefully controlled conditions are frequently reared to market weight of 225 pounds at a feed cost of less than 3 pounds per pound of weight added after weaning. Yearling cattle on full feed may add live weight at a feed cost of about 4.5 corn-equivalent feed units. Commercial broilers are raised to market weight in many flocks at a feed cost of about 2.3 pounds of feed, or 2.75 corn-equivalent feed units, since broiler feeds are higher in energy and protein than corn. To these costs must be added feed cost of the breeding stock used to produce the young to obtain a net feed cost of livestock production.

For the future, the estimated feasible increase in efficiency of milk production is small because the feed cost is higher for every pound of milk produced by adding more concentrate to the ration of the individual cow. Liberally fed cows substitute concentrate for roughage to a considerable extent. The national average production per cow is probably quite a bit below the genetic capacity of our cows, so it is probable that by feeding more adequately balanced rations in amounts proportionate to current milk production, about 1 pound of concentrate to 3 pounds of milk, some increase in efficiency can be realized. Self-fed pigs and poultry often waste much feed, and rodents eat a lot of feed put in the feeder. Better feeds and feeding, healthy flocks and herds, and stock bred for rapid gain can improve feed efficiency substantially. Cattle, calves, sheep, and lambs will improve realized efficiency as more and more of their gain in live weight is that of young stock fed carefully formulated, adequate rations, and as breeding improvement for rate of feedlot gain becomes effective. *(T. C. Byerly)*

Insects

Organic Insecticides

POTATO GROWERS in the Eastern States were alarmed in the 1860's by the advances of the Colorado potato beetle. Nothing was effective against it until someone began to use paris green, an arsenic compound that had been used for many years to color paints, wallpaper, and fabrics. Later it was found to be effective against cankerworm on fruit trees, the codling moth, and the cotton caterpillar. For many years the standard agricultural insecticides were paris green or london purple (another arsenical) for chewing insects and kerosene-soap emulsion for sucking insects. Pyrethrum was used for household insects. Efforts to combat the attacks of the gypsy moth in New England forests led in 1892 to the use of lead arsenate, which was more effective than paris green and less injurious to foliage. Great amounts of lead arsenate were used later in orchards against the codling moth and many other insects. Powdered lead arsenate was tried against the boll weevil on cotton. It gave some control and led to the development about 1916 of calcium arsenate, which came into use throughout the Cotton Belt. Lime-sulfur was used against San Jose scale beginning in 1880. Naphthalene was employed against grape phylloxera in 1882. The fumigation of citrus trees in California with hydrocyanic acid gas was started in 1886.

Agriculture meanwhile became more intensive, and insect pests were attracted in greater and greater numbers to crop areas to feed on the plants. Applications of insecticides became more frequent and heavier. Fears began to arise that fruits and vegetables sprayed or dusted with the arsenical insecticides might retain excessive residues of the poison. Western pears were condemned in Boston in 1919 because of excessive residues. A few years later British authorities objected to shipments of American apples for the same reason. The Department of Agriculture, which at that time was responsible for the enforcement of the Food and Drug Act, set up an arsenic residue tolerance of 0.025 grain of arsenic pentoxide per pound of fruit (about 3.5 parts per million) in 1927 and by 1932 had lowered this tolerance to 0.01 grain per pound.

Research was undertaken in two directions. One was to look for ways of removing or reducing residues present on the harvested crops. The other was to search for new insecticides that would be highly effective against insects but safer for man. The Department of Agriculture about 1927 began to investigate many different kinds

334

of organic (carbon-containing) compounds in a search for better and safer insecticides. Some of the compounds that were studied and tested were natural plant constituents, such as rotenone, the chemical structure of which was determined by three Department chemists, F. B. LaForge, H. L. Haller, and L. E. Smith. Others were synthesized especially for the tests. A few organic materials had been known for a long time to be toxic to insects—for example, carbon disulfide, paradichlorobenzene, and naphthalene among the synthetic compounds, and the constituents of such insecticidal plants as tobacco, pyrethrum, quassia, hellebore, and derris. From about 1927 to 1941, several new synthetic organic insecticides were discovered, among them ethylene dichloride, ethylene dibromide, ethylene oxide, and methyl bromide as insect fumigants; several organic thiocyanates for household and garden sprays; phenothiazine for codling moth; azobenzene as a greenhouse fumigant; and a number of dinitro derivatives of phenol and cresol as dormant sprays for orchards.

About the time the war started, in 1939, the synthetic compound DDT, which Othmar Zeidler, a German chemist, had first put together in 1874, started on its way to fame when a Swiss chemist, Paul Müller, discovered its insecticidal value. American entomologists and chemists verified its effectiveness when a sample was received from Switzerland in 1942. As soon as DDT was made available to civilians at the end of the war, it skyrocketed into wide use. DDT belongs to the class of organic compounds known as chlorinated hydrocarbons. Its full chemical name is 1,1,1-trichloro-2,2-bis(p-chlorophenyl)ethane. From a shorter, less exact name, dichlorodiphenyltrichloroethane, the abbreviation DDT was taken. Following its dramatic success, a series of effective chlorinated hydrocarbon insecticides made their debuts: Benzene hexachloride (or BHC), toxaphene, methoxychlor, chlordane, heptachlor, aldrin, dieldrin, endrin, perthane, and various others. DDT and its chlorinated relatives set a new high level of effectiveness. Some species of insect pests since have shown an ability to develop a tolerance or resistance to their action. When DDT was first introduced, house flies were so susceptible to its action that the application of a few ten-millionths of a gram to a fly sufficed to kill it. Now some flies that have been selected out by the treatment of many successive generations are so resistant that they can thrive in a screen cage solidly coated with DDT. These insecticides, however, are still effective against some species.

Other synthetic insecticides, the organic phosphorus compounds, were discovered during the war by a German chemist, Gerhard Schrader, who was looking for chemical warfare agents. Among his compounds were several effective insecticides, including schradan, parathion, and TEPP. An American team that visited Germany at the end of hostilities to obtain information on scientific advances brought back information on these materials. The research on organic phosphorus compounds since then has been active, and many potent insecticides have been discovered. Some that have come into use are malathion, methyl parathion, demeton, EPN, Dipterex, DDVP, ronnel, Co-Ral, Guthion, and Phosdrin. Many others are in use on a smaller scale or are still in the experimental stage. The organic phosphorus insecticides are extremely potent against a wide range of insects. Many also are toxic to warm-blooded animals because of their cholinesterase-inhibiting effect. Because they can be used at low dosages, however, and because most of them are somewhat volatile, they leave only negligible spray residues on crops. There has been relatively little development of insect resistance to these insecticides, as compared to the chlorinated hydrocarbons.

Several synthetic organic insecticides belonging to the carbamate class have been discovered. Among them are Sevin, dimetan, Dimetilan, Isolan, and Pyrolan. An unusual development in organic insecticides was the synthesis by Department chemists, M. S. Schechter, Dr. LaForge, and Nathan Green, in 1948 of esters similar to the pyrethrins, the active constituents of pyrethrum. This was accomplished after 15 years of study of the structure of the pyrethrins. One of these synthetic esters, allethrin, is produced commercially and has been widely used in aerosol bombs. Other somewhat related insecticides are barthrin and dimethrin. They were synthesized by another Department chemist, W. F. Barthel. This group of insecticides is about the safest known today.

Great interest has developed in materials that synergize them — that is, increase their effectiveness against insects although they themselves are not insecticides. A number of compounds have been discovered that are synergists for pyrethrum and the related synthetic esters. The first to be discovered was sesamin, a naturally occurring constituent of sesame oil. Later another constituent of sesame oil, sesamolin, was found even more effective for this purpose. A study of the structure of sesamin led to the synthesis of several good pyrethrum synergists containing the methylenedioxyphenyl group, which was found to be the essential factor in the synergistic activity of sesamin. Now in commercial use are piperonyl butoxide and sulfoxide. A few compounds of other types also have been found to synergize pyrethrum, including MGK 264. In general there has not yet been much success in finding good synergists for insecticides other than pyrethrum, although a few instances have been reported.

Chemists and entomologists in industry and in Federal and State research agencies are actively pursuing the search for even better and safer materials against which insects cannot build resistance. *(Ruth L. Busbey)*

336

The Battle with Cotton Insects

EVER SINCE cotton was grown commercially in this country there has been a constant war between cottongrowers and insects. Many times it has appeared that the insects were the victors, but always man has fought back, and at this point he appears to have the advantage. The Fourth Report of the United States Entomological Commission, published in 1885, put the average annual loss at about 15 million dollars for all the cotton States for the 14 years following the Civil War. The loss was attributed to one insect, the cotton leafworm, but the same report referred to the bollworm as the chief enemy known to cotton. Estimates of the loss it caused ranged up to 75 percent of the crop. It was an annual pest; the cotton leafworm appeared periodically.

The boll weevil appeared near Brownsville, Tex., in 1892. In the 30 years that followed, the time required for it to complete its spread to the northern extremities of the Cotton Belt and to the Atlantic Ocean, man was on the losing end of the battle. The entire economy of the South was affected. Farmers, bankers, and merchants all suffered. Many went broke. Farms were abandoned, and tenants moved away. The thriving Sea Island cotton industry along the Atlantic seaboard was wiped out, never to be revived— a casualty to an insect and an example of an insect's triumph over man. The area infested with the boll weevil remained fairly limited until 1954, when it was discovered in the Presidio Valley of western Texas. It since became the major cotton pest there and threatened to move farther west. Another threat came in 1917, when the pink bollworm was discovered in Texas. By then man had learned to take the offensive. Out of a vigorous research program developed effective cultural control measures. Quarantine and regulatory measures were enforced by the States and the Federal Government. Losses from the pink bollworm were kept low compared to those caused by the boll weevil. The insect has spread to New Mexico, Arizona, Oklahoma, Arkansas, Louisiana, and Texas, but it has not been a serious factor in the economical production of cotton, except in small areas following years when it is impossible or impractical to enforce the cultural practices designed to keep it under control. It was, however, a threat in Arizona and California, and an eradication program began in Arizona in 1959.

The weapons have steadily become more effective. Lanterns and

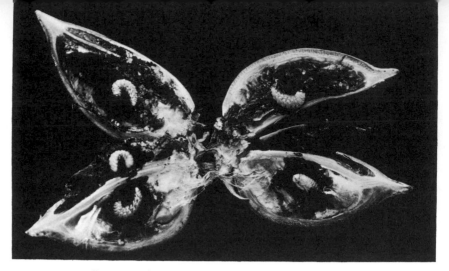

Larvae and a pupa of boll weevil inside a cotton boll.

fires once were used at night to attract and trap the insects. Dinner plates were placed on raised boards in cottonfields and filled with a mixture of vinegar and molasses to trap moths of the bollworm and cotton leafworm. Handpicking of insects or infested plant parts was done as long as labor was cheap and plentiful. The tactical approach to control cotton insects has centered around the use of chemicals. Paris green was officially recommended in 1873. Various compounds of arsenic also were used until the early part of the 20th century. Lead arsenate was used extensively until 1917. Man's first real victory over the boll weevil came with the development in 1916 of calcium arsenate, which also controlled the cotton leaf-worm and the bollworm to some extent. Complications developed, though. The insecticide also killed the beneficial insects, and the cotton aphid often developed to enormous numbers and sometimes caused greater damage than the boll weevil, which was being con-trolled. Certain soils, particularly the light, sandy soils along the Atlantic seaboard, were "poisoned" by the calcium arsenate and made unsuitable for the normal growth of many crops. Attempts to avoid these disadvantages were made, but calcium arsenate was not the answer.

DDT brought a new era of organic insecticides—DDT, BHC, toxaphene, chlordane, aldrin, dieldrin, and others. No one was the solution to the problem, although all were effective against several cotton pests. Combinations of them were tested. Millions of pounds were used. But then the insects developed a new tactical weapon and again became the aggressors. They developed a resistance to the new insecticides. In 1955 the boll weevil joined the group that had developed resistance to the chlorinated hydrocarbon insecticides. Other cotton pests also became resistant to the new organic insecticides. Thus again the insect had demonstrated its ability to fight back. Man, however, tried again. A new class of insecticides with a different mode of action had been discovered, the organophosphorus compounds, and they were sent to the battlefront. Some were effective against the resistant strains. Combinations of them and certain of the chlorinated hydrocarbons again gave man the advantage. Still another class of insecticides, having yet another mode of action, the carbamates, was found to be effective against many pests.

New chemicals and ways of using them are being developed. The use of systemic insecticides, which the plant will take up and translocate to all its parts, offers promise. The Boll Weevil Research Laboratory of the Department of Agriculture was completed in 1961 at State College, Miss. The ultimate goal of research there and elsewhere is the eradication of the boll weevil. An immediate objective is to relegate it to the status of a minor pest. It and other problems of cotton insects are being investigated in all the main cotton States. The scientists are changing their strategy from a running battle of applied research to one leaning heavily on basic research, which is expected to uncover new principles and open new approaches to control and possible eradication of some of the principal cotton pests. The war is not yet over. *(C. F. Rainwater)*

Dr. Erma Vanderzant developed ways to rear boll weevils in the laboratory on synthetic diets without cotton and so made possible continuous research on weevils.

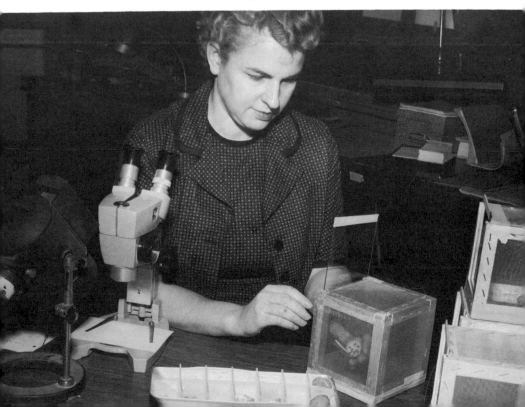

Systemic Insecticides

AN OLD, OLD hope for an insecticide that could be fed to plants or animals to protect them from insect pests approached reality in 1936, when two scientists of the Department of Agriculture discovered that selenium fed to wheat plants through the root system killed aphids feeding on the foliage. The entomologists, A. M. Hurd-Karrer and F. W. Poos, found that selenium, a poison, is absorbed by the roots and moves to the foliage, where it kills aphids at dilutions too low to cause visible effects on the plants. The wheat plants were normal, except that the poison persisted in the plants and grain. By 1945, however, the greenhouse industry was using a granular form of selenium mixed with phosphate fertilizer to control leaf-feeding spider mites in the commercial production of carnations and chrysanthemums. Selenium insecticide also became available in capsules for treating the soil of potted house plants to control foliage-feeding mites. Selenium has not been used extensively because of the danger of contaminating soils and making them unfit for growing food and feed, but its success as a systemic insecticide opened a new road.

Soon came a different type of systemic insecticide. R. A. Fulton and H. C. Mason, entomologists of the Department, observed in 1937 that after derris was applied to young bean plants, leaf growth was less palatable to the Mexican bean beetle than was similar new growth on untreated plants. Later studies made clear that the derris constituents were translocated from the outer surface of the treated leaves to leaves that developed after derris was applied. A big problem in the control of insects had been the distribution of insecticides to the inaccessible parts of the plants. Here was an insecticide that plants would redistribute and supply to new leaves. The amounts translocated were too low to be of much practical value, however.

Organic phosphates are the most practical systemic insecticides now available. The first one used commercially, schradan, was discovered in Germany in 1947. Work in Maryland on schradan demonstrated its value in the control of parathion-resistant spider mites on ornamental plants. Schradan is taken into plants through the root system, but its chief value has been in sprays and aerosols applied to the foliage of plants, from which it is absorbed and translocated chiefly to new foliage, flowers, and seeds. Its use in this country has been limited mostly to nonfood crops, because of persistent residues and subsequent development of more promising systemics, including demeton, Phosdrin, phorate, and Di-Syston. All four are used on commercial food crops, but all require great caution in their use. Demeton and Phosdrin are used mostly as sprays applied to foliage; demeton, for the control of aphids, spider mites, and leafhoppers; and Phosdrin, for the control of aphids and certain caterpillars. Demeton is persistent and cannot be used on vegetables close to harvest. Phosdrin is short lived and can be used up to a few days of harvest on many vegetables and other food crops. Phorate and Di-Syston have the advantage of being taken up from the soil by plants and distributed throughout the foliage, where they kill many species of aphids, mites, leafhoppers, and other insects without apparent harm to parasites and predators of the pests. These two materials apparently do not tend to be accumulated in the fruit or tubers of food plants. Both promise to be quite useful in the control of virus diseases by killing the insect vectors.

Research workers, however, are only beginning to learn how to use these two materials without adversely affecting the plants and without contaminating food and feed. Each is being widely tested on a variety of crops by scientists in industry, State agencies, and the Department of Agriculture. They have found commercial use on a few crops, including Easter lilies, birch, azalea, cotton, sugarbeets, and potatoes. Their early use on cotton and sugarbeets was as seed treatments, which under some conditions may damage the seed. In the control of potato insects, granules of the insecticides are merely placed in a band to the side of the seedpieces at plant-

In the foreground are untreated asters damaged by aster yellows, transmitted by the six-spotted leafhopper. In the background are asters grown in soil treated with 25 pounds of phorate per acre.

Cattle in the upper picture are infested with cattle grubs. Those in the lower picture were protected from grubs by a systemic insecticide.

ing time. Thus the day has come when with suitable equipment the potato grower can plant his crop, fertilize it, and apply insecticides to protect it from the potato leafhopper, aphids, and possibly the Colorado potato beetle, all in one operation. Experiments in California, Washington, Idaho, and Maryland indicate that bean-growers may soon be able to control the Mexican bean beetle as well as spider mites and leafhoppers by granules of systemic insecticide dropped into the seed furrow at planting time. In experiments, bean planters are equipped with extra hoppers to hold the insecticide, which is fed through a tube into the same planter shoe as the seed. Full use of systemic soil insecticides requires careful

342

studies to determine—for each crop, soil type, and insecticide—the best depth and position to place the chemical in the soil. Dosages must be established that will not injure the plants under various weather conditions and will not leave any harmful residues in the harvested crop.

The early successes with systemic insecticides applied to plants increased the desire for similar measures that would be applicable to livestock. A. W. Lindquist and other Department of Agriculture scientists fed DDT to rabbits and found that bed bugs feeding on the rabbits were killed. An intensive screening program was begun by Department workers at Corvallis, Oreg., and Kerrville, Tex., to find practical, safe systemic insecticides for livestock. The chlorinated hydrocarbon insecticides, dieldrin, lindane, and aldrin, showed systemic effectiveness, but their residues contaminated meat. The first real success came in 1955 with an insecticide called ronnel. Given by mouth to cattle as a drench, it killed all stages of the cattle grub throughout the treated animals. Ronnel was found to be effective at dosages below those toxic to cattle. Detailed physiological studies using radioisotope-labeled ronnel showed that some ronnel appeared in the milk, so that it could not be recommended for dairy cattle. Ronnel was briefly stored in the fat of cattle, but by 60 days after treatment no insecticide residues remained in the meat or fat of beef animals. Entomologists tried the method in various States and confirmed the effectiveness against cattle grubs. Thus, in 1958, ronnel became the first systemic insecticide recommended for use on livestock.

Ronnel was quickly followed by Co-Ral. Still newer systemic chemicals have shown promise in controlling the stomach bots of horses and the nose bots of sheep. To appreciate the impact of ronnel, which is given once orally, and Co-Ral, which is applied only once to the skin to control cattle grubs, one must compare these treatments with the earlier use of rotenone. Cattle growers were forced to wait through the warmer months while heel flies laid their eggs and the young cattle grubs burrowed through the tissues of the living cattle. Not until the grubs cut holes in the hide on the backs of the animals could they be reached effectively with rotenone. New grubs continued to burrow into the back muscles over a period of 3 to 5 months; thus the water-based rotenone sprays had to be applied again and again, often during the coldest part of the year. It was easier to take the loss on perforated hides and grub-damaged beef, which amounted to at least 100 million dollars annually. In the use of systemic insecticides, advantage is taken of the food distribution systems of the treated animal in reaching the pest insect with a killing agent. As in plants, this greatly simplifies insect control operations. *(L. B. Reed, R. C. Bushland, and G. W. Eddy)*

A Thief To Catch a Thief

SOME INSECTS kill other insects, and it would be to our advantage if we could turn the good ones—parasites and predators—loose on the bad ones, the many destructive species that are their natural enemies. A number of different species usually are on hand to attack all stages of a pest, but it is not entirely a simple matter, because the beneficial species are specialists. Those that prey on the gypsy moth, for instance, cannot survive on the forest tent caterpillar, a fairly close relative. That is why it is important to search in their native habitats for insect enemies of pests that have migrated to this country. About half of the worst pests in the United States are foreigners. We have put the main emphasis in biological control, therefore, on the introduction and establishment of beneficial species from their native homes. We are continuing this work, and we are hopeful of further successes. Better ways to transport these delicate, often tiny insects have been devised, and more precise knowledge regarding their biologies and ecological requirements is being discovered.

Work of this nature is being conducted against the balsam woolly aphid in the United States and Canada. It kills many fir trees in northern New England, the Maritimes, the Pacific Northwest, and even in the limited stands of Fraser fir in North Carolina. Sometimes the trunk of the tree is so heavily attacked it is covered with the white, woolly secretion of the aphid; their feeding stylets cause lesions, which soon girdle and kill the tree. Sometimes the buds of terminal branches are the main place of attack. Gouty swellings result, and eventually the twigs, treetops, and whole trees are killed. The aphid seldom kills trees in Europe and Asia. The species of fir there are less susceptible to injury by the aphid, and many native predators reduce the aphid populations tremendously. Some of the most important are small predaceous beetles, closely allied to lady beetles (or ladybugs or ladybirds). Both adult and immature beetles feed upon aphid eggs and adults. One of the most efficient European species, *Laricobius erichsoni,* has been collected there in rather large numbers and sent to this country, where it has been released in heavy aphid infestations. *Laricobius* is now well established at several liberation points in New England, Oregon, and Washington. We expect it will gradually spread throughout the whole infested area.

A species of Madremyia, native larval parasite of armyworms and cutworms in California.

A number of tiny flies also prey on the balsam woolly aphid. Only the larvae attack the host, however. One is a tiny cecidomyiid fly, *Aphidoletes thompsoni,* which is released in a special cage in order to insure its establishment. Each species, in fact, must be handled according to its special requirements. Usually it is necessary to import a number of different species, if economic control is to be achieved in the different climates where the host is a pest. The search for balsam woolly aphid predators is therefore being pushed diligently in many countries. Such work is being financed in India and Pakistan under Public Law 480, which provides money for research in those countries as payment for some agricultural products received from the United States. A number of promising predators have been found there, and it is hoped that the projects will add to our growing list of predators operating efficiently against the balsam woolly aphid in this country and Canada.

Another accidentally introduced pest against which an active program is being conducted is the alfalfa weevil. Most of its insect enemies are internal parasites, among which *Bathyplectes curculionis* is outstanding. This small, black wasp was collected in Italy in 1911 and released in Utah. It increased rapidly there, and now parasitization of weevil larvae infesting the first crop in our Western States often exceeds 90 percent. The alfalfa weevil, which established itself in the Eastern States in 1951, arrived without *Bathyplectes*. Arrangements were soon made to obtain the parasite, but first attempts to establish it apparently failed. It has now taken hold at several

An adult chrysopid or lacewing predator.

Bathyplectes curculionis parasitizing the alfalfa weevil.

Releasing Aphidoletes thompsoni on grand fir infested with the balsam woolly aphid in Oregon.

Eggs, larvae, pupae, and an adult lady beetle (ladybug).

Tetrastichus incertus placing eggs in the larva of alfalfa weevil.

places, and a program has been started to release it in North Carolina, South Carolina, West Virginia, New Jersey, and Pennsylvania in alfalfa fields that will not be sprayed with insecticides. The work is vitally important. The alfalfa weevil has increased to the point where it destroys some eastern fields in one season. We put our hope for its economic biological control in the East largely on *Bathyplectes,* and it is noteworthy that *Bathyplectes* can now be collected more easily in our Western States than in Europe. Additional parasites are also being collected for release in the United States by workers at the European Parasite Laboratory, maintained by the United States Department of Agriculture in France. Two, *Tetrastichus incertus* and *Microctonus aethiops,* have been recovered in New Jersey near the Parasite Introduction Laboratory in Moorestown.

Outstanding biological control has been achieved on citrus in California. The most famous was the introduction of the vedalia beetle from Australia in 1898. It was introduced to control the cottony cushion scale, which threatened to wipe out the California citrus industry entirely. This little lady beetle fed on the scale so voraciously and multiplied so fast that it brought the scale under complete control. The pest has never been a serious threat since then. Several other mealybugs and scale insects that attack citrus are serious, however, and a number of tiny internal parasites and predators have been introduced to fight against them.

The parasites and predators vary greatly in form and habit. Some of the commonest predators are ordinary beetles. Some of the commonest parasites are two-winged flies that look much like ordinary house flies. Others are four-winged, wasplike insects. We can make some general statements that will help to distinguish predators from parasites. Insect predators usually wander about and feed externally on a number of individuals. Insect parasites usually develop within the egg, larva, or cocoon of a single host. Lady beetles are predators, and all have rather similar habits. They feed on aphids, mealybugs, and related forms. The females lay eggs near their chosen prey, and the young feed on all stages of the same host species. Parasites show greater diversity. As a rule, adults feed almost exclusively on nectar or honeydew, which is a secretion from aphids. The immature parasites are the destroyers. Adults lay eggs in or on the host. The newly hatched larvae destroy the host, which is readily available. They complete their development on the single victim. Biological control undoubtedly can be used more extensively in the future. The development of more efficient strains of parasites, mass rearing so that large numbers can be released in restricted areas to effect direct control, and the use of parasites and predators in combination with insecticidal applications are some of the possibilities that are being explored. The last already has proved to be practical in many instances. *(Philip B. Dowden)*

Atomic Energy To Control Insects

INSECTS lose their power to reproduce when they are bombarded by gamma rays from a radioactive cobalt source. If large enough numbers of sterile insects are released to overflood the natural populations, the ability of normal insects to propagate is affected. If the sterile insects are released at a continuing high overflooding rate for a sustained period, the pest species may be eradicated.

The method works this way. Many millions of the insect pest are produced in an insect "factory." After sterilization by exposure to the gamma rays, the insects are released in areas inhabited by wild insects. When the released sterile insects greatly outnumber the wild insects, most of the matings that take place are not effective. As releases are continued, fewer and fewer offspring are produced, and it becomes more and more difficult for a normal female to find a normal mate. Calculations made by E. F. Knipling, an entomologist in the Department of Agriculture and the originator of this new concept, indicate that continued releases of large numbers of sterile insects may bring about the elimination of a species within a few insect generations.

Certain conditions govern the effective application of the procedure. It must be economically feasible to produce and distribute the large numbers of sterile insects required to overflood populations of natural pests. The radiation dosage needed to sterilize the insects must not damage them physically or seriously affect mating or other habits. Practical methods for distributing the sterile insects, whether from aircraft or on the ground, must be available. It was believed at first that the sterilization method would work only on insects that mate only once, but studies with tropical fruit flies have indicated that frequent mating will not be an obstacle. The method will not work or be practical for all kinds of insect pests. Some, such as the plant lice or aphids, which reproduce without mating, would not be controlled by releases of sterile individuals. Others are immobile for much of their existence, or they may not be able to invade the areas inhabited by the wild populations rapidly enough for the method to be effective. The sheer abundance of some pests, lack of suitable mass-rearing methods, or susceptibility to radiation damage are other limiting factors. The released sterile insects must not be harmful to crops, unless the injury they cause can be tolerated until eradication has been achieved.

348

The melon fly (Dacus cucurbitae), a serious pest of melons, tomatoes, cucumbers, and other crops. This fruit fly, and the oriental fruit fly (Dacus dorsalis), not shown, are subjects of radiation sterilization tests on Rota, an island in the western Pacific, conducted by the Department of Agriculture in cooperation with the United States Navy and Trust Territory of the Pacific Islands.

The effectiveness of the method was first demonstrated on the screw-worm fly, *Callitroga hominivorax,* a serious pest of livestock, by Dr. Knipling, A. W. Lindquist, R. C. Bushland, A. H. Baumhover, and their associates of the Department of Agriculture in field trials in Florida and on Curaçao, an isolated island in the Caribbean Sea. A cooperative program to eradicate the screw-worm throughout the Southeastern States was undertaken in 1958 by veterinarians and entomologists of the Agricultural Research Service of the Department and the Florida Livestock Board. Neighboring States contributed supporting surveys and regulatory programs. Eminently successful, the releases of sterile flies brought about elimination of all screw-worms in about 18 months. More than 3 billion flies were produced, sterilized, and distributed over about 75 thousand square miles of Florida and adjacent States to the north. The fleet of 20 airplanes from which the flies were released flew more than 3 million miles. Many tons of whale and horse meat were used to feed and rear the flies. The estimated savings from this successful project—one without parallel in applied zoology—are about 20 million dollars a year. Because the screw-worm was still present in Texas and other Southwestern States in 1962, a possibility remains that infestation originating there may make its way to

Efficient, low-cost methods for mass rearing insects are essential for application of the radiation sterilization method. Fruit flies are maintained in tiers of portable cages for egg production at the fruit fly laboratory in Hawaii.

Artificial devices are used to collect fruit fly eggs. The melon fly and oriental fruit fly insert their eggs through pin holes in plastic ice cream cartons. Many thousands of eggs can be collected in a carton.

Eggs of the fruit fly are deposited through pin holes in a plastic egg-collecting device.

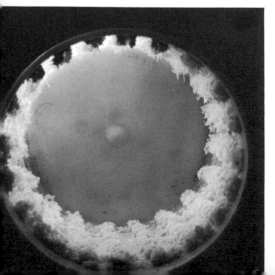

A colored wax shell is used to collect eggs of the Mexican fruit fly, which will not lay eggs in plastic receptacles with pin holes in them—it prefers to make its own punctures. The inverted plastic glass provides water. The small tray contains adult foods.

Fruit fly eggs on a small pad are placed on dehydrated carrot, a rearing medium, in trays. After hatching, the fly maggots complete their development in the carrot medium.

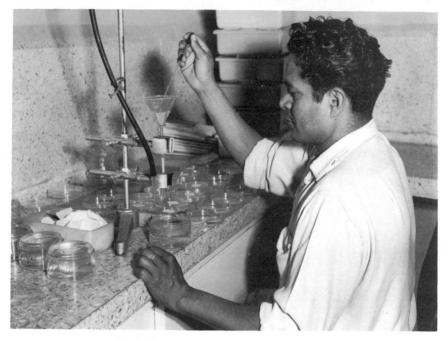

Fruit fly eggs are measured volumetrically.

Larvae of the Mexican fruit fly (Anastrepha ludens) are allowed to change to the pupal or resting stage in trays containing sand.

The carrot medium used to rear fruit fly maggots, first prepared from fresh carrots by University of California scientists and later changed to dehydrated carrots by Department entomologists, is prepared in a special mixing tank. After the trays are filled with the medium and eggs have been added, the trays are placed in a cabinet until larval development has been completed. The mature larvae leave the medium and fall into a drawer at the bottom of the cabinet, where they may be collected.

the Southeast. A reoccurrence of the screw-worm in a restricted area in Florida in the summer of 1961 was believed to have been taken care of by further releases of small numbers of sterile flies.

Unusually low infestations in several fruits following releases of many millions of sterile Mediterranean fruit flies, *Ceratitis capitata,* in a high, cool, semi-isolated area on Mauna Kea Volcano in Hawaii, in a test conducted by L. F. Steiner, a Department scientist, suggested the possible usefulness of the sterilization method to control this pest. Releases of sterile Mexican fruit flies by R. H. Rhode, another Department entomologist, in a village in Mexico have also appeared to reduce infestations. These and other radiation sterilization tests that were started or planned in 1961 on Rota in the Mariana Islands and in Greece, Costa Rica, Egypt, and elsewhere, should let us know within a few years whether control of tropical fruit flies with the sterilization method will be feasible. If results are favorable, an important new weapon may become available for eliminating infestations on isolated islands or continents that threaten our subtropical agriculture. Radiation sterilization studies with mosquitoes, the pink bollworm, codling moth, European corn borer, sugarcane borer, boll weevil, tobacco budworm, lice, cockroaches, the fall armyworm, tsetse fly, and other serious pests were in progress or under consideration in our country or other parts of the world. Even before the usefulness of radiation sterilization as a means of suppressing insect populations is fully determined, this technique may be supplanted to some degree by chemicals that void the reproduction of insects. Several compounds that render fruit flies, house flies, other insects and mites impotent or infertile when administered in food or externally to their bodies have been found. As yet, most of them are not safe for use on crops or animals. Chemists in the Department of Agriculture, other agencies, and industry have undertaken studies of new materials in the hope of developing completely safe sterilants. Effective chemosterilants will eliminate the need for irradiation and distribution of large numbers of laboratory-reared insects, if they can be applied to natural populations. Just as the radiation sterilization method may be limited in its application by damage resulting from exposure to the gamma rays or our inability to rear some insects, so may treatment problems influence the range of usefulness of chemosterilants. These methods may complement each other in the ultimate application that is developed for them.

Radioisotopes also are research tools. When certain radioactive chemicals are incorporated in the food of insects or applied to them in other ways, the insects then carry radioactive tags, which make

The pupal, or resting, stage of tropical fruit flies, which resembles a grain of wheat, is the most convenient one to radiate. The photograph shows many thousands of pupae, which have just been sterilized in Honolulu, being placed in a special container for air shipment to the radiation sterilization test site in the Mariana Islands. The aerated shipping container is shown in the background.

After attachment to the arm of the hoist, the cannister containing many thousands of pupae is inserted into the chamber in the lead cask, in the background of the photograph, which contains radioactive cobalt. Adult flies emerging from the treated pupae are sterile.

their later identification possible with a Geiger counter. Such radioactive markers facilitate studies of behavior, movement habits, length of life, and responses to various stimuli under natural conditions. Releases and recapture of radioactive insects may also be used to estimate the abundance of insects. This information has many uses, including the calculation of overflooding ratios needed in radiation sterilization experiments. Knowledge of the flight habits and dispersion of insects may be of help in the development of practical quarantine, control, and eradication programs. Radioactive chemicals have advanced our knowledge of life processes of insects.

The use of radioactive chemical tracers has enabled us to investigate problems of the rate of circulation and volume of blood; the absorption of fats, carbohydrates, and amino acids from the intes-

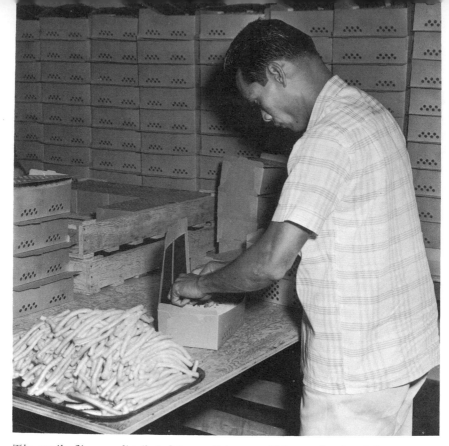

The sterile flies are distributed in small boxes, which may be ejected from aircraft with automatic equipment or thrown out by hand. Wicks saturated with nutrient solution help to keep the flies alive until distribution can be accomplished. Cardboard partitions within the boxes give protection from wind damage after the boxes are ejected.

tinal tract; the fate of sterols and the extent to which they may be provided through biosynthesis; and many more. We need to know everything that goes on inside insects. Entirely new control procedures may be suggested by the results of basic biochemical and physiological research. The research on insecticides likewise benefits from the availability of radioactive materials. Tagged insecticides have been especially useful in supplementing chemical assays in residue investigations and in studies to determine the fate of the insecticides and their metabolites in or on plants, animals, and soil. An example of one significant application has been the employment of labeled insecticides to demonstrate that they can be used safely on dairy cows for control of flies without fear of objectionable residues in milk.

Quarantine treatments, such as fumigation with toxic gases, or exposure to heat or cold to rid commodities of insect infestation,

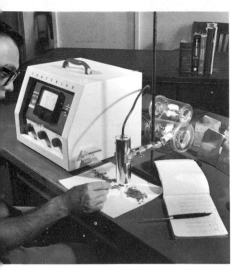

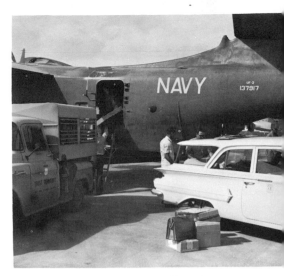

A Geiger counter is used to locate fruit flies tagged with radioactive phosphorus after their recovery in traps. Dispersal, behavior, and other biological studies are facilitated by this convenient means of identifying marked insects. Radioactive insects may also be used to obtain estimates of natural populations needed to calculate overflooding ratios in radiation sterilization tests.

Loading boxes containing sterile melon flies and oriental flies on a Navy flying boat for weekly distribution over Rota, test site in the Mariana Islands.

are methods now in use to protect our agriculture from invasion by foreign pests. Studies with tropical fruit flies have shown that the threat of their introduction may be eliminated by applying to infested commodities low dosages of radiation, which sterilize the flies without killing them. Most fresh fruit and vegetables appear to tolerate the small amounts of radiation needed to sterilize the fruit flies. Further work on this interesting possible application may indicate the feasibility of its practical application. We also have undertaken investigations of radiation to destroy the reproductive potential of insects in the travelers' baggage or other parcels and to eliminate or control insect infestation in grains and other stored products. The growing resistance of insects to insecticides and public concern over problems associated with the use of insecticides give entomologists the obligation to explore all possible new approaches to the control of insects. Future research on radiation and radioactive materials undoubtedly will be as productive in suggesting new concepts and experimental procedures as the ones we have developed. Progress is a product of good research. Seldom does it mark time or take a backward step. *(L. D. Christenson)*

Billions of Bombs

THIS IS THE STORY of a simple device that grew into a billion-dollar-a-year industry. It started about 1940, when a need arose for insecticides free of oil for use in mushroom houses. Searching for a way other than oil sprays to apply insecticides in the form of very fine particles, a chemist, L. D. Goodhue, and an entomologist, W. N. Sullivan, both of the Department of Agriculture, first tried burning mixtures of derris or pyrethrum, cornstalks, and sodium nitrate to produce a smoke. This was effective, but a large part of the insecticide was destroyed in the combustion process. A better method was found to be the spraying of a solution of the insecticide onto a hotplate or another heated surface.

Still not satisfied with the efficiency of the process, the scientists in 1941 got the idea of dissolving the insecticide in a liquefied gas under pressure in a container and letting the solution escape through a nozzle with a tiny opening. In that way they could produce a fine fog or mist that would stay suspended in the air for a long time. Such fine smokes and fogs technically are called aerosols. This liquefied-gas method of producing insecticide aerosols they found to be effective. A nonflammable, nontoxic liquefied gas, dichlorodifluoromethane (now commonly called propellant–12), which was used in mechanical refrigerators, was found to be suitable. The first insecticide aerosols of this type consisted of a solution of pyrethrum extract and sesame oil in propellant–12 in a steel cylinder and discharged through an oil-burner nozzle. Goodhue and Sullivan described this invention in 1941 and obtained a public-service patent, under which royalty-free licenses were issued for the manufacture of insecticidal aerosols until it expired in 1960.

Other workers have had the idea of using gas-propelled insecticide solutions. As early as 1882, carbon dioxide was used to pressurize large tanks of water solution of insecticides for orchard spraying. These earlier methods were not used generally. They did not include the idea of utilizing a liquefied gas as combined solvent and propellant or the use of a convenient, hand-held container. Just about the time that the liquefied-gas propelled insecticide aerosols had been shown to be practical, the United States entered the war. The armed services became interested in the device as a means for protecting their personnel from disease-carrying mosquitoes in airplanes, barracks, tents, and foxholes. It was found that small containers used for packaging 1-pound lots of dichlorodifluoromethane for refrigerators would make suitable containers. The armed services procured more than 40 million of the aerosol units. After the war, the aerosols were immediately accepted into civilian use. The need for a cheaper, lightweight aerosol container became apparent. This necessitated new types of aerosol formulations for use with lower pressures.

R. A. Fulton, a Department chemist, led this development. Manufacturers of cans helped to engineer and perfect a valve and container, and the first experimental units were filled March 7, 1947. Later in the year, two commercial filling plants for low-pressure aerosols were designed. In 1948, the first year of production, about 1 million units were sold. Since the use of insecticides is seasonal, the companies looked for other products to keep the plants operating on a yearlong basis. Aerosol deodorants soon appeared on the market. They were followed by a product known as Christmas snow, shaving cream, hair sprays, and others. In 1962 there were more than 120 aerosol contract loaders, 15 manufacturers of valves, and 14 manufacturers of containers. More than 290 types of products are used in aerosol containers, which are now produced in at least 15 countries. The annual production of all types approaches a billion units.

During this period of development, the Department of Agriculture continued research to find new uses for this method of applying insecticides. A standard aerosol formula was developed; any insecticide appearing on the market must meet this requirement. Many of the newer insecticides have been incorporated into aerosol formulations. Special pressurized spray formulas have been developed for applying residual insecticides to surfaces to control crawling insects, such as ants and roaches. Their particle size is somewhat larger than the true aerosols. Mothproofers, pet and animal sprays, and house and garden sprays of this type are used widely. The use of the organic phosphate insecticides applied by the aerosol method has revolutionized the control of insects in greenhouses through an increase in effectiveness and a reduction in labor.

Special insecticide aerosol formulas have been developed for the treatment of airplanes and ships to prevent the introduction of harmful insects. These formulas have become the accepted standard for this purpose throughout the world. This method of dispersing insecticides has also been applied to vaporizing fumigants and sterilizing agents. The method has the advantage of the additional force of the bursting effect of the particles at the nozzle to give uniform distribution. In a new method developed for sterilizing without heat, by using ethylene oxide, the nonflammable liquefied-gas propellant is used to eliminate the fire hazard of the active ingredient. *(R. A. Fulton and W. N. Sullivan)*

Resistance in Plants

THE GRAPE industry of Europe was threatened by the accidental introduction of a root-feeding aphid from America in the 19th century. The insect was native to the eastern part of the United States, and native grapes growing there had developed immunity to it. The grafting of European grapes on resistant rootstocks from the Eastern States gave control and saved the European grapes. It is an example of the value of resistant varieties as a means of curbing insects, but organized efforts to develop them began only 50 years ago. Since then collections of plants from all over the world have been screened; more than 100 species have been recorded, and 38 insect-resistant crop varieties were grown on American farms in 1958. Several others have been released since then or have been used in breeding programs. The development of insect-resistant varieties requires the cooperative efforts of entomologists, plant breeders, agronomists, and plant pathologists. The process of hybridization and selection takes 6 to 10 years, but insect-resistant selections occasionally can be made from a mixed plant population; if they are otherwise desirable, seeds of them can be made available to farmers in a shorter time.

The control of the hessian fly by the use of wheats resistant to it has been especially successful. The first such became available in Kansas in 1942. More than a dozen other varieties adapted to most of the infested area have been developed. Previously the only method for controlling the fly was delayed seeding, a method that was effective only for control of the fall generation. Farmers can now plant wheat earlier and get fall and winter wheat pasture for livestock. Some varieties of wheat can withstand other insects, including the sawfly. Rescue, a spring wheat, was developed in Canada; Rego, a winter wheat, and Sawtana, a spring wheat, have been released in Montana. All have been used for sawfly control. Resistance to the greenbug observed in barley during an infestation in 1942 by I. M. Atkins in Texas and Reynold G. Dahms in Oklahoma led to the development of resistant varieties of barley. The first wheat highly resistant to the greenbug was found in 1953 in greenhouse tests in Oklahoma, and breeding work was undertaken in Oklahoma, Texas, and Kansas to transfer the resistance to acceptable varieties.

The adults of some important cotton pests, such as leafworms,

Varieties of wheat with solid stems, like Rescue, make normal yields despite infestations of sawfly, but Thatcher is an almost total loss.

Damage to wheat by greenbugs: Ponca is a susceptible variety, DS28A is a resistant selection, and the hybrid of DS28A × Ponca is as resistant as DS28A.

Golden Regent sweet corn is resistant to the corn earworm; Spancross is susceptible.

A295, a variety of corn, is resistant to European corn borer; inbred WF9 is susceptible.

cabbage looper, bollworm, and pink bollworm, may stay out of cottonfields where varieties are grown that do not secrete nectar from the leaves and bracts. We grew common varieties and the new nectaryless plants in cages at Brownsville, Tex., and found 7 to 10 times as many leafworms in the common varieties as on the nectaryless cotton. The next step is to find out what effect the nectaryless cotton will have on insect infestations when it is grown in fields. Some varieties of sugarcane can withstand or escape injury by the sugarcane borer better than others. The use of relatively resistant varieties may help meet the borer problem and reduce the acreage that needs extensive spraying with insecticides.

Progress has been made in developing dent corn that resists the earworm. In a stand of southern field corn that would have yielded

Bountiful snap bean is susceptible to the Mexican bean beetle; Wade is resistant.

50 bushels an acre, loss was 3.2 bushels in the susceptible Mosby variety but only one-half bushel in resistant Dixie 18. In extensive breeding programs of field corn, sweet corn, and popcorn by Federal and State agencies, inbred lines and hybrid combinations have been tested for resistance to the European corn borer. Resistance and tolerance of certain lines are transmitted to their crosses. Many experimental inbred lines with effective resistance to the first brood of borers have been developed. A group of resistant inbred lines have been released by several State agricultural experiment stations, and hybrids with satisfactory resistance are available for some areas. The tolerance of some strains of corn to rootworms has been demonstrated by their ability to develop new roots above the point of injury almost as fast as the larvae eat off the roots. Susceptible strains lodge easily and produce poorly filled ears. Pollination may be affected adversely when lodging occurs at or before tasseling.

The use of resistant varieties of alfalfa to control the spotted alfalfa aphid illustrates how rapid this method of control can be accepted. Soon after the aphid was found in the United States in 1954, plant breeders and entomologists discovered that Lahontan, a variety developed for resistance to stem nematode, was resistant to the aphid. It was moderately hardy and adapted to parts of the West. Scientists concentrated on a program to develop resistant varieties for other areas. Moapa, a nonhardy variety adapted to the Southwest, was developed from African alfalfa at the Nevada Agricultural Experiment Station and was released there and the Arizona and California Agricultural Experiment Stations in 1957. Zia, adapted to New Mexico and similar areas, was developed and released in 1958 by the New Mexico Agricultural Experiment Station. Cody, developed from selections from Buffalo alfalfa at the Kansas Agricultural Experiment Station, was released in 1959. It is adapted to the area from southern Nebraska into Oklahoma.

Studies conducted with sorghums in Oklahoma and Kansas during an outbreak of chinch bugs in the thirties showed that in general the milos were very susceptible, the feteritas were susceptible, and the kafirs and sorgos were rather resistant. Data on hybrids showed that resistance was inherited, but the genetic factors involved were not determined.

Beans, cantaloups, collards, sweet corn, onions, peppers, potatoes, and squash are some of the vegetables that have been investigated for insect resistance. Men at the North Carolina Agricultural Experiment Station have determined the resistance of several vegetables to insect attack. They found no immune varieties, but some are less heavily infested and suffer less damage than other varieties. Control with insecticides is more effective on some resistant varieties and thus more economical than on susceptible varieties. A spectacular form of resistance was found by R. A. Blanchard, of the Department of Agriculture, in 1941 in a line of flour corn. He observed dead larvae of the corn earworm in the silks. The same or similar lethal factor has been located in a cross of corn $\times$ teosinte $\times$ sweet corn and from sweet corn $\times$ Mexican June, a semiflint variety. The lethal factor appears to be dominant. Thus, when either or both parents in a cross had the factor, it nearly always showed up in the progeny. The Purdue University Agricultural Experiment Station in 1959 released two inbred lines of sweet corn that showed this lethal factor. We do not know whether it is a toxic substance in the silk or the lack of some nutrient essential to the larvae of the corn earworm. Even in sweet corn developed without this lethal factor, some resistance to earworm has been developed. Some new hybrids have only 10 injured kernels in an ear; Golden Cross Bantam may have 25. Experimental hybrids have been tested that approach immunity.

The cause of plant resistance to insects is usually complex and varies with each insect and crop. It may be due to traits that cause insects to avoid a plant. It may be brought about by the lack of some nutrient in the plant necessary for development of insects. Specific chemicals, including toxins, may be responsible. Sometimes resistance may be due to the ability of the plant to withstand insect feeding or its ability to recover from injury. Varieties on which insects feed may exert a profound influence on their fecundity and other biological processes. For example, the spotted alfalfa aphid may produce about 30 offspring a week on a susceptible variety, but on resistant plants the aphid will produce only 4 or 5. An example of the effect of resistant varieties on the insect population in a wide area was reported in California. Two soft white wheats, Big Club 43 and Poso 42, resistant to the hessian fly, were released in 1944 and 1945 in California in places where the fly was doing serious damage. By 1946, further research on control of the insect was unnecessary because it was no longer a problem. Now even susceptible varieties grown on small acreages in these areas have low infestation. A variety that causes a reduction in the insect population of 40 or 50 percent each generation may eliminate the need for chemical control. Other natural forces may further reduce the number of insects.

Major efforts in developing resistant varieties have been to control insects that attack field crops. The progress has been so encouraging that undoubtedly research will be increased to develop insect-resistant varieties of fruit, nut, and forest trees, small fruit, vegetables, and ornamental plants. This means of control can be used without cost to the grower, without creating toxic residue to man and wildlife, and without damage to pollinating insects. It does not upset Nature's balance between insects and their natural enemies. *(Reynold G. Dahms)*

Lures for Insects

THE FEMALES of certain species of insects emit an odor that attracts to them males of their own species for mating purposes. Male gypsy moths can detect minute traces of female odor by means of their keen, highly developed antennae. Many other species depend for their survival on their sense of smell, not just to locate the opposite sex, but to find food, water, and plants and animals on which to lay their eggs. Sometimes an odor can evoke so compelling a response that the insect appears to have no choice but to follow the odor trail to its source.

We can take advantage of this behavior to help us combat injurious insects—in effect, the very trait that enables a species to survive or thrive in a hostile environment thus may lead to its destruction. Entomologists and chemists in the Department of Agriculture have pioneered in the use of materials capable of attracting insects, an approach that has been successful against the Mediterranean fruit fly and the gypsy moth. The lures, usually in traps, can help find foreign insect species before they can gain a firm foothold here. The insect, in getting caught, betrays its presence, and thereby assures the early detection of an infestation, which may then be eradicated before it can spread. Several of the insect lures now guard our borders at ports of entry. The baited traps do the work of detection more efficiently and at less cost than any other known method.

Should insects become established, detection of the extent and intensity of the infestation becomes important. Attractants show where and when control measures should be applied and when they may be ended. Thus we save time, money, and insecticides. Lures, by indicating a buildup of an insect population, can guide the timing of insecticide applications to give maximum effects. They have also shown promise in the direct control of insects. For example, by spraying an insecticide plus methyleugenol, a potent specific lure for the male oriental fruit fly, the Department's fruit fly laboratory in Hawaii obtained excellent control of the insect. Further experimentation on some Pacific islands may provide a way of eliminating a harmful species without affecting beneficial insects and wildlife.

Certain synthetic chemicals have been found to be potent insect lures. Like the sex attractants, they are highly specific, potent, effective at distances up to one-half mile, and attractive only to males. Curiously, we have found that compounds that attract females in

A gypsy moth, lured by a sex attractant, is about to enter a trap used in a survey.

The antennae of male gypsy moths are keen organs of smell.

Two segments, which contain scent glands, of the abdomen of a female gypsy moth are clipped into a bottle of solvent.

The top of a medfly trap is removed to show the cotton wick, which was impregnated with an attractive chemical, and a number of dead medflies.

laboratory tests do not attract them to any marked degree in the field. Weak lures can be useful, too. Once located, insects can frequently be controlled more effectively with a combination of lures and insecticides than with insecticides alone. Since the insect comes to the lure, the use of the combination eliminates the need for complete coverage. In this application, specificity and long-range action are not important, and the inexpensive food-based lures (for example, protein hydrolyzates), which usually are easily found, work well. The weak lures can therefore supplement the more costly specific ones.

Two examples show how lures can help us. Florida had two invasions of the Mediterranean fruit fly—the medfly. In the first, in 1929–1930, information on its distribution was obtained primarily by cutting and examining fruit. Eradication was achieved by 6 thousand workers, mainly through the removal of many trees and the destruction and burial of thousands of tons of fruit. In 1956–1957, 50 thousand lure-baited traps were used to pinpoint infestations, and

366

only 800 employees were needed to effect eradication. A mixture composed of insecticide plus a protein hydrolyzate attractant was sprayed by airplane, and about 5 percent of the soil was treated with a granular insecticide. Progress was excellent. The new methods, coupled with improved fumigation techniques, permitted almost normal harvesting and movement of crops to market; losses of crops and trees were nil. The total cost of the campaign was 11 million dollars over the 18 months; the cost of living with the pest has been estimated at 20 million dollars a year. In the early stages of the recent eradication, angelica seed oil, a medfly lure discovered in Hawaii by Department entomologists, led by L. D. Christenson and L. F. Steiner, was pressed into use. The flies responded avidly to this costly, spicy-smelling liquid, but in the midst of the campaign the world's supply of this oil ran out. Meanwhile Department chemists, led by S. A. Hall, had been synthesizing chemicals, and the Hawaiian entomologists were checking their attractiveness to the medfly. One of the chemists, S. I. Gertler, produced a group of synthetics that the medflies found most attractive. The best of these, siglure, was not so potent as angelica seed oil, but it could be made in any quantity, it was relatively inexpensive, and it did the job. Subsequently we collaborated with Mr. Gertler and introduced the synthetics known as medlure and trimedlure. These, especially the latter, are superior in potency to angelica seed oil.

Another example of lures at work pertains to the gypsy moth, which in its larval stage is a voracious defoliator of forest and shade trees. When it had reached an explosive buildup in numbers in 1889 in Massachusetts, entomologists attempted to use traps baited with unmated females for control purposes. Their efforts went for naught. They later discovered that the baited traps were efficient detectors of moth infestations and that the living female could be replaced by her last two abdominal segments or by an extract of those tips. Lure collected one year deteriorated by the time it was needed for trapping the following year. However, H. L. Haller, Fred Acree, Jr., and their coworkers in the Department of Agriculture discovered that they could stabilize the lure by chemical processing (hydrogenation), so that it maintained its potency for 10 years or more. Then the research men worked out the many details necessary for maintaining the survey and control operation now in use. With the traps pointing the way, insecticides are applied, usually by air, to hold down infestations and, applied to the fringe areas, to prevent the moth from spreading outside New England.

Some lures have been discovered by chance; some, by careful observation. An 8-year-old girl in Australia in 1907 noticed that medflies were attracted to kerosene that was being used to repel ants. For almost 50 years kerosene remained the best of the known medfly lures. Other discoveries were that automobile lacquer attracts the palmetto weevil *(Rhyncophorus cruentatus)*; wood and cigarette smoke attracts *Melanophila consputa;* the drycleaning fluid trichloro-ethylene attracts the kelp fly *(Coelapa frigida)*.

Most of those discoveries are only of academic interest. How do we set out to find a lure for a species having economic importance? There are two main routes. In one, the isolation approach, we start with a natural substance known to be an attractant and attempt to isolate, identify, and possibly synthesize the active ingredient. The attractant may be the sex scent of an insect, or it may be derived from a host plant or animal. A. Butenandt and his coworkers in Germany after 20 years of searching explained the chemical structure of the sex attractant of the silkworm moth. Long experimentation was carried on by Department workers on the gypsy moth sex attractant. Dr. Acree succeeded in concentrating and partly characterizing it. Martin Jacobson and his coworkers identified the chemical structure and synthesized it and a related substance that is easily produced. The yield of pure attractant from 500 thousand gypsy moth tips was one small drop of liquid, so potent that one ten-thousandth of a billionth of a gram of it can lure moths out of the woods. The availability of a synthetic gypsy moth lure has freed scientists from the expensive work of collecting the natural lure in the field. These examples show that the isolation approach can be long and arduous. The chemist's task has been eased considerably by the availability of modern instrumentation and techniques, but he must still develop procedures for extraction and purification and cope with such difficulties as the instability or high volatility of the lure.

The other method of finding attractants is to screen large numbers of chemicals of many different types to turn up attractive materials. We then obtain or synthesize compounds related to the best leads in an effort to get better lures. The ingenuity of the chemist comes into play here in deciding which compounds should be synthesized and in devising methods to prepare the chemicals. In general, this screening procedure is the same as the one used to find new insecticides, herbicides, pharmaceuticals, and other physiologically active agents. The program has turned up potent and useful lures for a number of important insect pests. In the course of our studies on insect attractants, more than 6 thousand chemicals have been tested against several different species. It is too early to draw any general conclusions in regard to structural types that would be attractive at our present state of knowledge, but a start has been made. It is interesting to note that the only two known natural sex lures, those of the silkworm moth and the gypsy moth, are both derived from unsaturated alcohols with 16-carbon atoms. Further research may indicate that other natural insect sex lures are closely related. *(Morton Beroza* and *Nathan Green)*

Problems in Greenhouses

EMPERORS, status-seekers, the prominent, and such people have had greenhouses for a long time. For common folk, however, the problems of pests and diseases were too much until a few decades ago. Now growing vegetables, fruit, flowers, and other plants under glass is a well established commercial practice and an entrancing hobby within the reach in money, time, and space of many. Against the insects and diseases, people used—to little avail—sulfur, tobacco, quassia, handpicking, washing with soapy water, brushing to remove scales, and so on. They would start crops in the fall, grow them during the cooler seasons, and abandon them when the pests became unmanageable.

Research projects on greenhouse pests were started about 1915 in the Department of Agriculture and several State agricultural experiment stations. They led to the development of pot fumigation with sodium cyanide and calcium cyanide powder, refined oil-emulsion sprays to replace kerosene emulsion, fumigation with various substances, and derris and pyrethrum sprays. None of those materials changed growing practices very much. About 1945 we entered a new era in pest control, which began with the appearance of many organic chemicals, including DDT, lindane, chlordane, dieldrin, endrin, TEPP, parathion, and malathion. They were especially effective against thrips, cutworms, leaf rollers and other caterpillars, centipedes, millipedes, chrysanthemum and rose midges, leafhoppers, plant bugs, many beetles, aphids, whiteflies, mealybugs, and scale insects. The control of spider mites by TEPP, parathion, and later by Aramite, Kelthane, Tedion, and Dibrom has been a notable accomplishment. Lindane in the soil was the first chemical that controlled the root-feeding symphylans without damaging the plants; on the foliage, lindane is highly effective against thrips and aphids. Metaldehyde for slugs and snails and Kelthane and Thiodan for the cyclamen mite have given us the first safe and effective controls for these serious old pests.

The elimination or reduction of many injurious pests on vegetable and flower crops in the greenhouse has resulted from the use of these insecticides that kill by contact, after ingestion, or through long residual action. Vapors of some compounds applied to foliage give a prolonged local fumigation action when the ventilators are closed. Some compounds, as demeton and schradan, are systemic poisons that may be applied to the soil, stems, or foliage and enter the plant. Most of these powerful new chemicals can be had as improved dusts, wettable powders, emulsion concentrates, aerosols, smokes, or concentrated sprays. Insects, nematodes, and disease organisms can be destroyed by steam sterilizing between crops; outmoded now is the former laborious practice of removing the soil from the bench and replacing it with new soil from the field.

By growing fewer crops in the greenhouse, the grower has greatly reduced the number of pests that he must combat. In this day of specialization, cuttings of chrysanthemums, carnations, poinsettia, and foliage plants are grown in a few places and supplied for scheduled planting dates to growers throughout the country. Occasionally certain pests, as the carnation shoot mite, spider mites, and leaf miners, are distributed widely on these cuttings and cause considerable damage before they are recognized and control measures are pursued. The newer chemicals and mechanical devices for automatic control of lighting, heating, ventilation, and watering have given the commercial greenhouse operator increased production per square foot of growing area and have improved the quality of flowers and vegetables. By controlling thrips and spider mites, he can now produce white roses and carnations for June weddings and late crops of tomatoes and cucumbers. That was almost impossible before modern insecticides were available. Efficient pest control has enabled him to take full advantage of new lighting and shading effects on plants and to produce crops throughout the year.

Floriculture and ornamental horticulture have changed a great deal in production practices during the past few years. Flowers grown in one part of the United States can be placed in markets in any other part of the country by overnight transportation. Keen competition exists between the northern operators of glass- or plastic-covered greenhouses and outdoor growers of the same crops in California, Florida, Hawaii, and other States that have long growing seasons. Specialists on Extension staffs in many States aid growers in developing more efficient ways of increasing production per square foot of greenhouse space by mechanizing growing operations and using better pest and disease controls and agricultural practices.

The present trend in building commercial greenhouses is to use plastic-covered houses as adjuncts to existing glass greenhouses. New greenhouse establishments and cloth-covered growing areas are being built in regions with favorable climate. Census reports indicate an overall increase of 50 percent in the valuation of crops and ornamentals during the past decade. This trend reflects the continued desire of American people for ornamental plants and healthy prospects for the future of commercial floriculture. Even more noteworthy is the construction of small greenhouses or conservatories

370

A lean-to type of greenhouse.

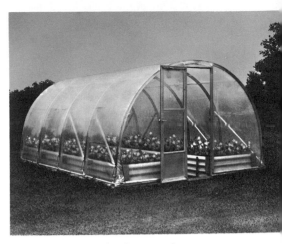

An inexpensive, plastic-covered greenhouse.

attached to private homes. One can spend considerable money for a greenhouse of masonry and glass, or one can erect a simple framework and cover it with plastic sheeting. Automatic controls for heating, ventilating, and watering take care of the plants during the owner's absence. *(Floyd F. Smith)*

A home garden greenhouse of metal frame, glass, and masonry. It has electrically controlled heating and ventilating units.

Combustible powders or smokes, developed originally for applying nicotine, are available with many of the newer insecticides and fungicides. Some are safe for use in home greenhouses—but read the label!

Carriers of Diseases

TYPHUS was brewing in war-torn Naples, Italy, in 1943. Unchecked, it would surely spread into a major epidemic, as it always had in wars, and in its wake take a toll of human lives equal to losses in combat. Typhus, a disease associated with wars and famine, is carried by lice. When living conditions become disorganized and people do not have facilities for keeping warm or for changing clothing regularly, infestations of body lice become heavy and widespread. Then, if typhus cases develop, the stage is set for an epidemic. Infected lice spread from one person to another in crowded sleeping quarters, as in compounds for prisoners and refugees.

When the Second World War began, we had no good way to control lice under conditions such as those that existed in Naples and elsewhere in Europe and northern Africa. Efforts to develop ways to control lice in time of war had been too meager—a strange and unexplained shortcoming in human judgment. History records that typhus rivals the enemy as a deterrent force to successful prosecution of major and extended wars. Yet, before the war, no country had made any determined effort to find a solution to the problem of body lice. Soon after our entry into the war, the Surgeon General's Office of the United States Army arranged for funds to support research by the Department of Agriculture on the control of the body louse. The investigations were started in April 1942, in Orlando, Fla. Within a year, control methods were developed that permitted the Army and the Rockefeller Foundation to stop typhus in Naples in 1943 and 1944, thereby demonstrating that typhus epidemics no longer need be a cause of human misery and suffering.

The achievements of the entomologists and chemists at Orlando were a major contribution to human medicine. Twenty-five men let themselves be human guinea pigs so that the chemicals could be tested and developed under conditions simulating louse infestations in the worst possible situation. In order to provide insects for evaluating many insecticides, it was necessary to develop and maintain a thriving colony of 25 thousand to 75 thousand body lice. The evaluation of the candidate insecticides began with a simple but reliable beaker test, in which patches of woolen cloth were impregnated with the chemical. If lice placed on the treated cloth were alive after 24 hours, the chemical was considered ineffective. If they were killed and if later tests showed that the treatment possessed

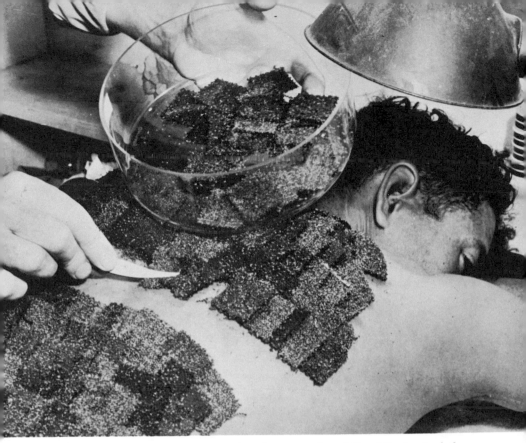

Thousands of lice were needed at Orlando, Fla., to test insecticides. Clinging to cloth patches, they were fed human blood twice daily.

lasting louse-killing action, the material was formulated in a powder for the next stage of testing. The Army wanted a louse powder that could be packaged in small cans and supplied to soldiers for louse protection and that could also be applied by hand or power dusters to masses of louse-infested people.

Then lice were exposed to cloth treated with a powder. If the treatment was effective for several days, the candidate insecticide was given a more critical test on a human subject. Cloth sleeves were dusted on the inside and taped to the arms and legs. Twenty-five lice from the colony were placed inside each sleeve. Examinations were made after 24 hours. If all lice were killed, more were added at intervals of several days to determine the residual action. The goal was to develop a powder that would kill all lice on a person at the time of treatment and also provide protection for several weeks to kill young lice that would hatch from eggs in the clothing or to prevent infestations from other sources. These techniques made it possible to develop a highly effective louse powder

373

within 4 months. The powder, containing synergized pyrethrum, killed lice quickly and prevented reinfestations up to 2 or 3 weeks. It was by far the best louse treatment known. The MYL formula was judged safe to use by pharmacologists of the Food and Drug Administration; it was tested by the Army, the Rockefeller Foundation, and the United States Typhus Commission and was found to be effective on naturally infested people.

Millions of cans of the powder were packaged and supplied to American and Allied troops. Research on new and even better louse powders continued at Orlando. In November 1942, the laboratory received the first sample of DDT from Switzerland. The test procedures demonstrated its value for control of lice. The Armed Forces purchased thousands of pounds of DDT dust. Millions of men, women, and children in war theaters were dusted for louse control. The threat of typhus in Naples was the first to be brought under control. Other epidemics in other war theaters were dealt with in the same way. Typhus is now controlled among civil-

The critical test: Sleeves containing lice were treated with an insecticide and put on men's arms and legs. If the lice died in 24 hours, new lice were added to determine how long the treatment was effective. If the lice were not killed, the men had to stand their crawling and feeding until records were taken.

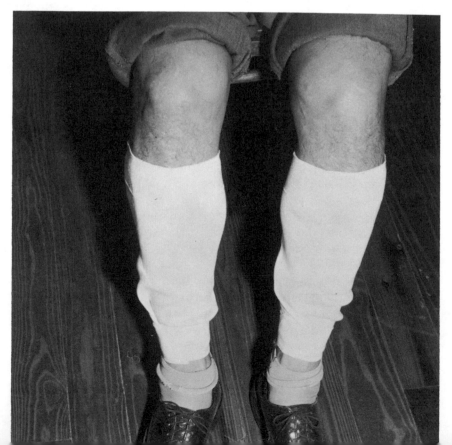

ians throughout the world, but research continues, because in many places the insect has become resistant to DDT. When lice became resistant to DDT in Korea, scientists cooperated with the Army in developing a lindane dust. By the time resistance to lindane appeared among lice in scattered localities, we had already demonstrated that a malathion dust was at least as good as lindane. We still have the original MYL formula, which is effective. Our chemists have also come up with allethrin, the synthetic pyrethrumlike insecticide, which is excellent.

Malaria is another example, of many, of the work and methods of scientists in the control of insects, ticks, and mites that can spread human diseases. British and Italian scientists proved in 1898–1899 that malaria is transmitted by *Anopheles* mosquitoes. This rural disease, common in many parts of the world, once was a serious obstacle to agricultural and economic growth in the South. Scientists in various countries soon made progress in dealing with the disease by controlling the vector. By draining swampy lands and applying oils and paris green to kill the larvae, such agencies as the United States Public Health Service, the State health departments, and the Rockefeller Foundation reduced the incidence of malaria in the United States during the early years of the century. Despite many contributions by medical scientists, entomologists, and engineers, malaria was regarded as late as 1943 as the chief health problem among hundreds of millions of people. When the Second World War began, military authorities, recognizing the threat of malaria and other mosquito-borne diseases to our war efforts, arranged for the transfer of funds to the Department of Agriculture to support research on mosquitoes, as they did for body lice. Methods of control that were effective and feasible among people in a stabilized community were too slow and uncertain of results to protect combat troops adequately against malaria and other mosquito-borne diseases. Research was undertaken at Orlando on mosquito repellants, mosquito larvicides, and on ways to destroy adult mosquitoes. With the assistance of various branches of the Army, Navy, and Air Force, the great superiority of DDT over other known materials for mosquito control was established. Suitable formulations and ways of applying the insecticide were developed. DDT was shown to possess outstanding effectiveness against adult mosquitoes as contact sprays and aerosols even when applied outdoors. As little as 1 to 2 quarts of 5-percent DDT spray per acre applied from the air just about annihilated all adult mosquitoes, even in the densest jungle. In a matter of hours, diseases transmitted by mosquitoes could be stopped among our troops; previously, weeks of control efforts were necessary if measures against larvae only were used. Even more important was the development of the idea of using a residual spray to control malaria. Swiss scientists had discovered the residual value of

DDT for control of flies. The scientists at Orlando developed the concept of residual insecticide as a way to control malaria.

In order to evaluate the several thousand insecticides and repellants received for test each year at Orlando, it was necessary to have an ample supply of all stages of *Anopheles* mosquitoes. Methods of rearing *Anopheles quadrimaculatus* in the laboratory in limited numbers had been developed by the Rockefeller Foundation. The Orlando laboratory devised procedures for producing thousands of *Anopheles* mosquitoes for use each day. Many larvae were needed for evaluating larvicides, and adults were required in even larger numbers to test repellants, space sprays, aerosols, and residual insecticides. Adult mosquitoes died after resting for less than an hour on the sidewalls of a cage treated with a light coating of DDT spray. A week after the cage was treated, mosquitoes were again introduced and they were killed almost as quickly. When the original treatment continued to kill mosquitoes week after week for several months, the entomologists sensed that the residual sprays might be the real solution to the malaria problem. The next step was to determine if adult *Anopheles* resting on the inside walls of treated houses or sheds would remain on the treated surface long enough to be killed following the application of DDT. A substandard house was used for the first field tests in 1943 in Florida. Small amounts of DDT were applied inside. Week after week, adult *Anopheles* entering the building from nearby breeding areas were found dead on the floors, thus confirming in field tests the observations made in the laboratory. Subsequent tests were conducted in many animal sheds, houses, and other favorite resting places for *Anopheles* in Arkansas and Mexico. The results further established the high degree of efficiency and long lasting action of DDT against the mosquitoes. The military services utilized the residual spray method to control malaria among troops, but the procedure has proved to be of greatest value as a way to control malaria among civilians in malarious areas throughout the world.

National and international health agencies adopted the residual spray method for general use in malaria control. Malaria, already on the decline, was eradicated from the United States by the Public Health Service within a few years. DDT was used by the Italians and cooperating agencies to eradicate malaria from Italy. Many countries reduced the incidence of malaria to low levels within a few years. Now, through the efforts of several international health agencies, the world has embarked on a global program to eradicate malaria. Resistance of mosquitoes to DDT and dieldrin is one of the major obstacles to success, but a worldwide effort, sponsored by the World Health Organization, has begun to find new residual-type insecticides that can replace these insecticides as resistance develops in various regions. *(E. F. Knipling* and *A. W. Lindquist)*

Quarantines

PASSENGERS going abroad by air and sea nowadays are handed a leaflet that in four languages sounds an important warning: "Did you know that plant pests and animal diseases that destroy crops and livestock often travel from one country to another in passenger baggage? This is why many countries, including the United States, prohibit or restrict the entry of fruits, plants, vegetables, seeds, meats, and meat products. Do not bring such items to the United States unless you have a permit from the United States Department of Agriculture."

Guests at hotels in Hawaii, Bermuda, Nassau, and Puerto Rico find cards in their rooms that inform them that for their convenience inspectors of the Department of Agriculture examine baggage before the travelers board the airplanes bound for continental United States. They are informed also that other baggage and all parcels mailed to the United States are inspected on arrival. Such precautions are necessary because the threat of invasion by plant pests from abroad has grown. Many destructive plant pests and diseases with which we have to contend today are of foreign origin. Thousands more have not gained entry. It is the responsibility of the Plant Quarantine Division to see that they do not. The United States was among the last of the major powers to recognize the need for protecting its agriculture against such invasion. After the passage of the Plant Quarantine Act of 1912, we moved promptly to halt the migration of foreign pests. We began to inspect and fumigate imported plants and plant products. We forbade entry to infested and infected products for which we had no satisfactory treatments. We soon found out that the importation of agricultural products was only one of many ways foreign pests could be brought into the country. Travelers bring back fruits and plants they have acquired abroad. Foreign mail, the food stores of ships, planes, and trains, and automobiles entering over our land borders may carry infested and infected products. As our plant quarantine service was developed, inspection was extended to cover all of these avenues for entry of pests.

It was relatively simple to maintain the defenses in the early days. Today the situation is different. The danger is greater. More people travel more, farther, and faster. Infested products can be brought from any part of the world in a few hours and, because of the open-

Preflight inspection helps prevent the spread of plant pests.

ing of new international airports in the interior of the country and the completion of the St. Lawrence Seaway, right into the agricultural area of our interior.

The Plant Quarantine Division maintains inspection service at all major air, ocean, Great Lake, and border ports of entry in continental United States. Stations also are in Hawaii, Guam, Puerto Rico, the American Virgin Islands, Bermuda, and Nassau. Importations of plants, fruit, vegetables, and other agricultural products are inspected to insure that they will not be the means of introducing new pests. Fumigation and other forms of treatment are applied when necessary. Baggage of incoming passengers is examined in cooperation with the Customs Service for plant material. Foreign parcel post is

Inspection at Idlewild International Airport, New York.

Prohibited plant materials collected from passengers' baggage and airplane stores during an 8-hour shift at Idlewild.

Nursery stock offered for import receives treatment to kill infestation
before being released to the importer.

Larva of the Japanese beetle family found in roots of nursery stock from Europe.

A plant quarantine inspector examines nursery stock that arrived by ship.

inspected in cooperation with customs and postal officials. Airplanes are searched for insect stowaways. Automobiles and trains are inspected at border ports, as are the effects and sometimes the persons of pedestrians.

Importations of nonagricultural materials also must be inspected. Khapra beetles, destructive snails, golden nematodes, and other pests have arrived with such products. Imported automobiles, dried hides, sheet steel, gums, barbed wire, and many other articles may be contaminated. Plant propagating material from abroad goes through plant inspection stations, the largest of which is in Hoboken, N.J. Their staffs are trained in the examination, treatment, and care of plants. Certain plants are held under quarantine for specified periods to detect any diseases that may not be evident when dormant material is imported. No more restriction is placed on foreign travel or commerce than is necessary to prevent entry of pests. No product is prohibited entry if it can be satisfactorily freed from pests by such treatments as fumigation, steam, dry heat, hot water, low temperatures, quick freezing, dips, fungicides, and aerosol sprays. Mechanical means may include high-density compression to kill pink bollworms in cotton bales and milling or other processing to eliminate pests in some products. Sometimes the quarantine defenses extend beyond our borders. Airplanes destined to continental United States from Hawaii, Puerto Rico, Bermuda, and the Bahamas are inspected before departure. Fruit is fumigated in Mexico before shipment to this country. Our inspectors examine flower bulbs in Europe before shipment to the United States. Certain kinds of fruit are given a low-temperature treatment, which is started in the country of origin and completed during transit.

In this endless battle we get help from many sources. Other agencies of the Department of Agriculture, State regulatory officials, the Customs Service, Immigration Service, and Public Health Service assist. Most important of all is the American citizen, whose understanding of the need for plant quarantines and cooperation in observing them are essential. He may not understand how big is his stake in the success of the battle, how much a new crop pest could cut the yields of our crops, and how much failure would add to costs of food, the expenditures for control and eradication of introduced pests, and so to taxes. We are sure of the citizen's cooperation when he understands that a small, innocent-looking plant or fruit in his baggage can harbor a serious threat to our agriculture—that, for example, the Mediterranean fruit fly, which cost more than 10 million dollars to eradicate, may have been introduced into Florida in one infested orange in a tourist's suitcase. That is why we supplement inspection and the other procedures with leaflets that inform travelers about quarantines and ask their cooperation in observing them. *(E. P. Reagan)*

Inspectors find larvae of the Mediterranean fruit fly in an orange taken from a passenger's baggage.

Technologies

Invitation to the 20th Century

THE FARMERS of Williamsburg County in South Carolina received their first invitation to participate in the 20th century on November 24, 1939. That day they were offered their first hope of purchasing electric power, a utility that had been a commonplace in United States towns and cities for several decades. Lacking electricity, rural families had been unable to use the technical innovations of this century and the 19th. They had missed out on the development of the radio. They had had no chance to use Edison's incandescent bulb. Farm women still cooked over wood fires. They washed clothes in black pots and ironed them with flatirons. They pumped and carried water by hand. They had no refrigeration for food. Many people in the South Carolina lowlands will tell you that, aside from events like births and deaths, the coming of rural power was the most important thing that ever happened to them.

Today the power supplier for 15 thousand rural families in Williamsburg and three adjacent counties is the Santee Electric Cooperative, an independent enterprise with headquarters near Kingstree. The people who receive their power over its lines own and control it. Santee's manager is Basil Ward, a South Carolinian who grew up, as one of nine children, on a tobacco farm not far from Kingstree. He was the cooperative's first paid employee when it organized late in 1939. "On our farm," he said, "we milked our cows by lantern light. We tried to keep our milk cool by pouring it into a jug and lowering the jug on a rope into the well. An electric line ran within sight of our house, but the power wasn't for us. It was going into town, but it might as well have been on the moon. Nobody figured we could pay the light bill. Nobody seemed willing to take a chance on us farmers."

Many city people and a new generation of farm youngsters are incredulous when they discover how recently it was that electricity came to rural America. Only about one farm in ten was electrified in 1935. Even by the end of the Second World War, nearly half of our farms and ranches still lacked power. More than 97 percent were electrified in 1962, along with millions of rural schools, churches, commuters' homes, and business firms. The task of pushing powerlines into every corner of the rural United States was accomplished during the past quarter century, in the years since the Rural Electrification Administration was created. REA was established by

384

Washday on the farm before electrification.

Executive Order of President Franklin D. Roosevelt on May 11, 1935, and it received statutory authority a year later with passage of the Rural Electrification Act. An agency of the Department of Agriculture since 1939, it makes loans to local organizations, like Santee, to finance the distribution, generation, and transmission of electric power to unserved rural persons. REA has approved more than 4 billion dollars in loans for this purpose; more than a billion dollars had been repaid with interest in 1962. Today REA's borrowers include some one thousand cooperatives, public power districts, and other organizations in 46 States and Puerto Rico. They carry power to more than half of all electrified farms in the United States. The rest are served by power companies or municipal systems. Whatever the source of rural power, there is no longer much question but that it was REA, together with local co-op organizers, that gave voice and substance to the demand of rural people for electricity. It was REA that first pronounced the goal of lighting every farmhouse in America, whether in Maine, Oregon, or South Carolina. Under the REA banner, rural electrification became much more than a Federal agency or program; it became a movement of rural people united in the desire to get themselves admitted to this century.

In his small brick office across the lawn from the Williamsburg County Courthouse, County Agent R. A. Jackson recalled how he helped organize the Santee Co-op in 1939: "Before REA, lots of men in these parts were agreeable if they'd stay alive. Once, when we had to ship hogs out of Kingstree for 5 cents, farmers got frightened and low, but when we got as much as 8 cents, they seemed plumb satisfied. There was no hope; people hadn't any spirit. In some ways, life was even harder on the womenfolks. On washdays, they'd draw water from the branch and carry it uphill to the pot. They'd heat the pot and scrub the clothes around for awhile, and then they'd boil the clothes and scrub some more. Electricity was the first promise of better times. I helped sign up the first members. I'd come down the road, taking 'em as they came, trying to talk them out of a 5-dollar membership fee. First thing that was hard was to get hold of 5 dollars, because 5 dollars looked as big as this tabletop in 1939. Sometimes I'd take 2 dollars cash and a note for the other 3 dollars. Second thing that was hard was getting people to believe that we could get them electricity. After we got our first REA loan in November and started setting poles, things started to pick up. Once we could show these people that power was on its way, they'd dig around and find 5 dollars hid out somewhere."

Guiding the destiny of the new co-op were nine directors, all farmers in the bright-leaf tobacco country, all serving without pay, all amateurs in the electric power business. They scraped together enough money to hire Basil Ward as an easement solicitor in the fall of 1939. Ward had volunteered to help the co-op sign up members a few months earlier.

"My only experience had been as a farmer and as an employee of the old Agricultural Adjustment Administration," Ward said. "I think I was hired mostly because I knew where people lived. When the time came to drive stakes to mark out the routes of the first lines, I went along to talk people into giving us easements across their property. As we moved along, you could feel the excitement begin to grow."

Among the most excited was Mrs. Kizzie Wilson, a schoolteacher in Clarendon County. After school, she trudged up roads to sign up members herself.

"I felt that people's lives were at stake," she said. "Before power came, whenever there was a public affair at the schoolhouse, everybody brought his own lantern to light up the building. There was always a lantern on the front seat of the buggy anyway, so that the driver could hold it over his wheels when a buggy passed coming the other way. We lit up the schoolhouse with them, but it was dangerous. In 1926, at Camden, S.C., a child knocked over a lamp, and it set the Cleveland School on fire. There was a lodge meeting upstairs and only one narrow curved staircase down. People piled up there, smothering and trampling one another. As I recall, at least 100 people lost their lives. In our own Hebron School, we heated our classrooms with potbellied stoves. On winter days, children would sit close to the windows, trying to see their books. There was a pump in the yard, and I used to urge the children to carry their own folding cups so that they wouldn't have to share the common dipper. There was no radio to hear educational programs;

Typical REA-financed construction on the farm of T. L. Burgess in Clarendon County, S.C. The pole is used also by the telephone cooperative.

Santee Electric Cooperative's Board of Directors (left to right): P. C. Stoll, S. C. Cooper, R. S. Burgess, Jr., J. D. Munnerlyn, W. L. Harrington, Board President B. C. Fitch, Manager Basil Ward, G. D. Jones, Amos A. Cribb, W. B. Davis, and F. H. Poston. All are farmers.

A church near Lake City, S.C., receives free yard light from the Santee Electric Cooperative.

Mrs. Kizzie Wilson, teacher of the first grade in Hebron School, remembers a fire in 1926, when a child knocked over a lamp in a schoolhouse.

Cecil Johnson, vocational agriculture teacher, shows boys in Hebron High School how to do electric welding.

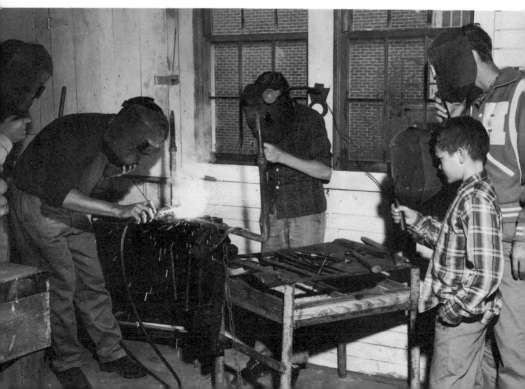

no record player to teach music. Some children complained that they got tired of studying by a kerosene lamp, and others didn't even have lamps at home. Some had to read by the chimneyside. To my mind, the coming of electricity began a new kind of life for most of us. I don't know how to say it, but it meant much more than gadgets and appliances. Tenant children used to quit school in the third grade. Now they go through high school, and many finish college. It all happened after Santee's lines came through."

Certainly electricity touched every life in the South Carolina lowlands. Gene Lane, Santee's young adviser on power use, starts out early to introduce you to some of the co-op members. At 8 a.m., Moultrie Bagnal O'Bryan unlocks the door of the Jordan Mercantile Co., his general store in Clarendon County, dodges an old kerosene lamp swinging from the ceiling, and gropes his way to a light bulb hanging over the soda-pop cooler. His is an old-fashioned crossroads store, filled with heavy boots, mule halters, and wood-burning stoves, but electric refrigeration has changed many of his goods. He sells soft drinks now, ice cream, fresh meat. "Before power," he said, "I sold salt meat only—pork and mackerel. I never saw any beef at all." Another storekeeper, W. B. Davis, a member of the Santee board, remembers: "We used to eat pork ribs until we were sick of the sight of them—just to save them from spoiling. For a while I bought ice to cool soda pop. Today my whole electric bill runs about the same as the cost of that ice alone."

As he roars up backroads, Gene Lane gives a few statistics: "Santee began with only 250 miles of line and 800 members. Today it serves 15 thousand, mostly farmers, over 3 thousand miles of pole lines. It began with only Mr. Ward. Now Santee has 65 employees and an annual payroll of more than 250 thousand dollars. We have 22 trucks and automobiles, and we have put more than 4 million dollars' worth of REA loans into our plant. Our rates are competitive. You could say that the folks around here started with less than nothing. Now, considering we've paid more than 2 million dollars in principal and interest to REA, we own 30 percent of our cooperative. More than 1 million dollars have gone back to members in patronage refunds. The Government doesn't own our co-op; we do."

Mr. Lane says that the chief worry when Santee started was whether farmers would use enough power to justify the expense of building lines in areas where there were only four homes to the mile. Many feared that farmers would buy a few light bulbs—and stop there. "They needn't have worried," he added. "By 1960, some 86 percent of our members had electric refrigerators; 81 percent had radios; 84 percent had electric washing machines; average usage was 268 kilowatt-hours a month—and climbing all the time."

Behind those figures is a changing way of life. You find E. I. Lawrence, a former teacher, at home. He resigned a few years ago

An old lamp reminds Moultrie B. O'Bryan of the days before his store had electricity, and he carried no fresh meat or dairy products.

A Santee crew, working while the lines are hot, installs a new cross arm on a pole.

At Santee's headquarters, Mrs. Agnes Wilkins takes payments from co-op members Jessie Gaines and L. O. McCutchen.

390

Cooking dinner in her own electrified home, Mrs. E. I. Lawrence practices what she preaches to members of Home Demonstration and 4-H Clubs.

to run his father's tobacco farms. Mrs. Lawrence is the Negro Home Demonstration Agent for Williamsburg County. A graduate of South Carolina State College, she spends much of her time working with 300 adult members of 13 Home Demonstration Clubs and with some 650 4-H Club members. "Electricity has changed so many things for us," she says, "that it's hard to say which is most important. Certainly washing machines. Certainly running water. But deep freezers are important, too. I know what families around here used to eat in the winter—dried peas, cornbread, rice, and sweet milk. A little salt pork. Now it's summer year-round for people with freezers. Peaches, greens, beans, even sweetpotatoes, cooked and ready for pies. I've taught women to raise 100 frying chickens at one time, to kill and dress them at one time, and to freeze them. Then they start another flock. There's no comparison between the old diet and the new one." Mrs. Lawrence's major objective for the 1960's is indoor plumbing, running water, and elimination of the privy: "Someday they'll all be switched over." As 1960 began, some 32 percent of Santee's consumers had modern plumbing.

Purchases of wiring, plumbing, and electric appliances on Santee's lines have been financed almost entirely through REA Section 5 loans. Santee has borrowed about 600 thousand dollars to finance the purchase of home equipment, and it has lent it in turn to several thousand customers, who buy their equipment from local dealers. The credit record of members has been good, on the whole, although the co-op once was forced to accept a live goat in lieu of a cash payment.

There seems to be no end in sight to the amount of power Santee's consumers will buy. Mrs. W. L. Harrington, wife of a Santee board member, shows you through her home, built shortly after the Civil War, and heated today by 23 electric panels. She has 21 electric appliances.

The promise of rural electrification, however, extends far beyond the rural home. You call on Randolph J. Matthews. A veteran of the Second World War with big plans, he moved to Lake Marion in Santee's area in 1945, a year before the powerlines finally pushed through the woods to the lakeshore. "I wanted to build a resort," he declared, "but it wouldn't work without power. I bought a GI surplus generator, but I spent more time cussing it and fooling with it than using it. Now, with electricity, we have 30 units, 15 with electric heat and air conditioning. We have a lighted dock, the whole works. Fifteen years ago, there was nothing here at all. Fifteen years from now, the whole shore may be filled. This is just the beginning."

Near Lake City, S.C., W. A. Nolen switches on his two-way radio and drawls orders to his lumber crew in the pine woods. Behind his office, you can hear the motor start and the sound of the big saw ripping into pine logs. "For years, I used a diesel engine to run my saw," reports this lumber company owner. "When it broke down, I switched to an electric motor. We had to learn to saw all over again, because we couldn't tell how we were doing by the sound of the motor any more. But we learned, and now nobody could pay me to switch back."

Sixty miles away, on a plantation near the ocean at Georgetown, Jack Hazzard takes you on a tour of inspection of his 32 thousand laying hens and 18 thousand pullets. "I run the biggest egg factory in the State," he says. "I've substituted electric power for manpower everyplace I can find. Electricity runs the whole business, and I just keep the books. Power grinds and mixes feed; carries food and water to the hens; cleans, grades, candles, and cools the eggs."

Santee consumers like Hazzard, Nolen, and Matthews already realize that with electricity it is possible today to do anything in the country that can be done in the city. Rural electrification, together with paved roads and expanding communications, has extended the frontiers of the 20th century to every corner of America. (*Hubert W. Kelley*)

A concrete-block plant on Santee's lines is typical of small rural industries that are springing up in the electrified countryside.

A lumber company now has an electric motor.

R. A. Jackson, the County Agent of Williamsburg County, helped found the rural electric cooperative in 1939.

Link with the World

IN AND around Powell, Tenn., everybody knows the Scarbro family. The telephone company they operate is a family affair. Mr. and Mrs. Scarbro have five sons and a daughter, all engaged in telephone work. Two sons, Kenneth and Malcolm, are on the staff of a telephone company in Knoxville, 10 miles east. Gene is manager of the Powell company's Rutledge exchange, 30 miles northeast. W. F. is plant superintendent in the Powell office. Charles, Jr., works part-time in public relations and other chores for the local company. Thelma is a telephone operator in Atlanta, Ga. The telephone experience of the family adds up to a couple of centuries.

Mr. Scarbro, Sr., (nobody calls him "Charlie") likes to tell about his more than 50 years of telephone service: "I had been with the Knoxville company for 19 years when the Powell system asked me to take over as manager. It was having a rough time of it. One day Al Schroeder, a hill farmer, came down from Clinch Mountain with his telephone set in his hands, marched into the office, and asked me to 'fix the danged thing.' Turned out there was nothing wrong with the phone; it was the wire outside Al's house. In those days, there were dozens of small farmers' mutuals around here, all magneto-operated and all with pretty poor 'whoop-and-holler' service. Some of the wire was strung along barbed-wire fences, some of it from tree to tree, and some of it just lay on the ground by the side of the road. If you could rouse 'Central' you were lucky. And if you could get your call through, you were luckier still. The mutual telephone system was owned and operated by the subscribers. It provided wire for a thousand feet away from the office, and that was all. After that, each subscriber was on his own. He bought his own wire, strung it up, bought the instrument, paid 10 dollars to get hooked to the system, a dollar and a half monthly for telephone service—such as it was. And I'll be the first one to admit that the service wasn't much."

The service in those days wasn't much in almost every part of rural America, either. There were more than 32 thousand rural telephone systems in the United States in 1912. Most of them were supplying "service" through the much-maligned magneto set. It was a big contraption, hanging on the wall. Often 20 or more subscribers were hooked to the same circuit. The subscribers not only failed to get privacy when they made their calls; they didn't even

Lillian Scales and Willie Dean Cooper operated the magneto switchboard in Powell, Tenn., in the old days.

Centuries of service: The Scarbro family of Tennessee. Seated, left to right: Charles N. Scarbro, Jr.; Mrs. and Mr. Charles N. Scarbro; Kenneth Scarbro. Standing: W. F. Scarbro; Gene Scarbro; Malcolm Scarbro.

expect it. They regarded the telephone as a news medium as well as a communications device. On many rural systems, the operator was the forerunner of the modern radio and television newscaster. Here and there, she rang all lines at 7 o'clock each morning to report the time, the weather, whose barn had burned, who was sick and needed help, and, in November 1912, the election of Woodrow Wilson. She answered questions, located the doctor and veterinary, and provided a local message center. But the service usually was limited only to daylight hours. Rural telephone service deteriorated in the years that followed. Insufficient maintenance, inadequate bookkeeping, and static caused by rural electric lines were some of the reasons. The telephone situation in and around Powell was no exception. It was definitely on the downgrade when Charles N. Scarbro, Sr., joined the staff of the Powell Telephone Co. At that time, it was operating a small magneto switchboard with 60 subscribers and two trunk lines to Knoxville, one of which was out of order most of the time. His wife, Mrs. Lula Scarbro, another telephone veteran, quit her job in the local store to take over running the switchboard in a backroom of their home. The Scarbro pantry was always well stocked. Farmers who could not raise the monthly telephone bill paid off in food—bushel baskets of tomatoes or corn, boxes of eggs, hams, turkeys, chickens.

The problem of getting good telephone service in rural areas was receiving attention in different parts of the country. In Washington, the Rural Electrification Administration was only 4 years old in 1939 when its Administrator, John M. Carmody, wrote a North Carolina editor: "It seems to me that rural people have just as much right to up-to-date communications as they have to up-to-date power. There's no question in my mind but that Government assistance will be required if the job is ever to be completed." Fewer farmers had telephones in 1940 than in 1920. The Powell system was feeling the pinch, too. Subscribers were slow to complain. Most of them were aware of the handicaps the company faced and its efforts to overcome them. One of the biggest obstacles was financing. The company scraped along, doing as well as it could under the circumstances, and always cocked an ear toward Washington, where the REA telephone loan program was being formed. The Scarbros knew that the new Government financing idea would be the answer to their predicament, and they were determined to hold on until the idea became a reality. It happened on October 28, 1949, when the telephone amendment to the Rural Electrification Act was signed into law. The amendment authorized REA to make loans for the purpose of improving and extending telephone service in rural areas. A major objective of the legislation was area-wide coverage, designed to avoid cutting off pockets of potential subscribers from future service. The Congress also directed that the program be con-

The Powell Telephone Co. follows the REA principle of area coverage and provides facilities where they are needed.

Margaret Peterson, of Powell, has a telephone handy in her kitchen.

ducted "to assure the availability of adequate telephone service to the widest practicable number of rural users of such service." A few months after the bill was passed, only 38.2 percent of all farms in the United States had telephone service.

REA itself does not own or operate any telephone facilities. The systems it finances are pledged to one basic national objective: To provide modern, adequate telephone service to people in rural areas. "For companies like ours," Willard Scarbro says, "REA offered exactly what we needed: Financing, technical assistance, management aids, engineering help, bookkeeping ideas—a complete package deal that spelled progress for us." Before long, the energetic Scarbros put that package together. Almost before the ink on the President's signature was dry, a letter was on its way to Washington, asking for information and a loan application blank. Then followed months of hard work, preparation of area maps, feasibility studies, right-of-way clearance, and equity collection. Meanwhile, the Powell company had lost no time in returning the loan application. The red-letter day came on February 8, 1951, when a telegram arrived, informing the Scarbros that the company's first REA loan had been approved.

Now that a sufficient amount of loan money was available at last, the company's modernization program swung into high gear. The line crew began the job of taking out old telephone sets and installing modern automatic dial equipment. The Powell office had estimated that about 600 existing subscribers could be accommo-

Broadacre Dairy Farm, near Powell, produces 900 gallons of milk daily and buys 4 thousand gallons from 60 other farms. Its 40 trucks serve eastern Tennessee.

Gene Parrott, who works in Broadacre's bulk milk room, keeps in touch with the front office.

dated by the new dial apparatus. Installation orders started flooding in. When the number stood at 825, the company had to call a halt, since the installation and line crews would have to work at top speed to finish their work in time to cutover (or "plug in") the new system. That day was celebrated in the fall of 1952. The Powell company was honored to be the first Tennessee REA borrower to cutover to dial—and fourth in the Nation. A capacity crowd in the Powell High School Auditorium watched as a Congressman placed the first call from the stage direct to the home of the REA Administrator in Washington.

Later on, Walter Burkhart, who operates a 300-acre dairy farm in Grainger County with his wife and son Jimmy, was a prime mover in the Rutledge exchange right-of-way program. Before the exchange could be converted to the new dial system, the telephone company had to get written permission from property owners along the line. Because of their strong desire for rural telephone service, the Burkharts appointed themselves a "committee" to talk their neighbors into signing the right-of-way easements, so that the whole area could be served. He trudged from farmhouse to farmhouse, obtaining the necessary signatures. He and his wife remember only too well the night when their young son woke up suddenly, suffering from an infected ear—and no telephone in the house to call a doctor. "I'd have given anything I owned," Burkhart said, "if I had

Walter Burkhart, a Grainger County dairy farmer, says the new telephone service saves him many dollars and hours.

Charles N. Scarbro, Jr., explains the intricacies of telephone equipment to the teacher, Crawford Sachs (at the right), and the pupils of the eighth grade of Powell Elementary School.

Thirty telephone booths are part of the service in the Powell area.

Mrs. Kathryn Martin takes an order at Groner's General Store.

only been able to pick up a phone and call for help. As it was, I set a few new speed records with my old truck, taking Jimmy miles down a bumpy road to the Jefferson City Hospital. When Jimmy recovered, we vowed that we would do whatever we could to get service in this area."

Mrs. U. H. Beeler, school lunch manager at Powell Elementary School, checks the menu for the next day.

J. T. Burchette, a lineman, works on a joint-use pole, which the telephone company shares with the REA electric cooperative.

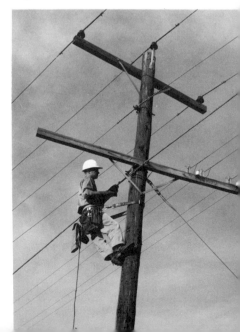

The coming of up-to-date telephone service in the Powell area was important to everybody. Commercial firms were quick to recognize their dependence on good service; it meant more profits, more expansion, and a higher payroll for the local business economy. For example, more than half of all the orders received by the Purity Packing Co. come in by telephone to its Powell plant. Founded in 1946, the plant provides employment to 125 people. It has 11 phones, takes orders from 100 miles around, and has 800 retail outlets in Tennessee. Its toll bill is the telephone company's highest. The J. E. Groner and Co. general merchandise store in Powell needs its telephone service for taking orders all year, especially when the weather is bad. A. H. Rhoads, manager and partner, has been with the store for nearly 40 years. "This town has changed a lot since I started here," he says. "People are willing to do without a lot of things if they have to, but they think twice before letting go of their telephone service."

In Grainger County, where Gene Scarbro manages the company's exchange, which serves almost a thousand subscribers, the only industry is the Rutledge Hosiery Mill. The mill, locally owned, sells its daily output of 700 dozen pairs of infants' socks to four or five chainstore outlets. The telephone is vital in accepting orders, keeping in touch with salesmen, and ordering raw materials and machine repairs. The Grainger County Health Department, through its Rutledge clinic, handles X-rays, inoculations, and dental care for schoolchildren. It also devotes much time to preventive activities, home visits to indigent families, and school health-education programs. Here again, good telephone service is essential, especially in time of accident or medical emergency. Schools in the Powell area always have received splendid cooperation from the telephone company. Mrs. Iris Johnson, principal of the Powell Elementary School, likes to talk about the friendly relations between her school and the Powell Telephone Co. The company provides telephone films (and a projectionist) for school assembly programs and donated and installed a system to connect the original school building with a new two-classroom annex.

Today's rural telephone service, provided by REA-financed borrowers in 45 States, is fast, efficient, and modern. With REA assistance, the Powell Telephone Co. is now an efficient local utility, providing modern communication facilities for more than 3 thousand subscribers in three counties in eastern Tennessee. Its headquarters building in Powell is a trim brick structure, designed for present and future efficiency. Its Rutledge exchange building is similar but smaller, and it also operates an unattended dial office building for its third, and smallest, exchange at Claxton. The people of Powell are proud of their local telephone system, the company that local people organized and support. *(Bernard Krug)*

The Uses of Electricity

WIRE COMMUNICATION by telegraph and telephone, wireless communication, and the transmission of electric power for industry had evolved by 1900 from the application of phenomena associated with electricity and magnetism to the point of having practical value. The basis of this progress, which in less than half a century has transformed agricultural production into a dynamic mechanized and scientific business, was the generation of power in central stations and its transmission long distances to the users. The initial uses of electricity for lights, water pumps, and refrigerators on farms have expanded to include a myriad appliances that use electricity for power and heating or are the control for other forms of energy. The use of electricity has reduced drudgery and made possible the doubling of production per man-hour of labor. The size of livestock enterprises has expanded greatly because it is possible to utilize mechanical equipment to replace much of the manpower formerly required for chore work.

The substitution of automatic controls for human supervision is one of the important principles of farm technology and mechanization. Electric circuits are simple, easy to operate, and versatile. It is nearly impossible to design control systems without electricity. The farm water system is one of the oldest of such automatic units in general use. The water pump, driven by an electric motor, pumps water into a storage tank. A pressure or level switch interrupts the electric circuit to the motor when the established level or pressure of water is attained. When the pressure or level falls to about one-half of the storage capacity, the circuit is reconnected, and the tank is filled. Thus, without human attention except for maintenance, the water is available on demand. An electric water system permits the use of water bowls or automatic float valves on troughs for livestock waterers. In winter the trough or bowl may be electrically heated. Water heaters in the milkhouse, as well as in the residence, provide hot water under pressure. To utilize offpeak electric rates, one or both elements of the heater may be controlled by time-clocks or radiofrequency relays.

The uses of electric motors seem endless. Household appliances, furnaces, air-conditioning equipment, refrigeration mechanisms, ventilating and drying fans, and milking machines are but a few. Electric timers and clocks on electric ranges, appliances, and feed-processing systems use small synchronous motors. Motors power automatic feed-processing systems, which, by means of preset controls, prepare feed on a daily basis without the presence of human operators. The various ingredients are metered into the grinder or mixer, and a master control starts the mixer, grinder, conveyor, and other equipment in proper sequence. Should one component fail, safety controls deactivate the system until the fault is corrected. When feed preparation is complete, the individual components are stopped in the reverse order. Automatic feed-processing units required development of remotely controlled ground-feed metering units and bin unloading mechanisms, particularly for conventional flat-bottom bins. An experimental high-pressure pneumatic system, using a thin-wall pipe 1 inch in diameter, can move ground feed about the farmstead.

Milking machines, also powered by electric motors, produce a vacuum, which, when pulsed by mechanical or electrical units, draw milk and convey the milk to pails or directly to a bulk-milk tank. Some milking claws, by electrical sensing of milk flow, release the milking unit when milking is complete. A milk-flow meter may be electrically connected to a feed-metering device so that the cow is fed grain in proportion to milk produced. Automatic washing systems permit parts of the milking equipment to be cleaned in place. Refrigeration systems for bulk-milk tanks have a compressor driven by an electric motor. One or more additional motors and fans are used to cool the refrigeration condenser, or, on water-cooled units, to pump water. The heated water, or air, from the refrigeration system may aid in heating the milkhouse in cool weather. Vacuum-type bulk-milk tanks with limited access are washed by water-powered rotary sprays inside the tanks. Hose connections to and from a pump are connected to the spray mechanism and the tank drain. A bulk-milk tank requires controls for safety and performance. The refrigeration system starts when warm milk enters the tank or the temperature of the milk rises. A stirring paddle driven by an electric gear motor operates simultaneously with the compressor and periodically to agitate cool milk held in the tank between milkings. Safety controls prevent overloading or damage if any part of the system malfunctions.

Electrical equipment also is useful to control environment. Ventilating fans remove moisture and help maintain temperature in livestock shelters. Fans controlled by thermostats or timeclocks assure positive air movement. If fans are used with evaporators, the air temperature is reduced, but there is a corresponding rise in humidity. Electric heaters equipped with controllers match their heat output to varying needs. Cooling units are less flexible and are controlled usually by simple on-off thermostats. Livestock shelters and crop storage buildings can be heated electrically. Thermostats for individual rooms or zones allow control of temperature according to occupancy and needs. Crop driers with electric heaters supplement natural air drying during humid or cool periods. Heat pumps either heat or cool by reversing the refrigeration flow.

Lighting extends or replaces daylight in poultry houses, livestock shelters, greenhouses, and outdoors. Length of day is a physical factor important in animal and plant growth and reproduction. Photoelectric units may activate lamps during dark or cloudy periods when natural daylight is not adequate. In greenhouses, plant growth chambers (or, in home basements, lighting for plants) can be controlled by timeclocks. Electric lamps, particularly ultraviolet lamps, attract night-flying insects. For this purpose, lamps can be turned on at dusk by a photoelectric relay or timeclock; in remote locations, a photoelectric relay can activate an inverter to supply alternating current to the insect trap from a storage battery.

Electronics—the field of electron tubes and related devices— includes communication equipment and control apparatus and instruments of an electrical nature. They use relatively small amounts of power. Electronic equipment for agricultural production must lower costs, give improved performance, or perform a new function. In farm operations, the evaluation must be based on additional returns, less physical labor, or saving of time. Citizens-band radio has made two-way radio communication available at reasonable cost on farm and ranch. From field to farmhouse, field to field, and from farm to farm, voice communication is a reality. Wireless and wired intercommunication systems installed in farmstead buildings save time and steps. Radio control, a means of remote operation without connecting wires, has had use in demonstrations of tractor safety. Remote switching by radiofrequency has limited use where relatively high costs can be tolerated. Similarly, radio telemetering—the transmission of qualitative or quantitative information automatically by radio—has applications in research, particularly in studies of animal physiology, wherein the scientist may wish to obtain physiological data without interfering with the animals.

Radio and radar-type apparatus can supplement conventional optical and hand means of surveying and measuring land areas. Future developments may include a radio reference signal as a basic control for land grading and leveling machinery. Guidance systems under development for machinery and equipment have utilized buried cables energized by radiofrequency or mechanical followers of physical surface guides. These guiding sensing elements activate servomotors to steer the unit as required—tractors, for example, follow rows of corn, and carts move along feed troughs. Electronic equip-

Warren W. Frye operates his 265-acre turkey farm near Peoria, Ill., with a minimum of manual labor and maximum use of electrical and automatic equipment.

Corn is the main ingredient of the feed for Mr. Frye's turkeys. He harvests his own crop and what he buys in the fields of nearby farmers with a picker-sheller.

Field-harvested shelled corn must be dried before it is stored. This automatic grain drier operates 24 hours a day during the corn harvest. Wet corn is quickly transferred from the truck to a holding bin. As the automatic drier completes its drying cycle, it is loaded with wet corn from the holding bin to repeat the cycle. The dried grain is put into one of the large storage bins.

The fully automatic feed-preparation system can prepare and deliver more than 14 tons of turkey feed a day to the turkey feeder. The unit proportions and grinds the feed ingredients from bulk storage as needed. The prepared feed is conveyed to the turkey feeders up to 400 feet away through 1-inch pipe with compressed air.

Purchased feed ingredients are delivered and stored in bulk. Automatically controlled auger conveyors deliver the ingredients to the grinding mill.

ment also is a great aid in quality determination and control of farm products. Grain moisture meters determine moisture percentages in grain based on radiofrequency conductivity. Thickness of tissue on live animals can be measured by ultrasonic reflectance; time difference of reflections or echoes of a sound pulse indicate the relative thickness and position of lean, fat, and bone. Apparatus is available for sorting of eggs, fruit, vegetables, and fibers by color. Photoelectric units and spectral elements detect colors more accurately than is possible by human eyes.

A visit to Warren W. Frye's farm near Peoria, Ill., will give a practical demonstration of the use of modern equipment. On his farm of 265 acres, 35 acres of which he rents, he raises each year about 30 thousand turkeys, which he sells processed and oven-ready. His investment in buildings is 100 thousand dollars and in machinery, 50 thousand. His payroll is 15 thousand dollars a year. He plants 220 acres of corn and 35 acres of oats. Buildings (including an eviscerating plant), waterways, and idle land account for 10 acres. Several other farmers nearby raise turkeys, but it is not generally considered a turkey- or broiler-producing area. Mr. Frye started the turkey farm in 1947, when he was 31 years old. He is a member and trustee of the Illinois Turkey Growers Association, a trustee of his school board, a participant in community affairs, and a frequent cooperator in extension and research programs of the College of Agriculture of the University of Illinois. He has the reputation of being a progressive poultry man, who is quick to adopt more efficient methods of operation, and an efficient manager in a business that has been beset by difficulties. *(Lowell E. Campbell* and *Hoyle B. Puckett)*

Prepared feed, delivered through 1-inch pipe to this feeder, is distributed throughout the house by a chain conveyor. Up to 1,500 feet of feeding trough and conveying chain can be attached to the feeder.

By means of air-operated pinch valves like this, Mr. Frye can route the prepared feed to as many feeding points as needed. The valves are remotely controlled to route feed to the proper location.

Mr. Frye points to the relays and switches in a control panel, which operate the feed-preparation and distribution system. They can start the system, open and close valves to route the feed, and stop the equipment after the need has been satisfied. The system may be controlled automatically or manually.

A switch that can be operated by the level of feed in a bin sets the automatic feed-preparation system in operation when the feed supply is low and stops it when the bin is filled.

An electronic voice communication system between the various buildings of the farmstead saves time and steps.

Mrs. Frye weighs one of the 30 thousand oven-ready turkeys produced each year.

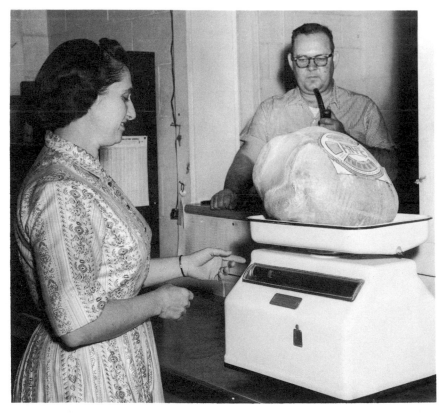

Two-way radio communication can coordinate activities on the farm during peak work periods.

Mrs. Frye receives and relays instructions.

Progress at the Farmstead

THE FARMSTEAD is the livestock farmer's place of business—his factory. As in any factory, his management practices, the layout of his facilities, and the methods and types of equipment he uses influence how much he produces and how long and hard he must work to do it.

The farmstead has changed greatly in the past century. In the early stages, engineers made trips to farms to note the ideas that farmers had built into their barns and other buildings. They pieced together a picture of the better features to provide construction details for an "improved" barn. Shortly after the First World War, research programs were begun in the Department of Agriculture to establish a sounder basis for the design of barns and sheds. Some State agricultural experiment stations had already worked on construction techniques and the control of environments with insulation and natural ventilation in the early 1900's. The programs gained momentum in the thirties. They began to answer many questions about the pressures that stored crops exert on storage structure walls, the testing of barn frames to predict more accurately their resistance to wind and snow, and environmental conditions that govern production, for example. Laboratory studies were started in 1940 to define the physiological responses of cattle, hogs, and poultry to environment. The Research and Marketing Act of 1946 enabled expansion of work on the curing and drying of farm crops and marked a change in the design of storage structures. A trend toward the industrial type of farming emphasizes the role of buildings as productive tools. Concentrations of animals are increasing in all phases of livestock production. Mechanization, work simplification, and control of environment for efficient production are the objectives of design. Ever since 1930, the Cooperative Farm Building Plan Exchange and the Midwest Plan Service have provided a unifying thread by incorporating the developments of industry and products of research into working drawings of modern farm buildings and equipment plans.

Some of the forces underlying the transformation in farm buildings—and, in a way, some of the results—are the use of improved implements and machinery; the development of transportation facilities; the transfer of some activities from the farm to the factory; the expansion of markets; and the establishment of agencies for

The old barn housed different kinds of stock, had a loft for loose hay, and sometimes space for grain and implements. It was a man-of-all-work. Specialization has brought many changes to farmsteads.

promoting scientific knowledge. The farmer no longer has to produce practically everything he consumes. He can buy more and more of his requirements ready made. He can concentrate on one major enterprise. Specialization has called for remodeling farmsteads and for specialized knowledge and facilities.

Managers of farms—like managers of factories—try to increase the quantity of production without lowering quality, reduce the shop cost per unit of product, and cut the overhead. The farmstead and factory must be located and arranged so that the product progresses in regular order from raw material through the different operations. Because of differences in sites, labor, power, and facilities, no two plants or farms will be exactly alike. Engineers specializing in farm structures have studied layouts to eliminate bottlenecks and promote the smooth flow of materials and performance of chores. They pay attention to ways of handling feeds into and out of storage and to the animal, handling the final product, supplying water, removing wastes, and doing other work, particularly milking. Among the many improvements in electrically operated equipment are feed grinders and conveyors, milking equipment, machines to remove

Push-button feeding on the Jones Farm near Fort Atkinson, Wis.

A pie-shaped dairy in San Diego County, Calif.

manure, and control devices, with which feed can be moved from storage, mixed to a formula, and delivered to the animals on a precise schedule.

Urbanization of formerly rural areas is forcing changes in the farmstead beyond expansion and mechanization. The confinement, or drylot, type of operation has developed greatly. It allows animals to be confined in a convenient enclosure, appropriate in size and provided with suitable shelter. Much use is made of electrical and mechanical power and little of hand labor. It is specialization of a high degree. The operator can buy all his feeds. They can be delivered on schedule to storage on the premises and mixed to his specifications. Water normally is piped and available for drinking and cleaning purposes at strategic points. Manure is moved by a power scraper or is flushed away with water.

The dairy farmstead is an example. In the middle 1800's, the cows usually were stabled in the general barns, which usually were dark and damp and had wooden stalls and very likely no running water. Ventilation was usually either too much or too little— depending on the size of the cracks and holes in the walls. Milking was by hand. Feed, water, manure, milk, and everything else was moved by hand. In 1910–1914 (and very likely in 1860) 3.8 man-hours of labor were required to produce a hundredweight of milk. A half century later, the man-hour requirement had declined to 1.9. (Some of that improvement was due, of course, to better breeding and nutrition of animals and better management practices.)

The milking machine came at about the turn of the century. Many farmers and agricultural workers wondered whether it was here to stay. There were complaints of injury to the cow, reduced milk yield, unclean milk, and a need for more highly skilled workers. The machine saved time and labor, though, and a good herdsman could learn to keep it clean and in good working order to avoid injury to the cow and to keep up the flow of milk. Today about 90 percent of our cows are milked by machine. The milking machine encouraged dairymen to enlarge their herds. It led to the milk pipeline, which eliminates carrying the heavy buckets or pails from the cow to the milkroom, and the bulk tank, which eliminates the heavy, cumbersome milk can and the lifting and handling that goes with it. In bulk handling, the milk now flows from the cow to the processing plant without any manual handling by the dairyman other than attaching and removing the machine. Another improvement is elevated stall, or parlor, milking, which generally is used in loose-housing systems and occasionally with a stall barn if the operator wishes to ease the milking chore. The cow stands on a platform that is elevated about waist high with respect to the man doing the milking. The tiresome stooping, squatting, bending, and reaching to attach and detach the machines in floor-level milking arrangements are replaced by a short, straightforward, elbow-height reach. The herringbone milking parlor is an elevated-stall, pipeline arrangement in which the cows stand next to each other in herringbone fashion in stalls on each side of an operator. Cows enter, are milked, and leave in batches the size of the stall. It is compact, fast, and convenient. Udders of adjacent cows are only about 30 inches apart, at elbow height and within easy reach. The operator's time, walking, and discomfort are cut considerably. To operate successfully a herringbone for five or six cows per stall (double-5 or double-6), a man working alone must be alert and reasonably agile, have well trained cows, know them well, and think ahead as he milks. Otherwise he may leave a machine on a cow too long and risk injury to the udder. A good operator can milk 50 cows or more an hour with a double-6 herringbone and travel less than 50 feet per cow in doing it. The double-4 arrangement is not quite so fast, but still faster than the side-entering or walk-through stall type of parlor, which may average about 30 cows an hour.

A pie-shaped or wagon-wheel corral is a time- and travel-saving layout for large dairy herds of 100 or more cows. At the center, or hub, is the milking facility. Gates and short lanes at the inner ends of each of the corrals provide easy access. The feeding area is around the outer perimeter. Fence-line bunkers are accessible for filling from a self-unloading wagon. Water is piped to troughs in the fences between alternate pens. Shelter, if any is needed, may be in the pens or along the perimeter and placed so as to give shade and protection against wind. This layout requires about one-third of the travel required in a rectangular layout of like capacity.

Another example of change is housing for poultry. The early immigrants from fairly cold climates erected tight poultry buildings with rather small windows so as to utilize the birds' output of heat to maintain warmth. Because the hen hatched and brooded replacement birds for the laying flock, a complete poultry house included setting, brooding, laying, and roosting rooms. Even with the generous spaces of 3 or 4 square feet of floor space per bird, the houses often were damp in the winter. Laying hens and broilers required a lot of care to achieve rather poor returns. The scratch house, popular in 1898, had two rooms. One was for roosting. A scratching room was open at the front and had a cloth curtain in a frame that could be lowered in cold weather. Investigations and farm trials before 1920 led to recommendations of many different designs. Most of the houses were less than 20 feet wide and accommodated 50 to 200 birds. The significant change was the fact that the birds lived in one room. The poultry range was still considered necessary. Farmers in the United States did not use artificial incubation to any extent until after 1900. About 100 makes of kerosene-powered

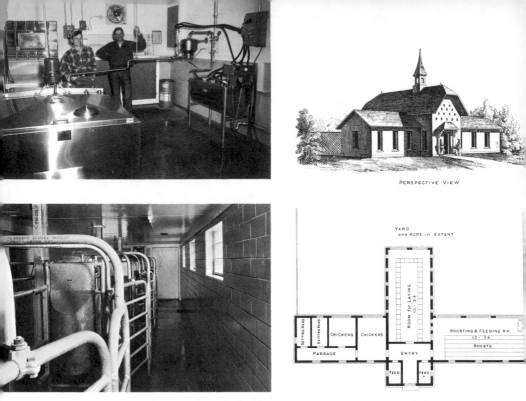

PERSPECTIVE VIEW

YARD
one ACRE in EXTENT

ROOM for LAYING 12 · 24

SETTING HENS
SETTING HENS
CHICKENS
CHICKENS

PASSAGE

ENTRY

ROOSTING & FEEDING RM
12 · 24
ROOSTS

FEED
FEED

Loren and Merlin Sprecher, Sauk City, Wis., and some of their dairy equipment in 1958.

A poultry house of the 1860's.

This modern broiler house at Bridgeville, Del., has a feed tank (at the left) and a fuel oil tank, which supplies oil to the chick hovers for heating. It houses 8 thousand broilers.

incubators were on the market in 1909. Most of them held 50 to 200 eggs, which often were incubated in the farm kitchen.

As the need for improved poultry houses grew, variations in climate over the country became an important consideration. A map published in 1920 divided the United States into four climatic zones to be considered in the design of farm buildings. More up-to-date maps show the dividing lines between the zones to have a slightly different location, but the map still functions well as a guide for designing farm buildings to suit the climate of a particular region. The map led to additional research that would be applicable to the development of poultry houses to fit each zone. Insulation was increased in colder sections. Attention also was given to the use of the heat of the sun to help raise the winter temperature of the house and to the use of flues for natural ventilation of poultry houses. Conditions in a tightly built shelter improved, but were not entirely satisfactory in winter. Improved buildings in the thirties were designed to accommodate larger flocks. By this time commercial hatcheries had taken over the task of incubation. Parcel post had been delivering chicks by mail since 1922. Separate brooder houses about 12 to 16 feet square also became prevalent about this time. Most of the poultry houses were 24 feet wide. The widest house recommended was one 30 by 30 feet. Larger producers housed birds within a long house divided into pens. It was still considered unwise to keep more than 100, or at most 200, laying hens in a single pen. Trials in the late thirties proved that as many as 10 thousand chicks could be safely brooded in one room. The idea grew, and the production of poultry boomed. Poultry housing has progressed to a mechanized unit where one man can easily produce 80 thousand broilers in a year or care for 10 thousand laying hens. The houses are much wider. Many have mechanical ventilation. Some are windowless. Laying hens may be kept in individual cages, colony cages, on deep litter, on slats or wire, or on a combination of slats and deep litter. These developments have intensified the need for more knowledge about the insulation, use of glass, width of house, and ventilation systems.

Economic and social trends and other indications tell us something of what we can expect the farmstead of the future to be. It will be closer to town and more accessible over better roads. Its sanitation and appearance will be more in keeping with the metropolitan area near it. It will be more highly mechanized. Probably it will be a specialized, drylot, or confinement type of operation, about which the farmer does more thinking, more planning, and more operating and monitoring of machinery or equipment and less shoveling, lifting, pushing, pulling, and carrying. Working conditions will be better. Chore labor will be less. Productivity will go up. *(John W. Rockey, Robert G. Yeck,* and *Norman C. Teter)*

Machines for Harvesting Fruit

ALL FRUIT once was picked—one fruit at a time—by hand and handled in small containers, also one at a time by hand. Few growers thought that fruit could be harvested by machines, because most fruit bruises easily, ripens unevenly, grows on trees of different sizes and shapes, even in the same orchard, and is harvested in a short season. The labor needed to harvest our 17 million tons of fruit has become costlier and scarcer each year since the Second World War. The cost of harvesting and handling by hand such crops as blueberries and cherries amounted to more than 50 percent of the cost of production.

The Department of Agriculture recognized the need for mechanizing the fruit harvest and in the fifties began research in cooperation with Michigan State University, the University of California, and Washington State University. It soon became apparent that complete systems would be needed—that handling could not be separated from harvesting. If fruit was separated from the tree mechanically, the rate of harvest would be too rapid for handling it in small containers one at a time. Bulk systems, which would be faster and cheaper, would be needed. Two such bulk handling systems were developed—bulk boxes for handling such fruit as apples, pears, peaches, prunes, and oranges, and the water handling of cherries. Both have come into widespread use. In Washington, for example, bulk boxes for handling fruit were nonexistent in 1957, but growers in 1960 handled about 14 million bushels of apples (more than half their crop) in bulk boxes. About 50 million pounds of tart cherries were handled in water in 1960 in the United States. A bulk box is a combination pallet and container, which holds 18 to 25 bushels of fruit. The pallet—platform—is part of the box. The filled bulk boxes weigh 800 to 1,500 pounds and must be handled with forklift equipment. Forklift units for orchard and field operation were not available in 1950. More than 25 companies now manufacture lift attachments for both front and rear mounting on tractors. In water handling of cherries, the fruit is put into pallet tanks, tank trailers, or tank trucks of cold water.

Some fruit crops that are destined for processing outlets can be separated from the tree by machines, which shake the tree. More than 55 percent of the fruit produced in this country is canned, frozen, dried, or processed into juice. Much of the 400 thousand-

An experimental machine for use in picking apples.

A boom-type shaker, collecting frames, and pallet tanks are used in harvesting tart cherries.

Harvesting blueberries with two-row equipment.

This is a bazooka-type impact harvester used in picking clingstone peaches.

Forty bushels of apples can be handled in bulk boxes like these.

ton crop of prunes in California is harvested by machines. Harvest equipment consists of self-propelled collecting frames and tree shakers. Each frame is 10 by 20 feet and is constructed with flaps, which seal around the tree trunk. One catching unit is used on each side of the tree. As the fruit is removed from the tree by a mechanical tree shaker, it falls on the catching frame and is conveyed into bulk boxes. A three-man crew can harvest 60 trees an hour. Labor costs are about 2 dollars a ton, compared with 12 dollars a ton for hand harvesting. A new model developed by Department engineers has a gasoline motor that furnishes power for moving the frame from tree to tree, operating the conveyor, and powering the tree shaker, which is mounted on the frame.

New equipment and methods for harvesting tart cherries are like those used for prunes, except that the cherries are conveyed or moved into pallet tanks or tank trailers of water instead of bulk boxes. About 3 million pounds were harvested mechanically in 1960. Six men can do the work of 33 handpickers at a cost of one-half cent to 2 cents a pound, as against 3 cents a pound for hand-picking. Hand-held shakers have been developed for harvesting cultivated blueberries. The ripe berries are shaken into small collecting frames. The shaking head has fingers that move the canes through an amplitude of one-eighth inch at a rate of 800–900 cycles a minute. The units are driven by a portable gasoline electric generator or a portable air compressor. About 25 percent of the blueberry crop in Michigan was harvested by machines in 1960. The labor cost of harvesting is reduced from 8 cents a pound for hand-picking to 3.5 cents a pound; one worker can harvest the same amount of berries (350 pounds) in a day that once took six workers to do by hand.

Mechanical picking aids are being developed for workers who pick tender fruit that is to be marketed fresh. A picker can almost double his output if he drops the apples immediately instead of putting them in a picking bag. An average picker spends about one-fourth of his time in nonpicking operations, such as climbing up and down the ladder. Equipment is being developed that utilizes most of the advantages of the pick-and-drop method and eliminates some of the nonpicking operations. It consists of a self-propelled machine with an adjustable-height platform, which positions the picker in the tree. Apples drop through a canvas funnel mounted in front of the picker and through a chute into a bulk box carried on the machine.

Harvesting fruit with machines is new and many problems exist, but growers have accepted the fact that mechanization is necessary. The development of mechanized harvesting methods and equipment and their commercial uses will be accelerated and will eventually replace most handpicking operations. *(Jordan H. Levin)*

Tillage Tools

THESE HUNDRED years are an era in which the tillage tools that were drawn by animals came to be drawn by tractors, in which ideas changed as to the purposes and methods of plowing, and in which the country gentlemen's studies of the plow, a mainstay for centuries, were supplemented by scientific and engineering achievements. The era began with the introduction of rotary power from the steam engine, which made possible the preparation of a seedbed in one operation. As an early writer, Chandos W. Hoskyns, argued: "It is not ploughing, it is not digging, it is not harrowing, raking, hoeing, rolling, scarifying, clod-crushing, scuffing, grubbing, ridging, casting, gathering, that we want: all these are the time honored, time bothersome means to a certain result. That result is—a seedbed." With the exception of the disk, all of the time-honored tools, including the mole plow and the moldboardless plow, were in full use. The practice of chilling and hardening cast iron to maintain cutting edges and the use of segmented steel tools so worn parts could be replaced were common.

The development of tillage tools was tied with the expansion westward, for which more and faster and larger tools were needed and in which different soils, vegetation, and climates had to be considered. Years of plowing with the moldboard plow created soil conditions in the Great Plains that winds turned into duststorms. The moldboardless plow of old was revamped into the subsurface sweep that kept protective plant residues on the soil surface. Special tools to anchor the surface residues, bring erosion-resistant clods to the surface, and plant seeds beneath the stubble mulch helped stabilize the soil. In humid regions, new tools were developed to stop the losses from erosion—terracers, ditchers, and other tools to control water and tools that could handle the protective winter cover crops. Irrigation in the West led to new concepts in leveling land to control water and make cultivation easier. The influence was felt in the East, where field conditions were refined through the use of landplanes and rock pickers, the removal of fences, and the enlargement of fields. The growth of the Nation was not without harm to the soil. The compaction of the soil by machines created harder soils for the tillage tools to break up. Farmers came to realize that with machines they could overtill and damage soil, and tillage systems that did a minimum amount of soil manipulation were de-

In research on tillage tools at the National Tillage Machinery Laboratory, Auburn, Ala., electrical signal outputs from electrical resistance strain gages, generators, and transducers are combined mathematically with transistorized analog computers, and final results are plotted by X-Y recorders.

To develop better tillage tools, the cohesive strength of soil is measured by a tension test.

vised. The pressures of growth brought into cultivation lands that were subject to periodic flooding or had poor texture; special tillage tools to reclaim and alter the texture of such lands were developed.

Such was the history. Such was the background. Such was the importance: The plow that tills the soil so seeds can grow is the symbol of agriculture, and the plowman is the farmer. Farmers over the centuries perfected the sticks, crooked beams, and shares they used to turn the earth and make a seedbed. Beyond a certain point they could not go. They could not make the necessary force measurements, which require the special skills of scientists and engineers. So the Department of Agriculture built the National Tillage Machinery Laboratory at Auburn, Ala. Nine soil bins 20 feet wide and 250 feet long were completed there in 1935 and filled with soils whose physical properties ranged from high contents of sand to high contents of clay. Special machines were made to prepare the soils and to make force measurements on experimental tillage tools. The work now includes studies of tractor tires and crawler tracks.

The purpose of the laboratory is to study the basic principles of the design and use of tillage tools. Engineers and soil scientists measure the forces that tillage tools apply to the soil and the way they break up the soil in order to find ways to increase effectiveness and efficiency of tillage. The type of equipment they use is different from the farmer's equipment. They remove tillage tools from their implements so that they can study only the working parts by special apparatus. It is necessary to control the speed and position of tools in order to make accurate measurements. Instead of the farm fields, they use the special bins; the different soils in them permit a wide choice of stickiness, cloddiness, and hardness, and the men can carry on their studies throughout the year. Artificial soils of clay, sand, and oil mixtures often replace natural soils for special studies with model tools. Electronic sensing devices and computers measure and record the forces exerted on tillage tools. These quantities must be exact so they can be fitted into the mathematical equations that describe tillage tools and their operating conditions. The aim in all this is the rootbed and seedbed.

The engineers give attention to the need to eliminate unnecessary tillage. An example is an attempt to separate fine materials already present into a seedbed rather than to pulverize additional soil. A new machine separates the clods and fine soil into different rows and layers. Crops can be planted in the seedbed rows of fine material and no power is wasted in breaking up large clods, which help prevent erosion between the plant rows. The engineers also study the time-honored tillage systems, in which harrowing and later operations may undo the earlier work of plowing and subsoiling. Repeated trips by heavy machines compact large volumes of loose soils in some places. Machine designs, like low-pressure tires, four-wheel drive tractors, and cultural practices, such as the so-called minimum tillage systems, are studied with the aim of preventing or minimizing compaction of soil. The engineers examine many new materials and designs for tillage tools to determine their suitability for increased effectiveness and efficiency. Studies of subsoilers have shown that the force required to pull tools with sloped shanks is much less than that for straight-shanked tools. Alternate methods of applying force to the soil by means of rotary, vibratory, or chemical means or compressed gases are investigated. It is likely that more tools will be powered directly from the engine, rather than pulled, so as to avoid power losses by slippage of tires.

A more intensive tillage system and consequently better tillage tools will be needed because of social and economic pressures in the future. The integrating of farm products into an industrialized processing network with scheduled delivery dates for products will make it necessary to till the soil under conditions once considered detrimental to the soil. The natural forces of climate that assist in the creation of tilth will become less important in some instances, and tilth may have to be created entirely by tillage tools. Four trends may develop. First, the construction of tillage tools may be by way of a scientific approach, in which designs are based on mathematical and physical principles; research data in this form can best be utilized by manufacturers, allied scientists, and farmers. Second, emphasis will be directed toward determining the best way to break up soil or to place it in a desired condition. The classical plow cannot be adjusted to varying soil requirements; its influence on the soil is unpredictable. It may be that the pulverization and movement of soil may be influenced by the size of cut and nature of tillage tools. When this is known precisely, the proper machine can be designed in terms of specific soil requirements. Third, the requirements of plants—soil tilth—will be studied more so that a minimum amount of time and energy will have to be expended in tillage. We have equipment to measure the force plants exert to emerge from the soil; better press wheels can be developed for planters to give the ideal firming conditions that different plants need for emergence. Fourth, we may have a new world of possibilities: Air vehicles that can hover above the ground and not compact the soil; atomic energy as a cheap source of power that can be used to grind up stones, level hills or mountains, and drive complex tillage machines; electronic systems that can guide tillage tools, test the condition of the soil, or control irrigation; materials, such as sintered carbides, may reduce wear on tools; plastics may be used to improve scouring; energy transmission systems, such as ultrasonic vibrations, may be used to loosen soil without tillage; electrical systems may be used to drain or heat soil or even melt snow to capture winter moisture. *(W. R. Gill and A. W. Cooper)*

A till-planter, developed by the Agricultural Engineering Department of the University of Nebraska, accomplishes tillage and planting in one trip over the field. Rows are planted in the same location each year. Research on equipment seeks ways to minimize tillage operations and traffic over fields.

Corn planted with the Nebraska till-planter without plowing. The till-plant system reduces cost and labor requirements, reduces soil compaction, increases the rate of water intake, and reduces the amount of volunteer corn in the rows over the conventional plow-harrow-plant system. Adjustment of equipment is more critical for till-plant than for conventional tillage.

New materials, such as Teflon, cause plows to scour better in sticky soils. Under some soil conditions, the force required to pull the plow has been reduced 25 percent. Other methods of accomplishing this may be the use of electro-osmosis or ultrasonic vibrations.

The use of models such as this disk accelerates the study of soil breakup. In this case, the soil is moved and the tool is stationary so that the action can be easily observed.

A plough used in the 1860's.

THE DOUBLE SHOVEL PLOUGH.

Ginning Today's Cotton

THE ECONOMIC development of the cotton States, a large export market, and the basis of mass production came about in no small measure because of the efforts of a schoolteacher from Massachusetts. Eli Whitney's inventions provided the means of filling the needs of a young and struggling America for fiber and firearms. His development of mass-production methods for the manufacture of firearms from standard parts helped build and defend this country. His development of the cotton gin opened up new industry and revolutionized agriculture in the South. The soldier on guard at a lonely outpost and the pioneer that followed him owed the shirts on their backs and the rifles in their hands to this man who taught school on Mrs. Nathaniel Green's plantation at Mulberry Grove, about 12 miles from Savannah, Ga.

The cotton gin Whitney patented in 1794 made it possible to separate lint from seed about 100 times faster than it could be done by hand. One man could do the work done by 100 men. The climate of the South was favorable for growing cotton, but production had been limited to the amount that could be removed from the seeds by hand. The invention of the gin broke that bottleneck. This first gin removed the fibers from the seed by means of spikes projecting through slots into a mass of cotton. The spikes pulled lint through the slots that were too narrow to pass the seeds. A revolving brush removed the lint from the spikes. Many refinements have been made, but the basic principle is unchanged.

One of the earliest gins was on Bryant's Creek near Oxford, Ga. It was powered by a water wheel. It and other early gins had no equipment for removing trash. As the acreage in cotton increased, the gin became a symbol of the prosperous plantation owner. With the expanding acreage, workers could hardly pick the cotton from the stalk as carefully as before; they became careless in their haste to gather the crop and picked more trash with the cotton. The trash— leaves and the hulls in which the seed cotton grows—made the fiber less desirable to the mills because it did not spin so well and there was more waste. For a while, the trash was picked from the cotton by hand, but for the laborer and his family sitting by the fireside at night this was a weary task after they had worked in the fields all day. In time, cleaners were devised that were relatively efficient in removing trash.

A person can pick about 175 pounds of cotton a day.

*A machine can pick about 15 thousand pounds of cotton a day—
the work of 75 to 100 men.*

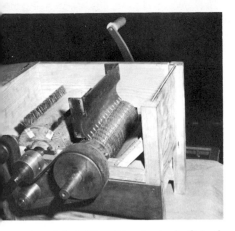

A model of Eli Whitney's gin, built in the shops of the Cotton Ginning Research Laboratory, Stoneville, Miss.

A model gin with modern saws and ribs.

Refinements in the gin stand and cleaning and packaging equipment in the 1800's and early 1900's met the needs of the plantation owner very well. Cotton could be harvested during clear weather and ginned during rainy weather. The costs of gins continued to

A seed cotton cleaner built of wood by a slave for the Blakley Plantation gin north of Vicksburg, Miss.

rise, however, because of the additional cleaning equipment needed to process the ever-rougher harvested cotton, and commercial installations began to replace the plantation gin. The more efficient gin machinery became for the removal of trash and moisture, the rougher the harvesting methods became, until a point was reached where the lowered grades were costing producers millions of dollars each year. The damp cotton brought to the gin could not be cleaned or ginned properly. It roped and twisted and tangled in the machinery. It would not spin well or make high-grade yarn, and buyers sometimes discounted the price of the fiber as much as 20 percent.

Farmers in 1926 asked the Department of Agriculture to develop a method for drying cotton to facilitate cleaning and reduce the losses due to rough preparation. Charles A. Bennett, who was stationed at Tallulah, La., developed and patented a drier, which was put into operation in gins in the fall of 1929. A Cotton Ginning Research Laboratory was constructed at Stoneville, Miss., where facilities for fiber analyses were also made available. The engineering research was under Mr. Bennett's direction. The work of fiber analysis and quality evaluation was directed by Francis L. Gerdes. They built a research program that continues today. Facilities for ginning investigations also were established later at Mesilla Park, N. Mex., Clemson, S.C., and Chickasha, Okla.

Thirty-two public-service patents have been granted or applied for. Among them are seed cotton drying apparatus, a process and method for ginning cotton with air-blast gins, a fractionation device and method, a cotton gin fan, lint cotton cleaner, stick remover for seed cotton, a baler, a moisture-measuring instrument, cotton turbo-cleaner process, methods of moisture restoration to cotton, cotton bale sampler, and a textile fiber sorter. The patents mostly cover basic items of equipment and keep the field open to all manufacturers. Some of the patents represent major advances; indeed, the seed cotton drier and the cotton lint cleaner rival the invention of the gin itself in importance to the cotton world. These two inventions helped make the use of mechanical cotton harvesters economically feasible. The drier made possible the more efficient use of gin machinery. Cottons that previously could not be ginned at all can be processed satisfactorily. Dry cotton will release its trash more easily, and more cleaning equipment can be used on it without damage to fibers, if the fibers are not overdried.

A shortage of labor gave urgency to developments in mechanical harvesting. A patent for a mechanical cottonpicker had been granted in 1850. The machine was unsuccessful, as were many others that received patents in the next 40 years, but in 1895 a patent was granted on a spindle-type cottonpicker to August Campbell; the principle on which it worked was developed by the International Harvester Co. in the 1920's and introduced in the early 1940's. A

Three hundred seventy-five truckloads of cotton waiting to be ginned near Lubbock, Tex. The growing use of mechanical harvesters has compressed the harvest season as much as 50 percent. To keep pace, many gins operate 24 hours a day, 7 days a week.

A modern cotton gin with elaborate drying and cleaning equipment for handling machine-harvested cotton represents an investment of about 250 thousand dollars.

Cutting bales to get samples of cotton at Greenville, Miss.

431

stripper-type harvester was introduced by the John Deere Co. in the 1930's. About 40 percent of our cotton was picked by spindle-type pickers and 15 percent by stripping machines in 1962. Mechanical harvesting was a giant step of progress, but it created problems for the ginner. Handpickers send seed cotton to the gin relatively clean and dry, but the machines send it in varying conditions, ranging from fairly clean and dry to very damp and dirty. The ginner must remove the moisture and trash in order to produce a quality of ginned lint that will give the farmer a profitable return. More elaborate drying and cleaning machinery in the gin therefore were necessary. The mechanical harvester also creates a problem of volume for the ginner. Hand harvesting used to extend over 3 to 5 months, but machines often complete the work in 4 to 6 weeks. Farmers deliver cotton to the gin faster than it can be ginned, and often they must wait many hours for their turn to unload.

Then came the lint cleaner, a device that cleans fine trash from the fibers after the large trash is removed. It made mechanical harvesting economically feasible; with it and other developments, the ginning of mechanically harvested cotton is today routine and profitable to the farmer. One mechanical picker does the work of 75 to 100 men and has cut the ginning season from months to weeks; the ginner's facilities are taxed thereby. Developments at Stoneville have increased the capacity of saw gins as much as 300 percent. Research on roller gins at Mesilla Park has resulted in increasing the capacity of roller gins as much as 500 percent. The roller gin is used for extra-long staple cottons in the Southwest.

These developments have not fully solved the ginning problem for mechanically harvested cotton. Cotton must be dried, cleaned, and ginned at a rate as high as 15 tons an hour. The lint must be packaged in 500-pound bales at 5 tons or so an hour for the average high-speed gin. The handling of this volume of material without fiber damage requires, for example, automatic drying systems to avoid overdrying the fibers, new types of seed cotton cleaners for efficient trash removal, more efficient lint cleaners, better trash disposal systems, and automatic controls for the ginning processes to reduce labor costs. The ginner must process cotton rapidly for his customer, the farmer, but at the same time the spinning quality must be preserved. Cotton mills, like the farmer and ginner, are demanding more from cotton than ever before. Spinning mills are running faster than ever in an effort to reduce costs. The gin of today cannot perform miracles, although it may seem to do so when compared to those built by Eli Whitney. The gin cannot improve cotton quality; at best, it can only preserve it. Ginning research is aimed at preserving the quality of the lint to meet the more exacting requirements of the farmers' customer—the textile industry. *(Vernon P. Moore* and *Rex F. Colwick)*

The Weather

A FARMER a century ago did his own weather forecasting by observing the "feel" of the air, such signs as low-flying swallows, and the way the sky looked. It was a matter of lore, superstition, tradition, or guesswork. The Congress recognized farmers' need for weather service in 1872, when it asked the meteorological branch of the Army Signal Service to include "such additional stations, reports, and signals as may be necessary for the benefit of Agricultural and Commercial interests." Since then, through the efforts of the Weather Bureau (which formerly was an agency of the Department of Agriculture and is now a part of the Department of Commerce) and others, the science of meteorology has undergone as great a revolution as has agriculture itself. Today's farmer uses information about weather and climate as one of his operating procedures. He can time his plowing, sowing, spraying, and reaping in accordance with reliable, scientific forecasts.

Forecasters, for instance, watch the movement of air masses southward from the Arctic so that Florida weathermen can alert vegetable and citrus growers that frost may be on the way. As the cold air moves in, meteorologists study its temperature and depth and the moisture it holds, and issue warnings of the low temperatures expected throughout a crop area. Growers check their thermometers in fields and groves and notify crews to stand by for firing heaters and running irrigation systems or hire extra crews for forced harvesting. The modern weatherman can follow the hour-by-hour changes in the atmosphere and report them to the farmers of America faster than ever before. Surveillance radar scans rural and urban areas and follows the progress of precipitation and severe weather. Radiosondes, carried aloft by balloons, send back profiles of the atmosphere. Detailed observations of weather elements are made hourly at hundreds of Weather Bureau stations throughout the United States and on many ships at sea. Thousands of supplementary weather observations from volunteers provide data on our climate, and they and information from other countries provide a vast number of details on which to base forecasts.

This wealth of information is collected at the National Meteorological Center in Washington, where meteorologists, atmospheric physicists, and mathematicians by combining their skills and by using high-speed electronic computers analyze and forecast global

One of the radar antennae used in weather detection by the United States Weather Bureau, the Department of Commerce.

weather patterns. Their product is transmitted instantaneously by modern communications systems to weather forecasting offices throughout the country. Forecasts of weather up to 5 days in advance are beamed across rural America by radio and television. Weather outlooks for a month in advance reach farmers through newspapers and magazines. Studies of the climate gleaned from a treasury of weather records compiled over nearly a century are available for long-range planning. A new farm weather service, which combines the sciences of meteorology and agriculture, was established in the Mississippi Delta in 1958. It makes special forecasts and probability estimates of weather that are important to current farming operations. The Weather Bureau and the agricultural experiment stations interpret the effects of weather conditions on

At 6:40 a.m., eastern standard time, April 1, 1960, the Thor Able rocket launched the weather satellite, TIROS I, from the Atlantic Missile Range at Cape Canaveral, Fla.

435

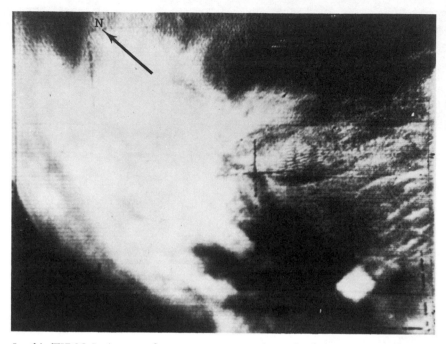

In this TIROS I picture, taken at 2 p.m., central standard time, May 19, 1960, a "square" cloud image (lower right), is centered about 50 miles west-northwest of Wichita Falls, Tex. Surface weather observations later indicated that the cloud moved northeastward, spawning tornadoes and hail. The large cloud area at the left is associated with a storm that was centered in Kansas.

farming and study the relationship of weather to agriculture. All of this information is carried on a round-the-clock weather teletypewriter service to news outlets. A complete farm weather advisory service thus is as close to every farmer as his radio, television, and newspaper.

What does the future of meteorology promise for the agricultural weather service? Will man someday control the weather? Will he perfect day-to-day weather forecasts for the entire crop year? Will he be able to eliminate evaporation loss from lakes and reservoirs? Will he be able to modify the climate to protect crops against frost? One can only speculate. Several events, however, have advanced our attempts to understand the basic nature of weather and, through this knowledge, to control it. TIROS I and TIROS II, our first weather satellites, enabled meteorologists to observe weather patterns around the globe. Future weather satellites will be equipped with more instruments and instruments of greater refinement. The weatherman's new ability to view the atmosphere from above gives him a tremendous boost toward his goal of complete understanding of the weather. *(Edward M. Vernon)*

Robert Gelhard, Eastern Hemisphere forecaster, and Raymond Green, Western Hemisphere forecaster, construct the daily series of prognostic charts for a 5-day forecast to be issued by the Extended Forecast Branch of the Weather Bureau.

More than 30 thousand weather reports from all over the Northern Hemisphere are plotted every 24 hours on maps, for later analysis, at the Weather Bureau's National Meteorological Center in Suitland, Md., near Washington.

Gilbert St. Clair, a Weather Bureau meteorologist, looks at a weather chart that is being transmitted via a facsimile network to several hundred stations around the country.

437

A Matter of Values

WE HAVE come a long way since a man got the idea that the skins of the animals he had been killing for food could protect his body and a later man found he could make the skins more comfortable if he softened them with animal fats or made them more durable by a process like tanning. Our processing has gone far beyond those primitive efforts, but we still have much to learn about such ancient farm products as hides and fats, even though we have the tools of modern research to work with. With them we can probe into the chemistry of plant and animal materials, their molecular and atomic structures, their physical properties, the reactions they enter into, and their response to controllable changes in environment.

Much of our knowledge of the properties of agricultural commodities we have obtained as part of the technological development of new products and processes, but a great part has been obtained in pure research. These are the findings for which no practical use may be evident at the time of their discovery, but from which we may later develop some building blocks necessary to a new product, an improved process, or a more advanced scientific concept. They may be useful in agriculture, medicine, other sciences, and industry. We who do utilization research study the inherent values of wheat, corn, and other grains; such natural fibers as cotton and wool; fruits and vegetables; animal products, such as meat, milk, hides, fats, poultry, and eggs; and oilseeds, sugar, tobacco, pine gum, and many others. The more information we have about their infixed values, the faster progress we can make to meet the increasing demands for better foods, improved feeds, and industrial products.

The research on fats is an example of our efforts to discover and utilize the inherent values of farm products. Fats are one of the three classes of organic substances that make up the main body of animal and plant tissues. Fats from animal sources usually are solids at ordinary temperatures. Liquid fats—usually called oils—are mainly of vegetable origin. Fats are considered insoluble in water and have a greasy feel. We can separate them from other materials by melting, pressing, or solvent extraction. Fats consist of carbon, oxygen, and hydrogen, combined in the form of glyceride molecules. A glyceride consists of three usually long-chain carbon compounds, known as fatty acids, attached to a glycerol molecule, which contains three carbon atoms. Fats differ in their fatty acid composition.

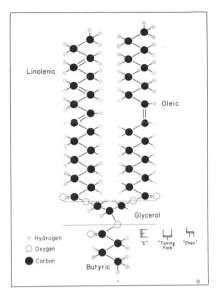

One of the glycerides (fats) found in milk, consisting of two 18-carbon fatty acids, oleic and linolenic, and a 4-carbon fatty acid, butyric, attached to a glycerol. The fatty acids can be attached to the glycerol in many possible configurations, such as a "tuning fork," an "E," or a "chair."

One, for example, might have two long-chain fatty acids, such as the 18-carbon linolenic or oleic acid, and one short-chain fatty acid, which might be as short as the 4-carbon butyric acid in milk fat. Some fatty acids are saturated—that is, they have no double bonds between the carbon atoms. Others, with these double bonds, are unsaturated. Some, like linolenic acid with three double bonds, are more unsaturated than others, like oleic acid, that have only one. The place in the chain where the unsaturation occurs can also vary. These differences in chemical structure—such as chain lengths, number of double bonds, and position of double bonds—explain the differences in the properties of fats. Melting temperature, for example, is generally lower for unsaturated fats and for those with shorter chains. The extent of unsaturation also has much to do with the reaction of fats with the oxygen of the air at ordinary temperatures. Linseed oil is a good base for paints, because linolenic acid, its main constituent, has three points of unsaturation and thus reacts quickly with the oxygen of the air to form a durable film.

We are now searching into even more subtle characteristics of the fat molecule. With our refined techniques for separating and analyzing the components of complex mixtures, we try to establish what the shape of the glyceride molecule is. It might be like a tuning fork, or a chair, or an "E," or something else. The attachment of fatty acids to the end carbons of the glycerol or to the middle carbons makes a difference in the properties of the fat. The stiffness or flexibility of the chain determines the extent of coiling that can take place and hence the reactivity of the fat and its mode

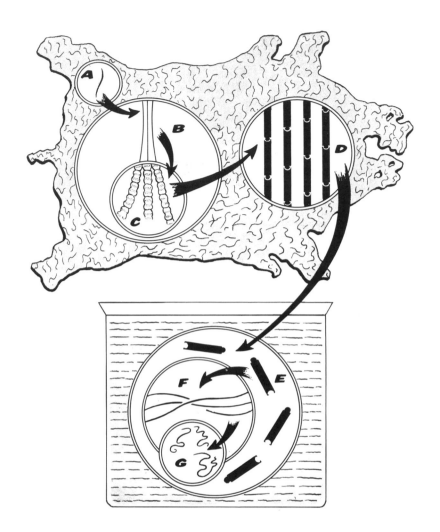

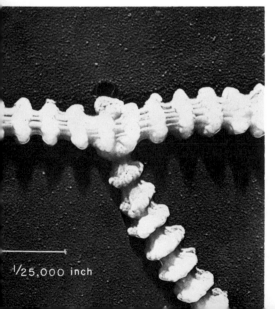

1/25,000 inch

The structure of hide collagen: A schematic representation of (A) visible fiber; (B) fibrils of fiber under light microscope; (C) fibrils under electron microscope; (D) structural arrangement of fibril shown by X-ray diffraction; (E) particles removed from fibrils in solution; (F) coiled formation of the molecular chains of a particle; (G) molecular fragments of a particle. Particles can be re-formed into fibrils with electron micrographic patterns apparently identical to those of native fibrils (C). Entirely different patterns can be formed, as the electron micrograph shows. This fibril, formed from collagen particles by Department scientists, is strikingly different from anything previously reported.

of crystallization. We must learn a great deal more about the branches that occur along the chains, about the effects of chemical groups other than hydrogen that are often attached to some of the carbon atoms, and about changes in the geometric form of the molecule that take place at the double bonds. We must also be concerned with other lipids besides "true" fats. These resemble fats, but they may have, for example, only two fatty acids, the place of the third being taken by some other compound; or the glycerol might be replaced by cholesterol or some other alcohol. Frequently an organism produces these other lipids in minute amounts along with the fats. Often they are difficult to obtain separately because they behave so much like fats. They can give rise to off-flavors in foods or create other problems in the utilization of a fat product. The purer and better characterized fractions of fats we are now obtaining give us a clearer picture of the chemical and physical changes in which they take part. This should lead to a better knowledge of structure and behavior and give us new possibilities for control. Some day we may be constructing our own especially adapted glycerides. Some day, too, we may know how to get rid of the other lipids that cause undesirable side reactions or perhaps prevent their formation.

From this glimpse of the nature of fats that we uncover by studying their chemical composition, we turn to animal hide, or skin—an example of how a consideration of physical properties yields information about a product. Animal hide is a complex of proteins, lipids, carbohydrates, inorganic salts, and water. When we consider its ultimate use, whether for making leather or glue products, we are concerned with its physical behavior—with such properties as strength and flexibility or stickiness. To understand why hide behaves as it does, we inquire into the size, shape, and the aggregation of its molecules. The basic component of animal hide is its matrix of complex fibrous protein, called collagen. Collagen contains only a few elements—carbon, hydrogen, nitrogen, oxygen, and a little sulfur—but their atoms are arranged in many combinations to form giant molecules consisting of thousands of atoms.

A close look at a piece of animal skin reveals a random interweaving of fibers. Magnified about a thousand times with a light microscope, one of these fibers is seen to consist of a group of smaller fibrils. Studies with an electron microscope, which permits magnification of a hundred-thousandfold, reveals the individual fibril to have a strikingly regular geometric pattern. We cannot see directly the ultimate unit of the fibril, even in the powerful electron microscope. We can, however, explore its organization at the molecular level indirectly by means of its diffraction of X-rays. The patterns we thus obtain tell us that the basic units of the fibril are arranged in a parallel and regular way. When we suspend the fibrils in certain solutions, we find that a few extremely long, thin, rod-

Scientists of the Eastern Utilization Research and Development Division of the Department of Agriculture study the characteristics of farm products.

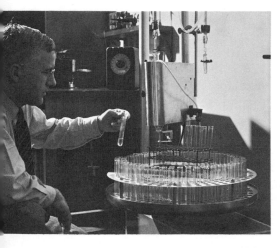

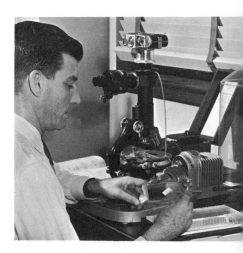

like particles are removed. Each particle contains more than 50 thousand atoms, which form long, threadlike molecules coiled around one another like strands of a rope. Although we have never seen these particles, we have deduced this information about them from the effects they produce when they are in solution—from the way they interact with light of various wavelengths, from the osmotic pressure they create when isolated on one side of a membrane, from their behavior under an enormous centrifugal force, and from other

effects. We can at present separate only a few of these collagen particles from the fibrils. The rest stay intact. We hope to learn the physical or chemical reason for this when we find out what and where the "hooks" are that nature has provided to keep these particles together in the fibril.

Now if we heat the liquid in which we have obtained these particles, we find that they separate into smaller molecules of unequal sizes and ill-defined shapes. In other words, the strands become unraveled. The solutions of these molecules behave like gelatin or glue. We do not know how and why these particles separate. Perhaps there are weak spots along their chains of atoms. We cannot tell yet because we have no way of determining the strength of a single molecule. Nor do we understand the interplay there is between molecules or even between portions of the same molecule. So we can fragment the collagen particle into smaller units. Can we put it back together? We think the process of subdividing the particles can be reversed. We actually have taken the isolated particles, before they were fragmented, and formed them again into fibrils in the laboratory. Some of our re-formed fibrils under the electron microscope appear to be similar to those of native fibrils, while others we have made produce entirely different micrographic patterns. Does this mean that we can take collagen apart and put it back together again, either in exactly the same way or in an entirely new form? It would appear so, but we are not sure.

So the search for the inherent values of agricultural products goes on. Looking back, we realize that at any given time, the exactness of the information available was dependent on the methods at hand for obtaining that information. We have had to modify our earlier concepts with the development of improved methodology. And we know that later investigators with their more precise instruments will be reexamining what we have done, thus giving the scientific world still better data leading to more uses. This search is an interdisciplinary effort, with chemists and biologists working alongside physicists, spectroscopists, statisticians, electronics experts, and other specialists, to develop more precise methods of measuring and analyzing the inherent values of agricultural products. The fruits of this research are shared by scientists in other apparently unrelated fields. The basic information about lipids and fibrous proteins we look for in the work on fats and hides, for example, is directly applicable in the biological sciences—human physiology, nutrition, animal husbandry, plant biochemistry—as well as such technological fields as plastics, textiles, food processing, and many others. Thus it is its dynamism, as well as its widespread implication in virtually all fields of science, that makes this research on the inherent values of agricultural products rewarding. *(P. A. Wells, G. C. Nutting, L. P. Witnauer, W. P. Ratchford, N. E. Roberts, and J. E. Simpson)*

Crops and the Chemical Industry

MORE THAN a billion dollars' worth of farm products are sold each year to the chemical industry, whose production totals about 40 billion pounds a year. It ranks fifth among all manufacturing industries in annual dollar sales, after the food, transportation, petroleum, and base metals industries. Its products are sold to every section of American industry and include fibers, surface coatings, plastics and resins, fertilizers, rubbers, medicinals, pigments, explosives, solvents, printing inks, pesticides, dyes, antifreezes, adhesives, bleaches, wood preservatives, flavorings, photographic chemicals, refrigerants, water-soluble gums, and paint driers.

We believe the chemical industry could be a much greater market for farm goods. Brakes on such expansion have been fluctuations in prices and supplies. Besides, chemical manufacturers have turned to raw materials derived from petroleum, natural gas, and coal, and industrial research has yielded raw materials of low cost, high quality, excellent stability, and dependable supply. These have cut deeply into the markets for agricultural products. Examples are the loss of soap markets to synthetic detergents, the invasion of wool and cotton markets by synthetic fibers, and the use of sheet plastics in place of leather. The complex carbohydrates, proteins, and fats and the lesser constituents of farm crops have characteristics different from those of other raw materials. It is possible technically to manufacture most of the end products of the synthetic organic chemical industry from agricultural raw materials, but in most instances the economics favor the petroleum raw materials. In planning a rational utilization program, therefore, we can take advantage of the unique properties the constituents of agricultural crops have. These materials can be used to manufacture new and different high-volume or high-priced products that cannot be prepared from other raw materials at less cost.

New research into the utilization of farm products has demonstrated that lost markets can be regained and new and better ones developed. Improved processing and modification of chemical and physical traits can give farm products all the properties of the most spectacular synthetic: Cotton and wool fabrics can be endowed with wash-and-wear qualities. Cotton can be made to resist weather and rot. Fat can be transformed to practical plasticizer-stabilizers, new and better surface coatings, and improved detergents. Wool can be

445

shrinkproofed, and processing wastes can be recovered and used. Fermentation can convert grain to new and more efficient feeds and feed supplements or organic acids and other raw materials for the chemical industries. Starches can be used in paper and textiles. Those are a few of the accomplishments of past and ongoing research, which we need for a thorough understanding of the properties of each agricultural commodity. For many purposes, some crops are almost interchangeable. For others, small differences may be of vital importance. Such research is done in laboratories in Wyndmoor, Pa., Peoria, New Orleans, and Albany, Calif. From them have come findings that create new outlets for farm commodities, improvements in the quality of farm products, and new processes, which have been turned over to industrial organizations for commercialization. Grains, starches, flours, vegetable oils, animal fats, naval stores, and sugar are among the materials on which we conduct utilization research.

The chemical industry uses about 1.3 billion pounds of vegetable oils each year in the manufacture of paints, varnishes, and other protective coatings; floor coverings; lubricants and greases; plasticizers (substances that give flexibility to plastics and make them pliable at low temperatures); and polyurethane plastic foams. Our research developed special types of chemically modified (epoxidized) fats and oils for use as plasticizers, an end use that currently uses 40 million pounds of these novel compounds. We also developed an internal plasticizer, vinyl stearate, for use in polyvinyl plastics. Unique fat- and oil-derived products, called acetoglycerides, have been developed and can be produced in a wide range of products from liquids to nongreasy, plastic solids. Some have been marketed and used in cosmetics. Others possess properties that can make them useful as plasticizers for plastic sheets or films used in food packaging, lubricants for food-processing equipment, and edible coating materials for foods. Other fat- and oil-derived products include sulfated and sulfonated products, which are used as surface-active agents; tallow derivatives, used as emulsifiers and jet lubricants; dimer acid (dilinoleic acid), used in special resins as a component in nondrip gelled paints and as a resin for polyurethane foams; a purified grade of oleic acid, used in plasticizers and other applications; and polyurethane foams from castor oil.

Cottonseed oil soapstock—foots—once found a ready market with producers of soap and fatty acids, before we had petroleum-based detergents, which replaced or supplemented soap in many applications. This surplus, low-cost, fatty acid material, including cottonseed as well as soybean and corn oil foots, is reacted with methanol (wood alcohol) on a commercial scale to yield a "methyl ester product," potentially useful in plastics and other industrial chemical products. Fifteen million pounds of the methyl ester product are

Department chemists made these textile fibers from amylose starch from corn in studies of the utilization of agricultural products.

Amylose, treated chemically, forms a fibrous material (right) that can be spun or made into a film. Amylopectin starch, from ordinary corn, given the same treatment, forms a powdery substance that has no film- or fiber-forming properties.

now marketed annually as high-energy additives for poultry and livestock feed. Oils from the seeds of parsley, carrots, fennel, dill, and coriander contain petroselinic acid, which is different in chemical composition from the fatty acids found in the common vegetable oils of commerce. Research has shown that many new chemicals made from this unique acid are suitable for use in paints, plastics, and elastomers. Many other novel oils from lesser known plants are being isolated and studied in an effort to uncover new, industrially useful products. New chemicals and protective coatings have been produced from tung oil, the ingredient in the famous lacquers of ancient China, and its principal acid, eleostearic acid. Other research led to paints with built-in fungicidal and antimildew properties and superior vehicles for floor sealers, primers, enamels, and flat wall paints. Commercial paint and varnish manufacturers are making coatings based on one of them. When we react tung oil with glycerin—a sweet, sirupy liquid used in toiletries and as a moistening agent—we can prepare tung oil monoglycerides, which have desirable properties as sticking agents for insecticidal sprays and as emulsifiers in water-emulsion paints. Its emulsifying action is fugitive— that is, after application to a surface, it can undergo air drying and increase the adherence of the emulsified material to the surface. About 1.7 billion pounds of lard and tallow are used in making soap and surface-active agents. Animal fats also are an important

Sheet of an acetoglyceride folded over a spatula and (left) lumps of a completely hardened fat.

E. T. Rayner, of the Southern Utilization Research and Development Division, prepares a new type of surface coating from tung oil.

The pilot-plant wing in the Southern Regional Research Laboratory, where processes developed in a laboratory are tried out on a larger scale.

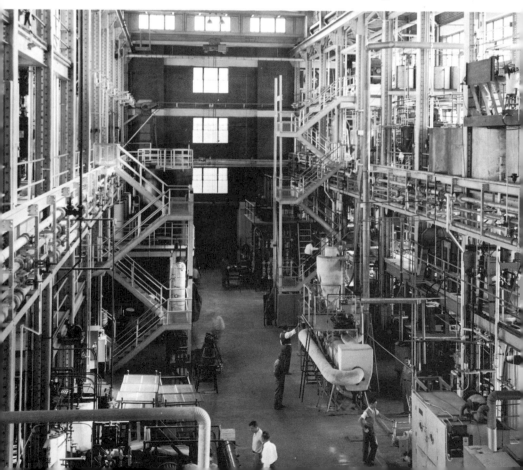

raw material in the manufacture of natural glycerin. The 1960 production of glycerin exceeded 300 million pounds, of which about one-half was derived from animal fats; the rest was supplied by manufacturers of synthetics.

Research on pine gum rosin seeks to improve its quality and reduce its cost. An estimated 300 million pounds of rosin are used for beater sizing in the paper industry. A new rosin size, made directly from partly neutralized pine gum, is being evaluated. Rosin salts are used as paint driers. Another important naval stores product is turpentine, of which the chemical industry consumes about 210 million pounds a year. Naval stores products also are being converted into pure compounds and derivatives for industrial application. Much of the synthetic GR-S "cold" rubber for automobile tire treads uses new, peroxide-type chemicals derived from turpentine. These chemicals are outstanding catalysts (or initiators for the reactions) to make rubber and plastics. Another turpentine-based chemical, myrcene, is used in making ingredients of perfume, such as geraniol, a fragrant oil normally found in geranium and rose oils. A new chemical, maleopimaric acid, produced directly from pine gum, is used in photographic processes and may find wide applications in plastics and printing inks. A process has been developed to isolate levopimaric acid from pine gum. This acid is potentially valuable as an intermediate for the chemical industry.

Fermentation research at the Department laboratories has developed improved processes for the production of penicillin and beta-carotene (provitamin A); processes for the production of dextran, important as an extender for blood plasma and other uses; vegetable gums, useful in a number of products; various acids; xanthophyll, a plant pigment; insecticides; and various antibiotics, needed in the treatment of plant rust, mosaic, and fungi, to mention but a few. Sugar and molasses are also highly useful raw materials for many industries. From these complex products come dextran; furfural derivatives for binders, resins, and plasticizers; detergents; acids, such as citric, fumaric, and itaconic, which are necessary in products ranging from foods to chemical intermediates; resins and plastics; glycerin; adhesives of several types; and mannitol and sorbitol, which go into foods and cosmetics. Certain microbial-synthesized polysaccharides have a potential of one-half billion pounds in secondary oil recovery. The food and feed industries still offer the largest markets for agricultural commodities, but expanded utilization in those markets will be dictated by increases in population, export demand, and per capita income. Any major increase in the utilization of these commodities must come then from industrial utilization. That this is possible has been demonstrated during the years in which we have carried on utilization research. *(C. H. Fisher* and *Johannes H. Bruun)*

Micro-organisms

ALMOST every phase of life is influenced in some way by a micro-organism or by a microbial process. Bacteria, molds, and yeasts are common micro-organisms. No less vital are the algae, protozoa, and viruses. Most micro-organisms are microscopic. They occur almost everywhere in air, water, and soil. Some cause diseases of man, animals, and plants, but most are harmless or helpful. Micro-organisms form diverse chemical products through growth and cell activity, according to the type of micro-organism, the nature and amount of the nutrient it has, and the conditions under which growth takes place. The organism *Clostridium botulinum* may grow and produce the poisonous botulinus toxin in underheated nonacid foods. Acid-forming bacteria ferment milk curd to various cheeses, shredded cabbage to sauerkraut, cucumbers to pickles, and plant materials to silage. The prime benefit of micro-organisms is in soil building. The continuous reduction of dead animal and plant tissue by microbial growth to more simple chemical substances improves the tilth, fertility, and water-holding capacity of soil. Another con-tribution to agriculture is the fixation of nitrogen by bacteria that grow symbiotically in the roots of legumes.

Scientists have studied micro-organisms since the early 1900's. Microbiologists and other specialists collect, describe, and classify the micro-organisms and their products. They seek to explain the nature of microbial enzymes in relation to the chemical reactions of the living cell. They look for ways to control microbial activi-ties, especially food spoilage and disease. Scientists learned to grow selected micro-organisms in pure culture under defined conditions as to nutrients and environment. This led to the development of industrial fermentation, one of the most important areas of science to benefit mankind during the past century. Hundreds of species of micro-organisms ferment agricultural materials, directly or indirectly, into chemicals, foods, feed supplements, drugs, vitamins, and anti-biotics. Carbohydrate-converting micro-organisms were first used to leaven bread, make alcoholic beverages, and produce vinegar and fermented foods. Since 1900 or so, many new industrial fermenta-tions designed to obtain specific chemical products by use of micro-organisms have been developed. The manufacture of citric acid by *Aspergillus niger* is the most important mold fermentation, aside from penicillin. Ethyl alcohol, produced by yeast from sugars, is the best

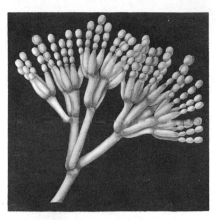

Growing colonies of Penicillium chryso-genum isolated from a moldy cantaloup. This is the parent of all present-day cultures used to make penicillin.

Characteristic structure, greatly enlarged, of Penicillium chrysogenum stalk showing chains of spores which can initiate new growth.

known chemical made in large volume. Many serious diseases are practically nonexistent today or are held in check with the products of microbial fermentation—antibiotics, antitoxins, vaccines, and cortical hormones.

The antibiotics deserve special comment. Penicillin, produced by species of molds, was first discovered in 1928 by Alexander Fleming, a British mycologist. It remained undeveloped for many years. Actually, the urgent medical needs of the Second World War provided the necessary impetus and financial support required for the rapid development of Dr. Fleming's basic finding. An appeal to the United States Department of Agriculture for assistance in developing a production process with his strain of the fungus *Penicillium* was answered by scientists of the Northern Regional Research Laboratory. The discovery by a staff member of a more productive mold, *Penicillium chrysogenum,* on a cantaloup, and the development of a process for growing it in deep-tank culture set the stage for the present antibiotic industry. Tests made with thousands of microbial cultures obtained from soil samples and other sources throughout the world have resulted in the discovery of several hundred new antibiotics. A few are outstanding for combating the disease-producing micro-organisms of man, animals, and plants. Some have proved useful as feed supplements to promote better health and growth of animals. The value of all antibiotics produced in 1961 was about 350 million dollars.

Riboflavin (vitamin B_2) is produced by two fungal species, *Eremothecium ashbyii* and *Ashbya gossypii.* Both are pathogenic to plants. Vitamin B_{12}, the most potent yet discovered, is made by

451

This is the apparatus used to freeze-dry micro-organisms for the culture collection at the Northern Utilization Research and Development Division, Peoria. The four small tubes (left-center foreground) contain cells of micro-organisms and blood serum. They are lowered into a pan containing dry ice, and the air is exhausted from them. When serum and cells are frozen and dry, the tops of the tubes are heated until the glass becomes molten, and the tubes are pulled off. This operation seals the tubes. This method, developed by Department scientists, keeps cells of bacteria, molds, and yeasts alive as long as 20 years.

Antibiotic produced by a species of Strep-tomyces. Vertical growth (left) is shown to inhibit adjacent growth of five different plant disease bacteria growing in horizontal lines at right. The sixth (bottom) micro-organism is unaffected by the antibiotic. This technique is used in searching for antibiotic-producing micro-organisms.

Dr. C. W. Hesseltine, a mycologist, examines the collection of several thousand cultures of bacteria, molds, and yeasts at the Northern Regional Research Laboratory in Peoria, Ill. The cultures are used in research and the development of processes for the conversion of agricultural products to new chemicals.

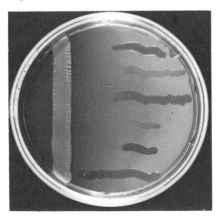

452

Dr. Harlow H. Hall and some of the equipment used at the Northern Regional Research Laboratory for developing fermentations to manufacture new products from agricultural materials.

several species of *Streptomyces,* as well as by the propionic acid-forming bacteria. A fermentation process, worked out by the Northern Regional Research Laboratory, produces beta-carotene, which is a precursor of vitamin A. This fermentation product is in demand as a supplement for animal feeds and for drugs and foods. The micro-organism used is the fungus *Blakeslea trispora,* commonly found on pumpkin, squash, and cucumber plant blossoms. One of the newest uses of micro-organisms in agriculture is to combat insects. Bacteria and molds that cause disease in a particularly destructive insect are spread through infested areas to induce plagues of the insect itself. Still another new use for micro-organisms is the production of plant growth hormones. One of them is gibberellic acid, a chemical that speeds up plant growth and the formation of blossoms and seeds. Industrial fermentation continues to be a fruitful area for research and development. More and more products from American farms are being converted to new products because of our knowledge of the action of micro-organisms. *(Harlow H. Hall* and *John L. Etchells)*

The Processing of Food

FOODS are processed to prevent spoilage by microbes and adverse chemical change. Micro-organisms are killed, as in canning; arrested, as in freezing or drying; or inhibited by fermentation or chemical treatment. Chemical changes are arrested by harmless food additives or by the control of temperature and the headspace gas in packages. Many processes used today developed after somebody learned the specific cause of deterioration and found a way to control the cause. Canning, for example, was invented by Nicholas Appert, who was rewarded by Napoleon after many years of attempts to preserve cooked food in jars. Appert found that if food were packed tightly in containers and heated long enough, most of the time it would not spoil. People did not know about bacteria at that time, and 80 years passed before the cause of spoilage was proved. Modern principles of heat transfer and knowledge of thermal death times of bacteria made possible the accurate determinations of process times for canned foods. Mechanical innovations revolutionized commercial canning practices. Open cookers gave way to pressure retorts for low-acid foods and to continuous pressure cooker-coolers. Hand-formed, hand-soldered cans were replaced by machine-formed and sealed cans, and manual operations were replaced by mechanical methods.

Caves, holes in the ground, and the cold water of springs and wells long served to refrigerate foods during the warmer seasons. Ice came into general use about 1811. Mechanical refrigeration had a marked effect on agriculture after 1900. It made possible wide distribution of perishable foods. The first cold storage warehouse was built in New York in 1865; 1,400 cold storage warehouses, capable of handling a million carloads of product a year, now serve the food industry. In quick freezing, foods are frozen quickly at low temperatures by the use of airblasts, contact plates, or brine immersion tanks. Fish and poultry were frozen on a commercial scale as early as 1865, but modern quick-freezing methods were pioneered by Clarence Birdseye in the early 1920's. Fish mostly were frozen at first. The commercial freezing of vegetables began in Oregon in 1927. About 700 food items now are frozen. Dehydrofreezing—the partial dehydration with freezing preservation—has been established as a process that preserves fresh quality as well as freezing does and reduces bulk, an important economic value. It is one of several

454

Women peel and core tomatoes in a cannery in the twenties.

combination processes applied to apples, peas, pimientos, and some other commodities.

Drying is an old way to preserve food. Natural drying, as of edible seeds and fruit, in time led to controlled drying. Sun drying of fruit still is in wide use, even though rain or dampness may lead to spoilage, contaminations by insects and rodents are difficult to prevent, and changes in weather mean that quality cannot be controlled completely. Controlled dehydration has become the rule. Many dried foods of today cannot be produced satisfactorily except by artificial drying. The place of dehydration will grow in time to come, especially because of the economy attending the removal of water. Most of our fresh foods contain 75 to more than 95 percent of water. Savings in transportation, packaging, and storage costs may more than pay for the drying. It is handier to carry a pound and a half of dehydrated mashed potatoes than a peck of fresh ones, and the dry potato keeps well on the pantry shelf and can be made ready for the table in a few minutes. A few years ago processed potatoes were almost unknown, but today nearly one-third of

A multiple-filling unit in a modern cannery.

High-speed filling and sealing equipment used in modern canning.

the United States crop is dehydrated, chipped, or frozen, and a long-term decline in potato consumption has been stemmed. Frozen orange juice concentrate has similarly expanded the demand for oranges at a time when surplus conditions had been feared as a result of large new plantings. Milk, eggs, tea and coffee, and fruit and vegetable juices are now marketed as dry powders that need only to be stirred into water. Stability of concentrated products is generally favored by low moisture content, low temperature, and protection against oxygen.

The natural forces of fermentative micro-organisms are part of the cycle of life, death, and decay. When conditions are just right, organisms of decay produce products in such concentration that the products inhibit further decay. Thus yeast produces enough alcohol to prevent its own further growth as well as that of many other organisms. Certain bacteria can get into wine and beer and produce enough acetic acid—vinegar—to prevent further decay. Other types of bacteria convert carbohydrates to lactic acid in such concentration that the pickles, olives, or sauerkraut will not decay further. The first basic understanding of these factors developed a century ago when Louis Pasteur was able to reduce the change of wine to vinegar by heat-treating grape must and inoculating it with pure yeast cultures. These processes, or their equivalent, now prevail in the alcoholic fermentation industry. Pickling and other acid fermentations have not yet completely yielded to the pure culture techniques, but conditions to enrich the fermentation by controlling the quality of the raw material and operating conditions have done much to assure a consistent high quality of such products. Small individual vessels once were used for fermentation. Now we have huge, efficient fermentation tanks. Bottling, filtering, pasteurizing, and other necessary operations have become highly mechanized.

Gail Borden's invention of condensed milk in the 1850's started an American epoch. This product was first viewed with suspicion but gained a solid footing after it was supplied to Union Forces during the Civil War. During those early days, milk often was produced in unsanitary conditions and was likely to carry disease, until pasteurization processes were developed to make it safe. Chicago adopted the first compulsory pasteurization law in 1908. All States today have laws that control cleanliness and safety of milk. It was discovered in 1924 that the vitamin D potency of foods containing ergosterol could be increased with ultraviolet light. Irradiated vitamin D milk appeared; later, milk also was fortified by the addition of vitamin D concentrate. Skim milk powder, which can be reconstituted quickly, has become a common item. Concentrated milk, a product distinct from canned condensed or evaporated milk, has become popular. The cream separator, invented by Carl de Laval about 1890, laid the basis for modern creamery operations. The past century has seen the shift from farm churning to creamery manufacture of butter. Ice cream now is manufactured the year around, and our per capita consumption is 2.5 gallons a year. Continuous freezing and automation have replaced hand-crank methods of making it.

The first canned meat line was introduced in 1878. Although sausage making dates back many centuries, the hotdog made its debut at the Chicago World's Fair in 1893. Canned spiced pork luncheon meat came on the market about 1930. Modern refrigeration and meat curing practices have displaced the historic smokehouse. Spices are no longer used for purposes of preservation but primarily to produce variations in taste in many meat products. Tough cuts of fresh meat can be tenderized with special enzyme preparations, some of which are injected into the animals' bloodstream before slaughter. Dehydration is limited in its application to meat, except for chipped beef. Freeze-drying is a process of removing moisture from the meat while it is held in the frozen state under high vacuum. A highly porous structure, retained by the dried product, makes rehydration easy. Freeze-dried cooked steaks, chops, hamburgers, and other products offer possibilities where stability or convenient preparation is important or refrigeration is not available.

Eggs once were produced for local use only. A St. Louis firm in 1878 was using a drying process to transform egg yolk and albumen into a light-brown, meal-like substance—the beginning of egg drying in the United States. Breaking and freezing eggs on a commercial scale for bakers and other food manufacturers followed soon after the development of egg dehydration. Early products were of poor quality because of lack of sanitation and inadequate refrigeration. Only the eggs that smelled bad on breaking were discarded. Spray-drying procedures, which had been used for milk dehydrating, were applied to whole eggs, yolks, and whites during the thirties. Egg drying was expanded during the Second World War in response to military needs for dehydrated foods, but the products had a short storage life and soon became unpalatable. Research resulted in improved stability of dried eggs in storage. Better processing of egg whites led to their extensive use in cake mixes.

Irradiation as a means of sterilizing foods, pasteurizing them for extended refrigerator storage, or reducing insect infestation is receiving much attention. When food is exposed to the proper dosage of ionizing radiation (as from cobalt 60), the spoilage organisms or insects in it are killed. Changes occur in the food, too, such as changes in color, texture, or flavor. Techniques for irradiation of food without adverse effects were not reliable in 1961, but we believe that in time there will be many applications of the process. Chef and waiter services in public feeding are giving way to less costly, sanitary vending machines, and this trend may continue. No cooking takes place in some restaurants—only the reheating of pre-cooked frozen foods. Specialty lines of foods are now on the market. Among them are infant foods; special low-calorie packs; single-item, balanced liquid food for calorie control; and salt-free foods and foods intended for diets of ill and aging persons.

Current emphasis is on preservation of natural appearance and flavor of customary foods. The future may produce a completely new concept. It is likely that in the next hundred years we will be striving to obtain foods that are more efficient nutrients rather than trying to preserve the form of natural meats and vegetables. We should not look askance at restructured foods that contain calories, balance of nutrients, and a pleasant taste, texture, and appearance, but little or no resemblance to familiar foods. The conversion of milk to cheese and of meat to sausage are early examples of such restructuring of foods. Public acceptance of such foods, made from different and unusual plant and animal sources, would open new vistas to the commercial processor and food scientist. Harvests of protein and carbohydrates from our almost limitless marine resources could be used, as well as chemically and microbially modified cellulose, lignin, and other inedible products of forest and jungle. Although great progress has been made in the field of food processing during the last century, a vast field has been left untouched. It awaits sufficient imagination and research to yield further methods of conserving our present food supplies and of converting the products of Nature's storehouse into new foods to nourish the underfed people of the world. *(M. J. Copley, Sam R. Hoover, W. B. Van Arsdel, and John R. Matchett)*

Machines for separating egg yolks and whites.

Cereals

THE STORY of wheat unfolds the changes brought by time and technology to an ancient foodstuff. Breadmaking remained much the same for centuries. Ground-up seeds of wheat or rye, from which some of the outer layers—the bran—had been removed, were mixed with water, a source of yeast, and salt to form a dough. The dough was molded into a loaf or dish-shaped piece, allowed to rise, and baked on hot stones or in some sort of oven. The basic principles have not changed greatly in the past century in the United States, but there has been a shift to mass production through mechanization and scientific control. Yeast fermentation to make the flavor-containing brews is carried out in large tanks in the newer large bakeries. The brews are mixed continuously with flour, water, and other ingredients at one end of a machine. At the other, extruded dough is formed automatically into loaves. The loaves go into pans, are proofed, and baked at a rate of 4 thousand to 6 thousand an hour. Loaves are cooled, sliced, and packed at the same fantastic rate. This large-scale operation has brought special problems to the baker, miller, farmer, seller, and consumer.

Different wheats vary in their baking quality. The requirements for wheat of suitable quality to behave properly in the new bread factories are especially critical. By experiment and observation, certain additives have been developed that help control properties of flour, but we lack a basic understanding of how and why these chemicals have effects and of how to achieve the best results. Scientists in the Department of Agriculture are developing this basic knowledge of chemical and physical bases for properties of flour and dough. They have separated individual proteins not previously known to exist in wheat and have shown that a specific chemical group, the sulfhydryl group, in the proteins is of special significance in controlling mixing behavior of flours in dough formation. This group is also involved in "maturing" effects in flours. The unique function of fatlike constituents of flour in controlling the volume of bread and cookie-spread has been discovered. The scientists also have found that certain water-soluble proteins, "albumins," are essential in combination with the gluten in order to get a good loaf of bread. Such lines of basic work are essential if farmers are to produce wheat for modern industry and if American wheat is to compete in foreign markets.

460

A factor in the accumulation of wheat in our warehouses has been a continuing per capita decline in our consumption of bread. A reason for the decline is that the larger, centralized production of bread requires more time for the product to reach the table. Thus bread no longer has the oven-fresh aroma and flavor it had when it was purchased fresh from the oven at the corner bakery or baked at home. Prepared mixes and partly baked goods for homemakers help solve this problem of freshness. The baking industry also is shifting to the use of freezing to preserve the highly unstable flavors of baked goods, for which research has provided a basis by defining the changes that occur during freezing, storage, and thawing of baked goods under varying conditions. Another ancient use for wheat is to parboil it to make bulgur. The Department of Agriculture has undertaken the development of convenient, instant types of bulgur in the expectation that it will open new domestic and export markets for American wheat. Another approach is the separation of fractions of wheat flour that have unique properties. A new batter process has been developed for the production of wheat gluten and starch from low-grade flours. The gluten is used to make high-protein breakfast cereals and to upgrade low-protein bread flours; the starch is available for industrial uses. A newer process accomplishes separation of high- to low-protein frac-

461

tions from wheat flour by fine grinding and air classification methods. Fractions may be selected that have suitable properties for pastry, cakes, or bread. The fractions of highest starch content and highest protein content are being investigated for industrial applications in sizing, coatings, and adhesives. Studies have started on the applicability of the process to corn, sorghum, and rice flours so as to obtain fractions suitable for specific food and industrial uses. Both the gluten and high-protein flours are being investigated for development of foods specifically designed for export markets.

Besides the cereals that go directly into our foods as bread, breakfast foods, pastries, and the like, much greater quantities reach the table through conversion into meat, milk, eggs, and other animal products. An increase in the efficiency of production of livestock and poultry since 1940 has lowered relative production costs. That and a larger disposable income have led to a shift to an animal type of economy. A continuation of this trend may mean a rise of 35 percent by 1975 in the per capita consumption of animal products and therefore a great overall increase in the consumption of grains, since 6 to 20 pounds of feed are needed to produce a pound of edible poultry or beef (dry-weight basis).

Cereal grains provide an abundant, annually replenishable, raw material for American industry. Wheat, corn, and sorghum flours serve a variety of industrial uses by reason of their paste, adhesive, and viscosity properties. Cereal flours as such and after chemical modifications find industrial applications as additives to petroleum drilling mud slurries, as flocculating agents to concentrate ores, in plasterboard to obtain better bonding to the paper cover, as extenders for water-resistant glues in plywood, and for use as adhesives and core binders. Scientists have developed a series of chemically modified flours with good performance as sizing and coating agents for paper and as paper adhesives. Research is continuing on the preparation of new chemical derivatives of flour with improved dispersibility, viscosity ranges, and increased adhesive properties of the protein part of the flour.

Starch, the main constituent of grain and cereal flours, has properties that adapt it to a great variety of industrial as well as food uses. This adaptability and its low cost make starch the most important industrial cereal product. The use of starch has grown tremendously. More than 150 million bushels of grain, mostly corn, were processed in 1962 for starch. A little more than half of the nearly 5 billion pounds of cornstarch produced annually in the United States is converted into corn sirup and dextrose sugar. Much of the remainder is sold without further treatment, but for many uses starch has to be modified by chemical or physical processes to meet the demands for specific applications. A starch-processing plant also produces corn oil, corn protein, and byproduct feeds.

Nearly every type of paper, except newsprint, uses starch in its manufacture. Added to the pulp, starch gives improved strength and rattle to the paper sheet that is formed. Paper is surface-sized with starch to improve its ink receptivity and printing properties. Clay-coated paper, such as used in books for the better reproduction of photographs and in magazines, commonly contains starch as the adhesive to bond the clay to the paper. Our annual per capita requirement for paper and paper products was about 450 pounds in 1961—with projections as high as 2 thousand pounds by the year 2000. Laboratory studies on the chemical conversion of starch indicate the prospect of incorporating significant amounts of starch derivatives, or cereal pulp, as an integral part of paper substance.

The properties of starch extend its utility far beyond the paper and paper products industry, its largest single market. Its dispersibility in water and its adhesive and film-forming properties account for its use in the sizing of cotton and rayon yarns in the textile industry. Its adhesive properties make it valuable as a core binder for binding the sand in intricately shaped foundry molds before they are heated; for its continued use as a laundry starch for stiffening fabrics and giving them a desirable finish; and for a multitude of other applications. The scientist has tailored the properties of starch to meet the needs of specific applications by adjusting the size of its molecules, by introducing new chemical groups, and by rearranging its molecular structure. These transformations are accomplished through the use of mechanical forces, heat, chemicals, enzymes, radiation, and microbial fermentations. The engineer makes the conversion practical by designing economical processes and equipment. Another route to new products is the selection and breeding of genetic lines of cereal grains having constituents differing in quality or amount from those present in varieties normally grown.

New fields of application for cereal starches have already been opened as a result of collaborative efforts of the corn breeder and the chemists in developing new varieties of corn that have starches with new molecular compositions. Waxy varieties of corn, sorghum, and rice are grown and processed commercially. Starch from waxy cereals consists wholly of nonlinear or branched molecules, called amylopectin. The amylopectin is responsible for the softer and more transparent nature of cooked waxy rice and starch pastes. Waxy corn and sorghum starches are used in special food products and in industrial sizes and adhesives. Recently developed high-amylose varieties of corn have starches containing much greater amounts of linear starch molecules, called amylose, as compared to ordinary cornstarch. Amylose forms strong, clear films much superior to those from ordinary starch and comparable in properties to many of the commercially used packaging films. Corn that contains starch of 50

Lightweight printing papers are made on large high-speed machines. About 450 thousand tons of cereal starch products were used in making more than 31 million tons of paper and paperboard in the United States in 1960.

Wheat flour after fine grinding is separated in an air classifier to obtain a number of fractions differing in particle size and composition. In the example shown, 100 parts of hard red winter wheat flour of 11 percent protein have been separated into 10 parts of high-protein fraction of 20 percent protein, 30 parts of low-protein fraction of 7 percent protein, and 60 parts of intermediate protein fraction of 11.5 percent protein. By blending the highest and intermediate protein fractions, one can get a superior bread flour of 12.7 percent protein. The 7 percent protein fraction is an excellent cake flour.

Cereal products, such as starches, flours, and their derivatives, are important raw materials in the production of pharmaceuticals and industrial chemicals by fermentation. Yeasts, molds, and bacteria can convert these raw materials, under controlled sanitary conditions, into important end products, such as alcohols, antibiotics, organic acids, and gums. A typical modern plant is shown with fermentors and accessory equipment.

to 60 percent amylose is grown commercially in limited amounts. Inbred lines have been developed that have as much as 80 percent of amylose. At the lower amylose levels, high-amylose starch finds use in special sizing applications. At contents nearing 100 percent, the high-amylose starch is of value for making transparent self-supporting films, special coatings, sizing, and adhesives. Both the high-amylose starches and the separated amylose hold promise as raw materials for the packaging film market. This billion-pound annual market continues to expand as more and more consumer items are protected by attractive packaging in transparent films.

Department scientists also have developed a new starch derivative called dialdehyde starch, which, when incorporated in paper, gives high wet strength desired in paper toweling, facial tissues, napkins, and similar paper products. Dialdehyde starch also acts to insolubilize certain proteins and holds promise for incorporation with casein in paper coatings to give superior wet-rub resistance. Similarly, it is expected to become an ingredient that improves water resistance of cereal, soybean, and animal protein glues when used in making plywood and wood laminates—products for which there is increasing demand.

Micro-organisms—the yeasts, bacteria, and molds—afford another route to new products from cereal grains. Whole grain, flour, starch, and protein may serve as sources of nutrients and energy in the growth of organisms which make new products such as enzymes, vitamins, hormones, and antibiotics. They may serve also as substrates which are modified or converted by microbial action into such new products as gluconic acid, sodium gluconate, lactic acid, grain alcohol, and microbial gums, wherein a larger amount of cereal substance is retained in the end product. Enzymes produced by molds and bacteria have come into large-scale industrial use for the reduction of viscosity of starch used in the sizing of paper, the liquefaction of starch to permit its removal from sized textiles, the conversion of starch into corn sirup and into dextrose sugar, and the saccharification of starch in grain alcohol fermentations. In all, the action of the enzyme has been to accomplish either a partial or complete degradation of the starch molecule. Micro-organisms can also perform the additional task of transforming the dextrose sugar unit of starch into other sugars and then recombining a mixture of sugars into a new carbohydrate of large molecular size. Scientists have used this type of conversion in the production of several new microbial polysaccharides. The new polysaccharides have properties entirely different from starch. Because of their high viscosity in dilute solutions, stability of viscosity in the presence of mineral salts, and other chemical and physical properties, they have potential utility in applications ranging from cosmetics to petroleum production. *(F. R. Senti* and *G. O. Kohler)*

465

Cotton and Wool for Today

COTTON AND WOOL, being usable in many ways, have been used for clothing and household fabrics for thousands of years. They and two other natural fibers, linen and silk, supplied most of man's needs for textiles until the beginning of the 19th century, when a manmade fiber, known first as artificial silk and now as rayon, became a member of the family of textile fibers. Nylon, the first truly synthetic fiber, in the thirties heralded a new era of scores of synthetic fibers of specialized properties. Competition for the consumer's favor began in earnest. Products made from plastics and paper began later to compete for the traditional uses of textiles. Enthusiastic believers in the power of modern industrial research thought these developments portended the beginning of the end of man's dependence on the natural fibers to supply his needs for textiles—but they reckoned without an appreciation of what directed research could do in endowing cotton and wool with new properties and in adding to their inherent properties, so that cotton and wool have become as modern as any of our textile fibers while keeping natural properties only they possess. The struggle for textile markets goes on. The consumer is the winner in it, for he will be even surer of getting the textiles he wants, but the lot of the producers of fibers will depend on the success of research conducted by them or in their behalf.

Cotton once was looked upon as primarily a versatile, durable, inexpensive workhorse fiber. Its many other virtues, such as comfort, were not appreciated and understood fully, for the consumer did not have for comparison the articles he has today made from one or more of the synthetic fibers, each with characteristics different from those of cotton. A few improvements in the performance of cotton textiles were made in the thirties—stabilization of garments and household articles against shrinkage, a treatment for water repellency that did not affect the hand of the fabric, a number of better dyes for cotton, and so on. Further improvements followed. The greatest was the development of easy-to-care-for, wash-and-wear, all-cotton shirts, dresses, trousers, and underwear. Another advance is in the full use of brilliant and varied colors, which tolerate washing and sunlight. Durable flame resistance for cotton, once available only through the use of treatments that added great weight to fabrics and made them less pliable, can now be imparted with little effect on flexibility. Flame resistance is achieved by combining a

The Wool and Mohair Laboratory at the Western Regional Research Laboratory, Albany, Calif., has equipment for studying wool from fleece to fabric.

Dr. Gordon Rose prepares to alter the fiber structure of wool by chemical means.

The electron microscope makes possible the study of changes in surfaces of wool fibers when a fabric is treated chemically to control shrinkage.

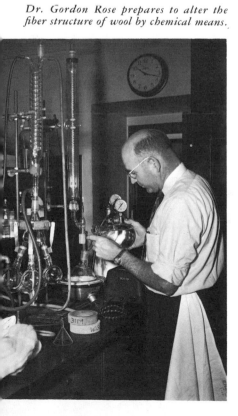

Technicians test new finishes for wool in the laboratory in Albany, Calif., by running a fabric through a chemical solution, then through a wringer, then a washer, and finally through a drying oven.

Yarns and fabrics are manufactured in this room in the laboratory in Albany. Other rooms are equipped for scouring and finishing wool.

small amount of nonflammable chemicals with the cellulose molecules of the cotton fiber. The treatments have been used mostly for special work clothing.

Fabrics that resist soiling to a high degree are achieved when certain chemicals that have a strong affinity for cellulose but little or none for substances of which soil is composed are applied to them. Fabrics that return to their original dimensions after stretching are produced by first shrinking the fabric in a solution of caustic soda, washing out the caustic soda, and then applying a chemical that forms microscopic links between the structural elements of the shrunken cotton fibers. When the fabric is stretched and then released, these links pull the fibers back to their unstretched position, and the fibers pull the fabric back to its unstretched dimensions. The performance characteristics of cotton fabrics are determined by the characteristics of the individual fibers. These in turn are determined by the chemical properties of cellulose, the substance of which cotton is composed, and by the complex physical arrangement of the cellulose molecules in the fiber. Research is adding to our knowledge of the chemical and physical properties and structure of the cotton fiber, and this knowledge is providing researchers with a clearer insight into how the properties of cotton can be modified to produce fabrics of greater usefulness.

People always have liked clothing of wool because it is warm, sturdy, good looking, and easy to make. Scientists now are finding that they can modify wool fibers and so open new possibilities, especially in making wool garments easier to care for. In the washtub era, wool underwear and socks were washed on Monday mornings, and scarves, sweaters, blankets, and shawls were washed as required. Special care was needed in washing them because of their tendency to shrink. The first reduction in drudgery came with drycleaning. Laundering has also undergone great change. Modern laundering has approached automatic methods that reduce time, cost, and labor, but wool fabrics, without modification, shrink in machine washing and come out mussy from tumble driers. Scientists have learned how to manipulate and modify the structure of wool to produce fabrics of superior launderability—without sacrificing the natural beauty and soft texture of wool. The Department's Wool and Mohair Laboratory in Albany, Calif., has found a way to give fibers a permanent, chemical surface coating. Suitings, knitted wear, blankets, and other articles so treated can be machine washed safely and repeatedly without shrinking and dried with little or no mussing. The applied coating is so thin that it does not alter significantly the handle or texture of the wool. The treatment can be applied easily in modern manufacturing equipment. The fabric is first immersed in a solution of one reactive chemical. The wet-out fabric is then run between rollers to remove excess solution. The

In carding, the first step in processing clean wool into yarn, the fibers are disentangled and alined and contaminating vegetable matter is removed.

Water-repellent cheesecloth has been treated with a silicon "alloy."

Scientists at the Wool and Mohair Laboratory have one of their colleagues and his family and three girls pose for photographs that display an end product of their research—good looking and easy-to-care-for clothing of wool.

damp fabric goes directly into a second treating liquid, and excess solution again is expressed. The whole operation can be carried out continuously at rates as high as 20 yards a minute. Chemical costs are less than 5 cents a yard of treated goods.

The new treatment has been called the IFP (interfacial polymerization) process because it involves combination of two chemicals under highly favorable conditions existing at the surface of contact (the interface) between the first and second solutions. When the first solution is on the fibers as a thin, liquid film, the moist fiber as a whole becomes the first surface. In this case the combination of the two chemicals occurs in such a way that it becomes part of the fiber itself and confers durable resistance to shrinkage. The treatment can be applied equally well to dyed and undyed fabrics, which can be dyed later. A sizable market outlet awaits an effective shrink-resistant treatment such as this new one, especially in the fields of children's and women's wear, slacks, sweaters, and blankets, which all together utilize somewhat more than 100 million pounds of wool every year.

Ever since the Prince of Wales made creases in trousers fashionable 100 years ago, men have had the problem of keeping a press in rainy weather. Now wool fabrics can be treated so they have built-in, long-lasting creases. The chemicals are applied along with the creases to the garments in the final stage of manufacture. The creases stay in through repeated exposure to rain and dampness and after cleaning. The creasing of wool fabrics involves the same general principle as the permanent waving of hair. Fibers are exposed to a chemical solution that penetrates their internal structure and unzips chemical linkages that tie together the web of thread-like molecules. The separated molecules can now slip past one another when the assembly of the fiber is strained, as during the pressing of a garment. New chemical crosslinks are formed almost immediately between the molecules in their new position. The treated goods do not develop odor when they are wet or when the humidity is high.

The only problem has been the appearance of slight change in shade in some light-colored fabrics. Further research may overcome this difficulty. The whole process of creasing trousers requires about a minute in a steam press. Scientists are seeking also to impart greater resistance to wrinkling, especially in lightweight wool fabrics. Research has been started to develop wools with greater soil resistance, resistance to yellowing, and increased resistance to wear. To that end, the scientists study minutely the fine details of the structure of wool fibers. They look for information that suggests where and how to modify the substance of the fiber to produce fabrics with almost limitless possibilities. (*Harold P. Lundgren* and *Mason DuPré, Jr.*)

The Search for New Crops

OUR FARM CROPS are the chief merchandise for the country's largest business enterprise. Like other businesses, agriculture tries to improve its merchandise. Every year excellent new models are brought out—a tastier tomato variety or a higher yielding corn hybrid or an improved variety of wheat, for example. New lines of merchandise are few, though. Many imports, such as the soybean, Korean lespedeza, avocado, safflower, and castorbean, have become or are becoming successful crops in this country. Still, fewer than 100 crops produced in the United States have cash values of a million dollars or more a year. Why do we not grow a greater variety of crops, particularly to provide raw materials for industry? Why, when thousands of species of seed plants are known to science, does world agriculture make use of less than 1 percent of this wealth? The answer is simple. Man has done the easiest thing first. Through the ages he has learned by trial and error which plants are most amenable to cultivation and are best suited to his needs. Then efforts of agricultural workers have been concentrated on improving the few crops selected.

The Department of Agriculture and State agricultural experiment stations conduct research to discover and develop practical new crops. Several factors have to be considered. Present and potential market opportunities must be evaluated. A new crop needs to fit existing or attainable cultural practices and produce economic yields. Practical processing procedures are essential. A new crop has to be profitable for the farmer, the processor, and the end user. The problems are complex and require years of work, but the rewards are high: A new crop as successful as the soybean would pay the costs of the program many times over. New tools of science permit us to probe the plant kingdom more deeply. Refinements of modern chemistry make obsolete complete reliance on human senses to evaluate the utility of a plant. Tests that once took months can now be made in days or hours. Developments in the plant sciences permit rapid, reliable evaluation of the potential of wild plants.

The first step in research on new crops is to decide on objectives. If we have in mind to find a new material for industry, for example, we may look for such major constituents as seed oils, proteins, and carbohydrate gums that offer promise of successful commercial exploitation. Then botanists send plant samples to the

473

chemical laboratory from their collecting expeditions in this country and abroad. They must recognize plant species at the site and note where and how the plants grow so as to guide future agronomic testing. The samples go to the Department's Inspection Station in Washington, D.C., where they undergo sanitary inspection and fumigation to avoid introducing or spreading disease organisms and harmful insects. They are then sent to the chemical laboratory, where each receives individual attention. Stalks are cut up for use in experiments to see if they are good for pulp or are ground for analysis. Seeds are separated from pods or other plant parts before they are milled. Such preparatory methods depend on the tests or analyses to be applied. Sometimes the technicians must improvise methods and apparatus, knowing that any process they develop may be mechanized if their findings are commercially acceptable.

The next step is to find out the kind and amount of the chemical constituents. For example, a seed sample is ground, and oil is extracted from a known amount of it with an organic solvent. It is weighed to determine the percentage. The makeup of the oil is found by a series of analyses and reactions. Natural oils are mixtures of a number of substances. The research chemist converts the oil to proper form for separation in a gas chromatograph. Each fraction separated in the machine produces a peak at a specified place on the paper chart of the continuous recorder. When a peak occurs in an unexpected position, the chemist knows he has a new compound. He can usually calculate from the size of the peak how much of the compound is present, and from its position on the chart he can make preliminary interpretations of the type of chemical structures involved. Further research proves what kind of new chemical has been discovered. All-glass apparatus for stepwise separations is employed in a procedure called countercurrent distribution. A combination of organic solvents, which are not miscible with one another, is used in each of a number of tubes. Provision is made for automatic separation of liquid layers and transfers from one tube to another. Some portions of the mixture being separated are more soluble in the upper layer and some in the lower layer in the tubes, so there is an enrichment of particular compounds in selected tubes. The use of this principle permits the separation of purified compounds so their chemical makeup can be unraveled.

The probability for successful development of new crops is enhanced by the large number of new types of chemical substances and new properties that we are finding. For example, the chemical structures of some of the newly found fatty acids of seed oils suggest important uses in plastics and lubricants and for numerous chemical intermediates for other uses. We must, however, first learn how to grow these species under practical conditions. Test plantings of the most promising ones are made in various sections of the

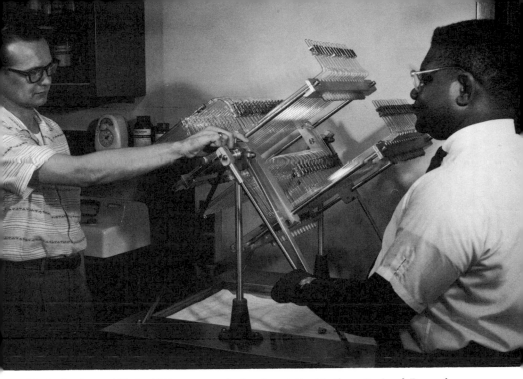

M. O. Bagby and T. L. Wilson, research chemists at the Northern Regional Research Laboratory in Peoria, Ill., operate an apparatus that separates complicated plant products into pure compounds.

L. E. Talley and D. E. Smith, physical science technicians, use a model of a commercial paper machine to convert experimental pulps to paper.

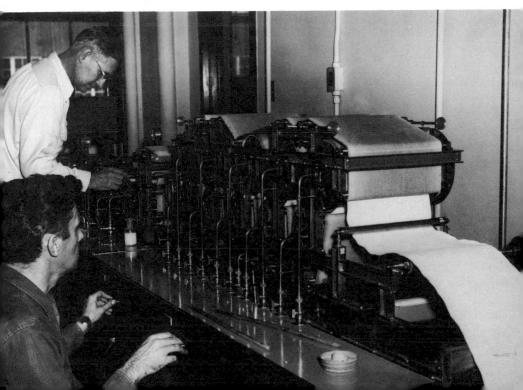

Karen O'Connor, a chemist, performs one step in chromatography.

country. Seeds of many legumes contain large amounts of carbohydrate gum. A little of this gum dissolved in water makes a solution almost too thick to pour. The gum increases the strength of many types of paper. Gums of this type are used also as thickening and water-retention agents in food and industrial applications.

Fiber plants that produce abundant growth are undergoing tests as possible new sources of pulp and paper. One of them, kenaf, sometimes reaches a height of 9 feet. After harvest, the chopped stalks are cooked under pressure in large steel autoclaves at high temperature with chemicals to dissolve the lignin and soften the fibers. Properties of pulps are then modified and controlled by various types of mills, which break apart the fibers further. Pulp is bleached to whiten it. A miniature laboratory paper machine provides a good indication of the quality of paper that can be prepared from the pulp. The paper is subjected to tests for measuring tensile strength, folding endurance, tearing resistance, and bursting strength. After the chemical investigations come evaluations by botanists and agronomists, who supply information on the possibilities of producing the species as a practical crop. Economists offer advice on potential markets and how the species may fare in competition with others. That is the final examination. The new plants that pass it are promoted to a place in the Department's research program. *(Ivan A. Wolff* and *Quentin Jones)*

476

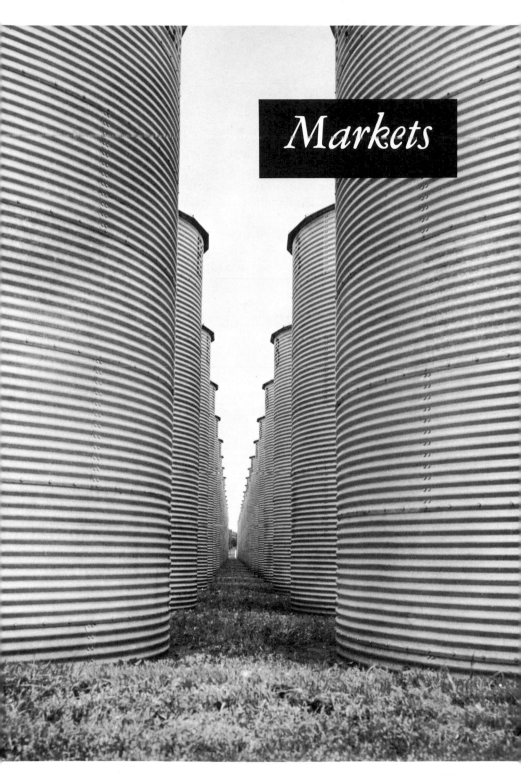

Markets

Getting Farm Products to Consumers

To GET the goods farmers produce to consumers takes billions of dollars of capital to establish and operate marketing facilities. Millions of workers assemble, transport, process, store, and distribute the products, for which American consumers spent about 100 billion dollars in 1962. Farmers today concentrate on production and leave most of the marketing to others. Consumers delegate more of the preparation and storage of food to the marketing system. Much of this change is due to the development of transportation and communications.

A few railroads reached inland in the 1860's, but most products were shipped by river or from Great Lakes, gulf, or ocean ports. Vessels sailing up and down the Pacific coast had to go around South America to reach the eastern cities. Travel between the Mississippi and California was a slow and hazardous overland trip by wagon train. Marketing then was both simple and difficult. It was simple because in most of the country farmers produced only for their own needs, and anything beyond that was sold or traded for other goods to the local storekeeper. When a farmer tried to market products outside his community, his problems multiplied. The difficulties were greater the farther he was from the nearest port or railroad. Until railroads spread out across the country, livestock had to be driven long distances to market. For about two decades after the Civil War, cattle were driven from as far south as Texas to railroad terminals in Abilene, Ellsworth, and Dodge City, whence they went to stockyards in the Midwest. Packers bought cattle from the yards, slaughtered the animals, processed the meat, and sent it to wholesale markets. Without refrigeration, fresh meat could not be stored for long or shipped very far. Hogs were slaughtered mostly in the winter, when cold weather made it possible to keep meat. Summer slaughtering did not become important until the development of refrigeration in the 1870's. Refrigeration also made it possible for packers to keep and use parts of the carcass that formerly had to be discarded.

In the years that followed, cities were getting bigger, calling for more food to be brought from farther and farther away. At the same time, however, more roads and railroads had been built, and shipping became easier and faster. These changes induced farmers to produce more than enough for nearby markets. As production increased, so did the number of so-called middlemen. Closest to the farmer was the country assembler. Because of trade connections in terminal cities, he could do a better job of finding markets than individual farmers or country storekeepers. The assemblers bought small quantities from many farmers and sold the lot at a few terminal markets. Elevators sprang up along railroads in grain areas. Small stockyards appeared for cattle and warehouses for tobacco and cotton. Country assembling of fruit and vegetables had to wait on the development of refrigerated freight cars. In 1872, a carload of fresh strawberries was shipped under ice from Anna, Ill., to Chicago, but long-haul shipments were not of any consequence until after the first refrigerated shipment of oranges and berries from California to New York in 1888. Transportation and communications had improved immeasurably by 1900. Railroad lines crossed the country, and branches served many small towns. About 8 thousand boats and barges were carrying merchandise on the Mississippi and its tributaries. Chicago, Duluth, and Buffalo were important shipping points, and shipments from eastern ports had increased. Although roads were still narrow and winding and the automobile and paved highways were still some years away, the so-called traditional marketing institutions had been established and would not change very much for several decades.

Large milling, baking, canning, and dairy industries were organized. Companies established brands and began advertising nationally; they believed they could promote their own products better than the wholesalers who had many brands to sell. Wholesale and retail outlets proliferated. At the end of the Second World War, retail food stores, particularly in cities, were too small to serve the expanding population without modernizing. Plants were in need of repair, and processing equipment was old or worn out. On the other hand, many firms and consumers had accumulated considerable capital during the war years, and others found it relatively easy to borrow money for construction and other capital investment. All these factors helped set the stage for the dramatic changes that took place in marketing after 1945. A significant change was the shift to fewer and larger and more specialized operations in marketing as in farming. Some farmers ship products directly to wholesale markets, but country assemblers are still an important link. There are fewer of them, but the size of their operations has increased, and products are drawn from a wider area. Because of the growing importance of trucks, assemblers depend less on railroads, and have a greater choice of routes to market and of quantities shipped. The networks of superhighways and local roads mean that trucks can be loaded by the farmer, assembler, processor, or wholesaler and unloaded at the door of the buyer. Market news reports allow flexibility in selecting markets.

Loading Texas cattle in Abilene, Kans., in frontier days.

Processing plants have changed considerably. Many small plants have been unable to compete with the big ones, which usually operate with a lower cost per unit. Another change has been relocating plants closer to sources of raw products—meatpackers are following cattle buyers and country auction markets; fresh fruit is packed near the orchard; and potato hydrators are in the growing areas. Food processors still sell a large part of their output to wholesalers, but retailers have been buying an increasing proportion. Some processors maintain sales organizations and warehouses in large cities, from which their goods are distributed to retail stores. Wholesale firms are larger and fewer. Some wholesale firms organize groups of retail stores into chains. Small retail grocers have formed cooperative groups that jointly own wholesale establishments. The aim of both groups is to give member stores the advantage of large-quantity, direct buying.

The final link in the marketing chain, the retail grocery store, probably has changed most of all. Groceries usually were sold in the 1860's in general stores—small, poorly lighted, cluttered places that smelled of pickled herring, coal oil, and stale tobacco smoke. In the center was a potbellied stove flanked by chairs and spittoons. Barrels, bins, boxes, and sacks of flour, sugar, and crackers

480

THE CITY MILK BUSINESS.

MARY, THE KITCHEN-MAID. "Why, John, what's the matter?"
MILKMAN. "Ah, Mary! if we don't have rain soon, I don't know what we'll do for Milk!"

were open to dirt, dust, flies. The customers hitched their horses in front. They traded their eggs, butter, and potatoes for molasses, sugar, kerosene, coffee, tea, spices. The clerks weighed the food items and put them into paper bags. Except for some local produce, no products were carried that needed special storage. Most foods other than staples were dried, smoked, or pickled. Canned foods were of dubious quality. One advertisement warned: "We sell the best in canned goods; we take no risks with our customers' health. There are certain brands of canned goods which should not be sold anywhere; these are never seen on our shelves." Many foods were adulterated. It was said that "even the products used for adulterating purposes are themselves adulterated and the evil has no limit." The old general store also sold yard goods, harness parts, ax handles, stove polish, washboards, pails, feather dusters, and playing cards. Often the post office was there.

—And a smell of herring in 1902.

Kiddie corners and music in 1962.

4:09 p.m., Nov. 23, 1904.

9:03 a.m., Nov. 22, 1961.

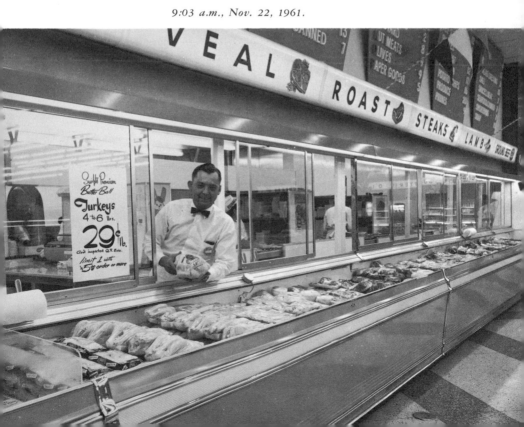

The typical retail food stores now are big, well lighted, well ventilated, and air conditioned. They average about 10 thousand square feet of selling space and carry about 6 thousand items. Most of them provide parking space. Some have check-cashing services, kiddie corners, and music. Some sell greeting cards, cigarettes, magazines, encyclopedias, phonograph records, toothpaste, hosiery, scrub brushes, shoe polish, dresses, pans, beer, brooms, detergents in super, giant, and mammoth packages, and food, also in packages. The packages are labeled, priced, and displayed with an artist's skill and the psychologist's knowledge of impulse buying. Packaging makes self-service easy for customers. It helps keep food clean and sanitary, maintain quality, and prevent excessive damage to the product. Refrigerated cases hold dairy products, meat, frozen foods, fruit, and vegetables. Many small neighborhood groceries have given way to the supermarket. The independent stores, such as the neighborhood grocery, and specialty stores, like bakeries, meat markets, and fruit and vegetable stands, still account for the largest share of stores, but supermarkets account for the largest share of grocery sales. Six percent of the chains accounted for 90 percent of the business done by these organizations in 1960; three corporations had nearly half of the sales. Some of the large chains buy products directly from farmers. Some operate processing facilities—bakeries, canneries, and coffee processing plants. Many chains maintain warehouses and have their own trucks. The big, new stores depend on a large volume and frequent turnover. To maintain this volume, they rely on quantity buying.

These changes have increased some of the farmers' marketing problems. Our marketing system today is characterized by a trend to fewer farmers producing larger quantities, which are sold in markets often controlled largely by a relatively few buyers. As farmers need assurance of buyers for their products and marketing firms wish to have dependable sources of products, more and more contract arrangements are being made between farmers and marketing firms. These contracts frequently require farmers to follow specified practices intended to produce the quality of product needed. In trying to offset some of the marketing pressures caused by large-scale buying, farmers have joined together in cooperative enterprises, in which they assemble and sometimes process farm products. Today's marketing system moves more food faster and farther than would have been conceivable a hundred years ago. Sweet corn is picked in the early hours of the morning, cooled, and sold in a distant market the same day. We have almost eliminated the calendar; most foods are available in some form the whole year. The future will see more of the same—newer foods, shorter marketing channels, greater efficiency, and less handling. *(Kenneth E. Ogren* and *Rosalind C. Lifquist)*

Market Research

MANY of the public markets for agricultural products were developed more than 100 years ago. They show their age. New ones are needed in some of our cities; new ones have been developed in more than 150 communities since 1958 with the help of marketing engineers, who studied the problems of antiquated facilities and the expected economies of modern installations. Examples are Columbia, S.C., where a new market has brought savings of 380 thousand dollars a year, and Philadelphia, whose new market was designed to save more than 3 million dollars a year in the cost of handling food products. Handling, which means putting down and picking up and storing and moving things from one place to another, takes time, money, and muscles or machines. Apples, for instance, used to be handled mostly by hand; many innovations in 1950–1955 in packing and handling saved a million dollars a year in the Northwest. Handling the fruit in pallet bins from orchards through packinghouses and to the retailer may save 4 million dollars a year. Less handling means a shorter, more direct line between two points: A vegetable, like corn, may be grown on contract with a farmer, picked at night, delivered to a store the next morning, and sold to the housewife 8 hours after it leaves the field. The marketing specialist also develops better techniques of quality control. Marketing officials in Vermont, for example, were able to reduce the off-flavor in milk products from 20 percent to less than 2 percent through the use of a testing laboratory designed to detect and correct off-flavor. Savings from reducing bulk in handling can be sizable. Carrots once were sold with tops on. Shipping costs were high because nearly half the weight was waste. Prepackaging carrots at the point of production reduced this waste, protected the product better, and saved 85 percent of the labor in retail handling.

The storage of agricultural products on the way to market also receives attention. New ways to aerate stored grain so it need not be turned, if used by one-third of the industry, should save millions of dollars a year. More than 400 firms have received help in designing aeration systems; at least 30 percent of commercial grain storage built in 1959 and 1960 was equipped for aerations. For sorting and packing eggs, automated equipment has been developed to detect blood spots and mechanize the weighing and packaging. This equipment has been adapted by more than 100 commercial plants.

The Lexington Market in Baltimore.

From colonial times, the Dock Street Market, Philadelphia, developed here.

The Dock Street Market, Philadelphia, in 1938.

Congestion in the Dock Street Market in 1958 was so bad that trucks often could not move for hours.

Plan of the new terminal market in Philadelphia.

An old market in Columbia, S.C.

The new Columbia Wholesale Farmers' Market, Columbia, S.C.

An electronic scale for weighing cotton does the work once done by 14 to 20 men.

Research workers of the Department of Agriculture and equipment manufacturers have helped develop automated packaging and pricing equipment, which wraps, weighs, prices, and labels packages of meat. The labor required for these functions has been reduced more than 70 percent. An example of refinements in work methods is the weighing of cotton in southern warehouses. Engineers mounted an electronic beam scale on a tractor; it and one operator do the job that crews of 14 to 20 men formerly performed.

Hourly costs of labor in food marketing have risen rapidly since 1945, but the labor cost per unit of product has increased only half as much. In the early postwar years, labor costs tended to rise almost as fast as hourly earnings, but unit labor costs more recently have risen at a much slower rate than wages. Large investments in new plant and equipment and greater emphasis on marketing research, public and private, apparently accelerated gains in labor productivity over the moderate gains during the war and the immediate postwar period. If labor costs per unit of product marketed had increased at the same rate in the 1950's as hourly earnings, the total labor bill in 1960 would have been up by an additional 7 billion dollars. This is a result of improved productivity of labor through better work methods, materials that cost less, and better facilities and transportation. *(Dale L. Anderson)*

Trucks are part of the transportation system that has made new marketing methods possible.

A blood-spot detector and packaging equipment for eggs.

Grapes for the New York market are loaded by forklift near Thermal, Calif.

Referee in the Market

THE FARMER and the consumer have become separated, and Federal, State, and local governments have had to take on more of the job of refereeing the marketing system—of making sure that the farmer gets fair treatment in the marketplace, the wholesaler and retailer get what they order, and the consumer gets the quality of food he wants. Housewives and chainstores alike want a uniform size and grade or quality in the products they buy. To get it, the stores use specification buying. That and long-distance hauling have furthered the use of the voluntary grading services provided by the Federal and State Departments of Agriculture. Wholesalers and buyers for large food retailers regularly order their stock by telephone and telegraph from producers and processors, who may be on the other side of the continent. The buyer is pretty sure of getting what he orders, thanks in large part to USDA grades. The supplier also can furnish Government certificates that the product meets the buyer's specifications; they are issued after the food is checked by Department or Federal-State graders.

The refereeing involves work that touches the operations of more than 3.5 million farmers; 100 thousand local buyers, processors, wholesalers, shippers, and handlers; and 500 thousand retail stores, restaurants, and hotels. Quality grading and inspection services, made available through the Agricultural Marketing Service of the Department of Agriculture in cooperation with the States, cover a wide variety of foods and fibers. In 1961, when farm marketings of agricultural commodities were worth approximately 35 billion dollars, more than 3 thousand Federal employees and 4 thousand employees of the State departments of agriculture and other local agencies were engaged in the grading of commodities for quality and condition. The grading program, largely voluntary, is financed by either a combination of Federal and State appropriations and revenue or revenue alone, paid directly to the Government agencies by the users of the service. The revenue paid by the users in 1961 amounted to almost 22 million dollars—more than 80 percent of the total cost.

When food products meet U.S. grade standards and the products have been graded by a Department grader, the seller may have the grade designation in the familiar USDA shield placed on the product or the package in which it is marketed at retail. Thus the

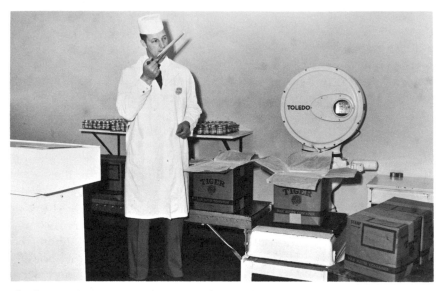

Floyd J. Mecham, Jr., a Department of Agriculture grader stationed at a creamery in Mason City, Iowa, uses a trier in grading a sample of butter taken from a bulk container. He examines the butter for flavor, aroma, color, body, and texture and assigns the appropriate grade in accordance with U.S. Standards for Grades of Butter.

Ruby G. Cartner, an employee of the Department of Agriculture, looks for the USDA grade shield on the package when she buys butter in a Washington store.

consumer also can be guided in his purchases by the grade designation. Eggs, chickens, turkeys, beef, veal, and lamb cuts, butter, and some fresh and processed fruit and vegetables are among the foods that commonly carry the Government grade shield. The Government grading program is not necessarily one of rating products as best, second best, and poorest. It is rather a process of subdividing highly variable products into uniform or standardized quality groupings. This subdividing and identification of quality by groups permits producers, buyers, processors and handlers, and consumers to select the quality group or subdivision that best suits their requirements.

A number of other inspection services, mostly nonvoluntary, are designed to assure the wholesomeness of food. Within the Department of Agriculture, the Meat and Poultry Inspection Services have been established by the Congress and directed to pass upon the wholesomeness of all meats, meat products, poultry, and poultry products that move in interstate or foreign commerce. These services are supported by appropriated funds and are compulsory upon all processing plants shipping these products in interstate commerce. The Food and Drug Administration of the Department of Health, Education, and Welfare is charged with the responsibility of protecting the public against adulterated, harmful, or mislabeled foods. All States also have food and drug agencies. Many State and local governments also have adopted various types of regulations, such as those governing the processing and distribution of milk, to protect the health of their citizens.

A related type of service, offered by the Department of Agriculture on a voluntary basis and financed from fees paid by the users, is the continuous inspection service for fresh and processed fruit, vegetables, dairy and egg products, and a number of other commodities. While the major emphasis of this service is quality control and quality grading, no plant may have this service unless it meets rigid sanitary standards. One such requirement, for example, is that each room and compartment in which any product is handled, processed, or stored must be designed and constructed to insure clean and orderly processing and operating conditions, must be free from objectionable odors and vapors, and must be maintained in a clean and sanitary condition. Other sanitary requirements cover equipment, facilities, and the premises on which the plant is located. Inspectors are stationed in a participating plant throughout its operating hours. They examine all ingredients utilized, check processing operations, and grade the finished product. Products processed under these services may bear the statement "Packed under the continuous inspection of the U.S. Department of Agriculture." They may also carry the U.S. grade designation on their label.

*Federal grades are used by the turkey
industry as a basis for paying producers
and as a mark of quality for consumers.
Nearly a billion pounds of ready-to-cook
turkeys are graded every year under a
voluntary grading service offered at cost
by the Department of Agriculture.*

*A Federal meat grader uses a roller to
stamp the grade on a carcass of beef.*

The classification of cotton by grade and staple length is another
example of the Department's role as a referee in the marketplace.
Cotton is made into heavy industrial fabrics, fine dress goods, and
many other products, for each of which a different quality is needed.
Cotton varies in length, color, strength, content of trash, fineness,
and so on. These properties must be identified, and cotton with
similar characteristics is assembled into lots of comparable quality.
Classification aids the textile manufacturer in getting the kind of
cotton he needs and helps the seller obtain a price based on its
quality. Practically every bale of cotton produced in the United
States is classed for farmers by the Department. Thus the farmer
knows its quality and value. All cotton tendered on futures contracts must be certified by the Department to insure a fair delivery.
The Department's cotton-classing services also are used in connection
with price-support operations and exports.

A. Elizabeth Handy, a home economist in the Department of Agriculture, examines federally graded turkeys in a supermarket. Seventy-five percent of all young turkeys sold off farms bear the Government grade shield, an assurance of satisfactory quality.

John Vilkaitis, a Department inspector, analyzes a sample of orange juice—a part of the official grade inspection procedure—at a processing plant in Florida.

A consumer selects a can of frozen concentrated orange juice that carries the USDA inspection shield and grade mark.

An inspector cuts a potato to determine the presence and the extent of internal discoloration.

Diane M. Moore, a Department technician, uses a fiber sorter to separate and measure cotton fibers.

Grading of wheat does not carry through to consumers on the loaf of bread, but the United States Grain Standards Act makes it compulsory for everyone selling wheat by grade and shipping it in interstate commerce to have it inspected for grade. This also applies to other grain. Domestic and foreign buyers use the grain grades to facilitate buying and selling without expensive and time-consuming personal inspection.

The Federal Seed Act provides for truth in labeling and advertising seeds shipped in interstate commerce. All States have similar labeling requirements, which apply at the local garden store. It also establishes minimum qualities for imported seed. Certain noxious weed seeds are specifically prohibited. Violation of this act is punishable by fines.

The Department of Agriculture also serves as an umpire in the marketing of livestock, meat, and poultry. The Packers and Stockyards Act of 1921, amended in 1958, regulates business practices of those engaged in interstate and foreign commerce in the marketing of livestock and live poultry and in the merchandising of meat and meat food products and poultry and poultry products. It is designed to protect farmers and ranchers from marketing practices that would deprive them of true market value of their livestock and poultry. It also protects consumers against misrepresentation of product and against unfair business practices that may cause excessive prices. It protects members of the regulated industries from unfair, deceptive, discriminatory, or monopolistic practices of competitors.

The Perishable Agricultural Commodities Act, enacted in 1930,

Elizabeth Wiseman, a seed technologist in the Department of Agriculture, determines the amount of inert matter and weed seeds in a mixture of grass seeds.

also serves as a watchdog over the operations of all who move fresh or frozen fruit or vegetables in interstate or foreign commerce. This act is designed to suppress unfair and fraudulent practices in the marketing of these products. Among the practices it prohibits are unjustifiable rejections or failure to deliver according to contract, fraudulent accounting, failure to pay, misbranding, and other forms of misrepresentation. Commission merchants, brokers, wholesalers, shippers, processors, and (under certain conditions) truckers and retailers are subject to the act and are required to be licensed. Farmers who sell only products they raise themselves need not be licensed. The Produce Agency Act authorizes still another umpiring job. This, a criminal statute, prohibits fraudulent practices in connection with consignments of fresh fruit and vegetables, dairy products, poultry, or any other perishable farm products. This law requires commission merchants or others to make fair and accurate accounting and full payment for any farm produce they receive on consignment. *(S. T. Warrington)*

Milestones in Cooperation

AGRICULTURAL COOPERATION in this country started with small, unincorporated organizations. "Associated," or cooperative, dairying began with the manufacturing and marketing of butter in 1810 at Goshen, Conn. Seventeen farmers in Bureau County, Illinois, in 1856 formed a pool for marketing hogs. Graingrowers built the first cooperative elevator in Madison, Wis., in 1857. The first known farm-supply cooperative was formed in 1863 to purchase fertilizer at wholesale for farmers at Riverhead, N.Y. It is still operating.

The growth of commercial farming and deflation after the Civil War aggravated the discontent of farmers, and they turned to organized effort to better their position. Through farm organizations, farmers registered protests against alleged exploitation by the railroads, the protective tariff, creamery and elevator companies, middlemen, financial interests and trusts, and general unfavorable economic conditions. For the next 50 years, general farm organizations influenced and guided cooperative effort. Each became deeply involved in farmer cooperative activity. Thousands of farmer cooperatives came into existence through their sponsorship. Its membership actually forced the Grange into cooperative business. By 1872 its half million members were united on a political and economic program that startled the Nation. Several important cooperatives today trace back to early Grange work. The American Society of Equity introduced the idea of pooling and market control. Its theory was tested in 1906 with the organization of growers of burley tobacco to resist low prices received for tobacco. "Night riders," seeking to enforce compliance with the planned production program, destroyed seedbeds and crops. As tobacco prices increased, the practices brought an end to Equity's operations in tobacco marketing.

Many early efforts failed, but farmers learned about cooperation from them. As a consequence, later endeavors of the Farmers Union and the Farm Bureau often proved more permanent. They sponsored marketing, farm-supply, and business-service cooperatives, many of which are in operation today. Springing up in response to pressing needs, many marketing cooperatives, however, began with no general farm organization affiliation. Between 1890 and 1921, cooperative marketing largely expanded on its own initiative and many of the associations organized in this period sparked further developments in the decades that followed. An important development in 1925 was the formation of the American Institute of Cooperation as a cooperatively supported educational institution to improve the understanding of cooperative enterprise in agriculture. The National Council of Farmer Cooperatives, organized in 1929, speaks for many farmer cooperatives in matters of national significance. Specialized national commodity organizations have also been established to represent the interests of various kinds of marketing cooperatives. Examples are the National Milk Producers Federation (1916) and the National Federation of Grain Cooperatives (1939).

As scientific farming expanded output and brought more specialized production, farmers increasingly called upon cooperatives for more service. By the midtwenties, cooperative marketing had become a well-recognized form of business activity and commodity marketing the cardinal principle. Tried first in California, the idea of large-scale commodity marketing rapidly spread across the country to include cotton, grain, and livestock. From California also came the concept of grower contracts, grading and standardization, and pooling of returns by grade and variety. These factors made effective marketing possible—a goal that farmers had sought vainly for a century. As farmers gained experience with marketing cooperatives, they saw more areas in which this form of business could help. To do a better job of production, farmers turned to cooperative farm supply and business services. Feed, fertilizer, petroleum products, and seed became increasingly important in modern farm operations and farmers soon found that cooperatives could effectively provide these items. Just as dairy, poultry, and fruit marketing cooperatives undertook an increasing number of services in moving products toward the consumer, statewide and areawide farm-supply cooperatives started to refine petroleum products and manufacture feed and fertilizer, thus moving farmer cooperative activities back toward basic raw materials. Cooperatives were first to use the open-formula principle in providing farmers with feed, fertilizer, and other supplies manufactured to meet their specifications.

In early days, farmer cooperatives were set up under the general State corporation laws. Soon the need for special legislation arose. A Wisconsin law of 1911 permitted the formation of stock cooperatives. In the next 15 years all States except one enacted similar laws. In Federal legislation, the Capper-Volstead Act (1922) gave farmers the right to act together in collectively processing and marketing their products, provided associations were operated for the mutual benefit of members and conformed to stated requirements. The Agricultural Marketing Act of 1929 provided for a Federal Farm Board with a revolving fund of 500 million dollars to be used in part to assist marketing cooperatives. For the first time, cooperatives were considered an important instrument of agricultural policy. Through a system of loans to some of these organizations, the Government looked to them to help control surpluses. The Farm Board, in addition to assisting cooperatives in financial difficulties during the depression, also helped establish large-scale cooperatives. The formation of the Farm Credit Administration in 1933 included a system of cooperative banks which, since the beginning, have made loans to eligible cooperatives and now provide over half of the loan capital borrowed by them. Through emphasis on complete loan service, these banks have contributed substantially to improved performance. Much credit for the steady growth and increased significance of cooperatives in marketing and purchasing is due the guiding influence of the banks for cooperatives.

The Department of Agriculture has worked on problems of farmer cooperatives for a long time. A document was prepared in 1901 to present possible dangers that should be avoided, the requisites for success, and the actual conditions encountered by cooperatives. The first formal work with cooperatives was centered in the Office of Markets in 1913. An important step was taken in 1926 with the enactment of the Cooperative Marketing Act, which created a Division of Cooperative Marketing in the Department of Agriculture. It established as national policy the principle of self-help for farmers through their own cooperatives. This act, now administered by the Farmer Cooperative Service, provides a program of research, advisory assistance, and education relating to management, organization, policies, efficiency, financing, and membership of farmer cooperatives.

The Federal Extension Service, since its beginning in 1914, has carried on educational work to extend the use of cooperatives by farmers. County agents have actively assisted in the formation of many local marketing associations and today agents and State Extension Services maintain close relations with cooperatives. The land-grant colleges assist farmer cooperatives through research, teaching, and extension. State departments of agriculture have assisted cooperatives, particularly on legal matters, organization problems, and accounting practices.

Cooperatives have played an increasingly important role over the past 100 years in helping farmers do a better job of producing and marketing food and fiber. This has come about through improved management, sound financing, increased use of research, and greater membership understanding and support. By working more closely together, by integrating operations, and by efficiently performing services needed by farmers, cooperatives can build upon their record in the future. *(J. Kenneth Samuels* and *Martin A. Abrahamsen)*

Farmer Cooperatives Today

FARMER COOPERATIVES have become an important factor in American agriculture during the past century. Whether in 1862 or 1962, farmers have looked to their cooperatives to help them increase income, build market outlets for an expanding output, and obtain supplies and services for an increasingly complex and mechanized farm production system. The farmer markets his products, purchases supplies, and obtains credit, electricity, insurance, irrigation, and other business services more conveniently and economically through cooperatives than he could by himself. At least four of every five farmers in the United States obtain some service from cooperatives. Nearly 10 thousand marketing, farm-supply, and related service cooperatives have memberships of almost 7.6 million. A farmer often belongs to two or more cooperatives. The estimated total marketing and farm-supply business, together with related services, of these cooperatives was 15.2 billion dollars, including intercooperative transactions. Their net worth—the amount farmers have invested in them—was almost 2.2 billion dollars in 1961.

Almost 15 thousand other cooperatives provide business services for farmers. More than one-half of the fire insurance farmers have in force is provided by their own mutual companies, 1,650 in number. About one-half of their electricity is obtained from some 975 Rural Electrification Administration cooperatives. About 25 percent of all irrigated land is supplied with water by more than 9 thousand mutual companies, mostly in the West. Farmers obtain credit for a variety of uses from 830 Federal land bank associations, 495 production credit associations, 550 rural credit unions, and a few agricultural credit corporations. Farmers also operate about 1,500 dairy herd improvement and 50 dairy-cattle artificial breeding associations. The net worth of these cooperatives is estimated to be almost 2.1 billion dollars. Thus, the combined investment farmers have in all types of cooperatives amounts to more than 4 billion dollars.

Cooperatives help to keep our free enterprise system competitive. By maintaining standards of business service and performance, they spread the benefits of their operations to all farmers. The presence of cooperatives often has brought about a decline in margins taken for marketing, purchasing, or related services. Farmer cooperatives range in size from small community enterprises to large regional associations that do many millions of dollars' worth of business annually. Three-fifths of them have business volumes of less than half a million dollars each. One percent have annual volumes of 20 million dollars or more. Local cooperatives serve a shipping point or trading center; their members are individual farmers. Regional cooperatives cover several counties in a State or all or parts of several States. Some are national in scope. They are of two general types. In a centralized association, the farmer is a direct member. In a federated association, the farmer is an indirect member, for he is a member of a local association, which is a direct member of the federation through an elected board. Each local association is controlled by its own members, who are the ultimate beneficiaries of the federation's operations. A characteristic of American farmer cooperatives is their interrelatedness. Many cooperatives may be defined as small or local organizations, but generally they are affiliated with regional federations. In turn, many of the regional federations are joined together in national federations for the purpose of functions that can best be performed on a broader basis.

Farmers, as individuals, have little influence in the marketplace. Organized cooperatively, they can meet power with power. Without cooperatives, they must accept available services. Cooperatives thus secure for farmers the advantages of big business—volume economies, access to managerial skills, and sufficient capital for research and development—preserving for them their status as individual operators. They perpetuate the values of small enterprise with its opportunities for individual expression and satisfaction. The family farm could not long survive as an atomist unit in a complex society without the aid of cooperative organization. Cooperatives give farmers a sense of belonging—millions of individuals feel they have a stake in the private enterprise system of this country because they are members of various kinds of cooperative organizations. Cooperatives increase the business capabilities of farmers. They share in management through membership meetings and in electing boards of directors. Cooperatives spread economic literacy through their educational programs, informative annual reports, membership meetings, and publications. They make information generally available on methods and costs of various marketing operations and functions. Without them, we would lack much detailed information regarding the working of businesses serving farmers, for cooperatives, as democratic organizations, must provide full and complete information to their members and to the public as well. Cooperatives contribute to the administration of various regulatory programs of value to agriculture, such as the milk marketing orders, which regulate the marketing of milk in many metropolitan areas.

The number of marketing, farm-supply, and related service cooperatives has gradually declined since the high-water mark of 12

The Farmers Cooperative Society of Rockwell, Iowa, which was organized in 1889, has the oldest cooperative elevator in the United States. S. T. Tomke (left) is its manager. J. B. McGaharen is cashier of the Community Bank in Rockwell.

The Lake to Lake Dairy Cooperative, Manitowoc, Wis., performs marketing services from farmers to consumers.

thousand was reached in 1930, largely because of consolidations, mergers, and acquisitions that have taken place as business units generally have grown in size. Cooperatives, like other forms of business, are affected by the economic forces calling for larger units. Farmers must provide themselves with organizations that are large enough to operate effectively in today's economy. The trend to

In the auction yard in Visalia of the California Farm Bureau Marketing Association, a wheel-shaped alley in the middle routes cattle into pens. A man grades the cattle and controls the yarding from a tower by the use of hydraulic gates.

mergers and consolidations has not yet reached its peak, for many cooperatives are exploring the possibilities of reorganization to achieve lower unit costs, more competent management, and greater efficiency. Cooperatives, to a large extent, are integrating organizations, with the farm as the foundation for the integrated structures. As cooperatives grow, they expand both horizontally and vertically, giving the farmer member the advantages that come from such extensions of his operations. By combining their producing and marketing functions to a greater extent in one organization, farmers can increase their operating efficiency with resulting enhancement of their economic position. Integration is growing in agriculture and its potentialities for farmers are great. By taking advantage of this trend, farmers can be the beneficiaries of this process, for it is obvious that the economy is going to be served by strong, integrated organizations capable of meeting the requirements of large, urban, mass markets.

As marketing cooperatives have expanded in business volume, they have increasingly concerned themselves with finding export outlets for their members' products. Sunkist Growers, Inc., formerly California Fruit Growers Exchange, as early as 1924 exported citrus products to customers in most parts of the world. Other cooperatives have developed extensive export operations in dried and deciduous fruit, rice, almonds, walnuts, poultry, honey, and other specialty products. A significant development is the formation of the Producers Export Co., which serves many of the grain marketing regionals and has started to expand its service to include oilseed products. The influence of American farmer cooperatives is worldwide. Students from all parts of the world seek information on how they are organized and operated. They hope to improve economic and social conditions in their own countries by setting up similar cooperative enterprises adapted to their own needs.

Cooperatives are adjusting their functions to changing production patterns. The increasing size of farm units brings the need for added services, such as production credit, farm-to-plant transportation, bulk distribution of feed and fertilizer, spraying, and harvesting. It also confronts cooperatives with the problem of varying costs incurred in serving both large and small farmers. Today's farmers are better equipped, more mechanized, better informed, and more demanding than their predecessors. They consider themselves businessmen in a specialized industry. They regard cooperatives as devices to help them improve their performance as farmers. They see farming on the move with new products, new methods, new problems. They demand cooperatives that keep up to date and out in front. That is as it should be, for cooperatives have a strong foundation built with 100 years of support from farmers and the Department of Agriculture. (*Joseph G. Knapp* and *Anne L. Gessner*)

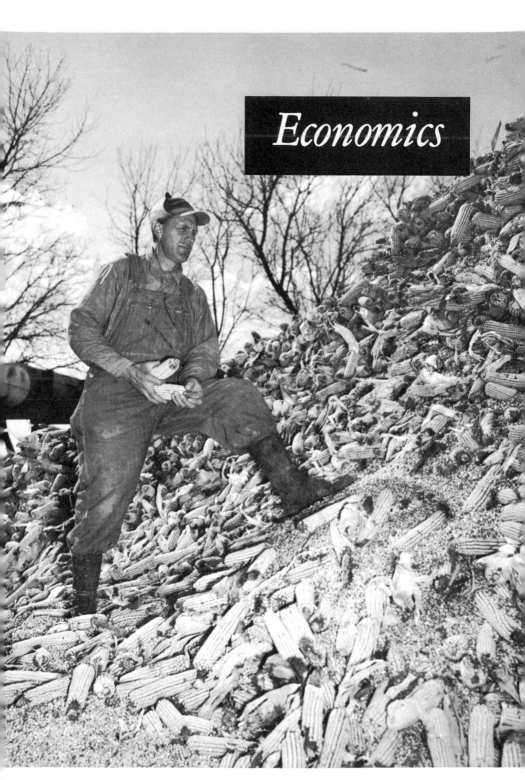

Economics

We Have Not Yet Learned

THE AVERAGE American farmworker in 1862 produced enough food and fiber to support fewer than five persons. That simple fact we should keep in mind when we consider how the productivity of American farms has increased since then to the point where the average agricultural worker can supply the needs of 26 persons and what that increase means. Only since 1920, the output per man-hour of farm labor has increased fourfold. The productivity of the American farmworker increased 6.5 percent a year after 1950; the output per man-hour in nonagricultural industry increased about 2 percent a year. Crop production was about 60 percent greater per acre and output per breeding animal was about 85 percent greater in 1961 than in 1919–1921. This success in agriculture has brought its reward—but the reward has gone to the American consumer and not to the American farmer.

The consumer in America works fewer hours to feed himself and his family than in any country and at any time in history. He can buy a balanced and varied diet for only about a fifth of his take-home pay. For comparison: In the United Kingdom, food accounts for about 31 percent of total expenditures for private consumption; in France, 32 percent; Austria, 36 percent; and Italy, 45 percent. The average American industrial worker was able in 1960 to buy much more food with his take-home wage than in 1947–1949—64 percent more pork, 32 percent more beef, 25 percent more milk, 5 percent more bread, 21 percent more potatoes, 62 percent more peas, and 100 percent more eggs. Retail costs of food have gone up, but they have gone up less than the prices of all goods and services the consumer buys. Retail food prices have risen about 17 percent in the period, but the cost of all items in the cost-of-living index has gone up more than 26 percent. The rise in food costs, however, is caused by an increase in marketing costs and extra services required by consumers. The basic cost of food—that is, the farm value of food—is 12 percent less than it was in 1947–1949. The farmer received only 39 cents of each dollar spent in 1960 for food; in 1945, he received 54 cents. The cotton farmer in 1960 received 27 cents for the cotton that went into a white shirt—not much more than a city man pays for having it laundered.

The decline in the prices farmers received for their produce and the increases in the prices they paid for machinery, fertilizer, and

The First World War stimulated mechanization. Tractors replaced horses, mules, and oxen. Food and fibers were grown on land that had been used to grow feed for animals. The use of improved varieties of crops, better practices, and more fertilization raised production in later years.

The world's need for food during the war period led to higher prices. Farmers went heavily into debt to get more land and machinery to grow the food. Then came the day of reckoning.

other production materials meant that farmers had less net income than nonfarm people in 1959. The per capita income of farm people was 965 dollars—about a third of which came from nonfarm sources. Nonfarm people received a per capita income of 2,216 dollars. Since 1950, the farm population's share of the national net income dropped from about 8 percent to about 4 percent—in other words, their share was cut in half. The decline in farm income has been almost steady and continuous during the fifties. The incomes of farm families were lower relative to the rest of the population

Should abundance be a problem?

in 1961 than at any time since the last days of the great depression. In view of the declining purchasing power of the dollar and the rise in the dollar income of the rest of the Nation, farm operators fell far short of the economic rewards their productivity and efficiency merited. Agriculture's success is the cause of agriculture's distress.

Increases in production and resulting decreases in price are an important part, but only a part, of the problem of agriculture. The farmer is at a disadvantage economically for three basic reasons: First, individual producers do not have it in their power to adjust production to current demand. American agriculture can produce more than can be marketed at prices that give farmers a fair return on their investment and labor. Second, farm costs have risen faster than farm prices—a cost-price squeeze that has put the farmer at an economic disadvantage. Third, wide underemployment exists in agriculture.

Industrial productivity has increased manyfold, but technological improvements and automation historically have not lead to unmanageable gluts of manufactured goods or demoralized prices. Industry can control output and thereby control prices received. Production of a manufactured item, such as a tractor, tends to be in the hands of a few large corporations, which can reduce production to the level of demand by reducing the amount of labor and raw materials they use. It is not feasible for farmers to reduce production when output exceeds demand. Millions of farmers, acting individually, cannot effectively influence the total output or the price of the products they sell. Actually, farmers tend to increase production when prices fall. They try to maintain their individual incomes by producing more units at the lower price per unit. This is because so many farm production costs are fixed and cannot be reduced when output is reduced. Mortgage payments fall due whether land is planted or lies fallow. Land is fixed absolutely and has few alternatives as to use, except when it lies close to cities. Buildings and machinery are also highly fixed. They have limited alternative use and are employed in farming as long as they will pay returns above their salvage value. The costs of labor cannot be reduced by limiting production—as they can in industry—since the farm family usually supplies the labor. The alternative is for members to find off-farm employment, but that is impossible in many sections for a variety of reasons. Farmers therefore continue to produce; production exceeds demand; agricultural prices continue to fall.

If a drop in agricultural prices caused demand to increase, there might be some relaxation of the downward pressures of excess production on agricultural prices. But the human stomach is relatively inelastic. American consumers are relatively well fed. They have changed their food habits, but individually they are eating no more

509

food today than they were in 1910. A little too much in the way of food supplies leads to dramatic declines in farm prices and hence to a farm income problem. A little too little in the way of food supplies leads to skyrocketing food prices—such as has been encountered in wartime—and to a real income squeeze on consumers. Because of the productivity of American agriculture, however, the "little too much" has been the more common occurrence. Population increases, programs to increase the consumption of food and fiber among the low-income groups, and programs that utilize food to assist in the development of underdeveloped countries all help to expand demand. Such increases in demand have not, and probably will not, be able to keep pace with the expansion of agricultural output.

The inelasticity of the human stomach and the increasing productivity of agriculture have meant that farm prices have trended downward. At the same time, prices paid for machinery, fertilizer, and other production materials purchased by the farmer have continued upward. This increase is the logical result of inflationary pressures in the economy. As incomes rise, consumers are willing to pay more for goods such as automobiles and appliances. Manufacturers of such "hard" items bid up the price of steel, petroleum, and capital. Manufacturers of goods the farmers buy consequently have to pay more for steel and capital, and so the prices of tractors, fertilizers, and other production materials rise. Seen on a graph, lines representing prices paid by farmers and prices received by farmers crossed in the early fifties. Since then the distance between them has tended to widen, with prices received by farmers falling well below prices paid. Even though the gross incomes of farmers rise, production expenses absorb more and more of this gross and leave smaller and smaller net incomes for farmers. This is the result of the cost-price squeeze.

Underemployment is a serious problem in agriculture. Many farmers reside on uneconomic units, which do not permit them to produce enough to earn a living wage. This is like a factory worker trying to live on a part-time job. In many cases, income from farming is supplemented by nonfarm employment. In other cases, a substandard existence is maintained. Department economists computed the unemployment represented by underemployment in agriculture. They concluded that if such underemployment were suddenly ended, 1.4 million workers would be added to the list of unemployed. The effect on the economy of such an increase in unemployment is a sobering thought. Surplus labor in agriculture has been responsible for a reduction in farm employment of about 45 percent since 1920, as farmworkers migrated to cities. It has also been responsible for uneconomic production.

A basic reason for underemployment in agriculture is the excess

Prices fell. Many mortgages on land and machines were foreclosed. Landless, homeless farmers were desperate. They did what they could; sometimes the sheriff had to come.

Action in the thirties by the Federal Government saved many farms from foreclosure. Thousands of farmers were given a start on new homes.

of births in the farm population over farming opportunities. The birth rate of rural America has been consistently higher than the urban birth rate. At the same time it has been increasingly difficult for a young man to begin farming on his own. Capital requirements in farming are rising, and an investment of 21,300 dollars for each farm employee was required in 1960—as against 15,900 dollars for each worker in the manufacturing industry. Few farm youths can obtain the capital needed to operate a farm. Established farmers have also moved out of farming as smaller farms have been absorbed into larger units. This has been the result of the tractor-power technology, which makes larger units more efficient and requires larger amounts of capital. The number of farms—which increased fantastically during the westward migration and reached a peak in 1935—has been steadily declining since the thirties, while the average size of the farm has increased. Although many farm youths and farm operators have entered nonfarm employment, many more lack the necessary education, skill, and experience. They remain on substandard farms and eke out a substandard existence. More jobs are needed, of course, since underemployment and unemployment are basically the same.

If a way can be found to adjust farm production to existing demand, assure farmers a fair return on their capital and labor, and reduce materially the agricultural pockets of poverty that characterize places of greatest underemployment, the farm problem will be

511

solved. Food would then be provided consumers at fair and stable prices, the potential for feeding a growing America would be preserved, and farmers would be provided with equality of opportunity with other Americans.

More is to be sought for than a recognition and an understanding of the farm problem. We need to realize the importance of agriculture to the economy. Agriculture is a creator of employment. Four out of every 10 jobs in private employment are related to agriculture. About 10 million people have jobs storing, transporting, processing, and merchandising agricultural products. Another 6 million provide supplies the farmers use. These workers, added to the approximately 7 million in farming, make up about a third of all employed workers. Those employed in farming alone, in 1959, exceeded those in either the steel or automobile industries. Investment in agriculture exceeds 200 billion dollars—three-fourths of the current assets of all corporations in the United States.

The farmer is a taxpayer. Farm real estate taxes in 1959 totaled 1.2 billion dollars. Personal property taxes paid by farmers totaled another 250 million dollars. Income taxes paid by farmers amounted to 1.25 billion dollars. License fees, permits, and taxes on motor fuels were 544 million dollars. Farmers also are consumers. They spend more than 25 billion dollars a year for the things they need to produce crops and livestock. They spend 15 billion dollars a year for the same things city people buy—food, clothing, drugs, furniture, appliances, and other goods and services. For tractors, motor vehicles, machinery and equipment, they spend about three times as much as the primary iron and steel industry spent in 1959 for equipment and new plants. The farmer buys enough rubber to put tires on nearly 6 million automobiles and enough electric power to supply the annual needs of Baltimore, Chicago, Boston, Detroit, Washington, and Houston. It may not be correct to say that depressed incomes of the farm segment of the economy lead to a general depression, but it is obvious that a decline in the purchasing power of the farmer materially affects the general economy. Apparent also is the threat to the city dweller of conditions which could drive nearly 1.5 million farmworkers into cities searching for jobs.

An understanding of agriculture's importance and its problems therefore is vital to all. We have moved from an age of scarcity to an era of abundance, but we have not yet learned how to live with abundance. Our political, economic, and social thinking must leave the economics of scarcity and move aggressively to cope with the problems of today. And time is running out. Conditions must be corrected soon, if America is to hold its position of world leadership and enjoy, during the next century, the economic growth and freedom that characterized the past 100 years. *(Kennard O. Stephens)*

Lean Years

A GROUP of photographers was assembled in the historical section of the Farm Security Administration in the midthirties and told to document with their cameras the agricultural world as they saw it. They took thousands of pictures. The pictures shocked and aroused Americans. City people knew there were duststorms, but they had not seen farmers and their families fleeing before clouds of dust. City people knew that soil eroded, but they had not seen gullies twice as deep as a house. City people knew there were poor farmers, but they did not see the potbellies of pellagra-stricken children. City people knew that lettuce and carrots were harvested, but they had never seen the jalopies that farm families rode to get to the harvest and the hovels of the migrants who harvested the crops. Many farm families had not seen these scenes, either.

The photographers, in the 7 years they worked together, made these scenes the common property of the Nation. The photographers included Arthur Rothstein, John Vachon, Ben Shahn, Marion Post Wolcott, Russell Lee, Carl Mydans, Walker Evans, Jack Delano, and Dorothea Lange. Their pictures have been printed and reprinted in books, magazines, and newspapers and used in exhibits. They are now on file in the Library of Congress. They were part of the education of America, and they still are: An education that accompanied and sometimes preceded a growing recognition that there were problems of people and soil and methods in America that were too big for any man or any group of men to solve on their own.

Roy Emerson Stryker, onetime gold miner, cowpuncher, professor of economics in Columbia University, and assistant to the Administrator of the Resettlement Administration, organized and directed this classic documentary endeavor. He has referred to the pictures as "important comments on United States life in the thirties." Some of them appear in the pages that follow.

"It was a troubled period," Mr. Stryker wrote in a review of the pictures in Harvester World. "There were depressed areas, depressed people. Our basic concern was with agriculture—with dust, migrants, sharecroppers. Our job was to educate the city dweller to the needs of the rural population. It was a troubled period, but as you look through the file, you'll detect counterpoints of dignity, hope, laughter." *(A.S.)*

Experiments in Survival

THE GRIM DAYS of the thirties demanded new programs, new assessments of direction, and new social action and experiment. The Government started several rural relief programs, some of which have continued, in somewhat altered forms, to this day. Others were short lived. Among the latter were a number of dramatic approaches to farm problems. Three of them we recall here—the resettlement projects, group medical care, and migrant camps. Perhaps the most significant part of them was that someone had the imagination to conceive them and someone was willing to try them out at a time when the Nation was going through a soul-searching experience. The accepted ways had failed.

The resettlement projects were efforts to develop more or less complete rural communities, in which low-income families, mostly farmers, could find a better way of life. In all, approximately 152 projects were occupied by 10 thousand families. The Government in some instances bought large tracts for the projects, subdivided the land into family-type farms, and equipped each farm with a modest house and a barn. In others, the Government added schools and community buildings and helped the families develop cooperative stores, cotton gins, and similar services. Several projects consisted of subsistence homesteads, where families who had industrial or other nonfarm employment could supplement their wages by raising a large part of their own food supply. In a few of these communities, the Government helped finance industrial developments. Nearly all the families selected by the Government to live on the newly developed farms were in distress: They had been farming wornout land. They had been sharecroppers. They had been on relief. The new communities offered an opportunity to get a fresh start. The projects that were made up of well-developed farms gave a number of farm families a real boost along the road to better living. In some instances, the farms that were originally laid out proved to be too small, and there was a general reworking of boundaries and consolidating of farm units, but even here the net result was the transfer of a group of farm families from the ragged edge to ownership of good farms.

The success of the subsistence homestead projects varied to the degree that industrial or other nonfarm employment was available to the homesteaders. Some of the projects ran into one difficulty

Officers of the LaForge Cooperative Association, LaForge Farms Project, New Madrid County, Missouri, hold a meeting in 1938. The Cooperative operated a cotton gin, a warehouse, a store, and a blacksmith shop.

A farmer and his wife in their new home on the LaForge Farms Project in 1938. The project consisted of about 100 family farms, developed to enable sharecroppers to obtain farms of their own.

after another. Many of them were doomed from the start, because skilled project managers were few. Many of them suffered from being in the limelight. Every disagreement the families had among themselves or with the Government was magnified by being in the public eye. The first of these ventures was started in 1933. By the midforties, the Government had finished the work of turning over to private hands all the farms and various community developments. Agencies involved in the planning, development, operation, and sale of the projects were the Division of Subsistence Homesteads of the Department of the Interior, the Federal Emergency Relief Administration, the Resettlement Administration, and the Farm Security Administration. No one has ever tackled the task of assessing the full value of this experiment. In broad terms, the allegations of the critics were that the projects cost too much and that certain developments were wildly impractical if not absolutely contrary to the accepted way of doing things. The proponents' main points were that they helped many families make a better living and that they laid the groundwork for real advances in various phases of supervised credit, farmhousing, better rural schools, family-farm management, farm cooperatives, and land settlement policies in general.

The farm families served by the Resettlement Administration—and its successor, the Farm Security Administration—had health problems. Because of their limited incomes, they tended to put off going to the doctor. Chronic conditions were not cared for. When emergencies occurred, such as appendicitis or pneumonia, they called a doctor and worried about the bills afterward. To pay the bills, they often had to sell a cow or use money they had set aside for seed, new machinery, or some other necessity. Often they were unable to pay all or even part of the bill, and their doctors for-

A former sharecropper looks at his new home from the porch of his old home in the Southeastern Missouri Farms Project.

A farmstead at Irwinville Farms Project in Georgia in 1938. Here 105 farms were developed for families who had been farming as tenants.

A camp built and operated by the Farm Security Administration for migratory farmworkers, Shafter, Calif.

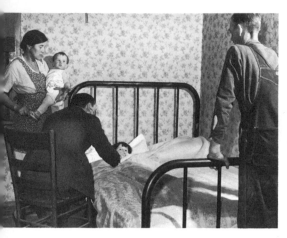

A physician visiting the home of a Farm Security Administration borrower in St. Charles County, Mo., in 1939.

Children of migrant packinghouse workers in front of shelters at Osceola Migratory Labor Camp, Belle Glade, Fla., in 1941.

The Osceola Migratory Labor Camp in Florida was developed by the Farm Security Administration to provide shelter for packinghouse workers.

gave the difference. During the 10 years that started in 1936, the two agencies encouraged the development of voluntary group medical programs as a method of enabling the borrowers to obtain needed medical care and of assuring their doctors a certain return for their services. These health insurance programs were voluntary on the part of the families and the doctors who participated. The borrowers paid a certain amount into a pool. The doctors charged for their services on a regular basis. If the funds in the pool were insufficient to cover all bills in full, the participating physicians agreed to accept a pro rata share for the services they rendered.

Some of the plans included dental, surgical, and hospital services, as well as physicians' services. The role of the Government was limited to helping set up the plan, encouraging its development, and, when necessary, including in the borrower's loan the amount needed to pay the membership fee. When the Government withdrew in 1946 from this type of participation in medical care, 706 plans were in operation in 1,029 counties. They were serving about 52 thousand families.

Another noteworthy experiment of the thirties was the migratory farm labor camps built and maintained by the Resettlement Administration and Farm Security Administration. Many migrant farm laborers even today live in appalling circumstances. In the thirties, thousands camped on ditch banks, in vacant lots, and in scrap-heap shacks on the outskirts of towns. The Government moved in on this problem by building camps where the migrants could be properly housed. The Farm Security Administration at the end of 1942 had 95 migratory labor camps, with accommodations for 20 thousand families. About half of them were permanent structures. The rest were mobile. In the permanent camps, the shelters were one-room structures built of wood or steel. The mobile camps had tents. Sanitation was stressed in all camps. The permanent camps had buildings provided with toilets, shower baths, and laundry tubs. The mobile camps had tents or trailers with shower facilities. The permanent camps generally had clinics and other community buildings. The mobile camps, where possible, had trailer clinics and community tents. Originally instituted as a relief measure to protect the health of the workers and the communities in which they lived, the camps during the war years developed into a mechanism for the better utilization of farm labor. The camps were sold in the midforties to local interests, and the Federal Government withdrew from this type of participation in easing problems of migrants. Some 15 years later, in the Housing Act of 1961, the Farmers Home Administration was authorized to insure loans for the development of housing for domestic farm labor. The loans may be made to individual farmers, groups of farmers, and public or private nonprofit organizations. *(Philip S. Brown)*

Facts for Decision

THE CROP REPORTING BOARD meets in the South Building of the Department of Agriculture in a locked, guarded room that no unauthorized person may enter and no one may leave until the Board completes its deliberations on one or another of the 500 reports it prepares each year. The reports touch on almost every phase of the production and utilization of farm products—the supplies and prospective supplies of food and fibers, prices received and paid by farmers, farm labor and wages, the storage holdings of commodities, and so on.

The actual session of the Board is the culmination of a complex, technical operation. The basic information is collected through State field offices, which cover a band nearly a quarter of the way around the world, on agricultural conditions from the Arctic to the Tropics. The State statistician and his assistants analyze the information they collect and send their report to Washington, where the State reports are analyzed again and the State official estimates are adopted and combined for the full, national reports. Because the Board's reports may affect the market and be of advantage to individuals or groups who could get them before their competitors, strict laws and rules of the Secretary of Agriculture govern the procedures. The State reports that might be involved in speculative operations are mailed directly to the office of the Secretary of Agriculture, where they are deposited, their seals unbroken, in a steel box that has two padlocks. The key to one is in the Secretary's custody. The other is kept by the chairman of the Crop Reporting Board.

Early on the day a report is to be released, the chairman and secretary of the Board and a few members meet a representative of the Secretary of Agriculture and proceed under guard to the locked box. Each lock is opened. The reports from the field are checked out and handed to the chairman. The group is escorted back to the locked quarters, where the window blinds have been drawn and sealed, telephone connections have been plugged, and buzzers have been disconnected. The door is locked and guarded during the entire meeting of the Board. Then the seals to the State reports are broken. Each member of the Board then analyzes the report from each State. The analyses of all the members are placed on a master sheet. The chairman reviews the conclusions reached by each member. After differences of opinion are resolved, the chairman adopts

On myriad details, such as measurements of the growth of a sample peach tree, the Crop Reporting Board of the Department of Agriculture bases its reports of crop yields and production.

To refine their estimates of production, agricultural statisticians check the damage a hurricane did to the cotton crop.

Eddie Anderson guards the room in which economists and statisticians prepare a monthly report on agricultural production.

the final, official figures, which are turned over to the computing section, a summary is compiled, and the total estimate or forecast for the United States is put together. Only at this point does any member of the Board or anyone else know the total figure. Comments are prepared. They and the statistical tables are stenciled and duplicated inside the locked room. The law requires that the Secretary of Agriculture, or in his absence the designated Acting Secretary, review and approve the final report. When everything is ready, the Secretary enters the room, reviews the report with the chairman and the members of the Board, and approves and signs the report. A minute or two before the official release time, usually 3 p.m. for the general reports and 11 a.m. for the cotton reports, the chairman signals the guard, who escorts the chairman and secretary of the Board to the official release room, where reporters are waiting. The reporters step back to a white line 6 feet from the instruments, at each of which the chairman places a report, face down. About 5 seconds before release time, the Secretary's release officer tells them, "Get ready!" When the clock points exactly to the time, he says, "Go!" At that instant the reporters man their telephones and teletype machines, and the report is released to the world.

The reports—like those of transactions on the stock exchanges, the statements on carloadings, inventories of major commodities, employment figures, and so on—are essential to the functioning of our free enterprise system, which can work only if the facts for vital decisions are freely available to all. Because our food originates on farms all over the country, only the Federal Government through the Department of Agriculture can provide all the people with the information contained in the Board's reports. The organization that provides this service is the Statistical Reporting Service. It employs fewer than a thousand persons, more than two-thirds of whom are in the various State offices. Individual States help strengthen the reports by furnishing personnel to provide information they believe is needed in connection with their services to agriculture in the State. The basis of the service, however, is the voluntary assistance of some 750 thousand farmers and businessmen who report periodically on their own operations. This service is an outstanding example of cooperation between the Government and citizens all over the country.

The need for this service developed long ago. As early as 1800, State agricultural societies became interested in statistics on crop and livestock production, when the transportation of food from farms to the cities was taken over increasingly by dealers and commission men and farmers contended that "speculators" robbed them of the fruits of their labors. Some of the societies attempted to collect information on the size of production and the progress of crops, but the job proved too big for such informal handling. On President Van Buren's request, the Congress in 1839 appropriated a thousand dollars to the Patent Office to collect statistics. The first crop reports were issued in 1841 but were discontinued after 1850. President Lincoln told the Congress "that an Agricultural and Statistical Bureau might profitably be organized." When the Department of Agriculture was established, a statistical reporting service was placed on a continuing basis. The first monthly crop report cited the condition, as of May 1863, of 19 crops in 21 Northern States and the Nebraska Territory. The more complete annual reporting of crop and livestock statistics and prices of farm products began in 1866-1867. The first appropriation specifically for crop and livestock estimates was 20 thousand dollars in 1865, and it was continued at about that level until the early eighties. The reports then were largely monthly reports of the condition of crops in the field without quantitative estimates. Final reports at the close of the year showed total acreage, yield, and production of crops; livestock numbers by species; average prices received by farmers for crops; and

The Crop Reporting Board in session. Seated at the end of the table, looking at you, is S. R. Newell, Chairman of the Board.

value per head of livestock. The crop reports had become increasingly important factors in the market by 1900 because of the activities on some of the commodity exchanges. The United States Crop Reporting Board was established in 1905.

At this time the realization grew that information was needed on happenings in the marketplaces that served the growing urban population. People began to urge that the Department of Agriculture establish a Market News Service. A start was made in 1915, when a simple report gave prices and market conditions for strawberries at Hammond, La. The reports today cover fruit and vegetables, livestock, meats, wool, dairy products, poultry, tobacco, cotton, cottonseed, and naval stores. These reports for the most part provide information on the prices, supply, and market conditions. The service is conducted through some 200 field offices in important producing areas, major assembly and terminal markets, and food distribution centers. For quick exchange of information, most of these offices are connected by more than 13 thousand miles of leased lines. The Crop and Livestock Reporting Service and the Market News Service supplement each other. Together they provide the

Reporters get set to flash news of crops and prices to the country. Left to right: Gaylord P. Godwin, United Press International; Barbara Spector, Journal of Commerce; Joe Western, Wall Street Journal; Ovid Martin, Associated Press.

Nation with a continuous flow of information from the time the farmer is making his plans to plant (the intentions-to-plant reports) to the sale of his products (the day-to-day market reports). Farmers, handlers and processors of food, extension workers, cooperatives, transportation agencies, producers of many goods, and people generally are among those who use the information to make decisions as to buying, selling, producing, and ordering. For that, accurate, complete, dependable facts are needed. *(S. R. Newell and S. T. Warrington)*

Interpreting the Facts

OVER THE YEARS we have developed a vast tool shed of facts that enable us to make systematic analyses of the economic and social problems of American agriculture. They help us answer any number of questions about farm management; the use of land and water; farm finance, income, population, and rural life; the agricultural outlook; and price analysis. How can a wheat farmer in Kansas best adjust his operations to current and prospective prices, costs, and Government programs? How can a cash-grain producer in the Corn Belt modify his farming in view of prospective prices, costs, and programs? The cotton farmer in the South? Dairy farmers in the Northeast and West Coast? What are the overall effects, now and for the next decade or two, of these actions and similar actions by other farmers on total production? What are the resulting implications for agricultural policy? Some of the answers have come from research in farm management, a field that developed about 1900. The main objective has been to provide information the farmer could use in adjusting his own operations to improve his income and to achieve a basis for making policy.

The early farm management studies in the Department of Agriculture were under the leadership of W. J. Spillman, who began his pioneer work with successful farms in 1903. His ideas, which centered on studying the best paying farms to obtain information applicable to other farms, dominated the Department's program in farm management until about 1915. His thinking was modified later by other workers, particularly G. F. Warren of Cornell University, who pioneered the use of farm surveys and the statistical analysis of large numbers of farm records. Farm budgeting came in later as a method of economic analysis. From this has developed more refined analytic tools such as linear programing, by which the most efficient combination of inputs to achieve a stipulated output can be systematically computed. When scientists and engineers develop better things for the American farmer, they answer the question, "Will it work?" The economist helps answer the question, "Will it pay—and how much, under farm operating conditions?" Pooling the results of the accumulation of physical and economic facts, their judgment of trends, and their knowledge of developments in the making, economists estimate what the yields may be 5 to 20 years from now. Such projections, subject to continual revision as new

Economists use electronic equipment to compile and analyze statistical data.

knowledge is gained, are valuable guides to farmers, policymakers, and others who must look ahead in agriculture. Much of the Department's work has been cooperative with the State agricultural colleges, although the Department's studies tend toward the national and regional aspects of the work, and the States tend to concentrate in developing information needed by farmers.

Studies of the utilization of the Nation's land resources began in 1912. The Department established a section on land economics in 1919. Early investigations centered on the need for land in agriculture, the extent of the lands suitable for farming, the expansion of farm production to meet the wartime requirements, and settlement opportunities for veterans and others. Secretary of Agriculture Henry C. Wallace appointed a committee to get and interpret the facts on the trends and outlook for crop and pasture acreages, consumption, exports and imports, and changes in productivity as a guide to private action and public policy. The findings were published in the 1923 Yearbook of Agriculture. Cropland requirements for 1950 were estimated at about 400 million acres, compared with 365 million in 1919. This estimate proved to be about 10 percent too high but was remarkably accurate in view of the facts and knowledge available in 1920. It led to the improvement of later projections.

Special research in water economics began when many irrigation projects encountered serious financial problems: What could be done to increase chances of successful reclamation ventures? More attention was given later to analysis of adjustments in land use, with emphasis on public responsibility for the improvement, use, and conservation of land and water. The depression, drought, and floods of the thirties brought home the need for a balanced use of resources. The results of studies of land utilization contributed to public action in the establishment of programs for shifting to forest, grazing, and other uses the lands that were ill adapted to farming and in the development of organized management for remaining public land areas. Programs have been developed for the protection and development of several hundred watersheds by local groups with Federal assistance. Techniques have been perfected for evaluating costs and returns of the programs.

Our growth in population has expanded the prospective requirements for land and water and has intensified the competition among the uses of land and water for agricultural, industrial, urban, transportation, and recreational purposes. Getting and interpreting the facts and evaluating alternative methods of meeting multiple requirements are a major task. An example is "Land and Water Potentials and Future Requirements for Water," prepared in 1960 at the request of the Select Committee on Water Resources of the Senate. To meet the needs of an estimated medium population of 329 million in the year 2000, 33 million acres of cropland and pastureland probably would be absorbed by urban expansion and other nonagricultural uses. About 78 million acres of grassland pasture and 36 million acres of woodland might need to be converted to cropland, along with necessary drainage, clearing, irrigation, and related improvements, unless research developments and adoption of technological advances exceed the rates that have prevailed.

Inadequate or costly credit and insurance services and inequitable taxation often have slowed the financial progress of farmers and sometimes have aggravated their financial difficulties. Research in agricultural finance has several purposes—to measure and explain changes in the financial situation of farmers, determine how farmers can be provided with improved credit and insurance services, and indicate relief from inequitable taxation. After the price crash of 1920, thousands of farmers lost their farms because they could not pay their debts and taxes. Failures of country banks and other farm credit institutions were widespread. These difficulties led to intensive investigations to learn why farmers and their credit institutions were so susceptible to a drop in farm prices and what could be done to prevent a recurrence. A major job of research in agricultural finance during the Second World War was to keep a close check on developments in the farmland market and in farm debts and taxes, so that any unhealthy tendencies could be detected. To aid in this work, the Department of Agriculture developed and began publishing an annual "Balance Sheet of Agriculture," which showed the trends of farm asset values, debts, and equities. Little, if any, active speculation in farmland occurred after the war, but land values and farm debts have increased year by year almost without interruption. The high level of farm income for several years served as a magnet to draw land values upward, and the rapid spread of improved farm technology has greatly increased the investment in land, livestock, machinery, and supplies.

The large increase in acreage and in value of production assets per farm and per farmworker has created new problems. Much research has been done on the capital requirements for efficient farming, the means by which farmers assemble their capital requirements, and the policies and practices of lending institutions in financing farm capital requirements. Farmers still need better guides in the use of credit and in means of reducing risks. Other problems to which future research must give more attention have emerged from the expansion of highways, the spread of industrial and suburban developments into rural areas, and other shifts in population. These developments have had striking effects on values of farmland and assessments and on the rates at which farmlands are taxed. They have created difficult revenue problems for local government units.

The greatest income crises in American agriculture developed after the price collapse of 1920 and during the depression of the thirties. In order to devise programs that would improve the income position of farmers, answers were needed to such questions as: How much income do farm people actually receive? How does this income compare with that received in the nonagricultural occupations? Are farm people sharing in national economic growth? Farm income estimates as we know them today received their real start in 1919, when national estimates of cash income from some of the principal crops were released. Since then, progress has been steady and tied closely to the expansion of crop and livestock statistics, which furnish the raw material for the estimates of farm income. We now have each month an estimate of cash receipts from farm marketings by States. This set of figures alone involves more than 7,500 separate statistical estimates.

On an annual basis, the Department now can estimate the total net income that farm people get from farming; the income that they obtain from nonfarm sources; and the per capita income of farm people from all sources compared with the per capita income of the nonfarm population. To get at the root of the farm income problem, however, we have to have more detailed information than national and State totals and averages. Different types and sizes of farms have totally different income patterns and problems. More than 90 percent of the value of total agricultural production is produced on fewer than half of the farms. There is a continuing upward trend in the number of farms that sell more than 10 thousand dollars' worth of products annually and a decline in those that sell less than 5 thousand dollars' worth. Both the larger and smaller farms are obtaining a greater proportion of their income from off-farm sources. The estimating of farm income is moving in the direction of obtaining more regular information on income by size and type of farm and by regions. But we need to know more about farm people than their money income. Statistics are necessary on the farm population, its composition and trends, on the farm labor force, and on the levels of living attained by farm families.

Statistical series were established in the twenties to provide annual estimates of the American farm population. The total number of persons on farms provides the denominator for such measures as per capita farm income. Continuous efforts have been made to improve estimates of farm population over the decades. One improvement came in 1944, when data were obtained on farm population from crop reporters and were coordinated with estimates for periodic enumerative surveys of the Census Bureau. Another improvement occurred in 1960, when the definition of farm population was brought into closer relationship to the definition of a farm, used in the Census of Agriculture and various other surveys. Under the old definition, many people whose livelihood was not gained from agriculture got reported as living on farms. This situation was substantially corrected in the recent census by eliminating many families selling little or no farm produce from the category of "farmers." Annual surveys are made also of the size, composition, earnings, and other characteristics of the hired farm force. It was found, for example, that of the 3,693,000 persons who performed some farm-work for cash wages in 1960, about 2.2 million worked 25 days or more. Indexes have been developed to indicate the level of living of farm-operator families for each county. These indexes are based on data from the Census of Agriculture, with the series beginning with 1930. Wide geographic variations exist in farm levels of living, but the regional differentials have changed little since 1940.

Many State and local area studies have been made on farm population, migration, farm labor, rural health, and rural education. These studies are usually made in cooperation with land-grant institutions and published as State experiment station bulletins. A few examples: At the time the Congress was considering the extension of the Social Security Act to self-employed farm operators, surveys in four States revealed that a substantial majority of the farm operators interviewed were in favor of bringing farm operators under the provisions of the act. The surveys also revealed that a majority of farm operators approved the existing provisions, which had extended Social Security coverage to regular hired farmworkers. A

study in 1957 showed that 37 percent of the 16- and 17-year-olds in three low-income counties in Kentucky had dropped out of school without completing high school. With expanded programs of rural development, we expect that research in the field of population and rural life will give greater attention to specific problems of education, health, and employment opportunities.

Because of the instability of the prices he receives for his products, the farmer stands in special need of accurate appraisals of his economic prospects if he is to plan and carry out his production and marketing activities efficiently and profitably. The typical farmer cannot afford to collect and analyze all the necessary statistical and economic information for himself. It has long been a goal of the Department to provide the farmer with economic facts and interpretations comparable to those available to business and industry. The beginning of outlook work dates from 1923, when the Department invited a group of leading economists and statisticians to meet in Washington to interpret the first intentions-to-plant report of the Bureau of Agricultural Economics in the light of the general economic conditions expected during the coming year. This was the first of the Outlook Conferences. The appraisals prepared by the Department's outlook analysts reach farmers through the

Department's regularly published Situation Reports, the State extension services, and through farm papers, daily newspapers, the publications of farm organizations, and radio and television.

Longer projections of the economic prospects for American agriculture also are issued. One was presented at the Annual Outlook Conference in 1936, with the general conclusion that desirable agricultural adjustment appeared to lie between a minimum reduction of 15 to 25 million acres and a maximum of 35 to 50 million from the average of 365 million acres harvested during 1928-1932. The greatest impetus to long-range projections came after the Second World War, when people were concerned that the contraction of wartime expenditures would return the Nation's economy to depression levels. The first effort in this direction was a series of four bulletins published in 1945 under the title, "What Peace Can Mean to American Farmers." This showed what full employment, moderate unemployment, and serious depression would mean for agricultural production, prices, and income. The Department in 1957 provided the Joint Economic Committee of the Congress with projections of food and fiber requirements to 1975, indicating that they would expand around 50 percent within two decades.

Statistical measurement of the factors affecting agricultural prices has been an especially useful tool in the study of existing and proposed farm programs. Policymakers need answers to such questions as these: How will a proposed program affect the competitive position of a commodity in the market? How will it affect the amounts that consumers will buy? Will farmers be encouraged to increase yields per acre or per animal and thus bring about excess production? How will the program affect farm income? What will it cost the taxpayer? Statistical studies of price behavior were used in the thirties to evaluate agricultural programs, but have been even more important since the war. An example is "Farm Price and Income Projections, 1960-65," published in 1960 in response to a request from the Senate Committee on Agriculture and Forestry. The Department was asked to make an objective report on probable market supplies and prices for the major farm products in 1960-1965, assuming that most production controls were removed and that price supports were maintained at levels that would permit an orderly reduction of excess stocks. The Department's analysis indicated that total farm output would rise 20 percent above the 1955-1957 average, prices received by farmers would drop about 17 percent, cash receipts from farm marketings would rise about 2 percent, and per capita food consumption in the United States would increase about 5 percent. Improved methods of statistical and economic analysis, including the use of electronic computers, will help us do a better job of analyzing the economic implications of alternative program proposals. *(J. P. Cavin)*

542

The Search for Parity

FARM PARITY, as a goal under which farmers and nonfarmers would enjoy equality of opportunity for income, usually is associated with the New Deal of the thirties. Actually, the search for income parity for agriculture has been going on a long time. The Virginia Colony attempted in 1621 to stabilize tobacco prices by limiting production and burning surpluses. The search began on a national scale with the close of the Civil War, when it became apparent that farm people would not long continue as a majority in the population and agriculture as a clearly dominant segment of the economy. America began its move from a rural society toward an urban one. The beginnings of the agricultural revolution made it possible for farm production to exceed demand, and farm income declined sharply. Rural discontent grew. Agitation for a living wage in agriculture began. The search fluctuated in intensity; farm prices rose and fell throughout the period from the Civil War to the First World War. Phases of the search included the Granger and Greenback movements, the Farmers' Alliance, and the Populist Party, whose supporters proposed the establishment of cooperative marketing groups, increased issues of currency, Government loans to farmers, control of rail shipping rates, and numerous social reforms.

The beginning of the First World War gave American agriculture an unprecedented stimulus. Spurred by high prices and patriotism, farmers set out to feed the world. They mechanized their farms and sold their horses. They diverted several million acres from growing feed for horses and mules to producing food and fiber. They plowed up 40 million acres of new land. They raised total production tremendously—but at high costs to themselves. To buy more land on which to grow more food and to buy machinery with which to operate it, thousands of farmers mortgaged their farms heavily at wartime values. The average mortgage debt per acre by 1920 was more than 2.5 times the 1910 debt. The demand for food continued at high levels for a short time after the Armistice. Farmers continued to produce an abundance as the extravagant postwar buying began to fade, as foreign nations rebuilt their agriculture and erected tariffs to protect themselves, and as the United States began to dam the flow of credit abroad. With incredible suddenness, it seemed to farmers, we lost our European markets. The production of food exceeded demand. Agricultural prices broke in

1935.

midsummer of 1920 and continued downward. The August index of prices received by farmers was 16 points under the June index, and the drop continued for the rest of the year at about the same monthly rate—a cumulative drop of 79 points during the second half of the year. In contrast, prices paid by farmers in 1920 were higher than those of any preceding year and higher than those of any succeeding year until 1947.

As prices declined, farmers increased their production even more in an attempt to maintain their income. They succeeded only in lowering farm prices further. Farmers produced surpluses to sell at whatever prices were offered. Industry could control its production and so was better able to maintain its price levels. Farmers were at a disadvantage. Farm income declined by more than half; with it went the farmers' purchasing power. Factories closed their doors. Workers went into breadlines. Our whole national economy was sick. By 1932 cotton had dropped to about 6 cents a pound, hogs to 4 cents a pound, wheat to 38 cents a bushel, and corn to 32 cents a bushel. Gross farm income dropped from nearly 18 billion dollars in 1919 to little more than 6 billion dollars in 1932. Net farm income also dropped—from 9 billion dollars in 1920 to 2.5 billion dollars in 1932. The total farm mortgage debt had increased 2 billion dollars since 1919. Foreclosures increased from 3.1 per 1 thousand farms in 1919 to 38.8 in 1933. Nearly 15 thousand banks closed their doors in 1920–1933.

These depressing conditions led farmers to band together and seek reforms. They joined farm organizations. They became increasingly able to exert political pressure. A Farm Bloc was organized in the Congress and succeeded in twice passing the McNary-Haugen Bill, which proposed that the Federal Government export surpluses to bolster domestic prices of farm products. President Coolidge vetoed it both times. Then, in 1929, the Agricultural Marketing Act became law. It set up a Federal Farm Board, whose operations were designed to stabilize farm prices. Its efforts were limited at first to loans to cooperatives, but the sudden drop in agricultural prices in 1929 caused it to organize stabilization corporations to purchase commodities and hold stocks off the market. Their efforts to support prices led to severe losses and little stabilization of prices, since the Board was attempting to cope with the world depression that was just beginning.

Farm parity, as a defined concept, probably had its beginnings during this period. George Peek, a leader during the McNary-Haugen fight, prepared a pamphlet, "Equality for Agriculture," in 1922. It defined a "fair exchange value" in terms of the relationship between agricultural prices and the general price index: Parity was achieved whenever the average price received by farmers and the wholesale price index of all commodities purchased by consumers had the same relationship as they did in a particular base period. The base period—the period in which these prices were in a fair and equitable relationship to one another—was generally agreed to be 1910-1914, the period just before the war. The thinking of Mr. Peek and other leaders was probably affected by Department of Agriculture Bulletin 999, "Prices of Farm Products in the United States," by George F. Warren. It appeared in 1921. Mr. Warren developed the first index of prices paid to farmers and compared farm prices with all wholesale prices in order to obtain a rough measure of the purchasing power of farm products.

It is not surprising that parity or "fair exchange value" was couched in terms of prices. Prices received were thought of as a measurement of purchasing power, and depressed farm prices were associated with depressed income for agriculture. Income, however, is affected by the number of units sold as well as the price per unit. Net farm income is affected by the cost of production as well as prices paid to farmers. Although parity of income is the goal of the search, parity as a measuring device is a price concept. Prices can be readily determined. The problem of determining the net income of farm families, of apportioning it among the several commodities or groups of farmers, and finally of selecting the volume of production to use in translating prices to income is difficult. Because of these difficulties and because no actual working formula has been developed so that parity income can be used as bases for guiding day-to-day operations, the simpler parity price standard was used in administering farm programs developed in the thirties.

Obviously, the price concept of parity had, and has, weaknesses. Parity prices do not measure the cost of farm production plus a fair profit. Neither will they provide farmers with incomes equal to incomes of nonfarm people—although, when prices of farm commodities are at parity levels, farm incomes are generally in better balance with those of nonfarm people. A parity price is not one received by a farmer for a specific grade, quality, or class of commodity at a specific place. Instead, it is a general or overall standard representing a United States average price for all grades, qualities, and classes of the commodity sold by farmers as a group. It is the dollar-and-cents price used to measure the degree to which farm prices—but not income—are in line with what the Congress has defined as a fair goal or objective. No definition of parity prices is as succinct, however, as the statement of a farmer: "If you sell a bale of cotton and buy with the money as much food, clothing, machinery, and fertilizer as you could in the base period, cotton is selling at parity."

As America moved into the thirties, cotton prices fell far below parity level, and so did the prices of other agricultural commodities. There was no doubt in farmers' minds that the Nation was experiencing a crisis in agriculture. By 1932, "the farm problem" became a phrase in everyday conversation and one of national concern. The enormity of the declines in farm prices and incomes and the volume of farm foreclosures made clear the need for stabilization of

Farmers in the 1920's.

prices. The Federal Farm Board had demonstrated the futility of attempting to control prices through purchasing and withholding operations, when no effective authority to control production was provided. When Franklin D. Roosevelt became President in 1933, new farm legislation held a high priority on his list of actions to correct economic conditions. The Agricultural Adjustment Act of 1933 provided production controls on wheat, cotton, rice, tobacco, corn, hogs, and dairy products and authorized benefit payments to cooperating producers. Payments were financed out of taxes imposed on processors. The Commodity Credit Corporation (CCC) was created under the President's emergency powers and given wide authority to purchase, hold, deal in, sell any and all agricultural commodities, and to lend money on them. The first price-support operations started on a permissive basis in October 1933, when loans were made on corn at the rate of 45 cents a bushel and on cotton at 10 cents a pound. The prices of corn, cotton, tobacco, and naval stores were the only ones supported before 1938.

In 1936, however, the Supreme Court declared unconstitutional the production control features of the Agricultural Adjustment Act of 1933 and ruled against processing taxes on the ground that they were an inseparable feature of the production control plan. Later in the year, the Soil Conservation and Domestic Allotment Act became law, but it was inadequate for production control. Heavy crops of wheat and cotton in 1937, accentuating the twin problems of surpluses and low prices, led to passage of the Agricultural Adjustment Act of 1938, which originally provided for mandatory price-support loans on corn, wheat, and cotton; permissive supports for other agricultural commodities; and, when necessary, marketing quotas on tobacco, corn, wheat, cotton, and rice. These quotas were keyed to acreage allotments and were intended to keep supplies in line with market demand. The act was amended in succeeding years, and the list of commodities for which support was mandatory changed. In 1961, however, the act of 1938, as amended, was still in effect and provided authority for acreage allotments and marketing quotas. Under this act, and related legislation, CCC has supported more than 100 different permissive commodities, including fruit and vegetables for processing and various types of seeds.

To encourage heavy production of farm products required to meet war and postwar needs, the so-called Steagall Amendment in 1941 made supports mandatory on all 14 commodities for which the Secretary of Agriculture publicly asked for expansion of production. High mandatory support levels were continued for most supported commodities under the Agricultural Act of 1948, but discretionary support was permitted for most of the "Steagall commodities." The 1948 act was superseded by the Agricultural Act of 1949, which continued supports at 90 percent of parity for basic commodities, provided for eventual use of flexible levels, and wiped out the Steagall classification. Although foreign agriculture had recovered to a considerable extent, crop production in the United States was increasing steadily, and surpluses were beginning to accumulate. The 1949 act was amended many times, but in 1962 it still provided the basic authority to support prices.

The Korean War strengthened farm prices, and most of the stocks acquired from the 1948 and 1949 crops were sold. Stocks began to accumulate again in 1952 and 1953, under programs that maintained a 90-percent support level for basic commodities and with no controls except for tobacco and peanuts. Acreage allotments on the 1954 corn crop and marketing quotas on 1954 crops of wheat, peanuts, tobacco, and cotton were imposed. The Agricultural Act of 1954 provided flexible supports for 1955 basic crops, but stocks continued to increase. The Agricultural Act of 1956 provided for a Soil Bank Program to assist farmers to divert a part of their cropland from the production of excessive supplies. Support levels and support prices trended downward during 1955–1960, in line with the philosophy of the administration of establishing supports at lower levels to lessen production for Government storage. Controls were minimized to the extent possible under existing law, and dependence was placed on the Soil Bank for diverting excess acreage from production and on Government export programs for removal of existing surpluses. Under the Agricultural Act of 1958, acreage allotments for corn were discontinued, after they were rejected by producers in referendum in favor of lower supports and unlimited production.

Low farm income in relation to nonfarm income, excessive production, and excessive Government stocks were issues of the 1960 campaign. With the change in administration, management of supply and the use of more and better controls began to be emphasized. Support levels of many price-supported commodities were raised in the spring of 1961, and emergency feed grain legislation— limited to the 1961 crop—provided substantially higher support levels for farmers who voluntarily reduced acreage of corn and grain sorghums by 20 percent or more. To maintain income of participants, payments were authorized to compensate farmers who were carrying out approved conservation practices on retired land. In addition to the acreage limitations, quantities of corn and grain sorghums eligible for support were limited to producers' 1959–1960 per-acre yield, multiplied by the 1961 acreage. That summer, the Agricultural Act of 1961 became law. It continued the 1961 feed-grain program for the 1962 crop, added barley, provided a similar program for wheat, and cut the national allotment 10 percent.

During the period of change in farm legislation, the need for a new parity formula became apparent. Although the 1910–1914 period was a statistically sound base for calculations immediately after the First World War, it began to be outdated as changes in both the supply and demand sides of agriculture developed. The Agricultural Acts of 1948 and 1949 provided for use of a modernized parity formula based largely on the relationship of individual commodity prices during the most recent, moving 10-year period. In effect, the new formula permits adjustments that have gradually developed among prices of individual farm commodities to be reflected in the parity price of individual commodities. At the same time, it maintains the 1910–1914 overall relationship between prices received and prices paid by farmers. The effect of shifting from the old to the "new" parity formula was cushioned by stretching the change over a period of years. Although legislation changed, programs designed to bring about farm parity are not greatly different from those established during the thirties. Programs have survived a succession of conditions, including a world depression and surpluses, dust-filled skies and farm migrations, drought of unprecedented degree, increases in demand during the Second World War and the Korean action, and later a decline in farm incomes and the accumulation of new surpluses. Throughout the period, the basic objectives and the tools of the programs have remained much the same. Over the years, many changes in the designation of commodities eligible for price support have been made. By 1961, changes in conditions had enabled the Department to discontinue price-support programs for nearly 50 commodities, many of which were minor crops. Prices were still supported for 21 commodities, 16 of which the law required to be supported.

Programs to stabilize or increase farm income have been greatly expanded since 1933. Those designed to stabilize farm prices may be classified as price-support, price-strengthening, price- or program-protection, and direct-payment programs. Commodities are acquired under the price-support program, and this necessitates storage and disposition programs. Programs that move stored commodities into domestic and export channels, other programs important to farm income, such as the agricultural credit and area development programs, and various utilization, research, marketing, and extension programs are discussed elsewhere in this book. Here we discuss only the "price programs," the Agricultural Conservation Program, and crop insurance.

Prices are supported directly by loans, purchase agreements, and purchases. The National Wool Program utilizes direct payments, but this program varies from other price-support programs and is described as a direct-payment program. Loans support prices in two major ways: By providing farmers a cash return for the commodity at the support level and by propping up market prices of the commodities through withdrawal of supplies from the market. They also help to bring about more orderly marketing by preventing market gluts at harvesttime. The loan method gives the farmer an opportunity to market his crop or keep it under loan, whichever is more advantageous. If the market price rises above the loan level, plus charges, he has the privilege of paying off the loan and selling his commodity in the open market. If the price fails to rise above the loan level, however, the farmer can deliver his commodity to the Commodity Credit Corporation (CCC) instead of repaying the loan. The loan program tends to even out marketings. Farmers are inclined to market their crops at harvesttime to obtain cash or because they lack storage space. This sometimes makes for market gluts, undue burdening of the transportation system, and lower prices. Farmers who utilize the loan program, however, can hold their crops without risk for later marketing. This tends to spread marketing over the season and thereby reduces the extent of price swings. Private lending agencies, mostly local banks, make most of these loans. CCC agrees to take over the loans, if requested. Price-support loans have been available in recent years on all supported commodities except dairy products, tung nuts, wool, and mohair. Loans have been available on tung oil, however.

A purchase agreement is an agreement on the part of CCC to purchase from a producer, at the producer's option, not more than a stipulated quantity of a commodity at the support price. Loans and purchase agreements provide support at the same level. A loan suits the needs of the producer who requires money immediately and who can meet loan storage requirements. A purchase agreement provides a convenient, inexpensive form of price insurance for the producer who does not have an immediate need for cash, who is not able to meet loan storage requirements, or who is not willing to encumber his commodity, as is required under the loan operation. Purchases are made of butter, Cheddar cheese, and nonfat dry milk from manufacturers and handlers to support the prices of butterfat and manufacturing milk. Cottonseed prices are supported by direct purchases from ginners and also from producers whenever nonparticipation by ginners makes such purchases necessary. Flaxseed prices are also supported, in part, by direct purchases from producers. Milk producers, except as members of cooperatives, do not deal directly with the Government in connection with the support program for manufacturing milk and butterfat. Purchases of butter, cheese, and nonfat dry milk by the Government maintain the overall price structure for dairy products, and the support level to milk producers is reflected in prices paid by milk handlers and manufacturers. In the case of cottonseed and flaxseed, producers deal with the Government.

Supply adjustment aspects of price-support programs are aimed at bringing supplies of agricultural commodities into line with national needs. Tools used to accomplish this aim include acreage allotments, marketing quotas, and payments for diverting land to conservation uses. Acreage allotments may be combined with marketing quotas to serve the double purpose of determining the maximum acreage that a farmer may harvest and still obtain price support and, at the same time, determining the amount that each farmer may market without incurring penalties. Acreage allotments represent the maximum acreage a producer may harvest and be eligible for price support. A marketing quota, as specified by law, is the quantity of a commodity that is produced from an acreage allotment. In combination, allotments and quotas can limit production more effectively than the use of allotments alone can. Nevertheless, the legal definition of marketing quotas permits farmers to increase production per acre without penalty, and the size of minimum national marketing quotas—set by law for cotton, wheat, rice, and peanuts—can also reduce their effectiveness.

Conservation payments for diverted acres is the third method practiced to limit production. The Soil Conservation and Domestic

President Roosevelt presents a Government check to William E. Morris of Nueces County, Texas, a participant in a program to cut cotton acreage. Henry A. Wallace, at the far right, was the Secretary of Agriculture. Marvin Jones, at the far left, was Chairman of the House Committee on Agriculture in 1933; he later became War Food Administrator.

Allotment Act of 1936 provided payments for shifting acreage of such soil-depleting crops as corn, wheat, cotton, tobacco, and rice to such soil-conserving crops as grasses and legumes and for carrying out soil-building practices. The Agricultural Act of 1956 established the Soil Bank. Under its Acreage Reserve Program, farmers agreed to cut their acreages below allotments. In return, they received payments to compensate for loss of income from the land diverted. Payments, based on normal yields, were made, and diverted land could not be cropped. Under the Conservation Reserve Program of the Soil Bank, producers could place any part or all of their entire farm under contract for periods of 3, 5, or 10 years. Under the 1961 feed-grain program, farmers who voluntarily reduced corn and grain sorghum acreage 20 to 40 percent (or more when bases were less than 100 acres) and placed these diverted acreages under a special conservation program received payments in negotiable certificates representing grain from CCC stocks. The majority of cooperating producers accepted payment in cash rather than grain.

The storage facilities program is necessary to maintain the quality of commodities acquired. Objectives of the program are to help producers finance storage facilities on their own farms—which permits farmers to participate fully in price-support operations and promotes generally more efficient marketing; to make maximum use of commercial facilities in the storage of Government-owned commodities; and to provide Government owned or operated facilities for storing acquired commodities (primarily grain) in areas where privately owned facilities are inadequate. Farmers' cribs or bins must meet the approval of the Government in order to be eligible for loans on farm-stored commodities. Commercial storage facilities are utilized under a uniform grain storage agreement, which establishes storage payment rates and requires the warehouseman to compensate the Government for any deterioration in quality of the commodities stored. In addition, the Government owns bins for the storage of grain and utilizes idle merchant ships of the reserve fleet for the storage of Government-owned wheat.

Price-strengthening programs utilize marketing orders and agreements but do not involve acquisitions of commodities by the Government. They seek to establish and maintain orderly marketing conditions for agricultural commodities moving in interstate and foreign commerce. A marketing order issued by the Secretary of Agriculture is binding on all handlers of a commodity in the specified production area. Programs for milk are in effect under orders without agreements, whereas most programs for commodities other than milk are under both. Milk order programs provide for the classification of milk on the basis of use and for the establishment of minimum prices that must be paid producers.

For commodities other than milk, such as fruit, vegetables, and tree nuts, both marketing orders and agreements are in effect. Prices are not established, but the program seeks to enhance or maintain prices for affected commodities and regulate their flow to market. Several types of regulations may be used. These include controls over the grade, size, quality, maturity, quantity eligible for marketing, and diversion of excess production into new or non-normal uses. Also included are the establishment of reserve pools for the control and disposition of surpluses; the prohibition of unfair trade practices; posting of prices; regulations of containers; and the establishment of certain marketing, research, and development projects.

Since efforts to maintain agricultural prices cannot be wholly successful if competitive foreign imported articles are allowed to take the domestic market away from domestic producers, the regulation of imports is authorized under certain conditions. These activities commonly are referred to as Section 22 operations, since Section 22 of the Agricultural Adjustment Act of 1933, as amended, authorizes them. The law permits the President to impose restrictions in the form of import quotas or fees in addition to existing tariffs, after a hearing held by the Tariff Commission.

Two programs are in effect that involve direct payments to producers. The commodities affected are not produced domestically in sufficient supply to meet domestic needs. The National Wool Program is essentially a price-support program, but loans, purchases, and purchase agreements are not involved. A grower sells his shorn wool in normal marketing channels. At the end of the marketing year, he receives a payment that amounts to the difference between a previously announced incentive price and the United States average price received by producers for wool sold during the marketing year. The same program applies to producers of mohair, but market prices have been high enough in recent years to make payments unnecessary. The Sugar Program provides for payments to domestic producers of sugarbeets and sugarcane grown for sugar, provided they comply with certain labor, wage, price, marketing, and acreage requirements prescribed by law. The Secretary of Agriculture is authorized by the Sugar Act of 1948 to determine in December of each year the sugar requirements of consumers in the continental United States for the next year. Of this quantity, the act apportions quotas to domestic and foreign producing areas. The total outlay of the Government for operating the program is more than offset by collections under a special tax of 50 cents per hundredweight of sugar, raw value, imposed on all sugar processed in the United States and all sugar imported for direct consumption.

The Agricultural Conservation Program (ACP) was established by the Soil Conservation and Domestic Allotment Act in early 1936 to assist farmers in making land use adjustments and in carrying out soil and water conserving practices. Designed to meet both current and long-range production needs, the program is flexible. It provided a fertility reserve, which was drawn on to increase production during the war to meet defense needs. Today, it stresses the twofold value of conservation and production adjustment by encouraging sound land use adjustments away from intensive crop production. It utilizes a farmer-Government partnership, which recognizes both the farmer's responsibility for protecting and improving his land and the public's responsibility for bearing its fair share of the cost. With the assistance of ACP, the farmers establish grass, legume, and tree cover; improve existing vegetative cover; establish or improve timber stands; build small dams for water storage; construct sod waterways and terraces; level land to conserve irrigation water; apply lime to make possible the growth of conserving cover; and carry out other needed conservation measures. The program provides emergency assistance to farmland damaged by drought, hurricanes, and floods. Through cost sharing, farmers and ranchers invest their own money, time, machinery, and labor, amounting nationally to about half the cost of installing conservation measures. ACP assistance in the form of materials, services, and financial aid accounts for the other half.

Financial difficulties of farmers due to crop failures prompted several private companies to write insurance against crop losses. These ventures, all of short duration, revealed that guaranteeing crop production is a risky and complicated matter. There was increasing demand that Government provide such protection since it was not available from private sources. The Congress preferred that private sources meet the need, but insurance representatives held out little hope for it unless the Government obtained experience indicating that such insurance could be operated on a sound business basis. The Federal Crop Insurance Corporation began operation of all-risk crop insurance in 1939 following passage of legislation in 1938. In 1948–1960, 94 cents of each dollar of premium was returned to policyholders through indemnity checks. The Corporation's Report to Congress in 1959 listed 118 causes of damage to crops, for which indemnities of nearly 450 million dollars have been paid. An all-risk policy covers damage beyond the farmer's control. It does not include losses due to negligence or poor farming practices. The policy provides protection from planting through harvest. Some crops are lost before they ever really start to grow, others are destroyed the day of harvest, and many are lost during the long period that lies between. Both production practices and insurance problems differ by crops, but knowledge and experience gained on each crop insured has resulted in gradual expansion of insurance to cover wheat, cotton, barley, oats, corn, flax, peaches, rice, tobacco, beans, grain sorghum, soybeans, and citrus fruit in about a thousand counties.

Farmers applied for price-support loans and Government aid offered during the troubled thirties.

Farmers in 1941 met to hear their county AAA representative explain details of a cotton program.

What are the results of the search for parity? Has it been achieved, or it is a goal yet to be reached? Prices of farm products today have greater stability than they did before we had price programs. We have a greater reserve of fertility and production potential than at any time in our history. Crop insurance has prevented economic distress during periods of crop failure. Net incomes of farmers are well above those earned when the programs were instituted. During the war and early postwar years, parity was achieved. Increased prosperity enabled farmers to substitute capital for land and labor. Increases in production per acre and per hour of labor were accomplished and resulted in more efficient production. Total production, however, increased at a much faster rate than demand, and agricultural prices began to slip in the last decade. Price programs slowed this decline, but could not affect rising industrial prices—the prices paid by farmers for the tools of production. The farmer was caught in a cost-price squeeze and, in 1960, netted only 80 percent of parity. On a per capita basis, farmers' incomes were a smaller percentage of nonfarm incomes than at any time since 1940. Lower incomes for farmers resulted from their inability to adjust production to demand and from a lack of purchasing power in underdeveloped countries that prevented America from fully sharing her abundance with the needy, except at heavy cost to taxpayers.

Farm programs are supporting farm income, but more consideration should be given to the causal factors of the farm problem. Programs should be of a type easily altered to permit rapid adjustments of supply to meet changing conditions and to prevent accumulation of stocks greatly in excess of needed reserves. In revising old programs and developing new ones, policymakers must seek to insure enough production of food and fiber to supply high living standards for all Americans and to assist our friends throughout the world to move toward these standards. To this end, more effective worldwide distribution must be sought. On the demand side, the utilization of agricultural products must be expanded with special concern for those in need at home and abroad. More emphasis should be placed on achieving parity of income rather than parity of price alone. Operators of efficient family farms should be assured the opportunity of achieving parity of income without losing control of their own enterprises and without exploiting either the taxpayer or the consumer. Farmers in marginal, depressed areas should be provided with either the assistance and guidance that will enable them to farm efficiently or the guidance, training, and employment assistance that will enable them to find economic opportunity outside farming. The search for parity is not ended. Parity has not been achieved, but neither is it lost. The search must go on. Our experience is a foundation for programs of the future. *(Murray Thompson)*

556

Farmers as Committees

AROUND 3 o'clock on the drizzly afternoon of March 22, 1961, the Congress put final touches on an emergency Feed Grain Act. By 4 p.m., the act had been signed by President Kennedy. Before nightfall, the Secretary of Agriculture, Orville L. Freeman, and some of his Department aides were airbound to Omaha, Nebr., for the first of three regional meetings to launch the new program. Five days later, the word had been carried firsthand to representatives of every State. Such fast action prompted favorable comment, but it went only part way toward meeting the signup urgency. A lot of seed was already in the ground. Some crops already were up in the Southland. Even in the middle country, farmers were literally at the field gate, tractor motors running. Skeptics doubted that widespread compliance could be obtained at such a late hour. Hundreds of local meetings would have to be held almost simultaneously to explain the new provisions and to remobilize cooperation of producers in a plan to limit plantings. As it turned out, despite the late start, the 1961 feed-grain program had surprising acceptance. By the June 1 deadline, complying farmers had pledged to divert to nonharvest more than 23 percent of their 1959–1960 average acreage of cornland and about 30 percent of their acreage of grain sorghum.

What accounted for this unexpectedly impressive response? The Washington correspondent for a newspaper in the Midwest summed it up: "Key to the successful implementation of the program lay with the State, county and community ASC committees. With strong urging from Washington, they performed in a way reminiscent of the early 1930's and the AAA." And so it was. Out across the Nation, in more than 3 thousand counties, nearly 100 thousand farmer-elected committeemen stood waiting as President Kennedy signed the new bill. Like the Department's staff, they, too, lost no time in calling local meetings, often of overflow size, to give out information about the program and conduct the signup. All this activity did, indeed, remind oldtimers of the emergency program actions in the early thirties. They recalled that it was in 1933 when the idea of the farmer-committee system first became a working reality.

Upon passage of the Agricultural Adjustment Act on May 12, 1933, Secretary of Agriculture Henry A. Wallace and other Department officials concluded that farmer-elected committeemen to admin-

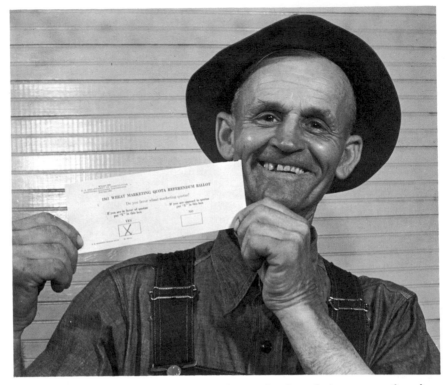

A wheat farmer who participated in the first national marketing quota referendum, May 31, 1941, holds up his marked ballot. Referendum voting actually is secret, however, and conducted by farmer-elected community committeemen.

ister the new programs at the county and local level would be commendably democratic in principle and intensely practical. They recognized that when it came time to set individual acreage allotments under the new production programs, those most capable of making these decisions fairly and acceptably would be local farmers acquainted with the farms involved and with the farming patterns of the community. Since any unsatisfactory committeeman could be removed from office by his own neighbors at the next annual committee election, they knew that attempts at partisan or organization domination of the programs could never succeed. At the same time, it was recognized that by relinquishing control of the selection of local personnel, the Federal Government ran the risk of inconsistent and uncoordinated relationships with individual producers. Any fears on this score were swept aside in the belief that farmers are devoted to the principle of fair treatment to all areas and thus would abide by reasonable regulations and administrative rulings developed at the national level. Experience proved this to be the case, especially as the national administration responded to requests from the field for practical and justifiable program revisions.

Temporary committees, either appointed or elected, handled the first stages of the original AAA programs. After the signup, cooperating producers in each community, usually a township, then elected permanent committeemen, many of whom had been on the temporary committee. The chairmen of the communities then met and elected a chairman and several (usually two to four) members from among their group to serve as a county committee. In some regions, however, notably in the South, leadership in local administration was shared at the outset with county agents and other officials of the Federal-State Agricultural Extension Service. This variation in administrative pattern developed out of the widespread assistance given by the Extension Service on the educational phases of the programs and the development of administrative machinery.

Farmers elected to the local committee posts soon discovered that theirs was no mere post of honor. They faced much hard, unfamiliar work, which required patience and many difficult judgments on individual appeals from producers. Nevertheless, the need for prompt action was great, and these committeemen soon gave an excellent account of themselves. The basic functional pattern for com-

Farmers visit the office of the county Agricultural Stabilization and Conservation (ASC) committee in Washington, Kans.

munity and county committees was set with the first programs. Working together, they subdivided the county acreage and production allotments among individual producers, heard and passed on any subsequent appeals by producers for allotment revisions, measured acreages or otherwise checked on producer compliance, obtained program agreements from producers and distributed benefit payments, determined the support loan or purchase agreement eligibility of individual producers and processed the necessary papers, shared responsibility for the erection and storage management of Government-owned bin facilities, furnished local direction on Federal marketing programs, made recommendations to the State and Washington offices as to local views on current and future program details, and held referendums pertaining to Federal farm programs.

In the beginning, at least in the major producing areas, each commodity had its own committee setup. In some States and counties, this meant that several committees functioned at the same time. After the supersedure of the original AAA with the Soil Conservation and Domestic Allotment Act in 1936, a single setup was authorized to serve all commodities in a county. During the Second World War, and also to some extent in the Korean conflict, the farmer committee system gave invaluable assistance by directing the collection of scrap iron and other needed salvage; by advising on allocation priorities for scarce equipment and other supplies, including feeds, needed to raise farm production; by aiding in defense bond drives; by handling livestock slaughter permits; and so on. Chairmen of the State and county farm program committees served as chairmen of their respective local war boards.

Several major changes in policy restricting the functions of State and local committees were adopted in 1953 and 1954. Worktime limits were imposed on the State committee members, and program operations were assigned to an administrative officer. In the counties, likewise, committeemen were put on a part-time compensation basis, with a concern henceforth primarily for policy matters. Each county was instructed to hire a county office manager to handle day-to-day operations. Some of these changes were later modified or reversed. Under further amending directives by Secretary Freeman, county committees were restored to full authority for conducting elections and directing the work of community committeemen. Operations at the State level also were realigned to provide more active participation by the State committeemen, all of whom must be farmers. In announcing these revisions on March 23, 1961, Secretary Freeman said: "It is our firm belief that the ASC farmer-committee system is the most effective and economical method of operation if it operates as originally conceived under the enabling legislation. We intend to see that the committee system functions with full authority and responsibility in the days ahead." *(Arthur T. Thompson)*

560

A Nebraska farmer reports his cropping layout to the ASC county office compliance checker with the aid of an aerial map.

Taking crib samples to determine eligibility of corn for price-support loans is one of many duties performed by county ASC offices.

Money

CAPITAL has been a quiet but effective agent in the development of our agricultural economy. Its importance has grown through the years.

When we talk of the settling of the West we talk in terms of a vast domain that could be had for the asking—plus sweat and an occasional broken hope. Even a homesteader had to have a team, plow, wagon, and a few tools, however. He had to erect a shelter, fence the land, and perhaps hire help to break the sod and dig a well. The development of 160 acres often took one or two thousand dollars out of the settler's pocket before the land produced a dollar. We take for granted now that whatever we are going to do, the doing will require money. We take for granted high costs and substantial investments, but it still shocks many of us to hear that a young farmer who wants to buy a well-developed, well-equipped farm in the Corn Belt can expect to invest 100 thousand dollars.

Most of the capital farmers have used has come from their own income, but our agricultural economy would have developed much more slowly if farm people had been forced to rely entirely on their own funds. Fred Garlock, writing in the 1960 Yearbook of Agriculture, reported that farmers in a recent 10-year period spent 363 billion dollars. Most of their funds were used to develop their farms and carry on their farming operations. About a third of their expenditures—125 to 135 billion dollars—was financed with credit. Without this extensive use of capital, the increase in the American farmer's productive capacity would never have occurred. Without the agricultural credit system, the pace of progress would have been more like a walk than a gallop. Credit has enabled farmers to take advantage of the results of research. Credit has helped farmers buy the feed, fertilizers, insecticides, fuel, improved seed, and other items that now form a part of the yearly cost of farming. Credit has helped farmers buy additional acres, increase the size of their herds, modernize their buildings, conserve their soil.

Farmers in the latter part of the 19th century were able to borrow from banks and insurance companies. Merchants extended credit. Most rural communities had a few individuals who had acquired a substantial amount of this world's goods and were willing to lend part of their capital to their neighbors. Some individuals in the East who owned or had access to capital hired agents, who located in Midwestern States and advanced funds to farmers. It is said that John and Ira Davenport of Bath, N.Y., sons of a wealthy merchant, lent more than 5 million dollars to midwestern farmers between 1868 and 1904. Much of the credit carried a high rate of interest. Most of it was on a short-term basis. The principal on real estate mortgages usually was due and payable at one time. Expensive renewal fees pushed costs higher. In certain areas credit was hard to come by. It is impossible to determine to what extent the supply of credit failed to meet the real needs of the farmers, but it is clear that protests were made—protests against the rates and terms of some of the moneylenders, and, in the "Greenback" and "free silver" movements, against the monetary system in general. It is also clear that improvements in credit systems have had a high priority whenever national programs have been drawn up to aid rural people. The Congress passed in 1916 the Federal Farm Loan Act, which created the Federal land banks and the Joint Stock land banks. Both institutions were designed to provide farmers with a dependable source of long-term credit at low interest. The Federal Government initiated in 1918 its first program of making direct seed loans to farmers.

An example of the role given agricultural credit when the Nation is seeking a solution to its farm problems is the rapid action taken in the early thirties. One of the first executive orders of President Roosevelt created the Farm Credit Administration. The nationwide system of cooperative Production Credit Associations was organized. Banks for farm cooperatives were established. A direct Government rehabilitation loan program was set up to help farmers who could not get credit from other sources. A system for the financing of rural electric powerlines was organized. The Government in 1937 provided direct loans to help farm tenants acquire land of their own and loans to finance water facilities in the West. There have been many improvements since then on these basic structures. The net result is that in 1962 we have extensive, well-organized, and experienced cooperative and Government agricultural credit systems that supplement the many other sources farmers turn to for their financial needs. Individuals and merchants held 39 percent of the debts owed by farmers in 1960; banks, 28 percent; insurance companies, 12 percent; the Farm Credit Administration (the cooperative credit system), 17 percent; and the Farmers Home Administration (the Government credit agency), 4 percent.

Several developments have marked the growth of the agricultural credit system. One was the use of the Federal land bank system to save thousands of farms from foreclosure during the most critical period in the thirties, when depression weakened the position of both farmers and financial institutions. The rate of foreclosure on American farmers had reached 38.8 per thousand by March 1933, and a substantial number of farmers who still held their land were in a risky position. Emergency legislation made available a type of real estate credit, the land bank commissioner loans. The loans were handled by the land banks and could be made on first or second mortgage security up to 75 percent of the appraised value of the farm. Their primary purpose was to help farmers avoid foreclosure. To increase the effectiveness of these loans, debt adjustment committees frequently prevailed on creditors to scale down their claims. The land bank and commissioner loans made by the Federal land banks totaled nearly 2 billion dollars between May 1933 and January 1936. Commissioner loans have long since been discontinued, but the Federal land bank system remains one of the major sources of farm mortgage credit. The system is a cooperative credit organization composed of 12 land banks and 800 land bank associations, which serve all parts of the United States and Puerto Rico and operate under the general supervision of the Farm Credit Administration. Each farmer who borrows purchases capital stock amounting to 5 percent of his loan in his local association. The associations in turn own the stock of the 12 land banks. The users of the system thus are also the owners.

The land banks were originally capitalized almost entirely by the Federal Government. They have been fully owned by the land bank associations since 1947. Members of each association elect their own board of directors from among their fellow members. The board determines the association's policies and hires a manager to run the day-to-day affairs of the association. Federal land bank loans are secured by real estate mortgages. The banks borrow additional funds for lending purposes in the regular money market by using the mortgages as security. Farmers usually pay off their land bank loans by making payments on the principal with each annual or semi-annual payment of interest. This method keeps interest at a minimum, enables the borrower to pay as he goes, and eliminates the alternative of paying all of the principal at one time when the term of the loan expires. The land banks have lent more than 8 billion dollars to farmers.

Copartners with the land banks in the cooperative credit system are approximately 500 production credit associations, which provide short- and intermediate-term credit. Like the land banks, they are under the general supervision of the Farm Credit Administration and utilized Government capital when they were organized. Almost all of the associations are completely member owned. They were established under the Farm Credit Act of 1933. The associations obtain their loan funds by rediscounting their loans with Federal intermediate credit banks, which in turn tap the regular money market through the sale of short-term bonds. Each farmer who borrows money buys stock, amounting to 5 percent of his loan, in his local association. Most members use the association's budget plan, whereby a member arranges for a loan sufficient to cover his financial needs during the entire season. He gets the money as he needs it. He repays the loan as he sells his farm products. Interest is charged only for the days the money is used. Most loans for production expenses (such as meeting current farm operating expenses) are written to mature within a year, but loans for capital purposes (such as buying machinery, foundation livestock, or improving land and buildings) can be made for periods up to 5 years. Members of a production credit association also elect their own board of directors from among their own members. Farmers have borrowed more than 25 billion dollars from the production credit associations.

The third member of the cooperative credit system is the banks of cooperatives. Under the general supervision of the Farm Credit Administration, 12 district banks and a central bank in Washington provide credit, accompanied by advice and counsel, to cooperatives engaged in marketing agricultural products, purchasing farm supplies, or furnishing farm business services. Cooperatives who use the banks buy stock in the banks. Rates of interest may not exceed 6 percent a year. The cooperative banks have lent approximately 10 billion dollars to cooperatives.

A development in the private credit system—the main institutional sources of farm credit—has been the trend toward the use of agricultural loan officers by commercial banks. More than 1 thousand commercial banks have placed a man on their staffs to look after the agricultural side of their affairs. Part of the farm loan officer's job is to draw more business to the bank. He works with the farmer customers of the bank and helps them make the best use of their credit resources. Trained in farm management and in money management, he is able to spot the weaknesses in the actual or proposed operations of his clients and offer suggestions as to the strengthening of the farm business. By helping his customers make wise use of their capital, the agricultural loan officer insures his bank against possible losses and attracts business that might otherwise never develop. His work also encourages the supplying of credit in amounts based on the needs of the farmers and their capability to repay and minimize the use of security as the governing factor in the amount loaned. The growth in the number of these specialists reflects the growing complexity of agricultural finance and is a tribute to the progressive spirit of the private credit system.

More than 14 thousand banks provide credit to farmers. The breadth of this phase of the American credit system constantly amazes foreign visitors, especially those from underdeveloped countries where banks are located primarily, if not entirely, in the larger cities. Most of the loans made by banks are made on a short-term basis. Through the years they have held the major share of the outstanding non-real estate debts of farmers. Commercial banks in 1940 held 900 million of the 1.5 billion dollars furnished by institutional lenders. In 1960, they held 4.8 billion dollars of the 6.7 billion outstanding.

Life insurance companies hold more farm mortgage loans than any other institutional lender. One feature of their operations that has helped round out the private side of the credit system is their custom, in many instances, of using banks as their local agents. This also helps the banks extend the scope of their service to their rural customers.

Private and merchant credit constitutes the biggest block of farm loan business. There is a trend in certain phases of this type of financing to shift the burden of financing the farm operations from farmer to supplier. In the production of broilers, for example, it has become customary for the farmer to enter into a contract whereby the supplier provides the chicks and feed and pays all other production expenses. The supplier takes the loss if his share of the sales proceeds does not cover production expenses. The farmer gives up any chance of making more than the predetermined return for his labor. The growth of this type of financing is a reflection of the increasing amounts of capital required for efficient farming, the narrowing of profit margins, and the competition for greater volume of business among dealers, processors, and manufacturers. The growth of this type of financing also chills the hearts of those who believe that the strength of our agricultural system lies in strong, independent, self-managed family farms.

The amount of capital invested in the average farm increased sevenfold from 1940 to 1960. Part of the increase was due to the increased use of machinery, fertilizers, and insecticides—inputs that take the place of farm labor. Part of the increase was due to inflation. With the increase in the amount of capital required went an increase in the amount of credit used. Farm costs rose faster than farm incomes.

Generally speaking, the Nation's agricultural credit system has been adapted through the years to meet farmers' needs. Further adaptations may be needed. Farmers traditionally have had the goal of clearing their holdings of debt in their lifetime. Some economists suggest that there may be a need and a justification for perpetual indebtedness on some farms. They argue that on a successful commercial farm with a high per-acre land value, earnings that might be used to amortize fully the mortgage loan might better be put to use to improve production efficiency. Federal land banks are now authorized to make loans on an unamortized or partially amortized basis.

Experimentation along these and similar lines is likely if past experience gives clues to the future. *(Philip S. Brown)*

Credit Plus

PEOPLE are the main element in agriculture—people who work to produce food so other people can live and fiber so people can be clothed. People therefore are the primary element in farm programs to the extent that they help farm families live better and farm better and so help everybody. This human side of agriculture is stressed in the supervised credit service of an agency of the Department of Agriculture. Its special concern is the farm people who are at the greatest disadvantage—those who have low incomes, meager resources, and inadequate skills. It was started in the depression of the thirties to help farm families get off the relief rolls. Through the years, it has continued to serve farm families who could not have made the adjustments they had to make without assistance.

In Morgan County in Georgia, for example, farmers once depended on cotton for their living, a living made risky by the boll weevil, a red soil that eroded easily, small acreages, and competition from other areas. They searched for something better. Dairying looked promising, and nearby Atlanta would be a good market. The transition would be expensive, however. Most of the farmers had no cash. Their average gross income was less than 1,500 dollars in 1940. They did not know the dairy business. Nevertheless, from about 1945 to 1955 more than a hundred good dairy farms were established in Morgan County. Sixty-two of the dairymen used funds lent them by the Farmers Home Administration. No two families are alike, but the average family who decided to switch from cotton to dairying in 1952 is typical of those who needed supervised credit to make the change. This family had been farming 71 acres, raising some cotton, and winding up with a net income of about 700 dollars for their year's labor. The family borrowed 32,400 dollars between 1952 and 1957. They used most of the money to enlarge their farm, buy cows and equipment, build a dairy barn, and establish permanent pastures. Some funds were used for operating expenses. When a local bank took over their short- and intermediate-term financing in 1958, they still owed 10,760 dollars on their real estate, but their net worth had risen from 3,400 to 15,500 dollars. They were milking 44 cows and had good equipment and 210 acres. Their home was modern.

To make this successful transition, the families used a special line of credit that had been developed to serve families who had finan-

The Farmers Home Administration Committee in Morgan County in Georgia: John Charles Maddox; Walter T. Pryor; Harry K. Neal, FHA Supervisor; and James N. Leckie, Jr.

cial problems that could not be solved by conventional methods and a combination of credit plus management guidance that substituted faith in a family's ability to acquire skills and resources, given the right kind of help, for more standard credit requirements. Specifically, the Morgan County families were using the credit and farm and money management knowledge available from Harry K. Neal, the Morgan County supervisor of the Farmers Home Administration. These men and their families spent long hours with Mr. Neal, figuring how many cows their farms would support, the costs of developing pastures, fencing, milking parlors, and other details they had to know before they could see whether this new venture had a strong chance of becoming a success. Only after they had developed complete farm and home plans, which listed their assets and debts, showed item by item what their incomes and expenses would be, told when and how they would make the necessary improvements, listed the farm practices they would have to follow, and indicated when and in what amounts there would be income available for debt repayment—only after all this was done did they borrow the amounts needed to finance their plans.

Once they were launched on their new venture, Mr. Neal con-

Mr. Neal explains details of loans to Mr. and Mrs. Gerald Cassaday, Buckhead, Ga.

J. K. West, County Agent, Janet Johnson, Home Demonstration Agent, and Mr. Neal look over house plans.

Charles E. Eagle, Madison, Ga., and Mr. Neal.

Mr. and Mrs. O. T. Harper, Morgan County, Ga., look at their record book.

tinued to be a guide to the knowledge and skills of all of the dairy and credit research and practice that accumulated in the world around them through the years. Mr. Neal visited with them on their farms, gave advice about problems that arose, and helped put theory into practice. At the end of each year, with him, the families spread their records on the table, analyzed the strength and the weakness of their operations, and drew up plans for further improvements. Anyone who drives through Morgan County can easily see the economic progress of these families and the other farmers who have used supervised credit to finance the expansion of poultry, beef, and hogs, to improve housing, and grow cotton better. No borrowers were delinquent in 1962. Only one had failed since 1950. The houses of almost all have running water, bathrooms, electric or gas stoves, and other conveniences. Businessmen of all types shared in their progress. The borrowers in 1960, for example, spent 1.25 million dollars in the county, compared to about 500 thousand dollars they spent the year before they began to build up their incomes with supervised credit.

Borrowers have become president, vice president, and directors of local farm organizations, members of the board of commissioners, and directors of breeding associations and farmer cooperative associations. Their sons have received 4-H Club awards and American Farmer degrees from the Future Farmers of America. Some have become lawyers and newspaper publishers. Daughters have become teachers and nurses and have won honors as Future Homemakers and State 4-H Club leaders. To suggest that all these gains came from supervised credit would be false and would discount the drive, spirit, and ability of people, whatever their circumstances. Education and community leadership, however, are easier for those whose income is certain and who have the backing of someone who is interested in what they can achieve when they get the tools.

The supervised credit system is available to farmers throughout the United States and Puerto Rico. The Farmers Home Administration has some 2,500 employees trained in farm and money management. Farmers can get in touch with them at offices located in all rural areas. A committee of three local farmers determines the eligibility of applicants. Funds for the loans come mainly from appropriations made by the Congress. The agency also makes certain types of real estate loans from monies advanced by private lenders. Repayment of the funds provided by private lenders is guaranteed by the Government. As soon as the farmer reaches a point where he is able to obtain credit from other sources, he does so. The services available through the Extension Service, the Soil Conservation Service, the Rural Electrification Administration, and other agricultural agencies are utilized fully at all stages.

The roots of the program go back to 1934, when small rehabilitation loans were made to farm families who had been on relief or faced that prospect. More than a million hard-pressed farm families were helped through the dreary days of the thirties with these loans and the grants that sometimes accompanied them. With the loans went help in many problems. Assistance was given in working out better leases, adjusting debts, and developing cooperative facilities and services. The basis of the program was the belief that if disadvantaged farm families were to move forward, the whole of their economic life—not just the financial side—needed adjustment. In the beginning, the loans were made for farm operating expenses— for feed, seed, fertilizer, mules, and such household expenses as pressure cookers and jars for canned goods; for family subsistence items like food and clothing; and for medical care. The scope of the loan assistance was considerably broadened in 1937 by the addition of real estate loans that tenant farmers could use to buy farms of their own. The result of several years of study by a Presidential Commission and congressional committees, these tenant purchase loans were a direct attack on the evil aspects of farm tenancy. At that point, 40 percent of the farms were operated by tenants and sharecroppers. There was general recognition that in many instances tenant farmers fared as well, or better, than owners of farms, but a great deal of concern was felt about the sizable group of landless farmers who had no assurance one year that they would be on the same farm the next and who were part of a system so unstable that neither landlord nor tenant, even when they were able, made any substantial improvements in land and buildings. A common result was constant erosion of the soil, deterioration of buildings, and a near-starvation level of living among many tenant families. The tenant purchase loans never reached a high level in the volume of dollars involved or the families aided. The ownership of land was so much a part of the American dream, and the drama involved in seeing a tenant farmer with almost no resources step into the ranks of farm ownership was so pronounced, however, that this type of credit attracted a great deal of attention.

That the Government was able to make 40-year, 3-percent loans for 100 percent of the cost of buying the farm and equipping it with a good house and buildings had a healthy effect on the financing of farm real estate in general. The operating loans had a similar effect. They had a rate of 5 percent and terms that could be extended up to 5—and later 7—years. The supervision that accompanied both types of loans, moreover, established a new pattern in the use of agricultural credit. Many lenders now use aspects of planning and on-the-farm assistance that accompany supervised loans. At the start of the Second World War, the emphasis in the supervised credit program changed from relief and rehabilitation to utilization of production potential of the small farmers to step up the production of food and fiber. When the war ended, thousands of veterans utilized this form of credit in making their adjustment back to civilian life. After the peak of the veterans' demand had been met, the credit service served to help family farmers make major adjustments in the size and the efficiency of their operations to keep pace with the technological revolution.

Through the years the original dual services of operating loans and tenant purchase loans have been broadened to include a wide range of loans to enlarge and develop farms. Special authorities have been provided for loans to develop water supply and irrigation systems for farmsteads, build and repair farmhouses and other farm buildings, and finance soil conservation measures. Loans have been made available when floods and frosts have wiped out crops and when windstorms have destroyed farm buildings. In times of severe drought, the extension of Government credit has been a bulwark for farmers, ranchers, and their conventional sources of credit. Most of the loans have been made to individual farmers, but supervised credit also has helped groups of farmers develop irrigation and

Mr. and Mrs. Carroll Clark, Morgan County farmers.

Charles E. Eagle and his son, Charles, Jr., in the woodlot of their Morgan County farm.

The H. S. Daws farm in Morgan County, Ga.

farmstead water-supply systems and drainage facilities. Loans have been made to local organizations to assist them in paying their share of the cost of developing watersheds. The supervised credit service has been administered by a number of Federal agencies. In 1934, the Federal Emergency Relief Administration was the parent body; from 1935 to 1937, the Resettlement Administration; from 1937 to 1946, the Farm Security Administration, which the Farmers Home Administration succeeded in 1946.

All told, by 1961 more than 2 million farm families had borrowed 5.5 billion dollars from the various agencies to equip, improve, operate, and buy farms. Repayments totaled 4 billion dollars. Most of the amount outstanding had not fallen due. The return to the Government in interest on the loans has been far greater than the amount that the Government has charged off as uncollectable. In the case of the rural rehabilitation loans, for example, 1 billion dollars were loaned and more than that were repaid in principal and interest. Although the real estate loans are made repayable over 40 years, more than half of them have been repaid, and the borrowers with outstanding balances have repaid more than has fallen due. Not that the program is intended to make a profit—if it were, there would be no point in the Government handling the loans. The cost of supervision plus other administrative costs, including interest on loan funds borrowed from the United States Treasury, adds up to more than the net return on the loans.

The gain lies in the progress made by the families who use the credit service and in the general strengthening of the economy of the farm communities in which they reside. Purchases made with loan funds and the increased incomes of borrowers have stimulated local trade. Improvements made by borrowers in their real estate have built a broader tax base to support improvements in roads, schools, and other community facilities. The gain also lies in the guide paths that have been laid out for other lenders to follow. There are national gains, too, for these loans are used primarily to strengthen family farms.

When the Department stepped up its efforts to help low-income rural communities in 1961, legislation was enacted to broaden and strengthen practically all of the authorities of the Farmers Home Administration and measures were taken to make maximum use of the supervised credit program. Because the program was essentially a means of helping disadvantaged farm families gain a firm foothold in their communities, because the program was primarily concerned with people, and because the program could help farmers work out a combination of farm and off-farm income opportunities, it was a main instrument in a program to develop rural areas. As such, it completed a cycle started in grimmer but somewhat similar circumstances 27 years before. *(Philip S. Brown)*

Sam Williams, a farmer near Madison, starts his spring plowing for cotton.

Mr. and Mrs. Elijah Book, who farm 114 acres in Morgan County, Ga.

Glenn Hall fills a trench silo with oats silage on his father's farm near Madison, Ga. The self-dumping wagon is homemade.

Conservation and Change

WE HAVE SEEN many changes. We shall see more changes soon. Farms will become larger. There will be fewer farmers. The farm business will become more competitive. Land values will increase. Lands not well adapted to low-cost production will shift to other uses. Yields will grow with the use of new technology. The changes are due not only to the technological changes in agriculture itself. Important also are the changes associated with nonagricultural uses of land. Greatly expanded requirements for recreation, transportation, and urban development already are bidding land away from agriculture. The trend will accelerate. Cities will continue to extend themselves across the landscape. More and more nonfarm families will take up residence in the country. The traditional division between city and farm will tend to disappear.

One thing is certain. Productive land will remain the basis of an efficient agriculture and a prosperous economy. The care of our soil and water will be as important tomorrow as it is today. The current and emerging trends in agriculture will lead to the need for more, not less, specialized services in the management of soil and water, whether private or public. As investments in land and outlays of capital mount, knowledge of the kinds of soil will become more necessary. Farm operators will have to give more attention to the fertility and moisture relationships of soils. They cannot afford to permit soils to erode and deteriorate. A higher level of technical competence thus will be needed by farm managers and from the conservationists and technicians who advise them.

Conservation has been an important part of the revolution in agriculture. Conservation itself has undergone a revolution. Modern science has changed its goals and methods in a generation. The fear of ultimate exhaustion of our natural resources, which prompted early efforts of conservation, largely has been removed by new knowledge. Instead of simple preservation, the goal today is to use and manage resources in ways to get the greatest benefit from them, now and in the future. Wise use, rather than restraint of use, is the keynote. Preservation, as such, is the primary concern only with those resources valued mainly for esthetic reasons. Today the practice of soil and water conservation consists mainly of applying the new technology in ways to keep land resources permanently productive and useful. The Department of Agriculture estimates

Poor drainage is manifest in this subdivision in Cook County in Illinois.

This round barn near New Lenox, Ill., which once housed 56 cows and is one of the few of its kind still standing, will soon give way to urbanization.

that by the year 2000 we may need more than twice the agricultural production we have today to supply an expected population of 329 million. This would equal the production from 400 million acres of additional cropland at present yields. We do not have 400 million more acres of land suitable for cultivation. The anticipated demand for farm products obviously will have to be met mainly from the land already in agricultural use.

We think this can be done. The acreage of harvested cropland has remained fairly constant in the past 50 years, yet farm production has climbed steadily. Very likely it will continue to do so. Gross farm output has nearly doubled in the past 50 years. Per-acre crop yields have increased by nearly one-half. The application of science to farming has made these gains possible with little net increase in cultivated acreage. Increased inputs of capital and the substitution of indirect labor in the form of machines, chemicals, and services for direct labor on farms have greatly intensified the use of cropland. For example, the number of tractors, virtually unknown on farms 50 years ago, has quadrupled in the past 25 years and now exceeds the number of farms. The use of other types of farm machines, chemicals, and electrical power has increased similarly. Moreover, the land used for crops today obviously is more productive than that cultivated a quarter or a half century ago. During this time there has been much shifting of crop production, both between regions and within single farms. These changes have tended to concentrate crop production on the more productive acres.

A national soil conservation program began in the 1930's to encourage adjustments in land use in accordance with the capabilities that soil surveys revealed. By 1960, more than half of the Nation's farmland had been covered by soil surveys, and a third of the farms had basic conservation plans based on the surveys. Several million acres of cropland, largely of inferior quality, had been converted to other uses and replaced in cultivation by better land taken from pastures and woodlands. Nearly 25 million acres of wet soils had been improved by farm drainage in soil conservation districts. Scientifically designed irrigation systems had been installed on nearly 4 million acres. More than 6 million acres of land had been leveled. More than a million miles of terraces had been constructed to control runoff water and conserve moisture in fields. Equally important improvements were made in methods of soil management. The conservation of soil and water traditionally has been primarily the concern of farmers. That, too, is changing, because land and water will be needed for other purposes besides the production of food and fiber. Additional millions of people must have space for homes, recreational areas, roads, airports, and industries. Extensive rural acreages will be taken over for their use.

Much land needing conservation treatment is no longer farmland. The intermingling in rural areas of nonfarm residents and nonagricultural enterprises creates new conservation problems. Conversion of open country to urban uses leads to many complex problems; such as finding stable soils to support structures, controlling floods and sedimentation, providing drainage and sewage disposal, and adjusting taxes. The new owners and users of the urbanized areas will have to cope with these problems, for the responsibility for conservation goes with the use of the land. In the years ahead, more and more nonfarmers will be deciding how land resources are used. Their decisions, like those of farmers, will determine whether resources are wastefully or wisely and beneficially used.

In order to plan intelligently, people need to know how soil and water resources are being used. The National Inventory of Soil and Water Conservation Needs, conducted by the Department of Agriculture in cooperation with other Federal, State, and local agencies during 1957–1959 in more than 3 thousand counties containing non-Federal agricultural land, supplies this kind of information. The inventory shows that our land-resource base is adequate, in combination with new technological developments, to meet the needs of our people in the foreseeable future. We are now (in 1958, the base date of the inventory) using about 450 million acres as cropland. The 1959 Census of Agriculture showed 311 million acres of cropland harvested. Other cropland is used for tame pasture, is idle or fallow, or is used for soil-conserving crops. Another 245 million acres of land in pasture and woodland are physically capable of sustained cultivation (class I to III). Still another 100 million acres of marginal quality (class IV) could be cultivated under intensive management. This does not mean that we can afford to let any of our farmland waste away or deteriorate in productivity, but it does mean that we have the physical resources for much greater agricultural ouput if and when economic conditions require it.

The inventory indicates that the acreage devoted to each of the major agricultural uses—cropland, grazing, and woodland—will change little in the years ahead. County-by-county projections of changes in land use to the year 1975 indicate that the amount of cropland will decline 2 percent, pasture and range will increase 2 percent, and forest and woodland will decline 2 percent. Cropland acreage in 1975 is expected to be about 11 million acres less than in 1958, pasture and range about 12 million more, and forest and woodland about 10 million less. These projections are based on the assumption that population will increase to 210 million, requiring about 30 percent more farm output than in 1953.

The greatest net change will be in land going into urban or other nonagricultural uses. The inventory indicates that by 1975 nearly 21 million acres will go out of agricultural use. This will be offset in part by about 5 million acres, mainly in the Western States, of new land from Federal ownership to be devoted to agriculture. Net conversion from agriculture to other uses will be 15.3 million acres, or an average of about 1 million acres a year. As population pressures increase, this trend may be expected to accelerate rather than slow down. Although the proportions of agricultural land devoted to each of the major uses are not expected to change greatly, there will be much shifting from one area to another as farmers adjust their operations to the capabilities of the land and as agriculture accommodates itself to the economic development of the country. The area of cropland will become smaller in the East and will increase slightly in the West. Pasture will increase sharply in the Southeast and decrease in the Northeast. Woodland acreage will decline in all regions except the Northeast. The total acreage involved in these changes will be much greater than the net effect on the allocation of land resources to the different uses. For example, we expect that 41 million acres of cropland will go into other uses by 1975; 30 million acres in other uses will be converted to cropland. Thus the use of 71 million acres will change, with a net reduction in cropland of 11 million acres. Shifts between other uses will also occur. Some 113 million acres, or nearly a tenth of our agricultural land, are expected to be in a different use in 1975 than they were in 1958.

These land conversions present one of the major conservation problems of the next few decades. Landowners will need reliable soil surveys and information on land capability to make wise selections of the areas to be shifted from one use to another. Each acre converted to a different use—from cropland to pasture, for example—will require the establishment of new types of vegetation or new crops and the installation of new soil and water conservation measures to protect and maintain it under the new use. The basic soils data of the inventory indicate the major conservation problems associated with the use of each class of land for agricultural purposes. Assuming the changes projected for 1975, about two-thirds of the land used for cropland, pasture, or woodland will need some kind of conservation treatment. About 270 million acres, or nearly two-thirds of the cropland, need conservation treatment and continuing attention to maintain and improve the soil. Erosion is the most prevalent problem. About 161 million acres, more than two-thirds of the cropland, still need treatment to protect them from erosion as the dominant problem. Removal, or control, of excess water is the major need on 60 million acres. Irrigation is needed on about 14 million acres. Corrective treatment for unfavorable soil conditions is needed on 36 million acres.

The acreage in non-Federal pasture and range will remain about the same or increase slightly, except possibly when a sudden need

Three-year-old spruce transplants are planted in soybean stubble on Dennis Frandsen's farm near Rush City, Minn.

On Henry Shephard's farm near Alford, Mass., trees were planted on a hillside retired from crop production.

arises to convert some arable pastureland temporarily to the production of crops. About 364 million acres, or nearly three-fourths of the non-Federal pasture and range, need conservation treatment, improvement, or protection. New stands of grass need to be established on about 72 million acres, largely land converted from other uses. Improvement of the existing vegetative cover is needed on about 107 million acres or about a third of the grazing land. The remaining 185 million acres need protection from overgrazing, fire, encroachment of brush and weeds, or other hazards. The acreage of non-Federal forest and woodland is likely to decline slightly. About 40 percent of it is on land suitable for the production of crops. Some of it will be brought into cultivation in response to mounting economic pressure.

The Timber Resources Review, conducted by the Forest Service in 1952–1955, projected a need for 83 percent more timber by the year 2000. That review also showed that the National Forests contain only 21 percent of commercial forest land. In view of the prospect of a smaller acreage of non-Federal forest and woodland, it is apparent that any increase in production of wood must come from increasing the yield of acreage devoted to this purpose. Most of the privately owned woodland needs some kind of conservation treatment or protection. About a sixth, 70 million acres, requires the establishment of new timber stands. A third, 160 million acres, needs improvement of existing stands. Protection from various hazards that threaten the timber stand itself, rather than the soil, is a major factor in conservation of woodlands. About 252 million acres need better protection from fire, 207 million acres need improved protection from insects and diseases, and 12 million acres need protection from rodents or other animals. This inventory does not include the 165 million acres on the United States mainland under the direct administration of the Forest Service.

The dual problems of water conservation—of correcting conditions of excess and shortage—will command greater attention. Withdrawals of water for agriculture, industry, and municipal use are expected to double by 1980 and triple by 2000. Although the expected total national requirement of 888 billion gallons a day in 2000 is somewhat less than the longtime average streamflow, many communities already are feeling the pinch of local water shortages. Industrial development in any area is contingent on a reliable water supply. The limit already has been reached in many places, and further development depends on making more efficient use of existing sources of water—especially in western river valleys where normal streamflow is already completely allocated under water appropriation laws.

Extension of irrigation will be important in increasing crop production to meet future food and fiber needs. In many places this will create a demand for additional water from sources that are already too small. Much of the additional water needed for irrigation—and, in some instances, for other purposes, too—can be met by more efficient practices by present users of water. For example, it is estimated that with expected improvements in conservation technology it would be feasible to irrigate 85 percent more land in 2000 with only 2 percent more water than was used in 1954. Unimproved irrigation methods sometimes make beneficial use of no more than 25 percent of the water withdrawn, although modern conservation practices with present technology can raise that level to 70 to 75 percent. Similar improvements can be made by water conservation practices in industry. Mounting competition and economic pressures will force increasing efficiency in water use in the years ahead.

Watershed protection on Ralph Holtung's farm near Elsberry, Mo., includes an inlet-type stabilization structure, a wildlife area, and plantings of hedges.

The need for more intensive use of agricultural land will also make prevention of flood damages and removal of excess water of increasing importance. Facilities for water control and water supply are being provided through community projects involving Federal, State, and local cooperation, such as those authorized under the Watershed Protection and Flood Prevention Act and the Small Reclamation Projects Act. The Conservation Needs Inventory delineated approximately 13 thousand small watersheds in the United States mainland. It found that about 8,300 of these need project action to deal with water management problems that are beyond the reasonable scope of individual action. The needed projects would embrace more than a billion acres, or half the land area of the United States. The prevention of floods is the worst watershed problem. About half the watersheds need projects for reducing floodwater and sediment damages that affect more than 62.5 million acres of flood plain lands. More than 4 thousand watersheds need projects to deal with critical erosion areas totaling 23 million acres. Agricultural water management for drainage or irrigation is a problem that requires project action in about a third of the watersheds. The inventory also revealed the need for recreation facilities on 2 million acres in nearly 2 thousand watersheds. More than 800 of the watersheds need to include provisions for municipal and industrial development of water supplies. The interest and initiative shown by local organizations since the Watershed Protection and Flood Prevention Act was passed in 1954 indicate that these projects will be a big factor in the development of water resources.

In summary: The public interest necessitates conservation of soil and water irrespective of the needs for agricultural production. The growing density of industrial, commercial, and residential improvements on flood plains gives further reason to manage the water in conjunction with the soil so as to minimize water damages to the agricultural and nonagricultural economy. This, too, points the direction of soil and water conservation. Soils must be kept in place in the fields and forests; water must be "banked" in the soil or in useful ground or surface reservoirs; and streamflows must be regulated by proper land use and man-made devices. Planning for expansion in nonagricultural uses of land and water is a task for the owners and users of land and for local, State, and Federal Governments. One of the big challenges of the next century is to make wise choices between the land and water areas to be devoted to producing material goods and others committed to urban and industrial uses or preserved for esthetic and recreational purposes. With the prospect of tremendous competition for land and water, the conservation and development of resources must be given high priority in national policy in the coming century. *(Donald A. Williams, Gladwin E. Young,* and *Ben Osborn)*

Rural America in Transition

A HUNDRED years ago a farm community and the small towns serving it were nearly self-sufficient. Most people farmed, and in one way or another farming supported the entire community. Now three of every five persons in rural areas do not live on farms, and 24 percent of our 3.7 million farms are operated by individuals who depend almost entirely on off-farm work or other income for their living. The trend to larger farms and increasing competition among commercial farmers for least-cost production have put severe pressures on the small farm. Thousands of farmers have turned to off-farm work since the Second World War. They have moved to cities if they could not find jobs near home.

In the face of these changes, which have produced difficult personal problems for thousands of farmers and their families forced to change their way of life, rural leaders are turning to area-wide development to maintain the economic well-being of their communities. This approach includes not only farm enlargement and improvement but also encouragement to industrial and other enterprises that add payrolls to the community. Dynamic programs having an area-wide impact also have been developed by Federal and State agencies concerned with farming problems and rural needs. New forms of extension service, the Tennessee Valley Authority, rural electrification, establishment of conservation districts, the small watershed program, farm security and credit programs, and Rural Areas Development are a few of them. The term "rural development" has gained increased acceptance as a method by which Government agencies and private groups and individuals can cooperate better to promote the economic development of entire rural areas.

The program started on a pilot or demonstration basis in a few counties in 1956. The Department of Agriculture in 1961 inaugurated a national Rural Areas Development Program. The Secretary of Agriculture established National and State boards and committees to help get work started in the localities as fast as their leaders wanted to move forward. The Secretary also ordered more emphasis on the programs of the Department that promote growth and expansion in rural America. The Rural Areas Development Program encourages rural and town leaders to take actions that will help their areas adjust to the farm revolution. The desires of local people to take the lead in their community's progress and growth are recognized: The program has the help of Federal and State agencies, but it belongs to local people.

An example is the Upper Peninsula of Michigan. Once isolated by the Mackinac Straits, where Lakes Michigan and Huron come together, the 15-county Upper Peninsula has long been a supplier of raw materials for the industrial cities of the Midwest. The area is now joined to mainland Michigan by a 5-mile bridge, opened in 1957. Mining, lumbering, farming, and tourism are the principal industries. A tourist who drives the entire 300-mile length of the area will pass through only two towns of more than 5 thousand population. The problems of the Upper Peninsula are traditionally those of an economy that produces raw material for manufacture somewhere else. With prices of raw materials as the barometer, the area's economy is one of boom or bust. Most of the 7,500 farms on the Peninsula are so small they do not produce an adequate living for a family. As in other rural areas, chambers of commerce in the small towns, farm leaders, and county agents for a long time tried to meet and solve these serious economic problems. School districts were consolidated to provide better education. Local roads were improved. Farmers were encouraged to expand, try new crops, and market more efficiently. Much emphasis was put on bringing in new industry and promoting tourism.

The whole drive for betterment was given new impetus and direction in 1956 by Michigan State University, working with the Department of Agriculture and other Federal and State agencies. The entire Upper Peninsula was designated as a rural development area. Most of the 15 counties surveyed their resources, such as timber, farmland, water, minerals, manpower, and capital available for expansion. Long-range development plans were prepared. To meet the changing educational needs of local communities, the University merged its Agricultural Extension Service and Continuing Education Departments into one field service program for the area. Its purpose is to help communities improve farming and marketing, gain more jobs, and modernize local facilities, such as schools and county governments. Since the start of the work, more than 1,500 businessmen, farmers, housewives, high school students, and professional people have helped gather and analyze facts about their communities. One such study produced facts and figures that resulted in county-wide approval of a consolidated high school costing 3.5 million dollars. Because tourism brings in 150 million dollars a year to the Upper Peninsula, nearly a thousand persons received training in ways to make the tourists' stay pleasant. Two counties sponsored food service clinics. Restaurant operators started an association to improve their services. County agents, after a course given by resort specialists in the University, helped motel and hotel operators with their business problems.

An Upper Peninsula Industry Development Conference is conducted each year to promote industry. Businessmen, county officials, members of chambers of commerce, and county agents meet to plan programs to strengthen present industries and attract new ones. Enterprises processing potato products, canning vegetables, turning timber into pulp, and producing handicrafts for tourists have started operations in the past few years. Much time and effort have centered on finding solutions to the local farm problems. Industry and tourist development are helping by providing new markets and off-farm work for some farmers. Some families have been able to put together a unit efficient enough to compete in the modern farm market. The dairy industry has grown in size and become more efficient. New crops, such as cranberries, have been introduced as an experiment. Small plants to process fruits and vegetables have grown. Besides the usual crops, many farms in the Upper Peninsula produce timber. Six demonstration woodlots were established to show farmers how to grow high-value timber. Extension workers send reports on the timber market regularly to local farmers. Several small wood-producing industries provide markets and work. A cedar fencing plant employs 50 men.

In just a few years, leaders in the Upper Peninsula and the public employees assisting them have worked out a comprehensive program of resource development. The key to their success, here as elsewhere, is the realization that farm development and improvement often depend on lifting the level of opportunities throughout the community. The leaders know that as long as markets are few, communities isolated, capital scarce, and opportunities for off-farm work limited, most farm families will be forced into a pattern of low-income, subsistence-type farming or will be forced out of the area entirely.

The rural development approach is taking hold in many different ways and in many different areas. About 4,500 farming and nonfarm rural communities were taking part in 1962 in organized programs of community improvement in the Southern States alone. Projects included building meeting places and recreation areas and ways to increase farm production and local markets. According to one estimate, 9,700 privately financed development groups (chambers of commerce, industrial committees, and utilities) were active. Probably the majority operated in small towns serving broad rural areas. Most of the 1,760 rural electric and telephone systems have a policy of promoting area development. They serve 2,700 counties.

Federal programs have been developed to reinforce these local-initiative activities. Other programs have been modified to be of greater service. The Rural Areas Development Program has helped greatly to get projects started in rural communities and small towns, especially in areas of extreme low income. State and Depart-

ment workers provide technical help that enables local groups to begin and maintain the work. Other Federal agencies also supply services and aid. Loans for small business, urban renewal in small towns, land reclamation, stream improvement, highway construction, vocational training, and employment services are some. The President in May of 1961 signed the Area Redevelopment Act, designed to deal with the specific needs of areas hard hit by declines in mining, railroading, farming, and other basic industries. Loans for industrial building, loans and grants for public works, technical aid in establishing new industries, and retraining are major features. In 1962, 686 primarily rural counties, 143 "labor market areas," and 47 Indian reservations were eligible to participate.

The great urban complexes of the Nation apparently will continue to increase in size, numbers of people, and difficulty of administration. If so, it will become evident to planners and policymakers that decentralization, economically viable countryside towns, and Rural Areas Development must be promoted in the interest of the big city. Indeed, the average citizen, struggling daily with problems of commuting, suburban sprawl, and the social and other

588

A new road is constructed in Monroe County, Ohio, as part of a rural development program.

costs of poverty in the central city may feel that a major national policy to promote decentralization is long overdue. The Secretary of Agriculture in a report on rural development in 1960 said: "During the next 10 years the Nation will turn increasingly to rural areas and the towns serving them. For here will be found the resources, manpower, living and working space, and recreational facilities needed to support economic growth and maintain a stable, vigorous national life." Within the next few decades—certainly before another century has passed—a new economic and social unit may grow up to rival the city in our civilization: The town-countryside area. This would be a balanced group of large and small towns and rural residential areas, with commercial farms, processing plants, and industrial enterprises interspersed among them. The area would be united by good transportation, common economic interests, and eventually perhaps by a common local government. The majority of families in the area would not farm for a living, although many might reside on small farms by choice. The rural revolution of recent years has already taken many parts of the Nation far in this direction. *(Joseph C. Doherty)*

Friends and Partners

AMERICAN AGRICULTURE has been propelled into the international arena by historic events that carry international responsibilities. Because the responsibilities are difficult to carry out unilaterally, the United States has joined with other countries to discuss mutual problems and ways to meet them. We have shared our technology with others to improve their agriculture and well-being. We have participated in international marketing agreements to achieve orderly marketing of commodities we have in surplus. We have participated in international organizations to study problems of international trade, finance, and exchange; regional economic integration; and the linking of effective control of supplies in "surplus" nations with the needs of underdeveloped countries. They have the common purpose of making the world a better place to live in. American agriculture has a direct interest in many of them.

Foremost among the international agricultural organizations is the Food and Agriculture Organization (FAO) of the United Nations, which developed from a conference at Hot Springs, Va., in 1943. It assumed some functions of the International Institute of Agriculture, founded at Rome in 1905. More than 90 countries, including the United States, are pledged to raise levels of nutrition and standards of living, improve efficiency of production and distribution of food and agricultural products, better conditions of rural populations, and thus contribute toward an expanding world economy. FAO and the United Nations General Assembly have moved to make more surplus foods available to food-deficit countries on special terms. FAO also has begun to study what better arrangements might be made for mobilizing surplus foods and distributing them in areas of greatest need, especially the developing countries. It launched a Freedom from Hunger campaign in 1960 to overcome in underdeveloped countries the twin problems of inadequate food supplies and rural poverty through an increased output of food. The Food for Peace program in the United States is one of the ways in which we support the FAO objective. The FAO Committee on Commodity Problems is an international forum responsible for dealing with problems that affect agricultural commodities.

International bodies established to foster cooperation in the solution of problems affecting commodities of major importance in international trade are concerned primarily with ways of insuring orderly

590

marketing and relatively stable and equitable prices and otherwise minimizing the cycles of price and supply that plague producers and consumers. The International Wheat Council administers the International Wheat Agreement, to which 35 importing countries and 9 exporting countries, including the United States, subscribed in 1961. The International Sugar Council administers the International Sugar Agreement, which included 8 importing countries, including the United States, and 28 exporting countries in 1961. Other commodity groups include the International Coffee Agreement, the International Coffee Study Group, the International Wool Study Group, the International Cotton Advisory Committee, and the International Seed Testing Association. The Inter-American Institute of Agricultural Sciences encourages agricultural sciences through research, teaching, and extension activities.

Operations of numerous international organizations are not primarily concerned with agricultural matters yet affect American agriculture. The United States participates in all of them as a member or observer. Some specialize in economic cooperation, some in technical assistance, and some in trade and finance. One is the Organization for Economic Cooperation and Development (OECD). Its aim is to achieve in the member countries sound economic development at a high rate of activity, promote economic expansion in underdeveloped countries, and contribute to the expansion of world trade on a multilateral basis.

The United Nations family includes four regional economic commissions: Economic Commission for Africa, Economic Commission for Asia and the Far East, Economic Commission for Europe, and Economic Commission for Latin America. These groups are charged with the responsibility for planning and developing programs aimed at raising the level of economic activity and levels of living in the four regions and for strengthening economic relations among the countries in a region and with other countries of the world. The Economic Commission for Latin America has taken the lead in the establishment of two "Common Markets" in Latin America.

The Organization of American States (OAS) has several ideals, among them to promote economic, social, and cultural developments in the Western Hemisphere. The Act of Bogota, adopted by 19 of the 21 American Republics in 1960, calls for strengthening the OAS to establish an inter-American program for social development and to use additional resources to finance plans and projects of basic economic and industrial development. The United States announced that it would establish a special inter-American fund for social development. The Caribbean Commission and the South Pacific Commission are advisory and consultative bodies, whose purpose is to improve the economic and social well-being of the people of the Caribbean and South Pacific Islands.

International forums for the exchange of technical information, techniques, and skills—generally called technical assistance—are provided in several organizations, including the United Nations Expanded Program of Technical Assistance; United Nations Special Fund; International Atomic Energy Agency; International Civil Aviation Organization; United Nations Educational, Scientific, and Cultural Organization; Intergovernmental Maritime Consultative Organization; World Health Organization; World Meteorological Organization; Pan-American Health Organization; Inter-American Statistical Institute; the International Council of Scientific Unions; and the International Labor Organization. The purpose of the Special Fund differs from that of the skill-sharing Expanded Technical Assistance Program in that it devotes its resources to relatively large projects aimed at facilitating new capital investment by creating conditions conducive to such investments.

Many of the programs and projects of economic development, particularly in underdeveloped areas, require extensive financing that is frequently beyond the means of the country that benefits immediately. To meet the need for such financing and to guide international investments into economically sound and productive channels, four international financial institutions have been established. One is the International Bank for Reconstruction and Development. On a "good risk" basis, the Bank lends funds or guarantees loans for reconstruction of industry and development of economic facilities. An affiliate of the Bank, the International Development Association (IDA), finances a wider range of projects, as it has considerable flexibility both in purposes for which it may provide funds and in the terms on which it may make loans. The IDA overcomes the limitations on lending that a weak foreign exchange position imposes. The International Finance Corporation encourages the growth of private enterprise in member countries, particularly in the less developed areas. It provides, in association with private investors, risk capital for financing productive private enterprises when other sources of funds are not available on reasonable terms. Fulfilling a need for an institution specifically designed to promote the financing of economic development in Latin America is the Inter-American Development Bank. Its broad objective is to accelerate the general economic development of Latin America with all Latin American countries sharing in the cost and in the responsibility for success.

In the spheres of international trade and foreign exchange, two institutions predominate. The General Agreement on Tariffs and Trade—GATT—has as its basic aims the promotion of cooperation in international trade, reduction of tariffs, and elimination of other governmentally imposed barriers to international trade. In serving these purposes, GATT operates as an instrument for negotiation

The development of improved nutrition represents one of the many significant goals of the Food and Agriculture Organization (FAO) of the United Nations. Here, Mary Ross, nutritionist of FAO, observes the reactions of Burmese children to an experimental meal, which includes fish flour.

and consultation for its 39 contracting parties. The International Monetary Fund is an association of nations (71 in 1961) for promoting international monetary cooperation and expansion of international trade. Members work together to provide a procedure for orderly adjustment of foreign exchange rates to insure that major changes in exchange practices will be submitted to international consultation before being put into effect and to remove restrictions on current exchange transactions.

The United Nations family includes one welfare agency, the United Nations Children's Fund. Best known for its emergency relief action among children and mothers in time of flood, earthquake, or other disasters, it helps with child and maternal care programs in the underdeveloped countries and territories. The Department of Agriculture has made large quantities of nonfat dry milk solids available to it for its worldwide child-feeding programs. (*Alex. D. Angelidis* and *Robert L. Tontz*)

Using Our Abundance

LARGE AMOUNTS of our agricultural commodities have been sold abroad or used to help other countries. They have been sold for dollars, for foreign currencies, or on credit. They may have been bartered or donated.

Most people and industries in the United States and overseas have been able to pay the dollar market price for the farm goods they use. Nearly 5 billion dollars' worth of agricultural commodities were exported in 1961. Seventy percent represented sales for dollars through regular commercial channels. Most of these exports have gone to the United Kingdom, the Netherlands, Belgium, West Germany, France, Scandinavia, Italy, and Japan. So that American exporters could compete in these dollar markets with exports from other countries, payment-in-kind programs were developed for the most important agricultural exports. These programs were designed to encourage exports from commercial supplies instead of from inventories of the Commodity Credit Corporation (CCC), a Government corporation that finances the agricultural price-support program and holds title to agricultural commodities acquired under it. This placed the merchandising functions in the hands of the private trade. Certificates at the applicable subsidy rates redeemable in commodities from CCC stocks were issued to American exporters on proof of export of commodities obtained from private stocks. The subsidy rates represent the difference between higher domestic prices and the prices at which an exporter had to sell in the foreign country in order to be competitive. No subsidy is allowed if there were no differential. Other commodities not under payment-in-kind programs were sold for export on competitive bid. Cash dollar markets were the most important markets, but other export programs were developed for countries that lacked sufficient gold and dollar reserves to pay cash.

The Commodity Credit Corporation Export Credit Sales Program, established in 1956, made possible the purchase of commodities in CCC inventory on a deferred payment basis for periods up to 3 years if an assurance of payment were furnished from a bank in the United States. Nearly 75 million dollars' worth of commodities were exported under this program in 1956–1961. Wheat, feed grains, rice, dry edible beans, nonfat dry milk, tobacco, and cotton were among them. An example of how this program has assisted

594

in economic development and expanded our agricultural exports is its use in El Salvador, Guatemala, and Honduras. To achieve greater economic independence, the countries began to construct their own flour mills. The credit program enabled them to utilize better their working capital, establish the milling industry, and encourage the consumption of wheat.

The Congress amended Public Law 480 by adding Title IV in 1959 to authorize the President to enter into long-term credit agreements under which the United States would receive payment in dollars for exported farm goods. The maximum credit period was set at 20 years; supply commitments up to 10 years were permitted. Proceeds of the sales in the foreign countries were to be used for economic development and not be earmarked as in the case of sales under Title I for foreign currencies.

Under the barter program, the Commodity Credit Corporation exchanged commodities in its ownership or control for certain materials, goods, and equipment produced in foreign countries. It was a way to move agricultural commodities into world markets that could not be exported for dollars. Sometimes the strategic and other materials received in exchange for agricultural commodities would not otherwise be acquired by the United States Government. To that extent, a market for these materials was created, and the effect on employment abroad, mining, processing and manufacturing facilities, and the general economic well-being of the countries was favorable. The additional purchasing power thus generated was translated into increased exports of United States farm and other products, and commodities that could not be sold for dollars were exchanged for materials of equivalent value, easy to store, virtually nondeteriorating, and not produced in sufficient quantity in the United States. Some materials acquired by barter—particularly those acquired for other Government agencies—would otherwise have had to be acquired for dollars. The resulting reduction in the outflow of dollars contributed toward a more favorable balance-of-payments position. Barter transactions took place under contracts that specified the material to be delivered and frequently stipulated the origin of the materials, the agricultural commodity to be exported, and the destination. They usually were separate foreign trade transactions, each through private competitive channels. In a barter transaction, an American firm bought a material abroad and sold it to CCC at or below the world price, took payment in a surplus agricultural commodity, and sold the acquired commodity on the international market.

Some countries lack both dollar reserves and strategic materials but need to import agricultural commodities. Under Title I of Public Law 480, government-to-government agreements were negotiated under which our farm goods were sold for foreign currencies, the greater part of which were lent back to the purchasing countries for various specified uses. This program, for example, provided much of India's expanded need for food supplies and the sales have provided local currency used in India's economic development. Out of total P. L. 480 rupee funds earmarked for loans and grants, 78 million dollars were expended by June 30, 1960. However, 316 million dollars were obligated as of April 1961, for 10 development projects in India. They include 12 river valley projects, which will provide additional irrigation for additional food production, dams, and hydroelectric power. Eight of the projects are expected to provide more than 12 million kilowatts of electricity and irrigation for some 9 million acres. Through another project, the Uttar Pradesh Agricultural University has been aided by a grant of 2 million dollars. A third project established the Refinance Corporation in accordance with the first Title I agreement with India, which reserved the rupee equivalent of 55 million dollars for relending to private enterprise through established banking facilities.

For many years, we have been sharing our abundant foods with hungry people abroad. As a new development in this tradition, the Food for Peace program, based largely on P. L. 480, was established in 1961. It enabled us to share food, agricultural resources, and technical knowledge with friendly countries everywhere. Surplus foods were distributed to needy persons overseas by private, non-profit charitable organizations, and some church organizations. All food was labeled "Gift of the People of the U.S.A." It was given without regard to race, color, or creed. An example was in the North African desert, southeast of Tripoli, where children were given daily a glass of reconstituted dry milk, a wedge of cheese, and a bun each. The Libyan Government supplemented this diet with other foods. The children's health improved, and so did attendance at school and (because hunger militates against learning) ability to learn.

Food donations at home began during the depression of the thirties and expanded steadily in the years between 1936 and 1941, after which rising incomes and high employment eliminated much of the need for public assistance. The Second World War reversed the situation. Surpluses disappeared, and rationing appeared. From the postwar period to 1961, unemployment and low incomes once again became a problem, and direct food donations were made again. State agencies helped donate to needy families and persons in charitable institutions foods acquired by the Department of Agriculture from America's abundance. Some 15 million schoolchildren also received foods made available from Federal funds and distributed by the Department. Nearly 23 million persons benefited from this expanded domestic direct distribution program in 1961. *(John H. Dean)*

Helping To Feed and Clothe the World

THE FARMERS of America in 1961 supplied nearly one-fifth of the volume of farm products that entered world trade. Farm commodities shipped abroad accounted for the output of about 60 million acres of our cropland and represented the production of 1 in 6 harvested acres. To ship these products abroad, arrangements were made for financing, inland transportation, storage, and ocean shipping for 41 million tons of cargo—enough to fill a million freight cars or more than 4 thousand cargo ships. The volume in 1961 was more than 12 times greater than the agricultural exports at the close of the Civil War. Traditionally, the major United States agricultural exports since the 1860's have been wheat, feed grains, cotton, and tobacco. More recently rice (also exported in the colonial period), vegetable oils, and oilseeds have become major export commodities. Animal products, fruit, and vegetables have been major items in years of surplus.

Our biggest agricultural surpluses in 1961 were cotton, wheat, feed grains, and tobacco, and they were our biggest agricultural exports. In the 3 years that ended June 30, 1961, exports averaged two-fifths of the cotton and wheat output, almost a third of the tobacco crop, and one-sixth of the feed-grain sales of American farmers. Of the total value, wheat and flour accounted for 23 percent. Grains and cotton together comprised almost three-fifths of the total. Animals and animal products, vegetable oils and oilseeds, fruit and vegetables, tobacco, and other commodities made up slightly more than two-fifths of the total.

More than 125 countries were involved in the agricultural export trade of the United States in 1961, but ten countries—Japan, the United Kingdom, Canada, India, West Germany, the Netherlands, Italy, Poland, Spain, and Belgium—each took more than 100 million dollars' worth of American farm products and together took nearly two-thirds of the total. The share of our agricultural exports relative to total exports is smaller today than in the historic past, when population numbers were lower and industrial production was relatively less important. In the early colonial period, agricultural exports accounted for most of the overseas shipments, as Europe provided manufactured goods to the colonists. At the time of the Civil War, they constituted about 75 percent of total shipments abroad. In 1961 they represented 26 percent. The volume of agricultural exports has been increasing, however, although at a slower rate than has been the case for nonagricultural exports. The volume of agricultural exports in recent years has been at its highest level in history, a continuation of a trend that got underway during the early years of the Second World War, following adoption of the lend-lease program. This upward trend was a reversal of a downward trend that prevailed from the late 1920's to 1940–1941, a decline brought on largely by the movement in Western Europe toward agricultural self-sufficiency and accompanying restrictions on trade.

Today's record levels have come about through recognition of the fact that the American farmer's foreign market actually has become two markets, each which must be approached in its own way. One is the "dollar market." The other is the "nondollar market." The dollar market is made up of the more prosperous, economically developed countries, able to pay dollars or other convertible currencies for the supplies they buy from the United States. It consists largely of Western European countries, plus Japan and Canada, although several other countries, including Venezuela, Mexico, and the Philippines, also are good cash customers. Of the 4.9 billion dollars' worth of farm exports in fiscal 1961, 3.4 billion dollars (about 70 percent) represented commercial sales for dollars. The nondollar market includes the less economically developed countries, which badly need products but lack convertible exchange. The nondollar countries are mainly in Asia, the Middle East, Africa, and South America. Exports under specified Government-financed programs make it possible to ship our farm products to the underdeveloped countries. Exports under the programs, identified as Food for Peace, amounted to 1.5 billion dollars (about 30 percent) of total agricultural exports in 1961. Sales for dollars are given top priority in the export programs. Dollar sales strengthen farm incomes. They contribute to meeting food requirements of the free world. The United States receives substantial dollar income that helps to finance its own imports from abroad. Further, this healthy trade between the countries of the free world is in itself a unifying factor.

In an effort to expand dollar sales, market promotion work is going forward in about 50 countries. Because promotion is primarily a responsibility of private industry, the Department of Agriculture has worked out cooperative arrangements with about 40 nonprofit, national agricultural and trade groups. Promotion includes exhibits and demonstrations of farm products, introduction of products, surveys and studies of market potential, publicity and advertising, education in nutrition and sanitation, exchange of management and technical personnel, technical assistance, and sales training. Agricultural exhibits have been one means of showing

598

Visitors at the Paris Trade Fair in 1961 learn about American dry milk.

foreign consumers the wide variety and high quality of American products. Nearly 100 exhibits, most of them in connection with international trade fairs, have been viewed by some 45 million visitors in recent years. In November 1961, in Hamburg, Germany, the Department of Agriculture staged its first large all-American agricultural exhibit—that is, an exhibit not connected with an international fair or other event. Also for the first time, commercial exhibitors were sold space for displays at which they were permitted to take orders for United States agricultural products. The Departments of Agriculture and Commerce opened a trade center in London in 1961. Agricultural market promotion work will be carried on the year around at the new center. Selected foods and agricultural products will be displayed at annual exhibits, which will also include demonstrations, receptions, lectures, and showings of slides and pictures. Plans were made to open a trade center in Tokyo in 1962.

Promotion alone is not enough, however. Our products also must have opportunity to enter a country and compete in its market. As part of its market development work, therefore, the United States

American foods at a large department store in a London suburb in 1961.

Robert N. Anderson, the United States Agricultural Attaché in London (left), Orville L. Freeman, Secretary of Agriculture, and F. J. Erroll, Minister of State, the British Board of Trade, visited the United States Trade Center in London in 1961.

constantly works toward the lowering of foreign trade barriers—variable tariffs, quotas, embargoes, bilateral arrangements, and the like—that interfere with the ready flow of our products. This is done through diplomatic channels, meetings in connection with the General Agreement on Tariffs and Trade, conferences with European Common Market officials, and in other ways. Barriers of one kind or another usually are erected because of a desire to protect some segment of their economy, or encourage self-sufficiency, or raise revenues. Another essential is current, accurate information about the markets and developments that affect them. A key factor in this information program is the flow of reports from United States agricultural attachés at 56 posts throughout the world, as well as surveys and analyses by marketing and area specialists.

The efficiency of American agriculture makes it possible to compete with a wide range of products in world markets. Domestic prices are higher than world prices for certain commodities, such as wheat, cotton, rice, feed grains, and dairy products, however. It is necessary in such cases that the Commodity Credit Corporation make export payments in cash or in kind or sell stocks below domestic market prices so these stocks can move. Of the 4.9 billion dollar total exported in 1960–1961, 2.3 billion dollars' worth moved with the assistance of export payments or sales at reduced prices. The estimated cost of these export payments was more than 600 million dollars, not counting donations valued at 300 million. Export payments, excluding donations, equaled 13 percent of the value of our exports of farm products. Even though the nondollar areas lack the cash resources to buy large amounts of American farm products, their need for such supplies is great. In recent years, Government-financed programs have made it possible for friendly countries to have access to our bountiful supplies even though they lack dollars. This Food for Peace concept specifies that the United States will do what it can to help foreign friends become adequately fed, because there is little chance for peace and progress in a world where millions of people go to bed hungry every night. Most of the Food for Peace exporting is done under Public Law 480, which has been in effect since 1954, although the idea is much older. During the Second World War, for example, the Secretary of Agriculture urged greater output because "food will win the war and write the peace." After the war, the United States gave food to rehabilitate war-devastated areas. A smaller amount of exporting under the Food for Peace program is done under Public Law 665.

Exports under Government programs, which account for about 30 percent of our total farm exports, are large enough to be important both to foreign producers and United States producers. These programs are carried out carefully. Established producers in a

Secretary Freeman (third from left) and several American agricultural and economic experts, who studied agricultural development problems in 11 European and Asian countries in 1961, visited the Agricultural and Jute Research Institute in Tejgaon, East Pakistan.

A marketing specialist checks the quality of American wheat when it is unloaded at a port in the Far East.

Foreign currencies received by the United States for surplus farm products shipped to developing countries have been loaned or granted back to the countries to finance public works, such as this irrigation project in the Middle East.

country receiving our products must not be hurt, and their incentive for producing must not be impaired. The availability of American farm supplies must not lower a country's efforts to feed its own people. Further, the world's commercial marketing mechanism, so important to the United States farmer, must not be damaged. Sales for foreign currency represent by far the largest of the special export programs. A substantial percentage of the foreign money "generated" by these sales is loaned and granted back to recipient countries to finance economic development. A substantial part also is used by the United States Government for various uses abroad, including market promotion. Barter has made it possible for the United States to swap stocks of surplus food and fiber for foreign-produced strategic and critical materials required for stockpiling. Credit sales for dollars also are authorized. Sales of commodities may be sold for dollars on credit at moderate rates of interest. Countries using this program have up to 20 years to make payment. Emergency donations are made by the United States to the governments of other countries. Other donations are made through voluntary agencies operating abroad or through such international organizations. Donated food supplies go for famine relief, aid to refugees, school lunch programs, and similar uses. *(Robert L. Tontz and Harry W. Henderson)*

603

Agricultural Intelligence

TO CARRY on their global trade in farm products, a business that bears directly on the lives of nearly 3 billion persons, the United States and many other countries have a system of agricultural intelligence whereby they get and assess facts to enable producers to market their crops abroad advantageously and to help consumers obtain the products they need. This global agricultural information can mean the difference between profit or bankruptcy to the world's farmers and traders, between soundness and unsoundness of a country's economy, and even between plenty and starvation. In the United States, this information is supplied largely by the Foreign Agricultural Service, an agency of the Department of Agriculture. Its program of reports, analyses, and publications yields information that helps the American exporter to sell wheat, the importer to buy coffee, and the public foreign-help organizations to learn where hunger exists and how to cope with it.

Agricultural attachés form the core of this system, which started in 1881, when Edmund J. Moffat was sent to London to provide "accurate reports of crop prospects, valuable statistical exchanges, and miscellaneous information of value to the United States Department of Agriculture and the agriculture of the country." The attachés do the same work now, but on a larger, more complex scale. They are stationed at more than 50 key posts around the world. They and their trained foreign assistants cover more than twice that many countries. They forward to Washington each year more than 2 thousand scheduled reports, 5 thousand spot news reports, and 3 thousand foreign publications. Their reports deal with the production, trade, and consumption of more than 230 commodities. They supply much collateral information on government policies, the formation of common-market coalitions, availability of foreign currency and credit, trade balances, labor situations, bilateral trade obligations, weather, demand, prices, and changes in farming techniques. The attachés interpret the information they gather and evaluate its usefulness to American producers, consumers, and Government officials.

Getting the data is not difficult in countries that have efficient statistical services and farming and marketing systems, but in many countries gaps exist in official figures, the basis of presentation seldom is constant, and the accuracy of available figures sometimes

604

Guy A. W. Schilling, a marketing specialist of the Foreign Agricultural Service, inspects cotton from the United States at the Burmese Government Cotton Spinning and Weaving Mill in Thamaing.

is questionable. Agricultural statistics are lacking in some developing countries, and the task of gathering data there often is made more difficult by uncertainties of highways and communications and the remoteness of producers. There the attaché may have to rely on interviews with parish priests, migrant traders, and tribal headmen and to undertake much arduous travel. A trip by car around one country in Africa, for example, takes more than 3 months.

Graham Quate, former agricultural attaché in Thailand, and his assistant ford the Ping River during a field trip to collect information on the rice crop.

Robert E. Adcock, United States agricultural attaché (right), sizes up the prospective coffee crop in Kenya. With him is T. E. Ritchie, of the Food and Agriculture Organization.

Sometimes the job of estimating the size of a crop is an individual project. An attaché in one country travels by jeep through the major cocoa-producing sections, stops every 2 miles, hikes into the groves, and counts the pods on a sampling of trees. Later trips to the same trees help him gage season-to-season differences in yield and quality. Often commodity specialists are sent from Washington to help the attaché evaluate the situation regarding a major crop. Help also is given by foreign technicians, officials, and farm leaders who have returned home after taking part in foreign training programs sponsored by the Department of Agriculture.

The reports from the attachés are fitted together in Washington by economic analysts who have expert knowledge of a commodity or an area or both. An instance: The attaché in Bangkok may report that the Thai rice crop is 3.5 million piculs larger than usual and that growers have raised their price 20 bahts. Thailand is a major source of rice, and rice is a mainstay of half the people in the world. The United States also is a major exporter of rice, although we produce only about 1 percent of the world crop. Thus the information about Thai rice becomes part of a larger picture— so important to millions who subsist largely on rice and to growers in Texas, Louisiana, Arkansas, and California, who rely on export markets. Against this background, the specialist of the Foreign Agricultural Service must decide: Does the Thai report coincide with other reports? How much rice may be exported—considering carryover stocks and domestic use? How does the price compare with comparable United States grades and qualities? How does it compare with world market prices? What is the situation in other rice-exporting and in rice-importing countries? How much of Thailand's rice is already committed through bilateral trade agreements?

The specialists who process such facts work in a dynamic situation that changes constantly as dietary habits change, farming methods advance, demand-and-supply patterns shift, and science fosters new agricultural products and bypasses others. For example, the Carolina indigo that was traded around the world a century ago has been replaced by synthetic dyes. The New England whale oil, once important in trade with Europe, has been supplanted by other oils. The uses of many natural products, such as rubber, are being extended or preserved by research on new uses and byproducts.

The Department shares its global information with everyone who wants it and needs it. International organizations and many foreign governments rely on the Foreign Agricultural Service for dependable facts and figures. The International Coffee Agreement, for example, sets its trading quotas on the basis of the world coffee estimates made by the Foreign Agricultural Service. The International Wheat Agreement makes use of our intelligence to get the billions of bushels of wheat in world granaries to the people who need it and yet protect both buyers and sellers. The primary clients, however, are American producers, processors, and traders. Many months ago, for example, a seed company foresaw increasing demand for higher yielding varieties of seed in the newly developing countries south of the Sahara. Our information on the staple food crops of those peoples, the varieties of seed that would grow best, and the limitations imposed by soil and climate benefited both trader and consumer. Other users of the data are bankers and brokers, farm and trade organizations, libraries, trade journals, shipping and railroad companies, universities and colleges, hotel suppliers, quartermasters, newspapers, TV and radio networks, manufacturers of pharmaceuticals, fungicides, and farm equipment, and other Americans who want to know what's going on in world agriculture.

The Department releases more than 5 thousand reports a year on some aspect of foreign agriculture in answer to individual queries and through a series of free publications. Foreign Crops and Markets, issued weekly since 1919, contains articles and statistics about commodities and developments in foreign trade. Foreign Agriculture Circulars advise specific segments of agriculture on world developments that affect sales or supplies of special commodities. Foreign Agriculture, a monthly illustrated magazine, reports and interprets developments in world agriculture. Information is also made available in press releases, fact sheets, chart books, economic studies, outlook reports, radio tapes, and films about special situations. *(Audrey Ames Cook)*

607

Agriculture's Man in Japan

THE MAN who represents American agriculture overseas has more activities than there are minutes in an hour. He seeks markets for American farm products. He is busy with agricultural reporting and analysis. He collaborates with other Embassy officers in negotiations with foreign officials. He advises the Ambassador. He assists official visitors and traders. He cooperates with his Embassy colleagues to remove trade barriers. All his activities advance his three basic duties: To represent United States agriculture abroad; maintain and expand overseas outlets for our farm products; and report on the production, use, and marketing of agricultural commodities overseas. He spends much of his time on aspects of the more formal programs of market development—government-to-government agreements for the use of agricultural products, participation in trade fairs, special commodity exhibits, distribution of samples, visits of Cotton Maids and Dairy Princesses, and similar undertakings that help in the development of markets.

The daily activities of the attachés vary considerably, depending on the nature of the agricultural economy and our interest in the areas they cover, but the attachés themselves have similar backgrounds and qualifications. An attaché usually comes from a rural area and is a graduate of a land-grant college, with one or more degrees in agriculture or economics. He has had work in price analysis, farm management, market structures, and statistics. He has had professional experience in domestic agricultural programs.

The daily round of our agricultural attaché in Tokyo epitomizes in large degree the day's work of the attachés who cover much of the world. Because Japan is a century-old customer for our farm products, it provides an appropriate example of an attaché's post. Japan sent its first diplomatic and commercial emissaries to the United States in 1860 and since has become a major industrial nation and a principal trading partner of the United States. Our exports of farm commodities have made up an important part of this trade. Japan ranks among the leading foreign markets for farm products of the United States. The agricultural attaché in Tokyo is an important wheel in the machinery that moves these products. He and his hard-working colleagues all over the world are truly the representatives—and eyes and ears and hands—of America and American farmers. (*Audrey Ames Cook*)

Dr. Charles M. Elkinton, American agricultural attaché in Japan in 1959–1962, and an interpreter interview a Japanese farmer in Yamanashi prefecture.

A Japanese farmer's wife gets the family water supply from a shallow, open well.

Kuniharu Kiyomiya and Dr. Elkinton talk to Japanese farmers about rice.

Japanese children get reconstituted milk, which they will distribute to fellow pupils as part of their school lunch.

Pupils in Takanawadai Elementary School for lunch have bread and milk, part of which was produced on American farms.

Dr. Elkinton and two local assistants, T. Takeshita and T. Sutani, discuss report data.

Most of the soap in Japan is made with tallow from the United States.

Removal of soil around the roots is one of the first steps in preparing bonsai for shipment to the United States.

Members of Japanese-American Soybean Institute discuss a market development project.

Japan imports sizable amounts of hard winter wheat for bread and rolls from the United States.

Andrew Wardlaw, American commercial attaché in Tokyo, and Dr. Elkinton watch the preparation of a shipment of tape recorders.

One brand of Japanese cigarettes contains 25 percent of American tobacco.

Dr. Elkinton poses with Japanese and European models who participated in the Leather Mode Show in Tokyo in 1961. Japan is a good customer for American hides and skins.

Dr. Elkinton and John D. Motz and Donald J. Novotny, assistant attachés, attend a luncheon meeting of the Japanese Feed Grain Council to discuss imports of corn and sorghums from the United States. Dr. Elkinton, a native of Eau Claire, Wis., holds three degrees from the University of Wisconsin. He formerly was a professor of economics in Washington State University and Iowa State University. He joined the Department of Agriculture in 1955.

So People May Know

The County Agent

OTIS R. GRIGGS is an educator, adviser, purveyor of information, executive, and representative of the United States Department of Agriculture in the conduct of educational farm programs in Reno County, Kansas, where he is the county agent. He is one of 6,343 county agents in the country. His training, activities, and responsibilities are much like those of the others, whose charter of operations is a memorandum of understanding drawn up in 1955 by the Secretary of the Department of Agriculture and the heads of land-grant colleges and universities. It specified that the Department would refer its educational responsibilities to State Extension Services. The county agent—who sometimes is referred to as agricultural agent, extension agent, and farm adviser—puts the programs into action in his county. He serves all segments of agriculture. In Reno County, for example, are farm-related industries that produce alfalfa meal, margarine, frozen and dried eggs, flour, feeds, grain and elevator equipment, dairy supplies, silos, farm machinery, fertilizer, and meat products.

Reno is the second largest county in Kansas. Its 2,289 farms in 1962 averaged 340 acres. Its population was 59,116. The population of Hutchinson, the county seat, was more than 37 thousand. Urban residents look to Mr. Griggs and his staff for information about lawn grasses, vegetable varieties, control of insects and diseases, fertilizers, landscaping, sprays for fruit trees, weed control, flowers, and other phases of the broad field of agriculture. Because the county agent is responsible for planning an educational program to meet the changing needs of the rural and urban residents of his area, Mr. Griggs keeps contact with an Extension council of 102 members. Individuals representing agriculture, home economics, and 4-H Clubs are elected annually from each township and incorporated city in the county. He works also with the board of county commissioners on the Extension budget and the district agent, who represents the State director. Reno County financed 82 percent of the 1962 Extension budget. Federal and State funds provided 18 percent.

In his day-to-day activities, Mr. Griggs informs residents of the county about new research findings, Government programs, such as the emergency feed-grain program, new varieties of crops, and the market outlook. Because Reno is in the center of the Kansas wheat

Mr. Griggs works closely with veterinarians on problems of animal health.

The Extension staff in Reno County, Kansas, comprises (left to right) James R. Childers, 4-H Club agent; Gertrude Hove and Gertrude Brown, home economics agents; Rae C. Luginsland, assistant county agent; and Otis R. Griggs, county agent.

belt, Mr. Griggs joined in a wheat quality improvement program in 1954. By 1961, the farmers had increased their acreage in strong gluten varieties from 4 to 33 percent. Kansas wheatgrowers increased their acreage in the desired varieties from 17 to 39.1 percent. Reno County was one of the pilot counties in the Plains States reforestation program of the thirties, and it still is interested in shelterbelts and windbreaks. Helped by the cooperative Forest Service-Kansas State University tree distribution project, started in 1957, farmers of the county ordered nearly 147 thousand trees in 5 years. Another project Mr. Griggs stressed, control of brucellosis in dairy and beef cattle, also was successful. The county became the sixth among the State's 105 counties to be declared a modified-certified brucellosis free area. Calfhood vaccination is emphasized now to limit the buildup of brucellosis in mature livestock. Much of Mr. Griggs' educational work is conducted through cooperating groups. A mid-Kansas swine marketing association, which originated in Reno County, now includes surrounding counties. Fat lambs are marketed on a graded basis through three outlets, which he helped to organize. Farm management long has been a strong point in the Extension program. One of Kansas State University's first district farm management associations, organized in the early thirties, included Reno County, which, in 1961, had more members than any other county in the association.

No day is like any other in a county agent's life, but one day, which we can consider as typical as any, Mr. Griggs began with a radio program at 6:30 a.m. He made another broadcast at 12:30 p.m., when he discussed the importance of deep watering and

617

Farmers get suggestions and detailed information about new structures and equipment from Mr. Griggs.

Keeping informed about results of research is a continuing responsibility of county agents.

timely mowing of bluegrass lawns and other topics of particular interest to urban residents. From the radio station, he stopped by the newspaper office to submit material for news releases. His first two or three hours in the office he spent with callers—for example, a businessman on his way to work brought in a twig from a tree affected by a blight. Mr. Griggs suggested the cause and treatment and later mailed the twig to the State Extension plant pathologist for further details. With another caller he discussed aspects of farm financing; those questions Mr. Griggs referred to the representative of the Farmers Home Administration. One man, who asked about soil conservation practices, was referred to the work unit conservationist in the county. Out of the office, the county agent inspected some of the 24 field demonstration plots scattered over the county. He checked with the superintendent of the State experiment field concerning tests with supplemental crops. He helped a farmer who was erecting a "hay keeper," in which chopped hay is dried and self-fed to livestock. He stopped to see a family whose farmstead he had helped landscape and wanted to show him how well the plantings had done and to get his suggestions on other plantings.

Otis Griggs was born in Brookville, Kans., in 1921. He grew up on a 160-acre farm. He is a graduate in dairy husbandry of Kansas State University. He and his wife, Roselma, have four children. He served 5 years in the Navy. Thereafter he was successively supervisor of the Marion County Dairy Herd Improvement Association, junior assistant county agent in McPherson and Lyon Counties, and county agricultural agent in Stevens County. He became associate county agent in Reno County in 1954 and the county agent in 1960. On his staff are an associate county agent, a home economics agent, an associate home economics agent, and a 4-H Club agent. *(Harold E. Jones* and *Harold Shankland)*

Extension in Oregon

THE EARLY Extension programs were geared mainly to short-term objectives. Simple questions of crop varieties, fertilizers, and the control of pests and livestock diseases were typical. Longer range objectives developed later as the need grew for sweeping agricultural adjustments, more attention to conservation of resources, and improved rural living conditions. Oregon is an example.

In the early 1920's it seemed apparent that Extension workers should be developing leadership to give a broad direction to the State's agriculture, which then was geared to produce large exportable amounts of many crops. In fact, Oregon can produce at some place within its borders any crop adapted to the North Temperate Zone. It seemed clear that its population could not consume more than 25 percent of its production then, and markets were far away. The only commodities that would pay transportation across the country would have to be ones with which Oregon farmers had an advantage in quality or in cost of production and high value and small bulk. Foreign markets changed drastically. The Extension Service was not entirely sure as to adjustments to suggest. Then came to mind the idea that has been the core of the Oregon Extension program since: To work with the people concerned in an analysis of the problem and agreement on steps toward a solution.

Topographical variations caused by elevation, relationship to mountain ranges, and moderating effects of the Pacific set out six types of farming regions, some of which differ from others as sharply as Maine differs from New Mexico. Some lands are farmed under protection of dikes to curb salt ocean water; others are at elevations of more than 5 thousand feet. In the five counties on the Pacific coast, 80 to 100 inches of rain fall annually on year-round pasturelands. On high plateaus in central Oregon, rainfall averages 7 to 8 inches, and the growing season is short. At some place under these widely differing conditions is opportunity for almost any fancy in production.

Oregon was by way of becoming an apple-growing empire. Land for orchards boomed in the early days of the century. Plantings that had been located on suitable soils were in production in the early twenties. Growers discovered too late that their market was nearly 3 thousand miles away, where in good apple years nearly 40

Growing grass and forage crops, including Alta fescue, for seed became a 30-million dollar enterprise in Oregon.

States competed for purchasers' favor. A freight cost of more than a dollar a bushel to New York or Boston as against 15 to 20 cents from upper New York or Michigan, for instance, set a handicap. But the die had been cast years before to the tune of more than 70 thousand acres on the basis of wishful thinking instead of logic. There also was a long list of hit-or-miss production patterns and other puzzling questions. Up to 1919, dairy products and eggs had been shipped in. Now there was surplus, and markets outside the State were desirable. Until 1920, eggs had been shipped in from Nebraska and Iowa. The degree of emphasis to place on development of these two enterprises was a question. Other commodities that could be produced faced uncertainty as to market. Among them were specialties like bulbs, holly, cranberries, nursery stock (including roses, for which the State had acquired high reputation), and cannery products.

Spokesmen of each commodity group, the School of Agriculture, State Extension specialists, and employees of the United States Department of Agriculture were invited to consider the problems. These leaders, including producers, handlers, bankers, and the press, met periodically over 18 months as special committees to study their particular segments of agriculture in Oregon. At the end of that time, conclusions were reached and presented by each of the committees at a statewide meeting of 600 persons on the campus of Oregon State College. With slight modifications in some cases, they were adopted as objectives in what shaped up as a well-defined State agricultural program.

After the State conference, the Extension Service directed its specialists to assist in setting up in every county appropriate counterpart committees to consider that county's relationships to the statewide conclusions. Two hundred to 4 hundred rural people in each of the counties participated in committee membership. From this came a county program of such content that every organization, both town and country, in each county could support it in some part or as a whole. It became the main educational program of the Extension agents. Each county in Oregon thus developed a full-fledged program of land use and county development, arrived at by agreement between Extension staff people and local groups. Five years later the same process was repeated to give recognition to possible changes and to evaluate results. This procedure has now been repeated five times in all the counties. Throughout the years, 80 percent or more of the effort of the entire Extension staff—administrators, supervisors, and specialists—has been directed to the advancement of the county programs.

The main focus of the Oregon Extension Service has been this concentration on county programs, but the State program has been rounded out by fulfilling other objectives. Time was taken to interpret the functions of other agencies of the Department of Agriculture. The purposes and operational methods of the Soil Conservation Service, for instance, were explained, and the organization of Soil Conservation Districts often became part of the county program. Policies of the Forest Service were interpreted, and the Director of Extension or his representative was a regular member of the State Agricultural Stabilization and Conservation Committee. County agents likewise were members of the county committees. The Extension staff members also interpreted the functions and regulatory program of the State Department of Agriculture and assisted in bringing all this into local focus.

The action of the people who took part in these program-making conferences has had a profound effect on farming in Oregon since 1925, as attested by increased returns. At the end of this time, a few farmers were farming just about the same acreage, and the income from farm sales and crops and livestock had been increased by 70 percent. The goals the leaders proposed have been accomplished in many instances. Some were exceeded. The farm economy of the State has been keyed to consideration of market possibilities as well as production possibilities. New enterprises resulted. The soundest ones already underway were substantially increased, and a start has been made on enterprises holding a promising outlook. For example, one committee, in 1924, recorded: "Because of its high value per pound and the higher average yield per acre of small seeds in Oregon, it is recommended that Oregon farmers on irrigated areas and in western Oregon enter more extensively into the production of such small seeds as clovers, grasses, and certain vetches. Figures indicate that these seeds may bring into the State an additional income of at least 2 million dollars annually for possible production of red, alsike, and white clovers, purple and hairy vetch, Grimm alfalfa, and grass seeds." Twenty-five years later, annual returns to the farmers from these and additional small seeds had exceeded the committee's estimate by 15 times. More than 30 million dollars annually was for a time the value to the farmers. This production has not been maintained, as other States have capitalized upon similar advantages, but it still is a sound enterprise in Oregon.

In fact, time disclosed that every one of the committees struck paydirt. The farmers diverted acres, mainly from wheat and other lesser income crops, to seed production in this instance, and attained top place in the United States in production of leguminous cover-crop seed and seed of ryegrass, Ladino clover, alsike clover, and bentgrass. A dairy business geared to high-quality butter for the California market was expanding encouragingly. A 42-percent increase in number of milk cows in 25 years resulted in production of 70 percent more milk. The poultry producers organized a cooperative marketing association to ship eggs east. Egg production increased three times to more than 50 million dozen by 1950. Apple acreage dropped to fewer than 13 thousand; more than 20 thousand acres of apples were replaced by winter pears, which meet

Dennis Belknap (left) and Frank L. Ballard look over an irrigated pasture in Willamette Valley, Oregon. It was a demonstration field to prove the value of irrigation, which now is applied to 125 thousand acres in the State.

less competition in distant markets. Acreage in prunes went down and was replaced by 14 thousand acres of sweet cherries, a better fruit for the markets available to Oregon farmers. Attention was focused on outlets for processing crops. As a result, the Extension Service employed specialists in the production of vegetables and small fruit and one to work with processors on the technologies of processing. Fruit and vegetable processing represents an annual value of more than 136 million dollars.

Several specialty crops were developed. Strawberries were established on 15 thousand acres. A special variety of green beans—Blue Lake—was established to the extent of 12 thousand acres. A water utilization project was established, and the irrigation of farmland in western Oregon increased from a few hundred acres to nearly 200 thousand in 35 years. In this development, the basic teaching method was the field demonstration, where results were measured on the ground by county agents. By similar teamwork by the Department of Agriculture, the college, and the county staffs, a nursery business that grossed about 13 million dollars was developed, and a million-dollar business in winter greenery—sword fern and huckleberry, mainly—was developed through eastern and mid-western outlets. Because neighboring California was growing rapidly in population and provided a market every day for all animal products except wool and poultry meat, the Oregon Extension Service

A field of Ladino clover grown for seed in Oregon.

heavily emphasized animal production. One result was that beef cattle became the number one agricultural product of the State in dollar returns in 1954.

Klamath County in 1924 did not produce the potatoes its population consumed. Yet farmers on the irrigation projects that account for the county's cropland urgently needed a cash crop other than alfalfa hay. A group met with the county agent to consider the wisdom of growing potatoes. At hand was the California market, recently joined by a shortcut railroad line and geared to receipts from irrigated areas much similar in soil and climate—but hundreds of miles farther away. The decision was to proceed. A carload of certified seed was brought in by one of the banks. County Agent C. A. Henderson was asked to establish cooperative trials of time and rate of planting, time and methods of irrigation, and fertilizer requirements and to keep up to the minute on harvesting and storage methods. These were carefully followed through year after year and progressively fixed sound methods. The new venture expanded continuously. In the midforties, annual shipments from the Klamath Basin—Klamath County and the northern edges of two California counties—had reached 12,500 carloads. The crop has brought a 10-year average of nearly 10 million dollars to the farmers to add to the tally for the State. This was not hit-or-miss farming. No overly optimistic pronouncements or land-boom dreams did all this in Klamath County. Instead, it was well-thought-out plans studiously and cooperatively and continuously applied that rang the bell. A market had been reviewed; physical resources as to climate, soil, and water had been appraised. From the first carload of seed, the sciences related to potato production had been canvassed and then applied. Mr. Henderson did not do all of these things as an isolated worker. He called upon the State Extension specialists in crop production, pathology, agricultural engineering, and soils in working out his demonstration program. Officials of the Reclamation Service and staff members of the Department of Agriculture were involved in the planning.

Meanwhile, the home demonstration agents organized programs of teaching in technologies applicable to the home. Family economics, home management, family life, health and safety, conservation, and citizenship were included in the county programs, besides projects in nutrition, clothing, and work simplification. A feature here was the organization of 700 study groups, which meet regularly 8 or 9 months of the year. The leaders comprise the County Home Extension Council, which leads in deciding the county programs. These study groups, which number 21,500 women, may include such groups as beginning homemakers, working wives and mothers, and young parents. Men and women participate together in many of the projects. These study club members number no more than half of the women reached by the home agent's teaching program. Some programs initiated and first advanced by these groups reach additional hundreds. Also cooperation is given to appropriate programs of other groups. In one county, for example, the home economics agent carries on a weekly radio program, gives appropriate service to the county safety organization, works with the home interest angles of civil defense, leads home interest features of the county fair, is an important consultant for the welfare program, and carries on a program with the women of the Junior Chamber of Commerce. Still further, she managed a winter-long group of 200 in family finance, held countywide meetings on care and cookery of game meats in the fall, and at Christmas reached 500 homemakers in a series of meetings on holiday foods.

Thus the Extension Service has made substantial, measurable progress toward achieving the basic goal—helping rural people— that was envisioned in the legislation establishing this cooperative educational enterprise: "To aid in diffusing among the people of the United States, useful and practical information in subjects relating to agriculture and home economics, and to encourage the application of the same." As Extension work was accepted more widely, more leadership from the college was required. In Oregon, for example, assistant directors of Extension do these things: Supervise specialists; recruit and train county and State staff members; maintain close working relationships with Federal and State agencies with overlapping fields; and work with special groups, such as civil defense, fire prevention, health organizations, and country pastors. Technical home economics is headed by a home economist, who serves as coordinator of all technical home economics work, directs specialists, and recruits all women personnel. A leader of 4-H Club work is chairman of the central office group that assists the county Extension agents with youth programs.

For closer contacts with local people, the counties have been divided into districts, with an agriculturist and home economist assigned to each. These field teams maintain cooperation with county governments, assist county Extension agents with their programs, and represent administration in all appropriate matters. Functions of the central administrative group, headed by the Director of Extension, are to establish and then guide the program in agriculture and home economics and related subjects. This includes establishing adequate budgets, recruiting competent staff, managing personnel, and maintaining a public information program. Most important of all is keeping a balance among these functions. A high level of competence in the staff is a first requirement. Once this is accomplished, financing becomes relatively easy, because people support a helpful program cooperatively decided and carried on by persons in whom they have confidence. *(Frank L. Ballard)*

Facts for People

GETTING FACTS about agriculture to the people who want them has been a basic part of the work of the Department of Agriculture since it began. The law signed by President Lincoln in 1862 directed the Department to "acquire and diffuse among the people of the United States useful information on subjects connected with agriculture." The phrase "among the people" was prophetic. The Department's work and information activity were geared in the beginning to the needs of farm people, but as the work grew from the conduct of research and the collection of statistics of crops and livestock to include educational, regulatory, service, conservation, credit, and action programs, its functions have come to touch the lives of people in the United States and in many foreign lands. Information therefore goes not only to the man behind the plow. It goes also to the people who process, market, and transport the food and fiber he produces and to consumers who eat and wear his products.

The importance of making agricultural information public and useful was recognized in formation of the progenitor of the present Office of Information. The first Secretary of Agriculture in 1889 set up a section of Records and Editing in the Department's Division of Statistics. Secretary Coleman said in his first annual report: "The very essence of the duties developing on this Department of the Government is that its results shall be made promptly available to the public by a comprehensive scheme for publication. Time and expense, ability and experience, lavished on the work of this Department can have no practical results unless we can lay their conclusions promptly before the people who need them." Farmers' Bulletin No. 1, "The What and Why of Agricultural Experiment Stations," in June of 1889 began the oldest continuous series of publications devoted to the purpose outlined by Secretary Coleman.

Publications still are a mainstay, but new ways come into use when their value is proved. The Department in 1912 became the first executive Department to establish an exhibit organization to take information to farm people at fairs and meetings. An office was established in 1913 to enable the Department to make more materials available to the press. Today an average of 3,600 press releases are issued a year, but an aim of the 1913 effort was to furnish two articles weekly to news syndicates, which supplied material in plate form to rural newspapers. The Department set up the first governmental motion picture operation in 1912. The Secretary of Agriculture at that time declared that the motion picture was "a work of the devil, a disreputable medium of expression." When he was enticed to see himself addressing a visiting group of corn club boys—photographed without his knowledge—he was amazed and delighted, however. From that moment, the Department's motion picture program became a going enterprise.

The enlarging activities of the Department and new methods of disseminating information sharpened the need for more effective direction and administration. To that end, the Office of Information was established in 1925. A radio service was added in 1926. The Motion Picture and the Exhibits Services became part of the Office of Information in 1942. In 1953, after some years of experimentation, a television service was initiated. The following year brought the production of all visual work to the central Office. Thus, through a process of evolution, the Office now includes facilities capable of meeting in all media the need of the Department to get information to all the people.

At the same time, a national agricultural communications network gradually came into being. Within the Department, the network begins with the information work that is carried on jointly by the Office of Information and the information staffs of the Department's agencies. The Office guides and directs the total information effort of the Department. It offers a number of services to the agencies, such as a point of contact and the distribution of materials to press, radio, and television; broad editing and policy guidance for publications; and production of visual materials—films, exhibits, arts and graphics, and photographs. A vital part is the information activities carried on in cooperation with the land-grant institutions. Information prepared by the Department is sent to the colleges through the Federal Extension Service for adaptation to local conditions and for distribution with their own materials based on research in the States. Another link is the agricultural industries that produce equipment and materials for farmers to use or that handle the products farmers produce. Through these outlets, much information is made available through trade publications, commercial information channels, trade associations, farm advertising, local dealers, and others. Through farm organizations and cooperatives, whose activities in behalf of their farmer members make them large users of Department-originated information, another way is provided to reach nearly every farm family in the United States. Cooperation is the key in all this: No group or agency dictates to another, for all depend on each other in carrying out their common task of keeping the public informed about agriculture, its achievements, and services.

The Department normally has about 4 thousand publications listed as available. They include farmers' bulletins, popular leaflets, and publications designed for use of farmers, homemakers, and consumers and technical or semitechnical bulletins for use as professional references or to carry out Government programs. About 600 of the publications are popular bulletins designed for use of farmers and homemakers. About 35 million copies of Department publications are distributed each year. By law, 80 percent of the farmers' bulletins are distributed by members of the Congress. A special listing of popular, up-to-date bulletins is made periodically for Congressmen to send to their constituents. Another 4 million copies are distributed by county agricultural agents and other State Extension offices. The Office of Information distributes an additional million copies to answer individual requests, and Department agencies usually use about 500 thousand copies in the course of carrying out their programs. Some publications are free. Others are sold by the

Publications were the first means of letting people know about developments in agriculture and the Department of Agriculture, and they remain the backbone of information work. The publications, which deal with many subjects pertaining to farming, gardening, homemaking, and so on, are available through members of the Congress, the Office of Information of the Department of Agriculture, and sometimes (as here) at exhibits.

Catherine A. Nawn, meat specialist in the Agricultural Marketing Service, illustrates the grades of meat and their use at a Department exhibit at the International Livestock Show in Chicago.

Superintendent of Documents, the Government Printing Office, Washington 25, D.C. To keep the materials up to date, 300 to 400 new publications are issued each year, and about 40 publications undergo revision.

In working with the public media (newspapers, radio, and television news outlets), the Department makes information freely available to all. Information of current interest is prepared in forms that will be useful to newspapers, magazines, and other publications. Writers, editors, and others come to the Department to obtain prepared information or to interview administrators and specialists. A prime source of information, particularly about policies, is the Secretary of Agriculture. A chief means of obtaining his views are his news conferences, which press, radio, and television news correspondents attend and report.

Many of the 9 thousand weekly newspapers published in the United States receive information from the Department through the State Agricultural Extension editors at land-grant institutions, who adapt and reissue the information. The Department reaches the

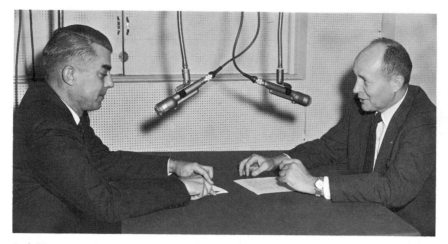

Jack Towers, radio specialist in the Department, interviews Howard P. Davis, Director of the Food Distribution Division, Agricultural Marketing Service, on the progress of the Food Stamp Plan, which was initiated experimentally in 1961, for Agri-Tape, a recorded weekly radio service for about 325 stations.

Inga Rundvold, who presents a women's show, "Inga's Angle," on WRC–TV, Washington, and Edith T. Swing, a radio and television specialist in the Department of Agriculture, discuss and demonstrate the uses of dry milk.

1,800 daily newspapers through the national news wire services, which cover the Department daily from the Department's press-room, and through other Washington correspondents. A weekly Farm Paper Letter and specialized services prepared especially for the farm press summarize developments in the Department. Close working relationships are maintained with two associations repre-senting the farm press—the Newspaper Farm Editors Association and the American Association of Agricultural Editors (farm maga zines). The newspaper farm editors reach about 10 million readers; the 150 farm magazines have a readership of about 22 million. Food and Home Notes, also weekly, is designed to meet the needs of more than a thousand editors of women's pages, food editors of newspapers and magazines, and directors of women's radio and tele-vision programs. Information of interest to homemakers and consumers is stressed, including such subjects as foods plentiful on the market, nutrition, clothing, and home management. News releases also are prepared weekly for the Negro press, which com-prises about 175 publications.

Many radio and television stations have people trained in agricul-ture who present programs for farm and city people. Most of them are members of the National Association of Radio and Television Farm Directors, and they have millions of listeners. Weekly tape-recorded services of the Department are used by about 425 stations and cover news and features of national and regional interest. Tele-vision stations are served with specially prepared package features made up of film clips, still photographs, slides, and other artwork and scripts. Occasionally newsreel-type films report on new develop-ments. These are designed for use within regularly scheduled live programs of interest to farmers and consumers, and reach an esti-mated 10 million viewers via about 300 stations. News and fea-tures are furnished weekly to two radio network outlets—the NBC Farm Review over the National Broadcasting Company and the American Farmer, produced cooperatively by the Department and the American Broadcasting Company. Radio material is regularly supplied also to the Mutual Broadcasting System and the Columbia Broadcasting System.

The Department makes and issues motion picture films that touch on almost every phase of American agriculture. Films that inform or instruct cover scientific discoveries and program activities. A few examples: In a nationwide program to eradicate brucellosis, "Back the Attack on Brucellosis;" in the continuing fight against plant pests, "Fire Ant on Trial;" in the effort to modernize rural America, "The REA Story;" in the multiple use of forest resources, "The Forest;" in watershed management, "Waters of Coweeta;" in agricultural economics, "Compass for Agriculture;" in conservation in the Great Plains, "The Dust is Dying." Usually

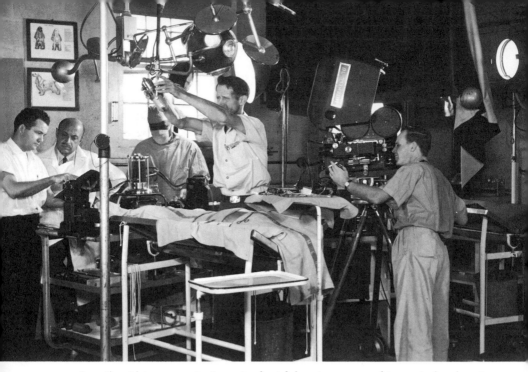

A motion picture crew prepares to shoot laboratory scenes of two veterinarians performing an operation on a dog in a film concerned with veterinary work. About 60 new agricultural films are produced by the Department annually. The crew includes (left) Homer Boor, Joseph J. Sanders, Jr., and Richard Milstead.

Secretary of Agriculture Orville L. Freeman at a news conference in his office in Washington gives press, radio, and television news correspondents—and, through them, people throughout the country—an opportunity to obtain information.

about 300 film titles are included in a catalog listing their availability. About 60 new films are made each year. For television programs, films that run up to 13.5 and 27.5 minutes are replacing the one- and two-reelers, and most films are cleared for television use. TV shorts, 10 to 60 seconds long, announce anything from currently plentiful foods to recommended agricultural practices. The Department's films are seen by millions of persons. The Department maintains a supply of films in Washington that are available on request and are listed in a catalog. Seventy film libraries, most of them at land-grant institutions, receive and distribute prints to county agents, schools, and other outlets in all States.

Exhibits are used at State fairs, conventions, field days, shopping centers, farm-and-home weeks, conferences, and other places to inform rural and urban audiences about agriculture. The exhibits tell the story of agriculture in dimension. They range broadly in size and cover subjects of current interest. Some exhibits are made for easy transportation from place to place and so can be seen at local meetings, in window displays, and as TV background. Others are of a size for display at fairs and conventions and for major displays at large expositions in the United States and abroad. Exhibits are shown in the Department's buildings in Washington or are distributed through arrangements with the agencies of the State Agricultural Extension Services. They have come to be important in the promotion of foreign trade. Some recent major exhibits in which the Department has participated include the Eleventh World Poultry Congress in Mexico City; the First World Agricultural Fair in New Delhi, India; International Agricultural Exhibition in Cairo, Egypt; World Forestry Congress in Seattle; and several agricultural trade shows, such as the British Food Fair in London.

Of great service in all this work are broadscale information "campaigns," art and graphics facilities, which support many types of information activities, and a photographic library, which makes subject-matter pictures available to editors and writers and has on file about 100 thousand prints.

All segments I have mentioned perform a useful and efficient service to the public. A new aspect has been emerging, however, of which we must be mindful: Even more vital in the future will be the service that information must do to interpret agriculture to the people who live in our towns and cities. At the end of the Department's first century, our farm people represent about 9 percent of our total population, a fact that has broad implications from the standpoint of the support and understanding that agriculture must have from labor, industry, and the general public. Information work in the future will have the obligation to tell about the problems of agriculture, its status in our economy, and its contribution to the health and welfare of all people. *(Harold R. Lewis)*

The National Agricultural Library

THE FIRST Commissioner of Agriculture outlined seven primary programs for the new Department. One was to establish an agricultural library that would "form a rich mine of knowledge," with publications accumulated through exchange, gifts, and purchase. The blessing of the Commissioner, an appropriation of 4 thousand dollars, and the transfer of the agricultural collection from the Patent Office brought into being the Library of the Department of Agriculture.

The published information it has collected provides the Department and the Nation with the literature of agriculture and the related sciences. The publications are in many forms—reports, books, journal articles, pamphlets, theses, translations, and microfilms, gathered from all the world. It is essentially a special collection in that it is devoted to the field of agriculture in its broadest sense. It specializes in the utilitarian rather than the rare—yet it has some very valuable rare publications. Among its holdings are fine collections of nursery and seed trade catalogs and stock, herd, and stud books. It has become known and serves as the National Agricultural Library. As a national library, it is a library of last resort in the field of agriculture in this country for libraries, scientists, and economists and the general public. As a Department library, its services are available to all Department employees. Almost half of the collection comprises publications from countries other than the United States. The need for scientific knowledge on a worldwide basis has resulted in active participation by members of the library staff in international organizations.

A main Department Library has existed since 1862. A system of bureau libraries closely connected with the main library was in effect from the early 1900's until 1942, when all libraries and all units of the Department that were providing library and bibliographical services were consolidated and transferred to the supervision and direction of the Department Librarian. Service to the field staff was expanded through branch and subbranch libraries and small station collections of library materials, including contractual service provided by five land-grant university libraries in the 1950's. The organization was again changed in 1959 by the cancellation of the contractual arrangements and the transfer of the six field branch libraries and a number of "station collections" to agency adminis-

The card catalog is a guide to the million-plus books in the Department's Library.

tration. The Director of the Library became responsible for the general direction and supervision of all library services in the Department and for the administration of all Department libraries in and near Washington. The system comprises the main Library, the Law Library, the Bee Culture Library, the Beltsville Library, and a number of agency libraries, which serve the Department's research laboratories and other groups of Department scientists at various field installations.

The Library has explored new and more efficient methods for acquiring, cataloging, and classifying its wide variety of publications and in making its information available. It began the printing of catalog cards for Department publications and making them available to other libraries in 1899. The Library of Congress took over this responsibility in 1902. The Library's cataloging is still being made available to libraries through the Library of Congress' AGR series of printed cards and through publication in the National Union Catalog.

It pioneered in the use of photocopies of library materials in lieu of loan of the originals. The Library was chosen by the American Documentation Institute in 1934 to serve as "the first experimental center for supplying microfilm and photocopy of articles on a large scale to all scientific workers." The Bibliofilm Service that was set up was later absorbed by the Copying Section of the Library. This service is part of the Library's Division of Lending. The development by Ralph R. Shaw, who was Librarian from 1940 to 1954, of a photocopying machine that uses a continuous-roll process enabled the Library to provide photoprints more cheaply. An experimental machine he developed was a forerunner of information storage and retrieval machines. Another of his improvements, the Photoclerk, an adaptation of his earlier photographic charging machine, uses photographic processes to replace manual typing procedures. The original handmade machine, built by Henry L. Flemer, of the

The Library—known as the National Agricultural Library—has 12.06 miles of bookstacks.

Library staff, according to Dr. Shaw's specifications, is still in use alongside a factory-made model.

The Bibliography of Agriculture is the chief device used to inform the Library's users of published material, including journal articles, numbered bulletins, and others, currently received in the Library. The Bibliography, issued monthly since 1942, is an index to the world literature on agriculture. Items are classified under broad subjects. Indexes of authors accompany the issues for January through October. The December issue is devoted to annual author and subject indexes. Useful features are the lists of publications of the Department, State agricultural experiment stations, State Extension Services, and the Food and Agriculture Organization. The bibliography supersedes and is an expansion of certain current lists, such as "Agricultural Economics Literature" and "Plant Science Literature," issued before July 1942 by the former Bureau libraries, and "Agricultural Library Notes," issued by the Department Library from 1926 through June 1942. From time to time the Library also has published informational lists, bulletins, accession lists, and so on. Over the years, too, the Library has compiled and issued bibliographies on specific subjects. These have appeared in various forms—Bibliographical Contributions, Agency publications, Library Lists, Miscellaneous Publications, Bibliographical Bulletins—but, however issued, were compiled to fill a definite need and usually in response to a specific request. The bibliographies cover a variety of subjects.

To attain a century is a distinction for any individual or institution, and the Library is proud of its age and its accomplishments. From a small collection transferred from the Patent Office, the Library has become one of the largest agricultural collections in the world and a rich mine of knowledge. It is rich also in the quality and the spirit of service displayed by its staff. It is rich in friendships with other libraries. Like other libraries, it has not been able to acquire all of the publications in its field of responsibility nor to meet all of the demands for service. Even more challenging is the outlook for the coming years, when there will be specialized needs of an age of space and automation and the constantly increasing flow of scientific publications. It hopes to serve better the Department of Agriculture and the Nation by obtaining adequate facilities to house its staff, collection, and patrons, by acquiring a more comprehensive collection of materials in the Department's subject fields, by further perfecting its publications exchange activities, by continuing its leadership in national and international cooperation among agricultural librarians, and by searching for the most effective and quickest method of acquainting and providing research workers with the published literature in the field of agriculture and the related sciences. *(Louise O. Bercaw)*

Books for Farm People

IT'S BEEN A LONG TIME since I've heard anyone use the term "book farmer," in which phrase "practical" farmers used to wrap up a measure of amusement or pity or suspicion for those whose operations were based on something other than habit or local custom or by-guess-and-by-gosh. Not that all farmers—or other persons—necessarily read more books now; that is a point we do not need to explore here. Rather, an awareness has grown among farmers (and other citizens) in this age of science that reading helps one do more things better, that books are practical tools, that the printed word deepens the meaning of life and work. Besides, farmers and their families can easily get books now; that is my point here, and an egregious one. To me, who admits to some bias in the matter, it is the outstanding development in the past century in rural America. Let him who challenges my enthusiasm wait with some small boy and his sister and maybe his father and mother for the arrival of the bookmobile at the general store near Norden, Nebraska, which is 49 miles from the closest library; or at Burton Crossroads, 37 miles from a city; or the one-room schoolhouse at Pony Lake. Let him see their anticipation of the joys it carries. Let him hear their excited, "Here comes the library!" Let him think of what books mean to those who thirst for the knowledge and pleasures in books but who until now had no books. Then he will get an idea of the importance of the Library Services Act, which made this possible.

Members of the Congress and of the American Library Association and all of us who live in the country had been aware of the lag in the development of library service to rural areas, especially in States where distances are great, population is sparse, and transportation is difficult. We all worked for it. We had the untiring leadership of Senator Lister Hill of Alabama. The Congress in 1956 enacted the Library Services Act, which provides funds to help States develop methods of bringing library services to residents of small towns, villages, and farming communities which are without such service. That was done by appropriations to the agencies of State Governments, which had been established as early as the 1890's to extend public library services and to improve public libraries already established, State library commissions, or library extension departments in State libraries.

Rock County Library in Bassett, northern Nebraska.

One of them is the Nebraska Public Library Commission. Our experience in the Commission is typical of what has happened in many States. It began to give direct library service to farm families and communities in 1901. All the service was by mail, and it did meet the needs of many citizens. We still have in our files a letter from a boy, who wrote: "What must I do to get a book? I have never seen any farm books, though I have read some papers. I should like to borrow something to help me prepare for agricultural college, especially something about increasing the fertility of

Extension Club No. 4 meets for book reviews and coffee in the South Central Regional Demonstration Library, Holdrege, Nebr.

Farmers and townspeople visit an art exhibit in the library in Holdrege.

"All mine for three whole weeks!" said Eddie Guy Bantam, District 60, Harlan County, Nebraska.

Sand delays for a little while the Rock County bookmobile, which Mrs. Velma Kaufman drives.

Mud, snow, rain, sand, or ice or gloom of night cannot keep bookmobiles from their appointed rounds in rural Nebraska.

the soil in the Sandhills, stock judging, hog raising, and tree planting." A farm wife, who had to count her pennies, even for postage, once wrote us: "Please send me five pounds of Shakespeare." We got many other letters from fathers and mothers, who would tell us about their children, their changing interests, and their progress in school. We came to think of them as friends and of ourselves as guides and mentors, but we knew this service by mail was not enough. We knew also that the town libraries that the Commission had helped to establish could not reach all Nebraskans, even though many of the libraries in the small communities extended their services to the surrounding trade area.

Among those who shared our hopes and impatience at the slow progress in taking libraries to rural Nebraska were farm organizations, especially the Agricultural Extension Service and the Home Extension Clubs. The latter, working with the Nebraska Public Library Commission in the late thirties, obtained grants from the Works Progress Administration for a few demonstrations of county library service. They, the Agricultural Extension Service, and the Commission in 1937 initiated training courses for 15 thousand reading-leaders. Books for the courses were supplied by local libraries and the Commission. The second year 25 thousand readers were enrolled. Each participant was asked to read at least six books and to choose them from three or more categories—home economics, biography, travel, history, fiction, and children's books. Keen enthusiasm for reading developed in many of the Home Extension Clubs, and the reading programs of the clubs expanded, especially after a Conference on Rural Reading, sponsored by the Department of Agriculture in Washington in 1951, gave a new impetus to such interests throughout the country.

One outgrowth was that two statewide reading conferences, sponsored by the Agricultural Extension Service and the Nebraska Public Library Commission and attended by the chairmen of the clubs' reading committees, were conducted. Their comments afterwards attested their gratitude. One wrote: "I graduated from high school in 1935 and could not go to college. Much of the lack of formal education is being made up for me because there are wonderful people like you—who care!" Another wrote: "Thank you for the privilege of attending the Rural Reading Conference. The speakers were wonderful and certainly gave us ideas to start the wheels rolling." A third: "The Rural Reading Conference was interesting, enjoyable, and certainly a most enlightening experience. I only hope that I can make progress in my county in order to show my appreciation and sincere belief in the goals you are trying to attain." Thus uncounted farm families have been encouraged to read more. They have come to understand the need for more and better libraries. Their desire to continue their education has grown, and so have their horizons, as we see in their letters that ask for information on estate and tax planning, area representation, Einstein's theory, Victorian jewelry, and a host of other subjects big and small that pertain to the world beyond their fence lines.

Funds from the Library Services Act have helped the Public Library Commission, in cooperation with the Home Extension Clubs, to carry on demonstrations of extended service with bookmobiles and larger units of service. An example is the South Central Regional Demonstration Library. From headquarters in Holdrege, it serves three counties and several municipalities in two adjoining counties. To a population of 26,337 in an area of 1,770 square miles, its bookmobile brings the same reading materials to rural homes as to those who live in town and so gives equal advantages to all. I think often of three farm boys in rural grade schools in Harlan County. From the bookmobile they borrowed

The staff of Nebraska Public Library Commission includes (seated, left to right) Dorothy Lessenhop, Margaret Richmond, Harriet Clark, Helen Dvoracek, and (standing) Louise A. Nixon, the Executive Secretary.

Story hour.

Books in Braille and Talking Books are sent from the Library Commission in Lincoln by Mrs. Flora Sams and Frank Hemphill.

science books. In their homes, one began experiments in chemistry, one in shortwave radio, and one in electronics. They soon moved beyond the resources of the Regional Library; then the librarian got books for them on an interlibrary loan from the Nebraska Public Library Commission and finally through the cooperative services of the University of Nebraska Library. A generation ago that would not have been possible.

From the little town of Bassett in northern Nebraska, far away from a metropolitan center, the red and white bookmobile travels to towns, community centers, and rural schools in Brown, Keya Paha, and Rock Counties. It carries 1,800 books—novels, children's books, books about philosophy, religion, science, gardening, art, literature, travel, history, biography. Children and adults in the sparsely populated area of 3 thousand square miles watch for it and the treasures it brings to their doorstep. Families who live miles from its route gather at one or another of the stops to choose books to read in the next 3 weeks. Any book they want that is not on the truck is obtained from another library or from the Commission and brought out on the next run. Patrons often write the librarians beforehand to ask that certain books be brought on the next visit. Don't think for a minute that the books they borrow and read are books only about silage and sheep and farm management and such. They have wide interests, and their requests are of just as great a range as are those made of a library in a city. They read carefully and critically—and thankfully. Thus, through wind, rain, and snow—over paved roads, gravel roads, and sandhill trails—bookmobiles take the wonderful world of books, friendship, and guidance of the librarians to rural residents of Nebraska. The Commission still sends large loans of books by mail to small public libraries, reading clubs, and rural schools. Small loans of books are made to individuals. Films are available for adult groups and children's films for story hours. Books in Braille and Talking Books are available to 885 blind persons in all parts of the State.

Much remains to be accomplished in Nebraska. Six counties had no public libraries within their boundaries in 1962. In many other counties, the local library service is inadequate. The 37 thousand women who are members of the Nebraska Council of Home Extension Clubs requested that a professional survey of public library service be made. The Commission and the Nebraska Library Association began such a study at once so that the findings and recommendations could be used as the basis for further library development in the State. With assurance I can repeat the words of the first Secretary of the Nebraska Public Library Commission, who wrote in 1904: "The future of the work is magnificent and inspiring and has no limits save the boundaries of Nebraska." *(Louise A. Nixon)*

Significant Books About Agriculture

THIS LIST was compiled by Elizabeth Gould Davis, bibliographer in the Library of the Department of Agriculture, with the advice and assistance of many members of the Department staff. It is not intended to be a list of the "best" books on agriculture; rather, it is a view of the agricultural literature published in the United States in 1860–1960. Books were chosen for inclusion on the basis of their influence on the agriculture of their day, the importance of the authors, or their lasting qualities. Federal and State Government publications were omitted.

Circa 1860. RUFFIN, EDMUND: *An Essay on Calcareous Manures,* edition 5, 493 pages, Richmond, Va.; J. W. Randolph. 1852. (First edition, 1832, reprinted 1961.)

1860. HILGARD, E. W.: *Report on the Geology and Agriculture of the State of Mississippi,* 391 pages, Jackson, Miss.; Barksdale.

1862. EMERSON, GEORGE B., and FLINT, CHARLES L.: *Manual of Agriculture for the School, the Farm and the Fireside,* 306 pages, Boston; Swan, Brewer and Tileston.

1862. GRAY, ASA: *Manual of the Botany of the Northern United States Including Virginia, Kentucky and all East of the Mississippi,* edition 3 revised, 606 pages, New York; Ivison, Phinney and Co. (First edition, 1848; Eighth edition, 1950.)

1863. JOHNSON, SAMUEL W.: *How Crops Grow, a Treatise on the Chemical Composition, Structure and Life of the Plant,* 394 pages, New York; Orange Judd Co. (Fourth edition, 1911.)

1863. RANDALL, HENRY S.: *The Practical Shepherd, a Complete Treatise on the Breeding, Management and Diseases of Sheep,* edition 31, 452 pages, New York; American News Co. (First edition, 1832.)

1864. FLINT, CHARLES L.: *Milch Cows and Dairy Farming,* new edition, 426 pages, Boston; Crosby and Nichols. (First edition, 1858; Third edition, 1889.)

1865. FRENCH, HENRY F.: *Farm Drainage; the Principles, Processes, and Effects of Draining Land,* 384 pages, New York; Orange Judd Co. (Third edition, 1884.)

1865. YOUMANS, EDWARD L.: *The Hand-Book of Household Science; a Popular Account of Heat, Light, Air, Aliment, and Cleansing, in their Scientific Principles and Domestic Applications,* 470 pages, New York; D. Appleton and Co.

1867. WARING, GEORGE E.: *Draining for Profit and Draining for Health,* 244 pages, New York; Orange Judd Co.

1868. ALLEN, LEWIS F.: *American Cattle: Their History, Breeding and Management,* 528 pages, New York; Orange Judd Co.

1868. HOOPES, JOSIAH: *The Book of Evergreens, a Practical Treatise on the Coniferae, or Cone-Bearing Plants,* 435 pages, New York; Orange Judd Co.

1868. THOMAS, JOHN J.: *Farm Implements and Farm Machinery, and the Principles of Their Construction and Use,* 302 pages, New York; Orange Judd Co.

1868. WARING, GEORGE E.: *The Elements of Agriculture,* edition 2, 251 pages, New York; Orange Judd Co. (First edition, 1855.)

1870. HARRIS, JOSEPH: *Harris on the Pig; Breeding, Rearing, Management, and Improvement,* 250 pages, New York; Orange Judd Co. (Third edition, 1889.)

1870. JOHNSON, SAMUEL W.: *How Crops Feed; a Treatise on the Atmosphere and the Soil As Related to the Nutrition of Agricultural Plants,* 375 pages, New York; Orange Judd Co.

1871. BRYANT, ARTHUR, SR.: *Forest Trees for Shelter, Ornament and Profit,* 247 pages, New York; Henry T. Williams.

1872. ALLEN, LEWIS F.: *History of the Short-Horn Cattle; Their Origin, Progress and Present Condition,* 266 pages, Buffalo, N.Y.; The Author.

1873. MARTIN, EDWARD WINSLOW: *History of the Grange Movement; or, the Farmer's War Against Monopolies: Being a Full and Authentic Account of the Struggles of the American Farmers Against the Extortions of the Railroad Companies; with a History of the Rise and Progress of the Order of Patrons of Husbandry, Its Object, Present Condition and Prospects; to Which Is Added Sketches of the Leading Grangers,* 539 pages, Philadelphia; National Publishing Co.

1875. HENDERSON, PETER: *Gardening for Pleasure; a Guide to the Amateur in the Fruit, Vegetable, and Flower Garden, with Full Directions for the Greenhouse, Conservatory, and Window Garden,* 250 pages, New York; Orange Judd Co.

1875. KELLEY, O. H.: *Origin and Progress of the Order of the Patrons of Husbandry in the United States; a History from 1866 to 1873,* 441 pages, Philadelphia; J. A. Wagenseller.

1878. HARRIS, JOSEPH: *Talks on Manures,* 356 pages, New York; Orange Judd Co. (Second edition, 1883.)

1879. ALLEN, RICHARD L.: *The New American Farm Book, Revised and Enlarged by Lewis F. Allen,* 526 pages, New York; Orange Judd Co. (Third edition, 1888.)

1881. HALSTED, BYRON DAVID: *Barn Plans and Outbuildings,* 235 pages, New York; Orange Judd Co. (Fifth edition, 1917.)

1882. FLINT, CHARLES L.: *The American Farmer; a Complete Agricultural Library,* with Useful Facts for the Household, Devoted to Farming in All Its Departments and Details, etc. etc.,* 2 volumes, Hartford, Conn.; R. H. Park and Co.

1884. CROZIER, WILLIAM, and HENDERSON, PETER: *How the Farm Pays; the Experience of Forty Years of Successful Farming and Gardening,* 400 pages, New York; Henderson and Co.

1884. FULLER, ANDREW: *Practical Forestry; a Treatise on the Propagation, Planting, and Cultivation, with a Description, and the Botanical and Popular Names of All the Indigenous Trees of the United States,* 299 pages, New York; Orange Judd Co.

1886. RICHARDS, ELLEN H.: *Food Materials and Their Adulterations,* 183 pages, Boston; Estes and Lauriat. (Third edition, 1906.)

1887. SANDERS, JAMES H.: *The Breeds of Live Stock and the Principles of Heredity,* 480 pages, Chicago; J. H. Sanders Publishing Co.

1888. COMSTOCK, JOHN HENRY: *An Introduction to Entomology,* 234 pages, Ithaca, N.Y.; Comstock Publishing Associates. (Ninth edition, 1940.)

1889. BAILEY, LIBERTY HYDE: *The Horticulturist's Rule-Book, a Compendium of Useful Information for Fruit-Growers, Truck-Gardeners, Florists and Others,* 236 pages, New York; Garden Publishing Co. (Nineteenth edition, 1917.)

1891. ATKINSON, EDWARD, and RICHARDS, ELLEN H.: *The Science of Nutrition,* 146 pages, Springfield, Mass.; Clark W. Bryan and Co. (Tenth edition, 1896.)

1895. WILCOX, LUTE: *Irrigation Farming; a Handbook for the Practical Application of Water in the Production of Crops,* 311 pages, New York; Orange Judd Co. (Fourth edition, 1913.)

1896. CAMPBELL, HELEN: *Household Economics,* 290 pages, New York; G. P. Putnam's Sons.

1897. HAMMOND, M. B.: *The Cotton Industry; an Essay in American Economic History,* 382 pages, New York; Macmillan Co. (American Economic Association Publication, number 1.)

1897. KING, FRANKLIN HIRAM: *The Soil; Its Nature, Relations, and Fundamental Principles of Management,* 303 pages, New York; Macmillan Co. (Sixth edition, 1914.)

1897. ROBERTS, ISAAC P.: *The Fertility of the Land; a Summary Sketch of the Relationship of Farm Practice to the Maintaining and Increasing of the Productivity of the Soil,* 415 pages, New York; Macmillan Co. (Eleventh edition, 1909.)

1898. HENRY, WILLIAM A.: *Feeds and Feeding, a Handbook for the Student and Stockman,* 657 pages, Madison, Wis.: The Author. (Twenty-second edition, by Frank B. Morrison, 1956.)

1898. HOLLAND, W. J.: *The Butterfly Book,* 382 pages, New York; Doubleday and McClure Co. (Latest edition, 1931.)

1899. SNYDER, HARRY: *The Chemistry of Soils and Fertilizers,* 277 pages, Easton, Pa.; Chemical Publishing Co.

1900. BAILEY, LIBERTY HYDE, editor: *Cyclopedia of American Horticulture; Comprising Suggestions for Cultivation of Horticultural Plants, Descriptions of the Species of Fruits, Vegetables, Flowers, and Ornamental Plants, etc.,* 4 volumes, New York; Macmillan Co.

1900. FAIRCHILD, GEORGE T.: *Rural Wealth and Welfare: Economic Principles Illustrated and Applied to Farm Life,* 381 pages, New York; Macmillan Co.

1900. KING, FRANKLIN HIRAM: *A Text Book on the Physics of Agriculture,* 524 pages, Madison, Wis.; The Author. (Sixth edition, 1914.)

1901. SHAW, THOMAS: *Animal Breeding,* 406 pages, New York; Orange Judd Co. (Second edition, 1907.)

1903. SNYDER, HARRY B.: *The Chemistry of Plant and Animal Life,* 406 pages, Easton, Pa.; Chemical Publishing Co. (Third edition, 1913.)

1905. BEACH, SPENCER A.: *The Apples of New York,* 2 volumes, Albany, N.Y.; J. B. Lyon.

1905. TAYLOR, HENRY C.: *An Introduction to the Study of Agricultural Economics,* 327 pages, New York; Macmillan Co.

1906. HILGARD, E. W.: *Soils; Their Formation, Properties, Composition, and Relations to Climate and Plant Growth in the Humid and Arid Regions,* 593 pages, New York; Macmillan Co.

1907. BUTTERFIELD, KENYON L.: *Chapters in Rural Progress,* 251 pages, Chicago; University of Chicago Press.

1909. BAILEY, LIBERTY HYDE: *Cyclopedia of American Agriculture; a Popular Survey of Agricultural Conditions, Practices and Ideals in the United States and Canada,* 4 volumes, New York; Macmillan Co.

1910. HOPKINS, CYRIL G.: *Soil Fertility and Permanent Agriculture,* 653 pages, Boston; Ginn and Co.

1910. VAN HISE, CHARLES R.: *The Conservation of Natural Resources in the United States,* 413 pages, New York; Macmillan Co.

1910. WHEELER, W. M.: *Ants; Their Structure, Development and Behavior,* 663 pages, New York; Columbia University Press.

1911. CARVER, THOMAS NIXON: *Principles of Rural Economics,* 386 pages, Boston; Ginn and Co.

1911. COULTER, JOHN LEE: *Cooperation Among Farmers; the Keystone of Rural Prosperity,* 281 pages, New York; Sturgis and Walton Co.

1911. SHERMAN, H. C.: *Chemistry of Food and Nutrition,* 355 pages, New York; Macmillan Co. (Eighth edition, 1952.)

1911. U.S. COUNTRY LIFE COMMISSION: *Report of the Commission on Country Life; with an Introduction by Theodore Roosevelt,* 150 pages, New York; Sturgis and Walton Co.

1912. HUNT, CAROLINE L.: *The Life of Ellen H. Richards,* 328 pages, Boston; Whitcomb and Barrows.

1913. BUCK, SOLON JUSTUS: *The Granger Movement; a Study of Agricultural Organization and Its Political, Economic and Social Manifestations, 1870–1880,* 384 pages, Cambridge, Mass.; Harvard University Press. (Harvard Historical Studies, volume 19.)

1915. HERMS, WILLIAM B.: *Medical and Veterinary Entomology; a Textbook for Use in Schools and Colleges, As Well As a Handbook for the Use of Physicians, Veterinarians and Public Health Officials,* 393 pages, New York; Macmillan Co. (Fourth edition, 1950.)

1916. WELD, L. D. H.: *The Marketing of Farm Products,* 483 pages, New York; Macmillan Co.

1918. BABCOCK, ERNEST B., and CLAUSEN, R. E.: *Genetics in Relation to Agriculture,* 673 pages, New York; McGraw-Hill Book Co. (Second edition, 1927.)

1918. GALPIN, CHARLES J.: *Rural Life,* 386 pages, New York; The Century Co.

1920. ASSOCIATION OF OFFICIAL AGRICULTURAL CHEMISTS: *Official and Tentative Methods of Analysis of the Association of Official Agricultural Chemists, with an Introduction by Harvey W. Wiley; Revised to November 1, 1919,* 417 pages, Washington, The Association. (First published in 1895 as Bulletin 46 of the U.S. Department of Agriculture Division of Chemistry.)

1920. WALLACE, HENRY AGARD: *Agricultural Prices,* 224 pages, Des Moines, Iowa; Wallace Publishing Co.

1922. PEEK, GEORGE N.: *Equality for Agriculture,* 47 pages, Washington; Harrington.

1923. CARRIER, LYMAN: *The Beginnings of Agriculture in America,* 323 pages, New York; McGraw-Hill Book Co.

1923. STEEN, HERMAN: *Cooperative Marketing: The Golden Rule in Agriculture,* 366 pages, Garden City, N.Y.; Doubleday and Co.

1924. HIBBARD, BENJAMIN H.: *A History of the Public Land Policies,* 591 pages, New York; Macmillan Co.

1925. BIDWELL, PERCY WELLS, and FALCONER, JOHN I.: *History of Agriculture in the Northern United States, 1620–1860,* 512 pages, Washington; Carnegie Institution. (Carnegie Institution of Washington, Publication 358.)

1927. BROWN, HARRY BATES: *Cotton: History, Species, Varieties, Morphology,* *Breeding, Culture, Diseases, Marketing, and Uses,* 517 pages, New York; McGraw-Hill Book Co.

1927. NOURSE, EDWIN G.: *The Legal Status of Agricultural Cooperation,* 555 pages, New York; Macmillan Co.

1927. ROSE, MARY DAVIES: *Foundations of Nutrition,* 501 pages, New York; Macmillan Co. (Fifth edition, by C. M. Taylor and G. McLeod, 1956.)

1928. METCALF, C. L., and FLINT, W. P.: *Destructive and Useful Insects,* 918 pages, New York; McGraw-Hill Book Co.

1929. BLACK, JOHN DONALD: *Agricultural Reform in the United States,* 511 pages, New York; McGraw-Hill Book Co.

1930. HUTCHINSON, WILLIAM T.: *Cyrus Hall McCormick,* 2 volumes, New York; The Century Co.

1931. HICKS, JOHN D.: *The Populist Revolt; a History of the Farmers' Alliance and the People's Party,* 473 pages, Minneapolis; University of Minnesota Press.

1931. ROGIN, LEO: *The Introduction of Farm Machinery in its Relation to the Productivity of Labor in the Agriculture of the Nineteenth Century,* 260 pages, Berkeley, Calif.; University of California Press. (University of California Publications in Economics, volume 9.)

1932. ISRAELSEN, O. W.: *Irrigation Principles and Practices,* 422 pages, New York; John Wiley and Sons. (Second edition, 1950.)

1932. SANDERSON, DWIGHT: *The Rural Community,* 723 pages, Boston; Ginn and Co.

1933. DUKES, HENRY H.: *The Physiology of Domestic Animals,* 391 pages, Ithaca, N.Y.; Comstock Publishing Associates. (Seventh edition, 1955.)

1933. GRAY, LEWIS CECIL: *History of Agriculture in the Southern United States to 1860,* 2 volumes, Washington; Carnegie Institution. (Carnegie Institution of Washington, Publication 430.)

1937. SNEDECOR, GEORGE W.: *Statistical Methods Applied to Experiments in Agriculture and Biology,* 341 pages, Ames,

Iowa; Iowa State College Press. (Fifth edition, 1956.)

1938. FAIRCHILD, DAVID: *The World Was My Garden*, 494 pages, New York; Charles Scribner's Sons.

1939. BAKER, GLADYS: *The County Agent*, 226 pages, Chicago; University of Chicago Press. (Studies in Public Administration, volume 11.)

1939. BENNETT, HUGH H.: *Soil Conservation*, 993 pages, New York; McGraw-Hill Book Co.

1940. CUMMINGS, RICHARD OSBORN: *The American and His Food; a History of Food Habits in the United States*, 267 pages, Chicago; University of Chicago Press.

1940. GAUS, JOHN M., and WOLCOTT, LEON O.: *Public Administration and the United States Department of Agriculture*, 534 pages, Chicago; Public Administration Service.

1940. ELY, RICHARD T., and WEHRWEIN, GEORGE S.: *Land Economics*, 512 pages, New York; Macmillan Co.

1943. HAGAN, WILLIAM A., and BRUNER, DORSEY W.: *The Infectious Diseases of Domestic Animals, with Special Reference to Etiology, Diagnosis, and Biologic Therapy*, 665 pages, Ithaca, N.Y.; Comstock Publishing Associates. (Fourth edition, 1961.)

1944. BROWNE, CHARLES A.: *A Source Book of Agricultural Chemistry*, 290 pages, Waltham, Mass.; Chronica Botanica Co. (Chronica Botanica, volume 8, number 4.)

1945. BAILEY, JOSEPH CANNON: *Seaman A. Knapp, Schoolmaster of American Agriculture*, 307 pages, New York; Columbia University Press.

1945. SHANNON, FRED A.: *The Farmer's Last Frontier: Agriculture, 1860–1897*, 434 pages, New York; Farrar and Rinehart. (Economic History of the United States, volume 5.)

1947. HARDING, T. SWANN: *Two Blades of Grass; a History of Scientific Development in the United States Department of Agriculture*, 352 pages, Norman, Okla.; University of Oklahoma Press.

1947. PINCHOT, GIFFORD: *Breaking New Ground*, 522 pages, New York; Harcourt Brace and Co., Inc.

1948. KILE, ORVILLE MERTON: *The Farm Bureau through Three Decades*, 416 pages, Baltimore; Waverly Press.

1949. KELSEY, LINCOLN D., and HEARNE, CANNON C.: *Cooperative Extension Work*, 424 pages, Ithaca, N.Y.; Comstock Publishing Associates.

1949. ROBERT, JOSEPH C.: *The Story of Tobacco in America*, 296 pages, New York; Alfred A. Knopf, Inc.

1949. TAYLOR, CARL C., and others: *Rural Life in the United States*, 549 pages, New York; Alfred A. Knopf, Inc.

1950. KLOSE, NELSON: *America's Crop Heritage; the History of Foreign Plant Introduction by the Federal Government*, 156 pages, Ames, Iowa; Iowa State College Press.

1951. GREELEY, WILLIAM B.: *Forests and Men*, 255 pages, Garden City, N.Y.; Doubleday and Co.

1951. WILCOX, WALTER W., and COCHRANE, WILLARD W.: *The Economics of American Agriculture*, 594 pages, New York; Prentice-Hall. (Second edition, 1960.)

1952. SHAW, BYRON T., editor: *Soil Physical Conditions and Plant Growth*, 491 pages, New York; Academic Press. (Agronomy Monograph, volume 2.)

1953. BENEDICT, MURRAY R.: *Farm Policies of the United States, 1790–1950*, 548 pages, New York; Twentieth Century Fund.

1953. KNAPP, JOSEPH G.: *E. A. Stokdyk—Architect of Cooperation*, 229 pages, Washington; American Institute of Cooperation.

1953. TAYLOR, CARL C.: *The Farmer's Movement, 1620–1920*, 519 pages, New York; American Book Co.

1954. FITE, GILBERT C.: *George N. Peek and the Fight for Farm Parity*, 314 pages, Norman, Okla.; University of Oklahoma Press.

1956. WALLACE, HENRY A., and BROWN,

WILLIAM L.: *Corn and Its Early Fathers*, 134 pages, East Lansing, Mich.; Michigan State University Press.

1958. ANDERSON, OSCAR E., JR.: *The Health of a Nation: Harvey W. Wiley and the Fight for Pure Food*, 333 pages, Chicago; University of Chicago Press.

1958. HIENTON, TRUMAN C., WIANT, DENNIS E., and BROWN, ORAL A.: *Electricity in Agricultural Engineering*, 393 pages, New York; John Wiley and Sons.

1960. GATES, PAUL W.: *The Farmer's Age: Agriculture, 1815–1860*, 460 pages, New York; Holt, Rinehart and Winston. (Economic History of the United States, volume 3.)

1960. MCGEARY, M. NELSON: *Gifford Pinchot, Forester, Politician*, 481 pages, Princeton, N.J.; Princeton University Press.

The Yearbooks of Agriculture before 1936 comprised sundry reports on agricultural developments and crops, statistics, and the Secretary's Report to the President. Since 1936, each segment has been issued as a separate publication, and the Yearbook has been devoted to the comprehensive treatment of one subject.

The annual report of the Secretary of Agriculture is published as a booklet of about 80 pages, copies of which can be had from the Office of Information, United States Department of Agriculture, Washington 25, D.C., or may be purchased from the Superintendent of Documents, United States Government Printing Office, Washington 25, D.C., for 35 cents (in 1960).

The statistical materials are published as a book, *Agricultural Statistics*, which includes statistics on agricultural production, prices, supplies, costs, income, land use, farm ownership, farmworkers, food consumption, and related subjects. There are also statistics on weather, freight rates, refrigerated warehouse storage, fisheries, forestry, world crops, and foreign trade in agricultural products. The data are grouped in 11 chapters. About 6,400 copies of *Agricultural Statistics* are purchased and distributed by the agencies of the Department to interested persons outside and within the Department. The Office of Information distributes copies to members of the Congress, libraries, and others who have need for them. Copies also are available (at $1.75 each in recent years) from the Superintendent of Documents. Richard K. Smith is chairman of the Yearbook Statistical Committee, under whose direction *Agricultural Statistics* is prepared.

The Administrative Regulations of the Department of Agriculture specify that the purpose of the Yearbook of Agriculture is "to make available, on the basis of need and interest, an authoritative and comprehensive treatment of research developments on an important agricultural subject for farmers, agricultural students and instructors, workers in agriculture, and others." Distribution is "to Congress as specifically required by law on the basis (since 1933) of 550 to each Senator and certain Senate officers, and 400 to each Representative and certain House officers. Department distribution (usually 12,000 copies) is limited to workers in the Department and to certain libraries, educational institutions, cooperating State extension and experiment station workers; on sale by the Superintendent of Documents to all others." Gove Hambidge was editor of the Yearbook of Agriculture during 1936–1942. Alfred Stefferud has been editor of the fifteen volumes since then.

In the list that follows, prices are given of the Yearbooks that were in print in April 1962. They may be obtained from the Superintendent of Documents.

1936. *Better Plants and Animals (Volume I)*, 1,189 pages.

1937. *Better Plants and Animals (Volume II)*, 1,497 pages.

1938. *Soils and Men*, 1,232 pages.

1939. *Food and Life*, 1,165 pages.

1940. *Farmers in a Changing World*, 1,215 pages.

1941. *Climate and Man*, 1,248 pages.

1942. *Keeping Livestock Healthy*, 1,276 pages.

1943–1947. *Science in Farming*, 944 pages; 136 pages of photographs. (A survey of advances in all agricultural sciences, primarily in the decade before 1947.)

1948. *Grass*, 892 pages; 32 pages of photographs. (Grass in a permanent agriculture; grass and conservation; forage for livestock; pastures; storage of forage; rotations; the range; enemies of grass; lawns, airfields, and playgrounds; research and grass; how to grow grass in all parts of the country.) $2.00

1949. *Trees*, 944 pages; 16 pages of photographs. (Shade trees for all regions, forests and soils, tree breeding, small woodlands, company forests, National and State Forests, diseases and pests, forest fires, wildlife, uses of wood, forestry, a vacation guide, questions and answers, how to identify trees.) $2.75

1950–1951. *Crops in Peace and War*, 942 pages. (The chemistry and utilization of agricultural products; the applications of chemistry, physics, biology, engineering, and economics in developing new uses and products; enzymes, allergens, and fermentation acids; starch; processing potatoes; preserving vegetables and fruit; sources of sugars; cotton and other fibers; rubber; oils; proteins; milk; hides; crops from the forest.) $2.50

1952. *Insects*, 924 pages; 80 pages of photographs and color plates. (How to know an insect; insects as helpers; insects as destroyers; the nature of insecticides; applying insecticides; warnings as to insecticides; resistance to insecticides; fumigants; quarantines; other controls; economic entomology; insects, man, and homes; insects on cotton; insects and vegetables; insects on fruit; insects on field crops; pests on ornamentals; livestock and insects; forests, trees, and pests; insects and wildlife.) $2.75

1953. *Plant Diseases*, 940 pages; 32 pages of color plates. (Bacteria, viruses, fungi, nematodes, and other foes of plants; how to control diseases of grasses, legumes, cotton, grain, vegetables, sugar crops, tobacco plants, ornamental plants, fruits and nuts, and other plants.) $2.50

1954. *Marketing*, 506 pages. (What is marketing? Why is it? What can it do for us? How much does marketing cost us? What are the problems we face? How efficient is our marketing system? Central markets, food retailers, storage, transportation, processing and packaging, prices, grades and standards, exports.) $1.75

1955. *Water*, 751 pages; 16 pages of photographs. (Our need for water, where it comes from, water and soil, watersheds, forests, irrigation, crops, ranges and pastures, gardens and orchards, drainage, water and wildlife, laws, pollution, water for farms and cities.) $2.00

1956. *Animal Diseases*, 591 pages. (The main diseases and parasites of cattle, swine, sheep, goats, poultry, dogs, cats, horses, mules, rabbits, minks, and other animals; the causes, symptoms, treatment, spread, and prevention of diseases.) $2.00

1957. *Soil,* 784 pages; 8 pages of photographs. (The nature of soils, their chemistry, fertilizers, soil care, moisture, cropping systems, soil management in all regions of the United States and special practices.) $2.25

1958. *Land,* 605 pages; 64 pages of photographs. (Our public domain; the increasing sizes of farms and our declining farm population; Government programs; Indian lands; military use of farmland; credit for buying land; insurance; land in subdivisions; highways; tenure; irrigation; forests; zoning and planning; regional problems; our future need for food and fiber; transportation and the future of cities; recreational lands; land laws; State lands; buying and selling property; taxes; conservation.) $2.25

1959. *Food,* 736 pages. (Vitamins, minerals, proteins, carbohydrates, fats, amino acids, calories and body weight, health

statistics, food allowances, needs of persons in each age group, quality in food, menus, recipes and plans, food habits, domestic and international food programs.) $2.25

1960. *Power to Produce,* 480 pages; 96 pages of photographs. (The mechanical revolution in farming, the use of tractors and other machines, electricity, communications, equipment for the land, power in harvesting, new livestock methods, effects of power, technological revolution and the future.) $2.25

1961. *Seeds,* 591 pages; 48 pages of photographs. (How seeds develop, travel, rest, grow, and carry life onward; how men produce, improve, clean, store, test, certify, and sell seeds of farm crops, vegetables, flowers, trees, grass; what modern science has learned about the effect on seed production of light, temperatures, growth regulators, insects, diseases, genetics; seed laws, frauds, good and poor seeds, weeds, costs.) $2.00

1962. *After a Hundred Years,* 704 pages; many photographs. $3.00.

Going to the Fair

ASK ANYONE who lives in Kenyon or Kandiyohi or Keewatin when the Minnesota State Fair is held, and you will get a startled reply, "Why, everybody knows the Fair is ten days before Labor Day!" Every Minnesotan expects every other Minnesotan, as well as outsiders, to know that. The farmer near Albert Lea has been planning all summer to see the new self-feeder on Machinery Hill. The barber in Minneapolis wants to see the races again. Children all over the State know that school starts the day after they get home from the Fair. The weatherman knows it, too, for he schedules fine, sunny weather for the Fair but changes it the day after Labor Day. To nostalgic Minnesotans away from their beloved native soil, the date and event are remembered as the end of the harvest season and the beginning of plans for the winter ahead. Yes, the Minnesotan knows the date as well as he knows Christmas or Thanksgiving.

Started as a Territorial Exposition before Minnesota was a State with the aim of displaying the best of the products of a country that extended from "the British line on the north, Wisconsin on the east, and the Missouri River to the west and south," the Minnesota State Fair is older than the Department of Agriculture. Early fairs were sponsored by agricultural societies for the display of the best or biggest products—cabbages that weighed 25 pounds, 3-pound potatoes, a radish of 15 pounds, "a turnip bigger than a peck measure, and a fine Devon bull named for our president and national hero, Zack Taylor."

Now, thousands from farms and cities visit the Fair each year; there are a million paid admissions. There are cabbages and radishes still, and 4-H demonstrations, art exhibitions, auto races, the Midway, and about 40 other classes of attractions and departments, which offer exhibitors more than 250 thousand dollars in prizes. It is big, bustling, comprehensive, exciting. It's a lot of fun, but it has a serious side, too—the exhibitions, contests, displays, competitions, in which proud Minnesotans display (and maybe get prizes for) jelly, cake, steers, corn, honey, butter, grain, flowers, vegetables, handicrafts, paintings, poultry, everything.

The Minnesota State Fair is not exactly typical of State fairs in the United States. Many are smaller. Few, if any, are larger; indeed, fair officials say theirs is the "largest 10-day agricultural show on earth." They also say that on the 300 acres of Fairgrounds near

the dividing line between Minneapolis and St. Paul are the "largest exhibit of farm machinery in the world, the largest show of draft animals in the United States, the leading dirt-track auto race cards in the country, and the world's biggest Midway." County fairs in the agricultural States also attract thousands of visitors annually. Altogether, 85 million Americans from farm and city visit our 2,158 agricultural fairs each year. They and the millions who have visited fairs since 1810, when an agricultural fair was held in Pittsfield, Mass., undoubtedly have been influenced by what they saw and did at them. Undoubtedly, too, the fairs have been catalysts in the spread of new information about farming and, indeed, in agricultural progress. They are a cohesive force that brings farmers together—and farmers and city folk.

Because Minnesota owes much of its rich heritage to the early settlers, the Minnesota State Fair honors them particularly. Special exhibitions are held. At special events, children dance to the folk music of their parents and grandparents, who came from lands across the sea. The display of prize-winning fruits and vegetables has changed little through the years. People like to discuss the judges' decisions, and the proud winners like to hang up their ribbons at home. On Machinery Hill the latest models are demonstrated, explained, discussed, and compared. Tractors sound off in loud blasts. Elevators race up to nowhere. Feedmills grind and pound everything into powder. Colorful manufacturers' brochures are given away to the visitors for reading at home. It is an exciting place for the farmer. In the months preceding each Fair season, contestants get ready for the big events. Horsemen practice. Flowers are given extra care. Artists and craftsmen create their masterpieces. Animals are groomed. Housewives practice their favorite secret cake recipes.

Children, spun candy, hotdogs, whirly-rides, Punch and Judy, magical wizard, and fun house all are a part of the Midway. It is a children's world, but parents, aunts, and uncles also ride the ferris wheel, enter the tunnel of love, and help steady young junior on the merry-go-round's galloping wooden horse. 4-H members and Future Farmers of America are active with exhibits and demonstrations. A large 4-H building houses several hundred young men and women during the Fair. Children from the cities often see farm animals for the first time close up. They are impressed. The Fair is a good place to relax, talk, exchange opinions with the people from up north or "the cities" or the western part of the State. It's all part of "going to the Fair," which Minnesotans have been doing for 100 years. *(David M. Granahan)*

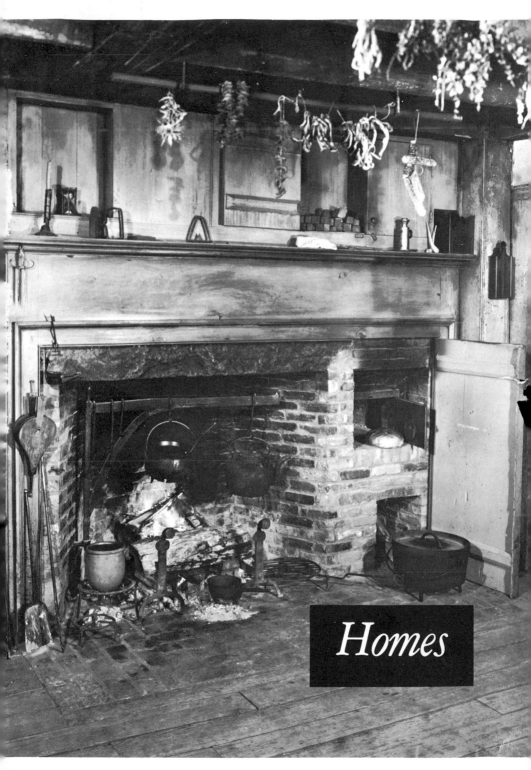

Homes

The House on the Farm

FARMHOUSES of the 1860's were the monuments of the times and the men who built them. There were houses of sod and adobe and houses of logs, columned plantation houses of brick or clapboard, and ornate Victorian houses with fancy fretwork. Variety there was, if nothing else, for more than anything they reflected the resources of time, money, skills, imagination, and materials that were available.

The westwarding pioneer was pressed to provide shelter for his family and could not wait for materials from the sawmill operator, the ironmonger, and brickmaker. Equally urgent was the need to establish croplands and herds; time was scant for fashioning a permanent home of finished materials or money to pay for it. So it was that the pioneer's other resources—manual dexterity and ingenuity to make do with materials at hand—were dominant in determining the type of house that first sheltered farm families in newly developing sections. The East had long since passed the crucial early days of settlement. There had been time and money to replace the first humble dwellings with more splendid ones. New England started building permanent homes during the colonial period and endowed domestic architecture with the well-proportioned clapboard house in villages and on farms. Interest in classic architecture spread to America early in the 19th century, left its imprint on the farmhouses of the Atlantic Coastal States and through the plantation regions of the South, and then moved on to the Middle West. Built of staunch materials, carefully crafted by hand, these colonial and Greek Revival houses were still in use in the 1860's. Midcentury saw an improvement in building supplies. Machines turned out construction materials and equipment formerly crafted by hand. New materials appeared. The domestic architecture was Victorian Gothic. Many farmhouses were built or remodeled into the style of the period. Traces of the gingerbread era can still be seen in the wooden lace around the eaves and porches of houses across the country.

"Beautiful birds built tasty nests," wrote O. S. Fowler in *A Home for All,* published in 1854. "As a general rule, a fancy man will build a fancy cottage, a practical man a convenient home." The American farmer, a practical man, may have paid some deference to popular styles in the exterior of his home and adopted new materials if they were more practical for the building, but he likely adhered to the philosophy that has traditionally governed the in-

The settler built his house of native materials.

Farmhouses were built of milled lumber and brick in well-established farming sections.

A kitchen in 1874.

659

terior design of farmhouses in this country—design for functional use. The early farmhouses had many functions. They were production plants for much of what the family ate and wore. "A house on a farm should be considered a place of business, and every provision should be made to fitly carry its business on," wrote Gervase Wheeler in 1855. He offered a house plan that would accommodate the several businesses of the farm household.

What was needed, several authors of the period agreed, were ways to lighten the workload of the farm household. The kitchen came in for the greatest attention, as it still does. "If any area of the house should be rendered comfortable, convenient and attractive, it is the kitchen, for it is in this room that the family will live," admonished one adviser to farm families. Another wrote: "A kitchen supplied with some modern conveniences and labor-saving implements and so cheerfully arranged that to do work in it is a delight rather than drudgery, is of infinite more value [than a parlor] if a choice must fall between the two." The "modern conveniences and labor-saving implements" available to the farm housewife of 1860 were meager enough. Consider the kitchen room itself. It was so big that it earned the description of "half-acre." Foods were stored outside the kitchen proper. The work surface was a table, too low to allow a person to work at it in comfort if it served also as the family's dining table, as many of them did. The fireplace and fireplace oven still were used for cooking and heating in many farm homes. The water supply was in a bucket kept in the dry sink.

The first step toward bringing modern convenience to the farmhouse likely was taken in the kitchen and in the direction of solving the problem of water supply and disposal. Running water for homes had been introduced during the 1830's, but even in the cities installation of plumbing facilities was slow. But there were other avenues of improvement: The well could be located close by the kitchen door. A drain could be installed in the dry sink. Next the pump came indoors, and the sink was no longer a "dry" one. Enameled plumbing fixtures were introduced about 1900 and met with immediate favor. The next step was piped running water. Not until electric power reached farther into the rural areas did plumbing facilities for farm homes become prevalent. Even as recently as 1950, more than half the farm homes of the country did not have running water. The inventor and manufacturer brought about the first real improvements through the development and mass production of radically different equipment for household chores and innovations in finishing materials. A wooden-tub washing machine was patented in 1863. Metal cookstoves began to supplant the fireplace and brick-lined oven. There was linoleum for the floors and oilcloth for tabletops.

No sooner had improvements been made in kitchen equipment

than the search began for ways of improving the improvements. By the early 1900's, a well-furnished kitchen was equipped with a manufactured kitchen cabinet in addition to the sink, ice refrigerator, wood or coal range, and perhaps an electric or oil stove for summertime cooking. Credit for the second era of improvement in kitchen planning goes to the women—to homemakers, who complained that, even with their new laborsaving equipment and materials, their backs still ached and their feet were tired, and to the women who were applying their newly won higher education to solving problems of home management (like Ellen H. Richards, the chemist who is acclaimed as the founder of professional home economics). Such women listened to the complaints and tried to help. The help that could be given was based mostly on common-sense reasoning and practical experience. A look at the posture of homemakers at work solved the mystery of the aching backs and instigated studies to determine the comfortable height for the kitchen sink and work surfaces. Rules emerged for arranging the equipment in the kitchen to save steps, rules made necessary by the fact that installed equipment could not be moved so readily as the dry sink, the kitchen cabinet, and table. Organization of the kitchen by work centers came to be emphasized. A bulletin on kitchen planning issued by the Department of Agriculture in 1926 gave this advice: "Group all equipment large and small into compact work centers for preparation of raw food, cooking, serving, clearing away, and dishwashing and any other activities done regularly in the kitchen." The compact small kitchen planned for efficiency came into being.

Compaction of kitchen areas was furthered by continuous built-in work counters and storage areas, which were introduced in the early twenties. With the introduction of tabletop ranges in 1930, a truly streamlined kitchen was possible but not always recommended. The kitchen planner was advised to weigh carefully the pros and cons of built-in and movable furnishings and to compare prices. The second era slid gradually into the third, an era born of experimental research. First efforts generally were in the field of equipment. Even before electricity became generally available to rural homes, the operating characteristics and performance requirements of dishwashers, refrigerators, ranges, and other equipment were being determined in the laboratories of some State colleges and the newly established Bureau of Home Economics in the Department of Agriculture. The growth of research on housing was slow, however, until 1931, when the President's Conference on Home Building and Home Ownership brought a new consciousness of the need for research on family housing problems.

Then farmhousing was established as a field of agricultural research. Under a grant from the Civil Works Administration, hundreds of specially trained workers were employed to obtain facts concerning conditions of farmhousing in 46 States. More than one-half million homes were included in this study, the first survey designed specifically for the purposes of housing research. Others also were exploring the possibilities of the experimental approach to housing problems. Maud Wilson, of Oregon State College, and Evelyn Roberts, of Washington State College, published the first research-based standards for working surface heights and other space units in farm homes. Thus the pattern was set for the research that was to receive its greatest boost with the passage of the Research and Marketing Act of 1946. The act authorized research relating to the design, development, and more efficient and satisfactory use of farm homes. Coordinated programs of work subsequently were conducted cooperatively by the Agricultural Research Service in the Department of Agriculture and 43 State agricultural experiment stations in four regions. The first study, an analysis of the kind and extent of activities carried on in farm homes and farm families' preferences for housing facilities, was followed by laboratory research to determine space needs and efficient arrangements of space for all major household activities and storage. Technicians started to translate the research-based data on space requirements into graphic standards for architects and families to use in planning homes for today's farm families.

We now have standards to guide us in making decisions as to how many inches of space to allow on the floor, on the work surface, or in a storage area for major household activities. We can position a wall oven within a range of heights that for the woman of average height has been found to require the least expenditure of energy. We can estimate in advance the difference in time and money costs of operating different types of household equipment. The concept of farmhouse planning for functional use has not changed, but changes in family living patterns have changed the functions of the house. Yesterday's farm kitchen had to be large enough to accommodate the extra workers who came to help with food preservation and feeding the harvest workers. Rarely do more than two persons work at a time in today's farm kitchen. When transportation was slow and one trip to town a week was the custom, large quantities of household supplies were purchased and stored in the farm home. With today's improved transportation, the amounts of goods purchased by the rural homemaker do not differ greatly from those of her city counterpart in most areas of the country.

Likewise the ice refrigerator that had to be replenished frequently was best placed near the back door so that it could be filled without tracking up the kitchen floor. Today's mechanical refrigerator may be placed for the user's convenience. As an example of what may happen in the second century of the Department, our suggestions for placement of the refrigerator today may not be suitable for the refrigerator of tomorrow, which may be several small units with different temperatures, each placed wherever it is needed. A similar division of cooking facilities is foreseen: Several surface cooking areas, ovens for baking, and ovens for warming, all placed for convenience. With the development of electronic cooking facilities, the organization and time required for kitchen work will change markedly, since cooking time will be reduced to minutes. These are only some of the anticipated changes that will influence the design of the kitchen of tomorrow. As social and economic changes continue to influence the living patterns of farm families, the concepts of what constitutes a good house will also have to change. We can expect that the farmhouse of 100 years hence will differ markedly from that of today, perhaps as much as today's differs from that of the 1860's. (*Avis M. Woolrich* and *Mildred S. Howard*)

The Beltsville Energy-Saving Kitchen Design No. 1 incorporated the results of research on human energy expenditures and on space requirements for household activities. Working drawings are made available to families through the Regional Plan Exchange, a cooperative activity of the Department and the State Agricultural Extension Services.

Food

MEALS a century ago probably differed little from our meals today. The common pattern for the main meal of the day was meat, potatoes, vegetables, bread and butter, and a dessert. People then ate about as much meat as now, much more grain products and butter, and less manufactured milk products (other than butter) and vegetables and fruit (except potatoes and apples). The chief differences in meals then and now are a greater variety in meals today, a greater similarity of the meals of rich and poor and of farm and city families, a lessening of the time needed to prepare food, and improvements in safety and sanitation.

A reason for the wider variety is the marked lessening of the seasonality in foods. With few refrigerated cars and little commercial preservation by canning, townspeople had to be content with such staples as flour and sugar, locally slaughtered meat, poultry and eggs brought in from farms, rather uncertain and unsanitary supplies of milk, and some other foods available in short seasons from nearby farms. There was some home canning. Root vegetables, apples, potatoes, and cabbage were kept in cellars, caves, or straw-lined pits in the earth. Some fruit was preserved in heavy sirup. In nutritive content, the seasonal swing in diets was most pronounced in vitamins A and C. Families could have fresh garden vegetables, berries, and other fruit in summer but not in winter; they took "spring tonics" and turned eagerly to early spring greens.

Richard O. Cummings in his book, *The American and His Food* (1941), wrote: "On the poverty level diet was very bad in the nineteenth century. Though in times of depression breadlines and soup kitchens were established, there were few systematic attempts to feed the poor. Families of unfortunates lived in squalor and ate wretched food." The greater similarity between diets of rich and poor reflects an upgrading of the diets of the very poor. Public welfare agencies today try to budget enough assistance for needy families to enable them to buy low-cost diets that are adequate in vegetables, fruit, milk, meat, and eggs, as well as cereals. Protein in the food consumed is a rough measure of the quality of a diet. The diets of the families in the lowest third of the income distribution contained 70 percent as much protein as those in the highest third in the 1930's; the percentage is now about 85. Old cookbooks give the impression that the dining tables of the well-to-do families were

The Atwater-Rosa respiration calorimeter, the first successful instrument designed to measure the energy requirements of people, was moved from the University of Connecticut to the Department of Agriculture in 1908.

groaning with food. Several kinds of meat, poultry, or fish, vegetables and fruit in season, hot breads, and desserts were there. We do not know how much of each of these dishes was eaten or how typical of actual practice the records are.

An account of one family's meals in the *American Agriculturalist* for November 1863 indicates simplicity and monotony. In an earlier issue, a correspondent had asked for "a list of meals for a week which should combine economy and good fare." A reply from a Rahway, N.J., family of five (three adults and two children, one an infant) was:

"Breakfast.—Each morning buckwheat cakes, cold meat, tea and coffee; excepting that on Monday and Thursday, eggs are served instead of cakes.

"Dinner.—Sunday, Monday, and Tuesday, roast beef, potatoes, turnips, and bread pudding—omitting the pudding on Monday. Wednesday, roast pork, potatoes, turnips and onion sauce. Thursday, the same with pancakes. Friday, corned beef, potatoes, turnips and batter pudding. Saturday, the same except bread pudding. Tea at each dinner.

"Tea.—Toast, preserves, tea and coffee, and twice, fried kidneys extra.

"Tea we drink weak; coffee very strong. Potatoes and turnips are my own growing, and preserves made from fruit of our own raising. Beef at 8 cents is the rump which hung for a week, roasted slowly, say 2½ hours, and well basted, is equal if not superior to porterhouse roast." The cost of the meals was 6 dollars and 16 cents a week and included, for example, 14 loaves of bread, 70 cents; 14 pints of milk, 42 cents; 5 pounds of pork, 50 cents; 1 quart of sirup, 14 cents; 3 dozen eggs, 60 cents; 2.75 pounds of butter, 77 cents; 5 pounds of sugar, 75 cents; 2 pounds of brown sugar, 20 cents.

Judged by modern recommendations for the various dietary essentials, this family's food was adequate, except for calcium and vitamins A and C. More milk, fruit, and green or yellow vegetables would have erased these shortages. Compared to the modern low-cost food budget of the Department of Agriculture, the New Jersey city family ate large amounts of sugar, fat, and eggs. It consumed less milk, fruit, and vegetables than is generally recommended for nutritionally adequate diets in this country today. Some of the difference in spending now and a century ago is related to food prices. Most prices were lower then, but not all. Sugar, for instance, cost 15 cents a pound wholesale in 1863—3 cents higher than the retail price reported by the Bureau of Labor Statistics in January 1961. It is surprising indeed to me that the Rahway family used 5 pounds of granulated and 2 pounds of brown sugar in a week. The average modern family of five probably uses a little more than 4 pounds. Of the foods the family bought in 1863, the cheapest, compared to now, were bread, beef, pork, milk, and eggs.

Families probably spent a larger share of their incomes for food a century ago than now, but we have no statistics to prove it. Food prices have increased on the average less than incomes, and the average working man's wage today buys more food than did the wages of wage earners 100 years ago. An hour's take-home pay of the average worker today will buy about 8 quarts of milk, 3.6 dozen eggs, or 10 loaves of bread. At the rate of 2 dollars a day for a 10-hour day in 1863 (a generous wage for most occupations), the average worker could have bought only 3.3 quarts of milk, a dozen eggs, or four loaves of bread on the basis of food prices quoted in the American Agriculturist.

It took longer to prepare meals, because families were larger, convenient equipment was lacking, few meals were eaten away from home, many foods were not available in our convenient forms, and getting food ready for the table or the stove took longer. Most cooks had to pluck and draw the chicken, and perhaps catch and kill it. Fish had to be scaled and dressed. The cook had to slice her ham and bacon and grind her own beef for beef patties. Bread had to be sliced. Coffee had to be ground. There were no ready-to-eat breakfast cereals, quick-cooking rice, instant mashed potatoes, frozen orange juice, TV dinners, chicken pies, cake mixes, canned baby foods, or canned soups. Almost all bread, cakes, pies, and other pastries were made at home. Recipes for many common foods 100 years ago looked much like those in cookbooks at the turn of the century. Today's recipes may contain the same items, but the measurements are more exact and the instructions are more specific. No longer do recipes say "butter the size of an egg" or "a generous mixing spoon of flour." Today's recipes and cooking directions, especially on cake-mix boxes and other such products, are precise and usually scientifically tested. They call for fewer procedures and utensils.

Pasteurization of milk was unknown a century ago, and milk was generally purchased by city families from a street vendor who ladled out milk from big cans into the customers' pitchers. Not until the late 1870's did milk begin to be bottled. Gradually codes were developed for regulating the bacterial content of milk. Today we enjoy a safe, unadulterated, and standardized supply of milk. Before we had refrigerated railroad cars, slaughtering of livestock was done by local butchers. The animals were frequently driven through the streets to local slaughterhouses, which sometimes were located in residential sections and gave rise to unsanitary conditions in streets. There were no ordinances concerning sanitation in the slaughterhouses. Adulteration of food was common. Beginning in 1883, when the Chemical Division of the Department of Agriculture was set up under the direction of Dr. Harvey Wiley, hundreds of reports were made on the presence of adulterants in a variety of foods— preserved meats, sugar, coffee, cereals, and canned goods. At the time the Department of Agriculture was founded, most retailers received their supplies in bulk. They displayed flour, sugar, cornmeal, rice, and crackers in barrels and boxes, often uncovered. Packaging made possible a cleaner product to the housewife, but it also provided opportunity for false weights and measures and encouraged false labeling and exaggerated claims for products. Toward the end of the 19th century, city codes and ordinances were beginning to be set up to prohibit short weight. Legislation was passed in the 20th century to protect consumers from false labeling, and the Federal Trade Commission was established to protect consumers from unfair advertising.

What I have written indicates how great are the improvements in our food supplies in the past century, so that many of us take for granted our abundant, safe, well-distributed supply of food and its relative economy. But we should not be complacent. There is room for improvement in production and marketing. As to consumption, we need more research, to discover what we should be eating for nutritional health; education, to tell and motivate us to eat what research points out is right; and additional purchasing power for some families, to permit them to buy nutritionally adequate diets. Available research in nutritional requirements is summarized periodically in the Recommended Daily Dietary Allowances of the Food and Nutrition Board of the National Academy of Sciences-National Research Council. When compared with these allowances, our present national food supply provides on the average enough calories, proteins, minerals, and vitamins. Dietary surveys, however, tell us that many families do not have food that furnishes the recommended amounts of these nutrients. About 3 households in 10 probably have diets that provide less calcium than recommended by the Council. One in four has food supplies with less than recommended amounts of ascorbic acid. Smaller proportions of households have food supplies that furnish less than recommended amounts of other nutrients.

Such figures do not mean there is outright malnutrition. They indicate that, on the basis of existing knowledge, the diets of some people are in need of improvement. The limiting factor for some families is lack of purchasing power, but for many it is lack of motive or knowledge to change their eating habits. Few instances of downright malnutrition exist in the United States today. Rickets, beriberi, pellagra, and scurvy are rarely seen by clinicians. No infor-

Flame spectrophotometric equipment is used in the modern laboratory of the Human Nutrition Research Division at Beltsville to determine the mineral content of foods.

mation exists on their prevalence a century ago, although there are many references to typhoid fever carried by bad water, milk, or other foods. Another indication of improved nutrition is the gain in body size of the population. Young men and women in the United States are about 2 inches taller than the average of even 50 years ago.

Many nutritionists believe that too much food in relation to our physical activity is our most pressing dietary problem today. It has been estimated that one-fourth of the adults in the United States are overweight. Insurance statistics have shown the association of obesity with high death rates from a number of diseases, including cardiovascular disease. Nutrition scientists are beginning to look closely at the upper levels as well as the lower levels of need for the various dietary essentials.

Many gaps exist in our knowledge of what are the minimum and optimum intakes of the many known dietary essentials. A challenge to research workers is the fact that the effects of various nutrients and the needs for them are interlocking and interdependent, and the scientist cannot study one without rigorous control of all others. Additional information is also necessary on the amounts of these dietary essentials in the foods we eat if we are to translate human nutritional requirements into guides for the selection of food. Another need is for more research on the quality of food, especially on the subtle changes in flavor due to changes in production and marketing practices. No amount of education will change dietary habits if people do not like the food.

An important function of education in nutrition is to combat faddism. False ideas about food are the stock-in-trade of faddists and promoters of many vitamin and mineral products. Some fads, such as the old idea that fish and celery are brain foods, are harmless, but many promotion schemes are harmful and wasteful of the consumer's dollars. Nutritionists agree that the best way to get the essentials of an adequate diet is through the foods provided in our abundant food supply—especially vegetables, fruit, eggs, meats, fish, milk, and whole-grain or enriched bread and cereals.

The daily food guide of the Department of Agriculture continues to be a good way to provide "food for fitness" for the Nation's families. Here is the Department's guide (from Leaflet No. 424): Milk group: 3 to 4 cups for children; 4 or more cups for teenagers; 2 or more cups for adults. Meat group: 2 or more servings—beef, veal, lamb, poultry, fish, eggs; as alternates, dry beans, dry peas, nuts. Vegetable-fruit group: 4 or more servings; a citrus fruit or other fruit or vegetable important for vitamin C; a dark-green or deep-yellow vegetable for vitamin A—at least every other day; other vegetables and fruit, including potatoes. Bread-cereal group: 4 or more servings— whole grain, enriched, or restored. *(Faith Clark)*

Clothing

WOMEN and children in the 1860's wore clothes in keeping with their slow pace of living. A dress, suitable for all occasions, had a long, full skirt, a fitted bodice, high neck, and long sleeves. Only the fabrics and trim varied. Women had no fashion periodicals (except Godey's Lady's Book), no commercial patterns, and no ready-to-wear things, except coats and mantillas. Their skirts, held out by ruffled and starched petticoats, were heavy, bothersome, and hard to take care of. Men's clothes a century ago were plainer and more somber than clothes of earlier years. Many men wore frock coats and stovepipe hats so they could look substantial and distinguished, but wide-legged trousers, wrinkled coats, and poor tailoring made them look seedy. The Victorian attitude meant that children had to act like adults. "Walking exercise" was regarded as adequate. Their clothes were what you would expect—long, full-skirted dresses, like mother's, for girls; outfits that looked like girls', for small boys; and baggy, man-tailored suits, like their father's, for many of the older boys.

The change over the years to clothing that is simpler, more comfortable and attractive, and better suited to a person's activities is due partly to the preferences of returning soldiers. They had become used to the practicability and comfort of research-based clothing, and they did not like padded shoulders, wider trouser legs, and all-over heaviness. Neither did they like shirts with high, close collars. Men's suits therefore have become lighter in weight, less restraining, more hygienic, more attractive, and easier to keep clean. Improvements in children's clothing, as in men's wear, started in 1920 or so. Preschoolers got the benefits first. In the early thirties, clothing specialists in the Agricultural Research Service developed a special garment that let kids make the most of sunshine and air. This sunsuit started a new freedom in clothing. Then came the first "self-help" clothes. They were compatible with a child's abilities and satisfied his normal desire to dress without the help of grownups. They are good for play and contribute to proper physical and psychological development. Functional one-piece outdoor playsuits for winter came next. Snowsuits made of water-repellent materials permit children to play outdoors in all kinds of weather. They are warm but light and allow for growth. They are practical. A child can button them up. The principles of these first functional garments for children were adopted for overalls, dresses, suits, and underwear.

During war years, Department clothing specialists developed women's work clothes suitable for man-sized jobs on farms and in war plants. Men's work clothes and the usual types of women's clothes were impractical for such work, but the clothing industry had never developed work clothes suited to women's needs. The results of research in the Department were welcomed by manufacturers of patterns and ready-to-wear clothes, and textile makers promoted fabrics recommended for the designs. Now slacks, coveralls, overalls, shirt blouses, and other work garments are made expressly for women. After the war, when many women returned to home-making, they were dissatisfied with housework clothing. The ruffled pinafores and clothes no longer good enough for Sunday failed to meet the new standards for simple and practical garments suited to a job. Department scientists developed designs that manufacturers readily adopted. The garments were designed for comfort, freedom for work activities, safety, convenience, and practicability. Such innovations directed attention to the fact that clothes also can be important in the rehabilitation of homemakers handicapped by accidents, disease, or age. A study of clothing problems of handicapped home-makers was made by the clothing specialists. The findings were applied to the development of garments with features designed to eliminate or lessen common problems and help the handicapped to increased independence, efficiency, and satisfactions.

Practically all clothes in the 1860's were made by machine; only a decade before, everything was made by hand. The change from hand to machine sewing came with the invention of the treadle sewing machine, which began to be used in factories at this time. The first factory-made suits and shirts were only mediocre in quality, but advancements in garment production were steady. Sewing machines were improved. Cutting machines were invented. The different operations were broken down into separate steps, so a worker could specialize in one or two operations. This was the beginning of our modern system of manufacturing clothes. The Census in 1860 reported that only 96 firms were making women's coats, mantillas, and accessories, such as hoops and corsets. Now there is an extensive ready-to-wear industry that has light, airy, modern factories. About 7 thousand establishments manufacture dresses and blouses for women, girls, and children; 5 thousand manufacture coats, suits, skirts, and outerwear for women, girls, and children; 4 thousand manufacture men's and boys' wear.

Women still do a lot of sewing. One report says that 40 percent of American women make clothing for themselves and their families. Improvements in home sewing machines are partly responsible for this. The treadle has been replaced by electric power.

Modern machines can be made to stitch backward as well as forward, hem, make buttonholes, embroider, darn, and sew on buttons. Many women who have the time find that they can make clothes at home less expensively than they can buy them. They can produce garments that wear and fit better than ready mades. Some enjoy creating clothes that express their individuality and are different from mass-produced garments. More than 1.5 million sewing machines are sold each year. Almost 500 million dollars are spent annually on piece goods. More than 33 million dollars are spent each year for patterns.

Every manufacturer used to use his own system of sizing. Many still do. In the late 1930's the Department of Agriculture undertook a study of body measurements. Under the supervision of anthropometrists and the Home Economics staff, 36 measurements were taken of each of 147,088 children and 58 measurements of 14,698 women. The measurements have been used by industry and Government agencies as a basis for establishing size standards for patterns and apparel for women and children. A recorded voluntary standard of the trade, CS 215-58, "Body Measurements for the Sizing of Women's Patterns and Apparel," based on these measurements, has been adopted by segments of the apparel industry. Similar standards for the sizing of boys' and girls' patterns and garments have been established. As a result, a larger proportion of our women and children can find better fitting clothing than formerly.

Only the four natural fibers—wool, silk, cotton, and some linen—were used to make clothing fabrics a century ago. Science to date has developed 17 new classes of fibers. Many are used for clothing. Among them are nylon, polyesters, rayons, and acrylics. These fibers have characteristics that impart new properties to fabrics. Many are thermoplastic, which means that fabrics made of them can be heat-set into shape. For example, circular-knit nylon hose can be set into a permanent full-fashioned shape, and pleats can be set so they will stay through washing or drycleaning. Because most of the new synthetic fibers are nonabsorbent, fabrics made of them can be dried quickly. So many new fibers were developed, and the claims for them so confusing, that the Congress enacted the Textile Fiber Products Identification Act, which makes it necessary to label the fiber content of all clothing fabrics according to their generic or class name. An earlier law insured the proper labeling of all clothing fabrics that contain wool. Since some materials are so flammable as to be dangerous when worn, another law was passed to insure that all such fabrics are labeled, as a protection to consumers.

Shrinkage was a big problem until the 1930's. Housewives had to wash and iron materials before they could safely start making them up. Today we can buy fabrics that will not shrink out of fit, no matter how often they are laundered. Many ready-to-wear and

A new cape coat.

Work clothes for women were designed by Department clothing specialists in the forties.

Self-help features were developed to encourage initiative and self-reliance.

Scientists in the Department have developed clothes that help the wearer do her work.

piece goods carry statements of the percentage of shrinkage that one can expect. Colors that faded in light or in laundering were also common problems in the 1860's. The range of colors was limited. Developments in the dyestuff industry have given us fabrics colorfast to sun, laundering or drycleaning, and perspiration. Time was when most washable garments had to be starched to restore body and dampened and carefully ironed to remove wrinkles. Many new fabrics no longer need to be starched. Some can be quickly ironed when dry. Some need no ironing. Most garments do not wrinkle so badly as previously. We now have materials resistant to rain, fungi, insects, and stains. Stretch fabrics, a product of the 1950's, had their start in sheer hose, but heavier weights have since been developed for such garments as slacks and swimwear. Nonwoven fabrics, another development, are made of cotton or synthetic fibers, held together by a bonding agent. They are generally stronger than felt and can be laundered like other washables. Some other nonwoven goods are made of paper with a synthetic fiber base, such as nylon. Because of this fiber base, they are stronger than ordinary papers of this type. They are particularly useful for disposable garments or articles, such as bibs, aprons, and uniforms.

Some shoes have been improved in styling. Children's shoes can be obtained with ample room for the toes and support for the ball and the arch; they have low and substantial heels. Modern parents understand the importance of safeguarding the development of their youngsters' feet, but fashion may decree that women wear shoes that flatten and pinch toes to a point or have heels so high they create a bad posture. Bootmakers in the early days used measuring methods handed down from one generation to the next. The hand was used for taking girth measurements and a strip of paper was used to measure lengths. There was no uniformity in the sizing of footwear, and no difference was made between rights and lefts. People simply shifted their shoes from one foot to the other so as to distribute the wear evenly. Little progress has been made during the past century in the basis for sizing shoes. During the Second World War, the Quartermaster Research and Development Command measured servicemen's feet as an aid in providing more comfortable footwear. In the 1940's the Department's home economists explored methods of measuring contours and dimensions of feet. No comprehensive study of foot measurements, however, has ever been made on which a scientific method of sizing shoes could be based. This is particularly true of women's and children's foot measurements. Manufacturers of lasts and shoes recognize this overdue need, as does much of the public. The surprisingly large number of men rejected for active duty because of bad feet is an example of the lasting effects of poorly fitting shoes. *(Clarice L. Scott and Margaret Smith)*

A 4-H Club

MORE than a generation has passed since organized 4-H Club work began in Shenandoah County, in northern Virginia. Children of many of the first members have become members; now grandchildren wait for their tenth birthday so they also can take part in this national movement for the growth of head, heart, hands, and health. The 4-H members in the communities organize into clubs with 15 to 35 members. They work and learn under the direction of the County Extension Agents and 35 adults, who as volunteer 4-H leaders are a vital part of the success of the clubs, a link between a person's formative years and the time he assumes his share of the county's agricultural, civic, and social responsibilities. They feel strongly about the values all through life of participation in 4-H activities, in which each member selects and carries out one or more projects in agriculture, home economics, or related fields and so is introduced to the latest research knowledge available from Virginia Polytechnic Institute, the agricultural college of Virginia, and the Department of Agriculture.

Training in leadership and character development are important parts of the program. The members are officers of their clubs and learn how to preside, give demonstrations, serve on committees, and express themselves before groups of people. They learn how to share responsibilities and to work together. Each club assumes one or more community responsibilities each year. One such project of the Meems Valley club was to equip a room in the Shenandoah County Memorial Hospital at a cost of more than 600 dollars. They raised the money by feeding baby beeves and selling them at public auction, growing hybrid seed corn, and raising potatoes. Other projects of various clubs have included painting and printing names on rural mailboxes; picking up trash and distributing litter bags to help keep roadsides attractive; placing first-aid kits in high schools; putting signs on the major roads to caution motorists to drive carefully; raising funds for landscaping the grounds of a new high school; participating in drives for funds to support health organizations; contributing books to a library in an elementary school; preparing baskets for patients in three nursing homes; soliciting donors of blood; buying a wheelchair for use in a community; and providing some items of equipment for a hospital. Thus members learn about their community, get to understand the problems to be solved, and become aware of their opportunities and responsibilities as junior citizens. The members plan and carry through to completion money-making activities when money is needed to support a community project. In doing so they learn about earning, banking, and spending money. Vespers in formal worship services are a part of 4-H programs. Members are encouraged to attend services of a church of their choice.

The 4-H work is one of the responsibilities of J. Carl Coiner, who became the county agent in 1936. Sallie Wetsel, home demonstration agent, and Stephen J. Beeken, assistant county agent, work with him. All are members of the faculty of Virginia Polytechnic Institute and are employed jointly by the Federal, State, and county governments. They have responsibility for 12 clubs, which have 330 boys and girls as members. They help each club plan and conduct its own program according to the needs and interests of all. Keystones in the activities are "learning to do by doing" and "to make the best better." Each club has a long-time program and an annual plan to reach its goals. Each scores its accomplishments annually and keeps a club history, which is submitted each year in a county competition.

First-year members are encouraged to complete one project their first year. More experienced members usually select more than one project. The most popular ones are food and nutrition, room improvement, health, clothing, beautification of home grounds, soils and crops, electricity, maintenance of tractors, entomology, forestry, gardening, livestock, poultry, beekeeping, song and game birds, and (for older members) automotive care, junior leadership, and career exploration. A vital part of the program is guiding young people toward their educational and vocational goals. One girl, who was the reporter for her club, later joined the staff of a weekly newspaper. One became interested in nursing during her health project and went on to become a graduate nurse. An active poultry project member continued his interest in college and then joined the staff of Virginia Polytechnic Institute to do research in poultry nutrition. Six girls in 1962 continued in college subjects their 4-H work introduced them to—home economics, dress designing, education, and field research. Income from sheep projects paid the tuition fees of two of them.

The activities in Shenandoah County are part of a big national movement that comprises 94 thousand local 4-H Clubs, which have more than 2 million members, 21 million alumni, 300 thousand adult leaders, and 110 thousand junior leaders. All of them subscribe to a pledge: "I pledge my head to clearer thinking, my heart to greater loyalty, my hands to larger service, my health to better living, for my club, my community, and my country." *(W. E. Skelton)*

676

And So, After a Hundred Years

THE YEAR 1962 finds the farm population continuing to decline in size, for the great recent advances in technology and productivity have not reached their peak. Farm operation has increasingly become a matter of sophisticated management and large investments of money, rather than a way of life for which only modest resources or training are needed. Many of the historic differences between rural and urban life have been eliminated or lessened, but many of those that still exist are of a problem nature, reflecting the fact that a disproportionate number of farm people still do not have adequate levels of income, education, sanitary facilities, health care, or other necessities of modern life.

But it will not do to overuse the word "problem," as we are prone often to do; talk and viewing with alarm can make a "problem" of almost any situation.

Nor should we overstress the decline in the size of the farm population; regardless of technological developments, people will be needed always on farms, and—as history shows—farm people always will have a strengthening influence on the whole population.

And so, after a hundred years, we have reached a moment in history that gives us opportunity for inventory and rededication.

We have traditions and history and—from them—facts and precepts for guidance in the years to come;

knowledge, ability, experience;

the spirit and genius to produce and the fruits of that production;

an eagerness to learn and ways to inform people who want to learn;

machines, tools, equipment, things;

science and technology that expand beyond our ability to see their end;

an awareness of the universe and our part in it;

land, rivers, lakes, mountains, forests, deserts, plains, valleys, space;

people, Americans.

We have a legacy.

The legacy sets our goals and responsibilities, such as those advanced at the beginning of this book and mentioned many times in later chapters: To insure a fair return to farmers; to provide for basic human needs; to care for our resources; to fulfill a duty to all Americans. *(A.S.)*

In a land where a head-high bush was called a tree, settlers had to use materials at hand, and houses were dug into the ground or made of sod.

Now, as on Hugo Meiland's farm in Barnes County in North Dakota, shelterbelts protect buildings and feed yards, stripcropping and rotations conserve the soil, artificial lakes provide water and pleasure, and the grim loneliness of frontier days is gone.

The Contributors

MARTIN A. ABRAHAMSEN, *Director,* Purchasing Division, Farmer Cooperative Service.

DALE L. ANDERSON, *Marketing Specialist,* Transportation and Facilities Research Division, Agricultural Marketing Service.

R. J. ANDERSON, *Director,* Animal Disease Eradication Division, Agricultural Research Service.

ALEX. D. ANGELIDIS, *International Economist,* Development and Trade Analysis Division, Economic Research Service.

GLADYS L. BAKER, *Agricultural Historian,* Economic and Statistical Analysis Division, Economic Research Service.

FRANK L. BALLARD, *Associate Director of Extension,* Oregon State College.

WARREN V. BENEDICT, *Director,* Division of Forest Pest Control, Forest Service.

LOUISE O. BERCAW, formerly Assistant Director of the Library of the Department of Agriculture.

MORTON BEROZA, *Investigations Leader,* Entomology Research Division, Agricultural Research Service.

MILTON E. BLISS, *Information Specialist,* Soil Conservation Service, Milwaukee, Wis.

HARRY A. BORTHWICK, *Chief Plant Physiologist,* Crops Research Division, Agricultural Research Service.

VICTOR R. BOSWELL, *Chief,* Vegetables and Ornamentals Research Branch, Crops Research Division, Agricultural Research Service.

C. A. BOWER, *Principal Soil Scientist,* Soil and Water Conservation Research Division, Agricultural Research Service, Riverside, Calif.

PHILIP S. BROWN, *Director,* Information Staff, Farmers Home Administration.

JOHANNES H. BRUUN, *Staff Specialist,* Product and Process Evaluation Staff, Office of Administrator, Agricultural Research Service.

T. S. BUIE, *State Conservationist,* Soil Conservation Service, Columbia, S.C.

RUTH L. BUSBEY, *Chemist,* Entomology Research Division, Agricultural Research Service.

R. C. BUSHLAND, *Entomologist,* Entomology Research Division, Agricultural Research Service, Kerrville, Tex.

T. C. BYERLY, *Deputy Administrator Farm Research,* Agricultural Research Service.

TOM BYRD, *Assistant News Editor,* Division of Agricultural Information, North Carolina State College.

J. J. BYRNE, *Director,* Division of Forest Products and Engineering Research, Forest Service.

LOWELL E. CAMPBELL, *Agricultural Engineer,* Agricultural Engineering Research Division, Agricultural Research Service.

J. P. CAVIN, *Deputy Director,* Economic and Statistical Analysis Division, Economic Research Service.

L. D. CHRISTENSON, *Entomologist,* Entomology Research Division, Agricultural Research Service.

FAITH CLARK, *Director,* Consumer and Food Economics Research Division, Agricultural Research Service.

L. C. COCHRAN, *Crops Research Division,* Agricultural Research Service.

REX F. COLWICK, *Leader,* Cotton Harvesting Investigations, Agricultural Engineering Research Division, Agricultural Research Service, State College, Miss.

AUDREY AMES COOK, *Information Specialist,* Foreign Market Information Division, Foreign Agricultural Service.

A. W. COOPER, *Director,* National Tillage Machinery Laboratory, Agricultural Research Service, Auburn, Ala.

M. J. COPLEY, *Director,* Western Utilization Research and Development Division, Agricultural Research Service, Albany, Calif.

JOHN L. CREECH, *Crops Research Division,* Agricultural Research Service.

REYNOLD G. DAHMS, *Entomologist,* Entomology Research Division, Agricultural Research Service.

WM. B. DAVEY, *State Conservationist,* Soil Conservation Service, Little Rock, Ark.

JOHN H. DEAN, *Deputy General Sales Manager,* Foreign Agricultural Service.

JOSEPH C. DOHERTY, *Information Specialist,* Farmers Home Administration.

679

WILLIAM W. DONNAN, *Branch Chief,* Soil and Water Conservation Research Division, Riverside, Calif.

PHILIP B. DOWDEN, *Entomologist,* Entomology Research Division, Agricultural Research Service.

MASON DUPRÉ, JR., *Assistant to Administrator,* Agricultural Research Service.

G. W. EDDY, *Entomologist,* Entomology Research Division, Agricultural Research Service, Corvallis, Oreg.

C. R. ELDER, *Director of Information and Extension Editor,* Iowa State University.

N. R. ELLIS, *Associate Director,* Animal Husbandry Research Division, Agricultural Research Service.

W. B. ENNIS, JR., *Agricultural Administrator,* Crops Research Division, Agricultural Research Service.

JOHN L. ETCHELLS, *Bacteriologist,* Southern Utilization Research Division, Agricultural Research Service, North Carolina State College.

C. H. FISHER, *Director,* Southern Utilization Research and Development Division, Agricultural Research Service, New Orleans, La.

H. A. FOWELLS, *Staff Specialist,* Division of Forest Management Research, Forest Service.

R. A. FULTON, *Chemist,* Entomology Research Division, Agricultural Research Service.

ANNE L. GESSNER, *Chief,* History and Statistics Branch, Farmer Cooperative Service.

W. R. GILL, *Soil Scientist,* National Tillage Machinery Laboratory, Agricultural Research Service, Auburn, Ala.

DAVID M. GRANAHAN, *Chief,* Exhibits Service, Office of Information.

HUGO O. GRAUMANN, *Chief,* Forage and Range Research Branch, Crops Research Division, Agricultural Research Service.

NATHAN GREEN, *Chemist,* Entomology Research Division, Agricultural Research Service.

HARLOW H. HALL, *Bacteriologist,* Northern Utilization Research and Development Division, Agricultural Research Service, Peoria, Ill.

MARGUARETTE M. HEDGE, *Publications Writer,* Information Division, Agricultural Research Service.

L. C. HEEMSTRA, *Director,* Animal Inspection and Quarantine Division, Agricultural Research Service.

MASON A. HEIN, *Assistant Chief,* Forage and Range Research Branch, Crops Research Division, Agricultural Research Service.

HARRY W. HENDERSON, *Assistant to the Assistant Administrator for Management,* Foreign Agricultural Service.

MARVIN D. HOOVER, *Division Chief,* Watershed Management Research, Rocky Mountain Forest and Range Experiment Station, Forest Service, Fort Collins, Colo.

SAM R. HOOVER, *Assistant to the Administrator,* Agricultural Research Service.

MILDRED S. HOWARD, *Housing Specialist,* Clothing and Housing Research Division, Agricultural Research Service.

C. DALE JAEDICKE, *State Conservationist,* Soil Conservation Service, Lincoln, Nebr.

K. F. JOHNSON, *Staff Officer,* Meat Inspection Division, Agricultural Research Service.

HAROLD E. JONES, *Director,* Division of Extension, Kansas State University.

QUENTIN JONES, *Botanist,* Crops Research Division, Agricultural Research Service.

H. R. JOSEPHSON, *Director,* Division of Forest Economics Research, Forest Service.

HUBERT W. KELLEY, *Assistant Director,* Information Services Division, Rural Electrification Administration.

CHARLES E. KELLOGG, *Assistant Administrator for Soil Survey,* Soil Conservation Service.

STEVEN C. KING, *Chief,* Poultry Research Branch, Animal Husbandry Research Division, Agricultural Research Service.

JOSEPH G. KNAPP, *Administrator,* Farmer Cooperative Service.

E. F. KNIPLING, *Director,* Entomology Research Division, Agricultural Research Service.

GEORGE O. KOHLER, *Supervisory Chemist,* Western Utilization Research and Development Division, Agricultural Research Service, Albany, Calif.

BERNARD KRUG, *Information Specialist,* Information Services Division, Rural Electrification Administration.

GEORGE M. KYLE, *Information Specialist,* Division of Information and Education, Forest Service, Atlanta, Ga.

JORDAN H. LEVIN, *Agricultural Engineer,* Agricultural Engineering Research Division, Agricultural Research Service, East Lansing, Mich.

HAROLD R. LEWIS, *Assistant Director of Information,* Office of Information.

ROSALIND C. LIFQUIST, *Food Economist,* Marketing Economics Division, Economic Research Service.

IVAN L. LINDAHL, *Leader,* Nutrition and Management Investigations, Animal

Husbandry Research Division, Agricultural Research Service.

A. W. LINDQUIST, *Chief,* Insects Affecting Man and Animals Research Branch, Entomology Research Division, Agricultural Research Service.

EDWARD G. LOCKE, *Director,* the Forest Products Laboratory, Forest Service, Madison, Wis.

MERLE S. LOWDEN, *Director,* Division of Fire Control, Forest Service.

HAROLD P. LUNDGREN, *Chief,* Wool and Mohair Laboratory, Western Utilization Research and Development Division, Agricultural Research Service, Albany, Calif.

PAUL C. MARTH, *Physiologist,* Crops Research Division, Agricultural Research Service.

MORRIS MASH, *Information Specialist,* Division of Information and Education, Forest Service.

JOHN R. MATCHETT, *Director of Product and Process Evaluation Staff,* Office of Administrator, Agricultural Research Service.

M. M. MERRITT, *State Soil Conservationist,* Soil Conservation Service, Indianapolis, Ind.

JOHN W. MITCHELL, *Physiologist,* Crops Research Division, Agricultural Research Service.

L. A. MOORE, *Leader,* Dairy Cattle Nutrition Investigations, Animal Husbandry Research Division, Agricultural Research Service.

VERNON P. MOORE, *In Charge,* Stoneville Cotton Ginning Research Laboratory, Agricultural Engineering Research Division, Agricultural Research Service, Stoneville, Miss.

L. O. MOTT, *Leader,* Virological Investigations, Animal Disease and Parasite Research Division, Agricultural Research Service, National Animal Disease Laboratory, Ames, Iowa.

F. J. MULHERN, *Associate Director,* Animal Disease Eradication Division, Agricultural Research Service.

C. H. HARRY NEUFELD, *Assistant Director,* Western Utilization Research and Development Division, Agricultural Research Service, Albany, Calif.

S. R. NEWELL, *Deputy Administrator and Chairman,* Crop Reporting Board, Statistical Reporting Service.

LOUISE A. NIXON, *Executive Secretary,* Nebraska Public Library Commission, State Capitol, Lincoln, Nebr.

G. C. NUTTING, *Chemist,* Eastern Utilization Research and Development Division, Agricultural Research Service, Wyndmoor, Pa.

KENNETH E. OGREN, *Director,* Marketing Economics Division, Economic Research Service.

BEN OSBORN, *Information Specialist,* Soil Conservation Service.

CLIFFORD D. OWSLEY, *Information Specialist,* Information and Education Division, Forest Service.

C. H. PALS, *Director,* Meat Inspection Division, Agricultural Research Service.

RUSSELL T. PRESCOTT, *Information Specialist,* Information Division, Agricultural Research Service, Albany, Calif.

HOYLE B. PUCKETT, *Agricultural Engineer,* Agricultural Engineering Research Division, Agricultural Research Service, University of Illinois.

C. F. RAINWATER, *Agricultural Administrator,* Entomology Research Division, Agricultural Research Service.

WAYNE D. RASMUSSEN, *Agricultural Historian,* Economic and Statistical Analysis Division, Economic Research Service.

W. P. RATCHFORD, *Assistant Director,* Eastern Utilization Research and Development Division, Agricultural Research Service, Wyndmoor, Pa.

E. P. REAGAN, *Director,* Plant Quarantine Division, Agricultural Research Service.

L. B. REED, *Entomologist,* Entomology Research Division, Agricultural Research Service.

L. P. REITZ, *Research Agronomist,* Crops Research Division, Agricultural Research Service.

L. A. RICHARDS, *Principal Physicist,* Soil and Water Conservation Research Division, Agricultural Research Service, Riverside, Calif.

N. E. ROBERTS, *Information Specialist,* Information Division, Agricultural Research Service, Wyndmoor, Pa.

JOHN W. ROCKEY, *Agricultural Engineer,* Agricultural Engineering Research Division, Agricultural Research Service.

J. KENNETH SAMUELS, *Director,* Marketing Service, Farmer Cooperative Service.

CLARICE L. SCOTT, *Clothing Specialist,* Clothing and Housing Research Division, Agricultural Research Service.

F. R. SENTI, *Director,* Northern Utilization Research and Development Division, Agricultural Research Service, Peoria, Ill.

HARVEY E. SHAFFER, *Extension Dairy Specialist,* The Pennsylvania State University.

M. S. SHAHAN, *Director,* Plum Island Animal Disease Laboratory, Greenport, L.I., N.Y.

HAROLD SHANKLAND, *Associate Extension Editor,* Kansas State University.

A. L. SHARP, *Research Investigations Leader,* Soil and Water Conservation Research Division, Lincoln, Nebr.

ELMER W. SHAW, *Technical Publications Editor,* Rocky Mountain Forest and Range Experiment Station, Forest Service, Fort Collins, Colo.

J. E. SIMPSON, *Assistant to the Deputy Administrator,* Agricultural Research Service.

W. E. SKELTON, *Assistant Director,* Virginia Agricultural Extension Service, Virginia Polytechnic Institute.

HENRY T. SKINNER, *Director,* U.S. National Arboretum, Crops Research Division, Agricultural Research Service.

FLOYD F. SMITH, *Entomologist,* Entomology Research Division, Agricultural Research Service.

MARGARET SMITH, *Clothing Specialist,* Clothing and Housing Research Division, Agricultural Research Service.

ARTHUR R. SPILLERS, *Director,* Division of Cooperative Forest Management, Forest Service.

LLOYD A. SPINDLER, *Principal Research Parasitologist,* Animal Disease and Parasite Research Division, Agricultural Research Service.

G. F. SPRAGUE, *Research Agronomist,* Crops Research Division, Agricultural Research Service.

WILLIAM J. STAHL, *Forester,* Division of Cooperative Forest Fire Control, Forest Service.

KENNARD O. STEPHENS, *Economist,* Price Division, Agricultural Stabilization and Conservation Service.

W. N. SULLIVAN, *Entomologist,* Entomology Research Division, Agricultural Research Service.

LLOYD W. SWIFT, *Director,* Division of Wildlife Management, Forest Service.

JOSEPH F. SYKES, *Dairy Husbandman,* Animal Husbandry Research Division, Agricultural Research Service.

NORMAN C. TETER, *Agricultural Engineer,* Agricultural Engineering Research Division, Agricultural Research Service.

ARTHUR T. THOMPSON, *Director,* Grain Division, Agricultural Stabilization and Conservation Service.

MURRAY THOMPSON, *Director,* Price Division, Agricultural Stabilization and Conservation Service.

ROBERT L. TONTZ, *Branch Chief,* Development and Trade Analysis Division, Economic Research Service.

W. B. VAN ARSDEL, *Assistant Director,*

Western Utilization Research and Development Division, Agricultural Research Service, Albany, Calif.

EDWARD M. VERNON, *Chief,* Forecasts and Synoptic Reports Division, Weather Bureau, United States Department of Commerce.

S. T. WARRINGTON, *Assistant to the Deputy Administrator,* Agricultural Marketing Service.

EVERETT J. WARWICK, *Animal Husbandman,* Animal Husbandry Research Division, Agricultural Research Service.

HAROLD A. WATERS, *Assistant to the Director,* Animal Inspection and Quarantine Division, Agricultural Research Service.

P. A. WELLS, *Director,* Eastern Utilization Research and Development Division, Agricultural Research Service, Wyndmoor, Pa.

DONALD A. WILLIAMS, *Administrator,* Soil Conservation Service.

R. C. WILSON, *Research Forester,* Division of Forest Economics Research, Forest Service.

L. P. WITNAUER, *Chemist,* Eastern Utilization Research and Development Division, Agricultural Research Service, Wyndmoor, Pa.

IVAN A. WOLFF, *Chief,* Industrial Crops Laboratory, Northern Utilization Research and Development Division, Agricultural Research Service, Peoria, Ill.

AVIS M. WOOLRICH, *Housing Specialist,* Clothing and Housing Research Division, Agricultural Research Service.

ROBERT G. YECK, *Supervisory Agricultural Engineer,* Agricultural Engineering Research Division, Agricultural Research Service.

GLADWIN E. YOUNG, *Deputy Administrator,* Soil Conservation Service.

Photographs and information for the chapter, "Profile of Farming," were supplied by RAYMOND G. PIERCE, *Extension Editor,* University of Alaska; JOHN BURNHAM, *Experiment Station Editor,* University of Arizona; DONALD N. HOLT, *Extension Information Specialist,* University of California; GEORGE E. BEVARD, *Associate Director,* Information Service, Colorado State University; JOHN A. MURRAY, *Agricultural Editor,* University of Delaware; M. H. SHARPE, *Associate Editor,* Extension Service, University of Florida; RICHARD ORR, *Assistant Editor,* Extension Service, University of Florida; GEORGE K. HINTON, *Extension Field Editor*, University of Georgia; JEAN A. GUTIERRES, *Extension Editor*, University of Hawaii; CEDRIC D'EASUM, *Assistant Editor*, Extension Service, University of Idaho; JACK C. EVERLY, *Assistant Extension Editor*, University of Illinois; R. L. REEDER, *Director of Agricultural Information*, Purdue University; JOSEPH G. DUNCAN, *Publications Editor*, University of Kentucky; NORMAN W. BUTTERFIELD, *Extension Specialist in Floriculture*, University of Massachusetts; W. LEE RUGGELS, *Assistant Agricultural Editor*, Michigan State University; WILLIAM GREER, *State Agricultural Society*, St. Paul, Minn.; DUANE B. ROSENKRANS, JR., *Extension Editor*, Mississippi State University; DELMAR HATESOHL, *Associate Agricultural Editor*, University of Missouri; HERBERT M. WHITE, *Assistant Director, Information*, Office of Information, Montana State College; MILTON H. COWAN, *Agricultural Agent*, Middlesex County, N.J.; JOHN M. WHITE, *Agricultural Editor and Head*, Department of Information, New Mexico State University; C. E. DEAN, *Chairman*, Agricultural Education Department, The Agricultural and Technical College of North Carolina; T. W. GILDERSLEEVE, *Extension Editor*, North Dakota State University; JAMES P. CHAPMAN, *Associate Extension Editor*, Ohio State University; RALPH A. PORTERFIELD, *Extension Dairy Specialist*, Ohio State University; RALPH W. SALISBURY, *Publications Specialist*, Oregon State College; HAROLD S. FOX, *Associate Extension Editor*, The Pennsylvania State University; MARIO L. CONDE-THILLET, *Press Editor*, Agricultural Extension Service, University of Puerto Rico; ROBERT J. STEINER, *Assistant Agricultural Editor*, University of Rhode Island; L. C. HAMILTON, *Agricultural Information Services*, Clemson College; EVERETT METCALF, *Agricultural Editor*, South Dakota State College; JACK T. SLOAN, *Visual Aids Specialist*, Agricultural and Mechanical College of Texas; THOMAS J. MCCORMICK, *Assistant Extension Editor*, University of Vermont; KIRBY BRUMFIELD, *Extension Information Specialist*, Washington State University; and GERALD JENNY, *Publications Editor*, University of Wyoming.

The Photographers

Abbott Laboratories, page 464; J. F. Abernathy Live Stock Photo Co., 629; Al Achtberger, 640, 641, 644; George Ackerman, 561; Ansel Adams, title page; Robert Alexander, 259; Jay T. Allison, 467; American Breeders Service, 300; American Can Co., 456; American Foundation for Biological Research, 293; Association of American Railroads, 3; Antonio Atiles, 91; M. C. Audsley, 442, 443; L. D. Bailey, 268; W. Brooke Ball, 302; Thomas J. Beavers, Jr., 532, 630, 635, 636; R. S. Beese, 298; Murray M. Berman, 40, 42, 117, 273, 308, 309, 322, 535; Paul S. Bieler, 268; C. Billett, 448; L. H. Binnie, 162; Bob Birdsall, 620; Robert B. Branstead, 182, 185, 200; H. E. Brown, 248, 251; G. M. Brune, 174; Hugo Bryan, 192, 194; S. Bunnag, 593; Melvin H. Burke, 256; F. Burns, 259; Norman W. Butterfield, 77; California Packing Corp., 455; Albert M. Candido, 663, 668; L. D. Christenson, 349; Roy M. Clark, XV, 683; Pat Coffey, 98; E. W. Cole, endpapers, 151, 161, 163, 164, 165, 166, 577, 581, 583; Jim Compton, 281; Russell S. Congdon, 255; Ray S. Cragin, 267; Emory Cross, 639, 641; Jim Dallas Studio, 489; Deere and Co., 428; Clarence Deland, 201; Jack Delano, 511; Dow Chemical Co., 342; Edholm & Blomgren, 643, 644; Roger L. Emig, 299, 303; D. R. Every, 214; A. Fayette, 448; Gaylor Field, 204, 206, 207, 208; Frank Flack, 263; William J. Forsythe, 39, 114, 134, 505, 531, 555, 673; R. G. Fowler, Jr., 89; R. E. Garrett, 453; Gillman Studio, 490; B. C. Goodell, 248, 251; R. M. Graves, 212; Great Plains Wheat, Inc., 461; O. Greeson, 142, 144; Lillian Guernsey, 139, 141; R. W. Haines, 451, 452; William E. Hallin, 220; E. Arnold Hansen, 241; L. C. Harmon, half-title page; Hasco Photographic Studio, 655, 656; Bradford Hatch, 190; Delmar Hatesohl, 81; Bartlett M. Hauthaway, 490; Herman J. Heikkenen, 264; Grant Heilman, 307; O. J. Henbest, 169, 170; George K. Hinton, 68; R. C. Hubbard, 93; Richard Hufnagle, 558; Edwin C. Hunton, 43, 104, 285, 308, 311, 333, 494, 496; Idaho Potato and Onion Commission, 72; S. A. Jackson, 622; L. L. Jacquot, 189; Johnny M. James, 467, 468, 470; James Manufacturing Co., 413, 416; Paul Jesswein, 82; William Jolly, 494, 531; Josetts, 464; A. B. Kennerly, 95; Kingston Photographic Supply, 600; H. R. Knaus, 74, 75; Charles Knell, 518; Frank S. Knoblock, 551; E. M. Kordwitz, 439, 440; George M. Kyle, 226; Dorothea Lange, 527, 544; W. H. Lathrop, 153; Le Bel's Studio, 661; Russell Lee, 523, 526, 527; Eugene Leedy, 160, 161; Libby, McNeill and Libby, 456; S. W. Lock, 492; Lord & Burnham, 371; L. D. Love, 248, 251; Lubbock Avalanch Journal, 431; Lummus Cotton Gin Co., 431; M. R. Lynch, 90; S. W. McBirney, 419; Thomas J. McCormick, 96; F. R. McDole, 157; B. C. McLean, 178, 189, 190, 198; D. J. McLellan, Jr., 87; Ray Manley, 270; Albert W. Matthews, 366; John Mattox, 54; R. C. May, 76; Wilfred J. Mead, 131, 140, 412; M. M. Merritt, 160, 166; Ralph Mills, 51, 52, 54, 55; John W. Mitchell, 138, 146; Masao Miyamoto, 70, 71; L. V. Monninger, 268; Bluford W. Muir, 121, 209, 239, 242, 261 268; Dorothy L. Murray, 471; William G. Murray, 46, 48, 49, 467, 468, 471; Lloyd E. Myers, 186; Keichi Nakamoto, 65; Navajo Agency, 62; Nebraska State Historical Society, 4, 5, 678; New York State Historical Association, 657; Marion Newson, 288; T. K. O'Driscoll, 142, 371; Ernest Orr, 437; Richard Orr, 67; Pan American World Airways, 378; Buford J. Poe, 170, 171, 173, 175; Hermann Postlethwaite, XIV, 11, 40, 127, 134, 135, 195, 307, 322, 339, 387, 388, 390, 391, 393, 395, 397, 398, 399, 400, 559, 568, 569, 570, 573, 575, 589; Poultry and Egg National Board, 330; Leland J. Prater, 218, 223, 224, 227, 230, 232, 244, 245, 260, 267, 270, 271; E. C. Purdy, 107; Rod Radford, VIII; R. C. Reeve, 205; L. A. Richards, 203; Lloyd W. Richardson, 121, 319, 320, 322, 405, 406, 407, 408, 409, 410, 416, 477, 482, 492, 495, 496, 534, 537, 630, 632; W. H. Riess, Jr., 140, 141, 144; Wells Riggs, 169; Frank M. Roadman, 183, 192; Duane B. Rosenkrans, Jr., 80; Arthur Rothstein, 515, 522, 528; W. Lee Ruggels, 78; R. B. Russell, 122, 215, 216; Dale Sanders, 267; Sante Fe Trail Highway Association, 4; Wm. F. Schaefer, Jr., 303; Otto Schallerer, 258; Fred Schlots, 189; Schneider Bros., Inc., 459; W. B. Sebens, 678; D. E. Smith, 86; Erwin E. Smith, 1; Smithsonian Institution, 23; Southern Pine Association, 212; Walter Sparks, 72; C. K. Spaulding, 270; Spotted Swine Record, 278; Stig C. Stabe, 83; L. F. Steiner, 350, 352; Robert J. Steiner, 349; W. E. Steuerwald, 240; Donald B. Stickney, 239; 255; L. R. Strickenberg, 263; Lee Sudlow, 94; K. D. Swan, 258, 271; Leobardo B. Terpan, 351, 352; Daniel O. Todd, 221, 227, 232, 234, 235, 236, 271; Elmer Turnage, 198; United Aerial Survey, 503; United States Bureau of Reclamation, 184; United States Information Service, 605; John Vachon, 516, 517, 518, 527; W. P. Venard, 452, 475, 476; Arthur L. Verdi, 581; R. Wenkam, 350, 351, 353, 354, 355, 357; L. Wernstedt, 254; West Virginia Pulp & Paper Co., 464; R. K. Winters, 221; George Winthrop, 437; Marion Post Wolcott, 528, 653.

Grateful acknowledgment is made of the help given by members of the Photography Division of the Office of Information: Charles T. Myers, Jr. (Chief), Albert W. Matthews, Russell T. Forte, Mina Q. Maxwell, Edna M. Phelps, Mary M. Cowell, Edith Fant, Peggy F. Waddell, Roy E. Sapp, Hermann Postlethwaite, Lloyd W. Richardson, Edwin C. Hunton, Murray M. Berman, Thomas J. Beavers, Jr., and Helen K. Hailstorks.

T. Swann Harding, whose period of outstanding service in the Department spanned its development from a few scientists and administrators in the old brick building to its modern eminence, graciously made available many old photographs and the unpublished manuscript of his history of the Department.

Index